in

OGY

Volume 9B

AMPHIBOLES:
PETROLOGY and EXPERIMENTAL
PHASE RELATIONS

DA... VEBLEN & PAUL H. RIBBE, Editors

The Authors

Barry L. Doolan
Dept. of Geology
University of Vermont
Burlington, VT 05401

Bernard W. Evans
Dept. of Geological Sciences
University of Washington
Seattle, WA 98195

M. Charles Gilbert
David R. Wones
Dept. of Geological Sciences
Virginia Polytechnic Institute
and State University
Blacksburg, VA 24061

Rosalind T. Helz
U.S. Geological Survey
959 National Center
Reston, VA 22092

Cornelis Klein
Dept. of Geology
Indiana University
Bloomington, IN 47401

Jo Laird
Dept. of Earth Sciences
University of New Hampshire
Durham, NH 03824

Robert K. Popp
Dept. of Geology
Texas A&M University
College Station, TX 77843

Peter Robinson
John C. Schumacher
Dept. of Geology
University of Massachusetts
Amherst, MA 01002

Frank S. Spear
Dept. of Earth and Planetary Sciences
Massachusetts Institute of Technology
Cambridge, MA 02139

Series Editor

Paul H. Ribbe

Department of Geological Sciences
Virginia Polytechnic Institute and State University
Blacksburg, Virginia 24061

MINERALOGICAL SOCIETY OF AMERICA

COPYRIGHT

1982

Mineralogical Society of America

PRINTED BY

BookCrafters, Inc.
Chelsea, Michigan 48118

REVIEWS IN MINERALOGY

(Formerly: SHORT COURSE NOTES)

ISSN 0275-0279

VOLUME 9B: AMPHIBOLES: Petrology and
Experimental Phase Relations.

ISBN 0-939950-09-X
0-939950-11-1

Additional copies of this volume as well as those
listed below may be obtained at moderate cost from

Mineralogical Society of America
2000 Florida Avenue, NW
Washington, D.C. 20009

REVIEWS in MINERALOGY

Volume 9B. AMPHIBOLES: PETROLOGY and EXPERIMENTAL PHASE RELATIONS

FOREWORD

This is the tenth book of a series which began in 1974 under the title *Short Course Notes*. In 1980 the Mineralogical Society of America changed the name and institutionalized this serial under the title *Reviews in Mineralogy*. The books published thus far are listed on the opposite page (p. ii); they are available at moderate cost from the Society.

Volume 9B, "Amphiboles: Petrology and Experimental Phase Relations," was begun in 1981 in preparation for the Short Course on Amphiboles and Other Hydrous Pyriboles presented at Erlanger, Kentucky, October 29 - November 1, 1981, prior to the annual meetings of the Geological Society of America and associated societies. Unfortunately, only the first chapter was in manuscript form at the time of the short course, and publication was delayed by one year. Its printing coincides with that of Volume 10, "Characterization of Metamorphism through Mineral Equilibria," edited by John M. Ferry.

The contents of the sister volume (9A: "Amphiboles and Other Hydrous Pyriboles -- Mineralogy") are listed on the cover.

As is the case in most of what is published in the *Reviews in Mineralogy* series, the chapters have not been subject to review other than by the scientific editors and the authors themselves, which in the case of Chapter 1, at least, involves a formidable number of qualified individuals who have had the better part of a year to find any serious problems with the text. The substantial portion of Chapter 2 written by Rosalind T. Helz was approved for publication by the U.S. Geological Survey.

This series editor is grateful to the following individuals who have contributed to the final preparation of the manuscript at Blacksburg: Margie Strickler, Ada Simmons, Ramonda Haycocks, Lisa Duncan (typing), and Sharon Chaing (drafting). Ms. Jeanne Atkinson cheerfully and ably supervised the printer's efforts in dealing with our sometimes not-so-camera-ready copy; Sarah Veblen and Mark Miller assisted with the proof-reading.

Paul H. Ribbe
Series Editor
Blacksburg, VA

PREFACE and ACKNOWLEDGMENTS

Although it includes some discussion of chemically complex reactions and the chemographic relationships among amphiboles and other rock-forming minerals, most of Volume 9A of "Reviews in Mineralogy" treats amphiboles and other hydrous pyriboles as isolated systems. In contrast, Volume 9B is dedicated more to an exploration of the social life of amphiboles and the amphibole personality in real rocks and in the experimental petrology laboratory. The chemical complexity of amphibole, which Robinson *et al.* refer to as "a mineralogical shark in a sea of unsuspecting elements," permits amphiboles to occur in a very wide variety of rock types, under a large range of pressure and temperature conditions, and in association with an impressive number of other minerals. The description of amphibole petrology and of petrologists' attempts to understand amphibole phase relations are therefore not simple matters, as the length of this volume suggests. Although they do not cover every type of amphibole occurrence, it is hoped that the papers in this volume will provide the amphibole student and researcher with an up-to-date summary of the most important aspects of amphibole petrology.

Many people were instrumental in the production of this volume. Institutional support was provided to David R. Veblen by Arizona State University and The John Hopkins University, and to Paul H. Ribbe by Virginia Polytechnic Institute and State University and Mobil Research and Development Corporation, Field Research Laboratory, Dallas, Texas. The National Science Foundation, Earth Sciences Section is acknowledged for sponsoring some of the editors' own research efforts that were in simultaneous progress with the preparation of Volumes 9A and 9B; it was not always easy to keep the two from overlapping.

John Grover of the University of Cincinnati provided invaluable local organization for the Short Course for which these reviews were prepared.

David R. Veblen
Baltimore, Maryland

Paul H. Ribbe
Blacksburg, Virginia

September 1982

AMPHIBOLES: Petrology and Experimental Phase Relations

TABLE of CONTENTS

Chapter 1

PHASE RELATIONS of METAMORPHIC AMPHIBOLES: NATURAL OCCURRENCE and THEORY

Peter Robinson, Frank S. Spear, John C. Schumacher,
Jo Laird, Cornelis Klein, Bernard W. Evans & Barry L. Doolan

(Authors are listed in reverse alphabetical order; the individual's
name appears in this list with the sections he has written.)

Chapter 2

EXPERIMENTAL STUDIES OF AMPHIBOLE STABILITY

M. Charles Gilbert, Rosalind T. Helz, Robert K. Popp & Frank S. Spear

Chapter 3

AMPHIBOLES in the IGNEOUS ENVIRONMENT

David R. Wones & M. Charles Gilbert

Chapter 1

PHASE RELATIONS of METAMORPHIC AMPHIBOLES: NATURAL OCCURRENCE and THEORY

Peter Robinson, Frank S. Spear, John C. Schumacher,
Jo Laird, Cornelis Klein, Bernard W. Evans & Barry L. Doolan

INTRODUCTION

From the earliest days amphiboles have played a central role in studies
of metamorphic rocks. This is obvious from the original and revised metamorphic facies classification of Eskola (1920, 1939; Fyfe *et al.*, 1958) based
on rocks of basaltic composition. In the greenschist facies amphiboles are
subordinate but significant. In the hornblende hornfels, amphibolite, and
glaucophane schist (blueschist) facies they are dominant, and an extensive
portion of the literature of metamorphic petrology is concerned with reactions that form amphiboles from other, usually more hydrous, mineral assemblages, or by hydration of less hydrous primary igneous rocks. Amphiboles
become less prevalent in the pyroxene hornfels, pyroxene granulite, and
eclogite facies, but major reactions needed to achieve assemblages characteristic of these facies involve the dehydration of amphiboles. Recent experimental work has shown that amphiboles are not stable below the uppermost
mantle because they are less dense than the sum of high-pressure anhydrous
phases plus highly compressed aqueous fluid. Thus, amphibole-rich rocks
formed by metamorphism of mafic igneous rocks represent a broad middle ground
in terms of pressure, temperature, and H_2O content.

Amphiboles, like pyroxenes and feldspars, are abundant in a wide variety
of rocks, because they lie also in a central position in terms of the range of
bulk chemistries of rocks. For example, they can occur in SiO_2-rich rocks with
quartz or in SiO_2-poor rocks with olivine and nepheline. Similarly, they
crystallize or break down by reactions between minerals that lie on opposite
sides of the amphibole composition space, much the same as pyroxenes do
(Robinson, 1980). This is no surprise to crystallographers and crystal
chemists, who emphasize the related structures of these two mineral groups and
the fact that amphibole compositions can commonly be expressed as *pyroxene plus
sheet silicate* (Thompson, 1978, and Volume 9A). This position in a chemical
middle ground means that amphiboles can play a role in the metamorphism of a
very wide variety of rocks, as long as H_2O or equivalent F or Cl is available.
For example, the occurrence of tremolite is a major feature in the metamorphism
of siliceous dolomite (Bowen, 1940). An amphibole stage precedes the highest
metamorphic grade for ultramafic rocks and is crucial in the metamorphism of

a variety of chemical sediments, including iron-formations. Amphiboles also can be crucial in the metamorphism of igneous rock compositions other than basalts, including andesites, dacites, rhyolites, and granites, in altered and metasomatic rocks, and in a variety of calcareous sedimentary rocks. About the only rock type in which amphibole is not important is in potassium-rich, calcium-poor aluminous sedimentary rocks, the pelitic schists, and even these, with a little calcium, can succumb to the blandishments of amphibole and develop the muscovite $\pm$ kyanite $\pm$ staurolite-hornblende assemblages of the so-called "garbenschieffer" of the Alps and New England (Frey, 1969; Doolan *et al.*, 1978).

Amphibole has been described as a mineralogical "garbage-can" or "waste-basket" (Ernst, 1966) or "sponge" (Engel and Engel, 1962) that does not discriminate among the constituents tossed into it.[1] Petrographers, however, know it as a highly translucent garbage-can that can accurately transmit through color, optical properties, and chemistry much information about its history and conditions of formation. This message is written by the interactions of the amphiboles with other minerals that surround it in chemical and physical space occurring in response to chemical and physical conditions. It is the objective of the metamorphic petrologist to attempt to interpret the message told by amphiboles and the purpose of this chapter to assist in this work.

The multicomponent composition space of amphibole is controlled by three types of limits, all of which vary as functions of pressure and temperature:

I.   Internal limits governed by the coexistence of two or more amphiboles. Such limits are strictly a function of amphibole crystal chemistry and details of competing amphibole structures.

II. Limits governed by the coexistence of two or more other minerals on opposite sides of amphibole composition space. These combinations of minerals can be the chemical equivalent of amphibole under more volatile-rich (commonly lower temperature), or under more volatile-poor (commonly higher temperature) conditions, and hence provide terminal limits on amphibole stability.

III. Controls on amphibole compositions provided by interactions of amphiboles with one or more minerals, all of which lie on the same side of the amphibole composition space, including ion-exchange reactions between amphiboles and other minerals.

Because the number of chemical components in amphiboles is very large, the number of other minerals that provide limits and controls on amphiboles is also

----

[1]A mineralogical shark in a sea of unsuspecting elements!

2

very large and leads to consideration of a very large number of equilibria. A purist approach would be to make a systematic chemographic and theoretical study of such equilibria that could be used in interpretation of any kind of amphibole rock. We have chosen instead to provide a more limited survey of the behavior of amphiboles, from a variety of chemical environments, prepared by a variety of petrologist-mineralogists, using a diversity of chemographic and analytical approaches. This is preceded, however, by a general survey of metamorphic amphiboles, including evaluation and comparison of analyses, systematics based on analyses, composition ranges and miscibility gaps. The question of amphibole nomenclature, covered extensively by Leake (1978) and summarized by Hawthorne (Chapter 1, Vol. 9A — the companion volume to this one) is only mentioned here where essential to understanding of other matters.

GENERAL REVIEW OF METAMORPHIC AMPHIBOLE COMPOSITIONS

The amphibole formula

Effective comparisons of amphibole compositions can only be made if the analyses are cast into a reasonable structural formula based on what is known about site occupancies from crystallographic studies. Because of the complex nature of amphibole structures, even the most sophisticated crystallographic studies leave many uncertainties; hence, site assignments based solely on chemical analyses would seem foolhardy at first. However, even if such systematic site assignment is wrong in local details, it often bears some similarity to truth, and better yet, provides a *uniform basis* for making chemical comparisons and evaluating chemical analyses.

Leake (1978) summarizes the standard formula for amphiboles and the procedure for calculation from an analysis (see also Hawthorne, Chapter 1, Vol. 9A): $A_{0-1}B_2C_5^{VI}T_8^{IV}O_{22}(OH,F,Cl)_2$. This formula translated into the site terminology of crystallographers reads:

$$A_{0-1}(M4)_2(M1,2,3)_5^{VI}(T1)_4(T2)_4^{IV}O_{22}(OH,F,Cl)_2 \ .$$

These formulae, broken down into pyroxene-like and mica-like sites as proposed by Thompson (1959, 1970, 1978), are as follows:

Pyroxene-like		Mica-like
$B_2C_2T_4O_{12}$	or	$A_{0-1}C_3T_4O_{10}(OH,F,Cl)_2$
$(M4)_2(M2)_2(T2)_4O_{12}$		$A_{0-1}(M1)_2(M3)_1(T1)_4O_{10}(OH,F,Cl)_2$

The six- to eight-coordinated (M4) site of amphibole is equivalent to (M2)

3

of pyroxene. The six-coordinated (M2) site of amphibole is equivalent to (M1) of pyroxene. The (T2) site is linked to two adjacent tetrahedra as in pyroxene, and the (T1) site is linked to three adjacent tetrahedra as in sheet silicates.

In these terms, tremolite $[Ca_2Mg_5Si_8O_{22}(OH)_2]$ is 2 diopside $[CaMgSi_2O_6]^0$ + 1 talc $[Mg_3Si_4O_{10}(OH)_2]^0$; glaucophane $[Na_2Mg_3Al_2Si_8O_{22}(OH)_2]$ is 2 jadeite $[NaAlSi_2O_6]^0$ + 1 talc $[Mg_3Si_4O_{10}(OH)_2]^0$; and edenite $[NaCa_2Mg_5(Si_7Al)O_{22}(OH)_2]$ is 2 diopside $[CaMgSi_2O_6]^0$ + 1 soda biotite $[NaMg_3AlSi_3O_{10}(OH)_2]^0$. However, due to the strong ordering of Al into the (T1) mica-like sites (Hawthorne, Chapter 1, this volume), tschermakite $[Ca_2Mg_3Al_2(Si_6Al_2)O_{22}(OH)_2]$ is *not* 2 CATS $[CaAlSiAlO_6]^0$ + talc $[Mg_3Si_4O_{10}(OH)_2]^0$, but $2[CaAlSi_2O_6]^{1+}$ + $1[Mg_3Si_2Al_2O_{10}(OH)_2]^{2-}$, and pargasite $[NaCa_2Mg_3Al_2(Si_6Al_2)O_{22}(OH)_2]$ is *not* 1 CATS $[CaAlSiAlO_6]^0$ + 1 diopside $[CaMgSi_2O_6]^0$ + 1 soda biotite $[NaMg_3AlSi_3O_{10}(OH)_2]^0$, but $1[CaAlSi_2O_6]^{1+}$ + $1[CaMgSi_2O_6]^0$ + $1[NaMg_3Si_2Al_2O_{10}]^{1-}$. The possibility occurs to us here that these differences in distribution might be what makes these amphiboles more stable than the equivalent pyroxene-mica combination.

Hawthorne (Chapter 1 in Volume 9A) has shown that for highly aluminous amphiboles the four T1 sites are, on the average, half-filled by Al, whereas T2 sites only begin to fill substantially in rare, extremely aluminous, Si-poor amphiboles, where this average mean half-fill of T1 is achieved. Average half-filling of T1 is the maximum possible to achieve Al avoidance. Presumably to achieve higher values of tetrahedral Al, for example to 2.7 in extreme gedrites (Schumacher, 1980) or to 3.5 in extremely subsilicic hastingsites (Shimazaki *et al.*, in press), further Al must go into T2.

Calculations of a structural formula from a complete wet chemical analysis should begin with evaluation of the H_2O, F, and Cl analyses and evidence for replacement of OH by O. If these analyses are considered extremely reliable, then the formula should be calculated on the basis of 24(O,OH,F,Cl). If there is uncertainty, it is usually safer to assume 2(OH,F,Cl) and to calculate the formula on the basis of 23(O). Cations are then assigned to sites as follows:

T *site*: Add Si, then Al, then Fe^{3+}, then Ti^{4+} to sum to 8.00.[2] If Si is greater than 8.00, this probably indicates an analytical problem. If there is not enough Si, Al, and Fe^{3+} to sum to 8.00, there is also probably an analytical problem.

----

[2]Hawthorne (Chapter 1 in Volume 9A) indicates there is little crystallographic evidence for assigning Fe^{3+} to tetrahedral positions. However, such assignment is documented in pyroxenes and sheet silicates and is an apparent necessity in some well founded amphibole formulae.

C sites (M1,M2,M3): Add left-over Al, Ti, Fe^{3+}, Cr^{3+}, Mg, Fe^{2+}, Zn, Mn, Ca, Li, and Na in that order to sum to 5.00. If Ca or Na are required to bring the sum to 5.00, there may be an analytical problem, although assignment of Ca in small amounts may be reasonable in some sodic amphiboles (Hawthorne, 1976).

B sites (M4): Add left-over Mg, Fe^{2+}, Zn, Mn, Ca, Li and Na in that order to sum to 2.00.[3] If the sum is substantially less than 2.00, there may be an analytical problem, unless the possibility of site vacancies is entertained.[4] For orthorhombic amphiboles and members of the cummingtonite-grunerite series, assignment of large amounts of Ca or Na to the B (M4) site throws suspicion on the analysis because these are essentially small-cation structures.

A site: Add left-over Ca, then Li, then Na, then K to sum not exceeding 1.0. If Ca must be assigned to the A-site, this probably indicates an analytical problem. If the total calculated occupancy of the A-site exceeds 1.0 then there is an analytical problem. Crystallographic data suggest that occupancy by any amount of Na + K between 0 and 1 is possible, and it is this variability in total cation occupancy that makes amphibole chemistry difficult to deal with.

No attempt has been made to prescribe exact limits beyond which an analysis should be rejected. One can, for example, reject *all* analyses in which Ca is assigned to C (M1,2,3) or to A, or one can be more tolerant. An objective for crystallographers in the future will be to ascertain as precisely as possible what the limits of site occupancies are, including the abundance and distribution of vacancies, if any. It goes almost without saying that another important objective is to weed out those analyzed phases, claimed to be amphiboles, which in fact are not amphiboles (Veblen, Ch. 4, Vol. 9A) or which are mixtures of amphiboles and other phases. To an extent limited by the resolution of optical microscopy, analyses by electron microprobe eliminate many of the problems caused by sample impurity and the common chemical zoning in amphiboles, but they pose other problems discussed in the next section.

----

[3] Leake (1968) suggested that an analysis of a calcic amphibole should be rejected if Mg + Fe^{2+} in B is greater than 0.25. However, some natural hornblendes with a strong cummingtonite substitution contain more than this limit and are legitimate.

[4] If the M4 sum is less than 2.00, then the total M-site sum is less than 7. This shortage *could* show up as a vacancy in any site, for example in M3, thus tending toward an amphibole analog of the dioctahedral micas.

Formulation of electron probe analyses

Electron probe analyses are capable of determining proportions of most atoms heavier than oxygen with an accuracy satisfactory for mineral formulation. However, they are incapable of distinguishing O and (OH), or Fe^{2+} and Fe^{3+} (or Mn^{2+} and Mn^{3+}). The first problem can commonly be ignored by assuming 22 oxygens plus 2(OH,F,Cl) in the formula, and calculating the cations to 23(O). Unfortunately, a very large number of amphiboles contain both Fe^{2+} and Fe^{3+}, which play very different roles in the crystal chemistry, so some attempt *must* be made to distinguish them. An excellent method in clean homogeneous material is to make a purification of milligram amounts and perform a wet analysis for FeO.[5] This can be combined with the results of a probe analysis and Fe_2O_3 determined by difference from total iron. Other direct methods of estimating Fe^{2+}/Fe^{3+} on small separates include Mössbauer spectroscopy (Goldman, 1979; Hawthorne, Chapter 2, Volume 9A) and optical absorption spectroscopy (Goldman and Rossman, 1977; Hawthorne, Chapter 2, Volume 9A). Aside from these direct approaches, reasonable indirect estimates can commonly be obtained by evaluating the analysis in terms of various chemical and crystal chemical limits outlined below (Stout, 1972; Papike *et al.*, 1974; Robinson *et al.*, 1971b; Laird and Albee, 1981).

Chemical limits. Two chemically limiting formulae for any amphibole analysis are formulae assuming all Fe as FeO and assuming all Fe as Fe_2O_3. The first assumption is used all too often in published papers, with resulting formulae that violate one or more reasonable crystal-chemical limits. In fact, the results are often so discouraging that the authors completely abandon formulation and merely present raw analyses. The "all FeO" assumption yields the largest number of cations, the largest A-site occupancy, and the largest Si content. Conversely, the "all Fe_2O_3" assumption, equally unreasonable in most cases, expands the oxygen framework relative to the number of cations, minimizing the A-site occupancy and the Si content. Some authors have used bulk rock analyses to estimate the Fe^{3+}/Fe^{2+} ratio. This certainly gives some clue as to a happy middle ground but can be truly accurate only when the amphibole in question is the only Fe-bearing mineral present. Generally, more satisfactory results are obtained by evaluation using crystal-chemical limits.

Crystal-chemical limits. Several papers have stated that amphibole formulae can be corrected for Fe^{3+} using charge-balance criteria. This is just not so! The fact is that any combination of oxides can be constructed into an

---

[5]Maxwell (1968).

amphibole formula. It may look utterly ridiculous from the point of view of
crystal chemistry, but the charge *will balance*! Charge *imbalance* can only be
obtained by making a silly assumption, for example that Ca in the A-site has
a 1+ charge, or that a vacancy in the M4-site has no effect on charge. The
"imbalance" can then be "eliminated" by recalculation until there is no Ca in
the A-site or no vacancy in the M4 site. The fact is that the mineralogist is
completely free to recalculate the formula to any number of cations he wishes
between the two chemical limits. The task then is to decide which recalculation makes the most *crystal-chemical sense*.

Before one can begin, assumptions about the crystal-chemical limits of
cation substitution in amphiboles must be made. These are based on single-
crystal X-ray diffraction studies and can be justified on the basis of size
arguments. These limits involve restrictions of what site a particular cation
can or cannot enter. They are in some ways the antithesis of the site assignments listed above. A list of reasonable crystal-chemical limits might be:

K -- A-site only	Mg -- M1,M2,M3 or M4 site
Na -- A-site and M4 site only	Fe^{3+} -- M2, M1 or M3 site
Ca -- M4 site only	Ti -- M2 site
Mn -- M1,M2,M3 or M4 site	Al -- M2 or T sites
Fe^{2+} -- M1,M2,M3 or M4 site	Si -- T site only

Another common assumption is that vacancies are not present in any site other
than the A-site.

With these assumptions in mind, a series of recalculations can be done on
fixed numbers of cations to derive amphibole formulae. When the analysis has
been normalized to the chosen number of cations, the amount of associated
oxygen or the number of positive charges is totaled, *still* treating all Fe as
Fe^{2+}. If oxygens are totaled, then add 2 for R^{4+} ions, 1.5 for R^{3+} ions, 1
for R^{2+} ions and 0.5 for R^{1+} ions. The oxygen total should be some number
less than 23; the charge total should be some number less than 46. In the
special case where the sum is *greater* than 23 oxygens or 46 charges, the
cation option violates the chemical *all FeO* limit and must be rejected. In
the normal case, oxygen is then added to bring the total to 23, or charges
are added to bring the total to 46. *For each amount of oxygen thus added,*
convert twice that amount of Fe^{2+} to Fe^{3+} and so reduce the Fe^{2+} in the list.
For each positive charge added convert that amount of Fe^{2+} to Fe^{3+} and so re-
duce the Fe^{2+} in the list. If the calculated amount of Fe^{3+} exceeds the amount
of Fe, then this option should be rejected because it violates the *all Fe_2O_3*

chemical limit. In the formula list, ions are best listed and assigned to sites as prescribed under the earlier discussion of amphibole formulae.

In general, one can find two recalculations that represent upper and lower bounds for Fe^{3+} and that fit within the chemical limits *and* within reasonable crystal-chemical limits. If the microprobe analysis is good, the real answer should lie within these bounds. The following options for normalization can be considered.

(i) Total cations to 16 (all sites filled): For most amphibole analyses this assumption would yield more cations than the "all FeO" assumption and hence would be chemically impossible. However, for a few amphiboles extremely rich in Na_2O and K_2O and hence rich in cations relative to oxygen, the "all FeO" assumption would give *more than the 16 cations*, which is the absolute limit. Recalculation of such analyses to 16 cations gives a minimum amount of Fe^{3+}. Further increase in Fe^{3+} could be considered by assuming still fewer cations, but would probably not be undertaken if it would result in placing substantial Ca in the C(M1,2,3) position or more Fe^{3+} in tetrahedra. Natural examples of such 16 cation formulae from probe analyses are the following   hastingsite, katophorite-taramite (Shearer *et al.*, 1981), and high Al gedrite (Schumacher, 1980, unpublished data):

$$(K_{.39}Na_{.71})(Na_{.35}Ca_{1.64}Mn_{.01})(Mn_{.14}Fe^{2+}_{2.79}Mg_{1.14}Fe^{3+}_{.54}Ti_{.26}Al_{.13})(Al_{1.85}Si_{6.15})$$
$$(K_{.33}Na_{.67})(Na_{1.45}Ca_{.55})(Ca_{.08}Mn_{.20}Fe^{2+}_{3.09}Mg_{.56}Fe^{3+}_{.78}Ti_{.28})(Fe^{3+}_{.07}Al_{1.42}Si_{6.51})$$
$$(Na_{1.00})(Na_{.12}Ca_{.01}Mn_{.05}Fe^{2+}_{1.83})(Fe^{2+}_{.04}Mg_{3.05}Fe^{3+}_{.60}Al_{1.31})(Al_{2.79}Si_{5.21})$$

(ii) Total cations to 15 exclusive of Na,K: This assumption excludes all Na,K from the B(M4) site, and has the crystal-chemically sound effect of excluding Ca from the A-site. Aside from this provision, it maximizes Mn, Fe, or Mg in the B(M4) site. Since these are already likely to be large in ortho-amphiboles and cummingtonites, whereas Na in B(M4) would necessarily be small, a formulation close to this often works well for such FeMg amphiboles.

(iii) Total cations to 15 exclusive of K: This assumption excludes Na from the A-site and forces it into B(M4). It can be effective for glaucophane and riebeckite, where the amount of Ca is small and is not forced excessively into the C(M1,2,3) sites. This formulation can be a disaster in overestimating Fe^{3+} in Ca amphiboles, while excluding Na from the A-site, and reducing or eliminating any Mn, Fe, or Mg from B(M4).

(iv) Total cations to 13 exclusive of K, Na, Ca: This assumption excludes Mn, Fe^{2+}, and Mg from B(M4), thus automatically eliminating any "cummingtonite

8

component." Depending on K, Na, and Ca, the Na may be reasonably distributed between the A-site and the B(M4) site, as seems to be common in many calcic amphiboles, such as the following:

$(K_{.38}Na_{.48})(Na_{.23}Ca_{1.77})(Mn_{.05}Fe^{2+}_{3.82}Zn_{.01}Mg_{.23}Fe^{3+}_{.43}Ti_{.29}Al_{.17})(Al_{1.81}Si_{6.19})O_{22}(OH)_2$ [Jaffe *et al.*, 1978].

$(K_{.107}Na_{.136})(Na_{.109}Ca_{1.891})(Ca_{.014}Mn_{.027}Fe^{2+}_{1.018}Ni_{.004}Mg_{3.161}Cr_{.007}Ti_{.043}Fe^{3+}_{.446}Al_{.281})(Al_{.961}P_{.007}Si_{7.032})O_{22}(OH)_2$ [Ashwal, 1974].

Another modification is to calculate to 13 cations excluding K, Na, Ca, and Mn. In fact, a split of Mn between B(M4) and C(M1,2,3) can often give a very satisfactory result.

(v) <u>Total Si to 8</u>: In some high Si amphiboles, an all-ferrous calculation can yield an Si value greater than 8. In this case, Fe_2O_3 can be added until Si = 8.000, thus giving a *minimum* value for Fe^{3+}.

(vi) <u>Total Si + Al to 8</u>: In some low Al amphiboles, calculation of Si + Al to 8.000 can give a reasonable *maximum* value for Fe^{3+}, assuming one is unwilling to assign Fe^{3+} to tetrahedral sites. Riebeckite formulae published by Klein and Gole (1981) are averages midway between the two limits Si = 8 and Si + Al = 8. For amphiboles containing significant Al, these two crystal-chemical limits are usually well outside the chemical limits.

If two of the above crystal-chemical limits both give reasonable formulae and both fall within the chemical limits, then an average number of cations can be used intermediate between the two ideals (Stout, 1972). Alternatively, if wet chemical data from adjacent occurrences suggests certain characteristics for the formulae, these characteristics can be adopted. For example, if hornblendes in the district seem to average about 0.180 Na in B(M4), hornblende formulae can be normalized to 14.820 cations exclusive of Na and K. If gedrites average about 0.08 Na in B, gedrite formulae can be normalized to 14.92 cations exclusive of Na and K (Schumacher, 1981b). The emphasis then should be on careful scrutiny to obtain a formula that makes the most sense crystal-chemically. To further familiarize the reader with formula selection criteria, formulae for seven analyzed amphiboles are presented in Table 1 and discussed in the caption.

The composition range of metamorphic amphiboles

For the average undergraduate or graduate student of mineralogy and petrology, encounters with amphibole crystal chemistry can be dismaying.

Table 1. Structural formulae of selected amphiboles calculated according to various chemical and crystal-chemical limits. All are calculated to 23 oxygens assuming 2(OH,F,Cl).

Chemical Limits:

Fe^{2+} — All Fe as FeO.

WET — FeO and Fe_2O_3 of the wet chemical analysis.

Fe^{3+} — All Fe as Fe_2O_3

Crystal Chemical Limits:

15eNK — 15 cations excluding Na and K

15eK — 15 cations excluding K

13eCNK — 13 cations excluding Ca,Na,K.

16CAT — 16 cations

a Hornblende with Cummingtonite - Vernon

	Fe^{2+}	15eNK	WET	15eK	13eCNK	Fe^{3+}
Si	6.566	6.542	6.529	6.398	6.388	6.359
Al	1.434	1.458	1.471	1.602	1.612	1.641
	8.000	8.000	8.000	8.000	8.000	8.000
Al	.783	.751	.733	.558	.545	.506
Fe^{3+}	.081	.168	.254	1.117	1.249	1.447
Ti	.080	.080	.080	.078	.078	.078
Mg	2.964	2.952	2.947	2.888	2.883	2.870
Fe^{2+}	1.172	1.049	.986	.278	.203	.043
Mn						.056
	5.000	5.000	5.000	5.000	5.000	5.000
Fe^{2+}	.321	.271	.245			
Mn	.044	.044	.044	.023		
Ca	1.635	1.685	1.682	1.648	1.645	1.582
Na	.029			.328	.327	.326
	2.000	2.000	2.000	2.000	1.972	1.908
Ca	.056					
Na	.044	.335	.306	.043	.043	.043
K	.437	.379	.349			

b Hornblende with Epidote - Ashwal 13-1

	Fe^{2+}	15eNK	13eCNK	WET	15eK	Fe^{3+}
Si	7.107	7.092	7.049	7.032	6.977	6.885
Al	.893	.908	.951	.961	1.023	1.115
P				.007		
	8.000	8.000	8.000	8.000	8.000	8.000
Al	.361	.344	.293	.281	.208	.100
Fe^{3+}		.122	.400	.446	.865	1.434
Ti	.044	.043	.043	.043	.043	.042
Cr	.007	.007	.007	.007	.007	.007
Mg	3.196	3.188	3.169	3.161	3.137	3.096
Ni	.004					
Fe^{2+}	1.392	1.303	1.067	1.018	.587	
Mn			.028	.027	.028	.027
Ca			.014		.105	.294
	5.000	5.000	5.000	5.000	5.000	5.000
Fe^{2+}	.087	.051				
Mn	.028	.028	.028			
Ca	1.885	1.922	1.910	1.891	1.758	1.572
Na				.109	.242	1.240
	2.000	2.001	2.000	2.000	2.000	1.812
Ca	.041					
Na	.247	.246	.155	.136		
K	.397	.354	.397	.262	.243	.105
				.107	.107	.105

c Riebeckite - Bocquet 2248

	Fe^{2+}	WET	13eCNK	15eK	Fe^{3+}
Si	7.751	7.467	7.426	7.397	7.319
Al	.249	.533	.574	.603	.681
	8.000	8.000	8.000	8.000	8.000
Al	.534	.221	.175	.143	.058
Fe^{3+}		1.692	1.931	2.101	2.568
Ti	.023	.022	.022	.022	.021
Mg	2.286	2.202	2.191	2.183	2.159
Fe^{2+}	2.157	.863	.675	.495	
Mn				.006	.006
Ca				.050	.188
	5.000	5.000	5.000	5.000	5.000
Fe^{2+}	.563	.065			
Mn	.006	.006	.006	.033	.136
Ca	.344	.331	.330	.279	.136
Na	1.087	1.598	1.670	1.721	1.703
	2.000	2.000	2.000	2.000	1.839
Na	.716	.139	.058		
K	.038	.037	.036	.036	.036
	.754	.176	.094	.036	.036

d Cummingtonite with Hornblende - Vernon

	Fe^{2+}	15eNK	WET	15eK	Fe^{3+}
Si	7.662	7.630	7.629	7.608	7.313
Al	.338	.370	.371	.392	.450
Fe^{3+}					.237
	8.000	8.000	8.000	8.000	8.000
Al	.134	.100	.099	.077	
Fe^{3+}	.013	.191	.200	.323	1.860
Ti	.013	.013	.013	.013	.012
Mg	4.289	4.271	4.271	4.259	3.128
Fe^{2+}	.564	.425	.417	.328	
	5.000	5.000	5.000	5.000	5.000
Mg	1.633	1.572	1.570	1.530	.965
Mn	.100	.100	.100	.100	.096
Ca	.267	.328	.328	.327	.314
Na			.002	.044	.042
	2.000	2.000	2.000	2.001	1.417
Ca	.062				
Na	.044	.044	.042	.050	.008
K	.009	.009	.008	.008	.008
	.113	.053	.050	.008	.008

e Anthophyllite with Hornblende Robinson and Jaffe - 6A9X

	Fe^{2+}	15eNK	WET	15eK	Fe^{3+}
Si	7.336	7.336	7.316	7.251	6.992
Al	.664	.664	.684	.749	1.008
	8.000	8.000	8.000	8.000	8.000
Al	.485		.463	.388	.087
Fe^{3+}		.025	.127	.535	2.160
Ti	.013	.025	.025	.025	.024
Mg	3.966	3.966	3.955	3.920	2.727
Fe^{2+}	.564	.522	.430	.132	
	5.000	5.000	5.000	5.000	5.000
Mg	1.744	1.744	1.702	1.572	1.053
Mn	.091	.091	.091	.090	.087
Ca	.112	.112	.112	.111	.107
Na	.041	.041	.095	.227	.207
	2.000	2.000	2.000	2.000	1.466
Ca	.176	.176	.134		
Na	.044	.003	.003	.003	.003
K	.009				
	.179	.179	.137	.003	.003

f Ferri-gedrite - Lal and Moorehouse 80

	Fe^{2+}	15eNK	WET	15eK	Fe^{3+}
Si	6.622	6.163	6.124	5.934	5.853
Al	1.778	1.837	1.876	2.066	2.147
	8.000	8.000	8.000	8.000	8.000
Al	.703	.621	.566	.300	.188
Fe^{3+}		.093	.092	.089	2.721
Ti	.093	.092	.093	.127	.088
Mg	3.331	3.301	3.279	2.484	2.003
Fe^{2+}	.873	.557	.340		
	5.000	5.000	5.000	5.000	5.000
Mg		1.878	1.784	.632	
Fe^{2+}	2.000	.036	.035	.034	.033
Mn				.085	.082
Ca		.086	.096	.559	.551
Na					1.797
	2.000	2.000	2.000	2.000	
Fe^{2+}	.018				
Mn	.035				
Ca	.087				
Na	.586	.582	.481	.020	.020
K	.022	.021	.021		
	.748	.603	.502	.020	.020

g Richterite - DNZ-55-9

	Fe^{2+}	16CAT	WETKFe³⁺
Si	7.791	7.775	7.756
Al	.209	.225	.232
Fe^{3+}			.012
	8.000	8.000	8.000
Al		.024	.009
Fe^{3+}			.089
Ti	.011	.011	.011
Mg	3.983	3.975	3.966
Fe^{2+}	.206	.117	
	5.000	5.000	5.000
Mn	.290	.265	.230
Ca	.842	.840	.839
Na	.868	.895	.931
	2.000	2.000	2.000
Na	.712	.683	.642
K	.318	.317	.317
	1.030	1.000	.959

DISCUSSION OF ANALYSES from Table 1, opposite page.

a) The all-ferrous formula is unsatisfactory because of 0.056 Ca in A. The all-ferric formula is unsatisfactory because 0.056 Ca is assigned to M1,2,3 and the M4 sum is only 1.972. The 15eK formula is preferred over 15eK because the former is in agreement with observed lamellae of cummingtonite in the sample (0.245 Fe^{2+} and 0.044 Mn in M4). It is closest to the WET analysis.

b) The all-ferrous formula is unsatisfactory because 0.041 Ca is assigned to A. The all-ferric formula has 0.294 Ca assigned to M1,2,3 and an M4 occupancy of only 1.812. The 15eK formula has 0.105 Ca assigned to M1,2,3 and WET formula has 0.014. Although both the 15eNK and 13eCNK formulae have none of these unsatisfactory features, the latter is more consistent with an amphibole saturated with epidote and not with cummingtonite. It is closer to the WET formula.

c) The all-ferrous formula does not show blatantly unsatisfactory features although such a content of Fe^{2+} in M4 in a sodic amphibole is unheard of. The all-ferric formula is unsatisfactory because it has 0.188 Ca in M1,2,3 and only 1.839 cations in M4. A 15eNK formula in this case would lie outside the chemical limits. The 15eK formula also has 0.050 Ca in M1,2,3, while the 13eCNK formula has no objectionable features. It is closest to the WET formula. In this case 13eCNK is superior to an average between 13eCNK and the ferrous formula.

d) The all-ferrous formula is unsatisfactory because 0.062 Ca is assigned to A, likewise the all-ferric formula because the M4 sum is only 1.417. The differences in 15eNK, WET, and 15eK are not large as is expected where the amount of Na is small. It is probably a better choice for cummingtonite, in this case one with hornblende exsolution lamellae, to let the Na go into A in the 15eNK formula. It is also closer to the WET formula. 13eCNK formulae are impossible for Fe-Mg amphiboles.

e) Only the all-ferric formula with an M4 occupancy of 1.466 is blatantly bad. A 15eNK formula would be outside the chemical limits. An average between the all-ferrous and 15eK formulae would be reasonable. Still better would be to take the mean value of about 0.08 Na in M4 for plagioclase-saturated orthoamphiboles and normalize to 14.920 cations excluding Na,K.

f) The all-ferrous formula is extremely unsatisfactory with 0.018 Fe^{2+}, 0.035 Mn, and 0.087 Ca in A. The all-ferric formula has an M4 sum of only 1.797. The 15eK formula is improbable because 0.559 is assigned to M4. The 15eNK formula is not blatantly bad, but the A-site occupancy of 0.603 is unknown for good wet analyses of gedrites of similar compositions. Again, the mean value if 0.08 Na in M4 could be used to obtain a very satisfactory formula very close to the WET formula.

g) The all-ferrous formula is impossible because A-site occupancy is >1.000. The 16CAT formula is reasonably close to the WET and all-ferric formulas, which coincide. All other crystal-chemical limits are outside the chemical limits.

11

With good luck he or she may be able to retain names and structural formulae of many of the ideal end members. By the time this struggle is over, there is little time left to explore the questions of how commonly these ideal end members are approached in nature, and what is the composition range of natural amphiboles. These are questions we will attempt to answer for natural metamorphic amphiboles in the next two sections.

In order to study the composition range of natural metamorphic amphiboles, it is necessary to obtain a representative sample. This is no easy task for many reasons. Because of the importance of Fe_2O_3 in amphiboles, we have chosen, at this time and for this particular purpose, to rely on published wet-chemical analyses. The results are thus heavily dependent on the often uncertain purity of mineral separates, and the effects of compositional zoning and exsolution lamellae can be badly obscured. Such difficulties are overcome by the electron probe, with, however, other uncertainties that have been discussed in the previous section. Because of the chemical complexity of amphibole, a large number of elements must be measured with accuracy. When any important oxides are omitted, as Na_2O and K_2O commonly are, especially for actinolites, cumming-tonites, and orthoamphiboles, the analyses cannot be used.

Fortunately for us, there are available the compilations of wet chemical analyses of Deer *et al*. (1963) and of calcic and sodic-calcic amphiboles of Leake (1968). Still more fortunately, we have available an extension of these lists of calcic and sodic-calcic amphiboles prepared by Steffe (1979). In this last work, all formulae were recalculated on the basis of 23 oxygens and 2(OH,F,Cl) and site assignments made in the preferred sequence outlined above. To the Steffe list we have added analyses and derived formulae of Fe-Mg and sodic amphiboles from Deer *et al*. (1963), Rabbit (1948), Bocquet (1974), Ernst *et al*. (1970), Coleman and Papike (1968), Klein and Ito (1968), and a variety of other sources. In all formulae there is essentially charge balance, provided proper account is taken of various ionic valences and the charge effects of vacancies, if any, in the M4 sites. A few of the Steffe formulae had to be recalculated where he had included P_2O_5 in calculating the oxygen sum but omitted it in the cations.

Evaluation of analyses was carried out in a subjective and somewhat arbitrary way, which, nevertheless, we hope, is reasonably in line with known amphibole crystal chemistry. For the Steffe list all analyses were discarded if Si > 8.000, if Ca was assigned to M1,2,3, if Ca was assigned to A, or if the sum for M4 was less than 2.000. The number of analyses discarded because of Ca assignment is, however, shown in histograms of Ca in M1,2,3 (Fig. 3) and A (Fig. 5). For the remainder of the sample, which was far less abundant, the standards were relaxed somewhat to allow Si slightly above 8.000, to allow Ca in M1,2,3 or A, or to allow the M4 sum to go as low as 1.91 to 1.94 (depending on certain plotting parameters). Without these concessions, a much higher proportion of sodic and Fe-Mg amphibole analyses would have been discarded.

A fall-out from this evaluation process was the understanding that it is much harder to get an "acceptable" analysis of a simple amphibole such as tremolite [$Ca_2Mg_5Si_8O_{22}(OH)_2$], cummingtonite [$Fe_2Mg_5Si_8O_{22}(OH)_2$], or riebeckite [$Na_2Fe_2^{3+}Fe_3^{2+}Si_8O_{22}(OH)_2$], than it is to get an "acceptable" analysis of a compositionally complex hornblende or gedrite, where there is much greater flexibility in site assignment, particularly of Al and Na. It is interesting that even with the "relaxed" criteria, *not one* out of 11 wet chemical analyses of riebeckite from iron-formations survived the evaluation process.

To evaluate the composition range of metamorphic amphiboles, a series of histograms was prepared (Figs. 1 through 5), based on the derived structural formulae from the site assignment scheme described earlier. It must be remembered that these assignments are not absolute, particularly for ions like Fe^{2+} and Mg, which undoubtedly have a more complex distribution that can be a function of temperature, local structure, and cooling rate (Seifert, 1978; Hawthorne, Chapter 1 in Volume 9A). On the histograms separate symbols are used for orthorhombic amphiboles, for cummingtonites, for calcic amphiboles, and for sodic amphiboles. For sodic-calcic amphiboles, the symbolism is somewhat arbitrary and inconsistent; sodic-calcic "hornblendes" are grouped with calcic amphiboles, whereas richterites are grouped with sodic amphiboles. In addition to the histograms, a list has been prepared (Table 2) giving structural formulae for analyses showing the *maximum* assigned occupancy by each ion in each site (underlined) for each of the four amphibole groups. A few formulae derived from recent electron probe analyses have been added which extend these maxima considerably, and the interested amphibole extremist will find ways of his own to extend these maxima with additional probe analyses.

Because tetrahedral Si and Al are essentially complementary, except in those few formulae with tetrahedral Fe^{3+}, it is not necessary to discuss Si separately. The maximum tetrahedral Al (Fig. 1) in the sample is 2.551 in a calcic amphibole (14-5038). This limit is greatly extended to 3.487 (Shimazaki 1) in some recent probe analyses from Japan. In the distribution of calcic amphiboles there is a broad peak between 1.4 and 1.8, and a more or less continuous distribution down to zero. The peak must represent a strong bias toward amphiboles of common amphibolites. The lack of a comparable peak close to zero for common actinolites, must, in part, represent the analytical problems of this simple amphibole. The maximum tetrahedral Al in an orthoamphibole is

13

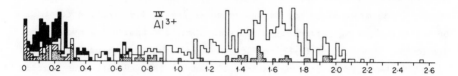

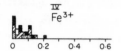

Figure 1. Histogram of inferred tetrahedral Al and Fe^{3+} in "accepted" wet chemical analyses. The key to the shading patterns is given in Figure 2 below.

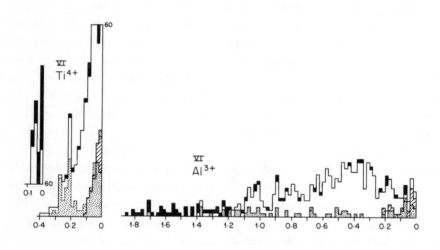

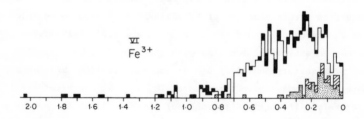

Figure 2. Histogram of inferred octahedral Al, Fe^{3+}, and Ti^{4+} in "accepted" wet chemical analyses of amphiboles. Stippled pattern represents orthoamphiboles; lined pattern, cummingtonites; unpatterned, Ca amphiboles and barroisites; solid, Na amphiboles and richterites. Fine-dashed pattern indicates Ti in calcic amphiboles from charnockites and other granulite facies rocks.

2.047 (I34I), although this also has been greatly extended to 2.795 (JCS) by recent probe analyses. Two major concentrations near 1.4 to 1.6 and near 0.1 to 0.2 represent common gedrites and anthophyllites, respectively, roughly near the limbs of the anthophyllite-gedrite solvus. A minor concentration near 0.7 to 0.9 represents "hypersolvus" orthoamphiboles. Cummingtonites and sodic amphiboles are concentrated especially between 0 and 0.3, with maxima at 0.810 for cummingtonite (DHZ-36-3) and 0.692 for a crossite (DHZ-53-6). The former is remarkably aluminous for a cummingtonite, hinting at analytical or separation problems.

In the entire Steffe list there was not one hornblende in which Fe^{3+} was assigned to tetrahedral positions. However, our additional collection showed a number of orthoamphiboles, cummingtonites, and sodic amphiboles where such assignment seemed necessary. Tetrahedral Fe^{3+} can be a natural consequence of minor analytical difficulty in any amphibole with low Al. Hawthorne (Chapter 1, Volume 9A) has stated that there is no crystallographic evidence for tetrahedral Fe^{3+} in any amphibole. However, in view of well demonstrated Fe^{3+} in tetrahedral positions in both pyroxenes (Hafner and Huckenholz, 1971) and sheet silicates (Faye and Hogarth, 1969), we think it should remain as an option for amphiboles for the present.

Al in octahedral positions in calcic amphiboles is broadly distributed between zero and a maximum of 1.389 (16C-5319), with a broad peak near 0.4 (Fig. 2). The maximum of about 1.4 octahedral Al is the value that has been so thoroughly documented by Leake (1965, 1971), although Doolan *et al.* (1978) have probe analyses where octahedral Al reaches nearly 1.9. Orthoamphiboles show the same broad distribution but with a higher maximum value of 1.706 (DHZ-34-10). Cummingtonites mostly have very low values of octahedral Al with a rather isolated value of 0.667 (DHZ-36-3; see comment above). Sodic amphiboles show a broad distribution with a peak near 1.5 to 1.8 with a maximum of 1.858 (LM-4) in the closest "accepted" formula to pure glaucophane.

The distribution of Fe^{3+} in octahedral positions bears some similarity to that of Al, but the peaks are steeper. Calcic amphiboles range from 0 to a maximum of 1.190 (19B-5223), with a peak centered near 0.35, lower than octahedral Al. Orthoamphiboles show a decided peak near 0.13, with a maximum at 0.800 (B616). The range for cummingtonites is mostly below 0.2, with a maximum at 0.233 (DHZ-36-5).[6] For sodic amphiboles the Fe^{3+} range is the broadest, with a maximum of 2.033 in a riebeckite (DHZ-54-14). The largest concentration

----

[6]Maximum on the histogram is at 0.243 for DHZ-36-16, which Klein (1968) proved is an anthophyllite-tremolite mixture, and which should have been deleted from our data.

of analyses is at low values of Fe^{3+}, because analyses of metamorphic glaucophanes are more abundant than those of crossites and riebeckites.

Ti^{4+} in octahedral positions in calcic amphiboles has a sharp peak at
0.05, with a maximum value of 0.393 (12-5132). Thus, *no* metamorphic amphiboles in the sample qualify as "kaersutite" with more than 0.50 Ti. However,
recent probe analyses on calcic amphibole in a skarn from Japan contain 0.520
Ti (Shimazaki 2). Within the calcic amphiboles there is a special subset from
charnockites and other granulite facies rocks (dashed pattern) that shows a
distinct peak between 0.20 and 0.27. This is a function of the increasing
solubility of Ti in amphiboles of rocks saturated with a Ti mineral such as
ilmenite or rutile with increasing metamorphic grade. This change is usually
accompanied by an increasingly brown color as noted by Shido and Miyashiro
(1959) and Binns (1965b), among others. All other amphibole groups show a Ti
peak close to 0. Maximum for orthoamphibole is 0.111 (R13). Despite this low
solubility, orthoamphiboles are noted for their fine exsolution lamellae and
needles of ilmenite or rutile (Robinson and Jaffe, 1969a,b). The maximum for
cummingtonite is 0.067 (DHZ-36-4). For sodic amphiboles the maximum is 0.234
(DHZ-57-7) in arfvedsonite. When compared to pyroxenes (Robinson, 1980, Fig.
2), the octahedral Al, Fe^{3+}, and Ti in metamorphic amphiboles is remarkably
similar (taking into account that in pyroxene there is only one M1 site, as
compared to two M2 sites in amphibole).

Cr data were not easily available in our data set, but the maximum amount
we could find, in a hornblende from a foliated lherzolite, is 0.272 (Varne,
1970). This is a larger proportionate occupancy in the appropriate site than
in any chrome diopside in the representative pyroxene sample (0.136 vs 0.058
when normalized to one cation site) (Robinson, 1980, Table 1).

The histograms of Mg and Fe^{2+} in M1,2,3 (Fig. 3) are complementary, because these two ions are the essential building blocks of all amphiboles. When
one is maximized the other can be minimized. Mg in calcic amphibole ranges
from a minimum of 0.395 (17-5497, see bottom of Table 2) to a maximum of 4.920
(18-9), with a broad peak of abundance near 2.5. Orthoamphiboles cover nearly
the entire range of Mg values from a minimum of 0.007 (DHZ-34-10, maximum Fe^{2+}
in ferrogedrite) to a maximum of 4.948 (DHZ-34-1). Cummingtonites have similar
distribution ranging from 0.010 (DHZ-36-14, maximum Fe^{2+}) to 4.855 (YK-1).
Riebeckites and glaucophanes are necessarily confined to the lower part of the
range, below 3.4, because nearly two positions are always occupied by Al or
Fe^{3+}. Arfvedsonites and particularly richterites (black dots in Fig. 3) can
have higher Mg, reaching 4.863 in a natural richterite (DHZ-55-2) and 4.930 in
synthetic richterite (DHZ-55-1).

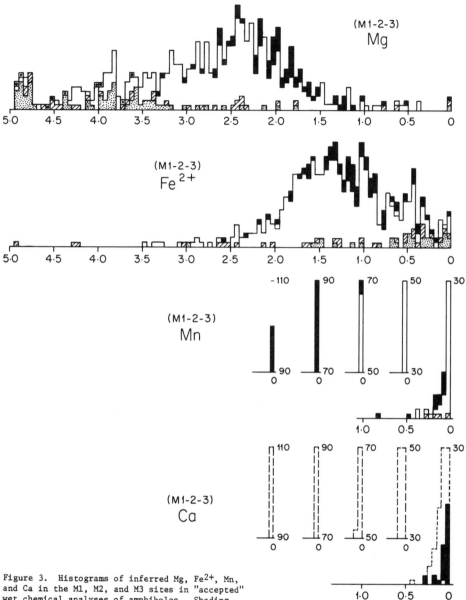

Figure 3. Histograms of inferred Mg, Fe^{2+}, Mn, and Ca in the M1, M2, and M3 sites in "accepted" wet chemical analyses of amphiboles. Shading pattern as in Figure 2 (above) except that dotted squares indicate Mg in richterites. Dashed outline for Ca indicates number of calcic amphibole analyses not accepted because Ca was assigned to M1,2,3. Because the vertical scale was not great enough for Ca and Mn, these peaks have been chopped into several sections.

Because of the site assignment scheme adopted, Fe goes to M1,2,3 only when they are not filled with Mg. Thus, in calcic amphiboles Fe^{2+} ranges from zero to a maximum of 3.463 (17-5521), with a broad peak near 1.40. In orthoamphiboles the range is zero to 2.969 (DHZ-34-10), in this case limited by octahedral Al and Fe^{3+} in ferrogedrite. Cummingtonites, including grunerites, cover almost the entire range of Fe^{2+} content from 0.066 (YK-2, Table 2, bottom) to 4.938 (DHZ-36-14). Fe^{2+} in sodic amphiboles is limited to 2.595 (Hashimoto, 1973) in a riebeckite.

Zn and Mn are assigned to M1,2,3 only in cases where Al, Fe^{3+}, Ti, Mg, and Fe^{2+} total less than five. This occurs in a few calcic and sodic amphiboles and a few Zn- and Mn-rich cummingtonites, but in no orthoamphibole. Zn in M1,2,3 reaches 1.049 in a calcic amphibole (KL13), 1.186 in a cummingtonite (KL65), and 0.862 in a zincian manganoan winchite (89407). Mn in M1,2,3 reaches 0.376 in a Zn-rich calcic amphibole (KL13), 0.201 in a more normal hornblende (17-495), 0.275 in a manganoan cummingtonite (KL2), and 0.831 in a manganoan richterite (DHZ-55-9).

As discussed above, assignment of Ca to the M1,2,3 sites was used as a basis for rejection of Ca amphibole formulae. However, these analyses are plotted in dashed lines in Figure 3 to show the extent of this rejection, along with a few sodic amphiboles in which Ca was assigned to M1,2,3. Such an assignment is tentatively justified by Hawthorne (Chapter 1, Volume 9A). An alternative possibility is that there are actually vacancies in M1,2,3, tending toward a "dioctahedral" amphibole component as suggested by Thompson (1978).

The occupancy of the M4 site is most important in characterizing the calcic amphiboles, cummingtonites, and sodic amphiboles. Assignment of Mg to this site occurs mainly in Mg-rich orthoamphiboles and occurs in only six monoclinic amphibole analyses (Fig. 4). The largest value of 1.702 (Zotov and Sidorenko, 1967) is in an extremely Mg-rich gedrite.

In calcic amphiboles modest amounts of Fe^{2+} in M4 are characteristic, with a sharp peak at 0.05. The maximum amount of Fe^{2+} is 0.615 (ESHBL) in a hornblende separate coexisting with cummingtonite. Sodic amphiboles show a similar distribution with a maximum of 0.530 (KL13) in a riebeckite. Fe^{2+} in M4 is characteristic of both orthoamphiboles and cummingtonites, which show a broad distribution with a concentration near 1.80. The largest amount in an orthoamphibole is 1.952 (R1) in an intermediate gedrite, whereas cummingtonites reach 1.961 (KL12A).

Modest amounts of Mn are assigned to M4 in numerous calcic amphiboles, orthoamphiboles, and sodic amphiboles, but it can be a major constituent in manganoan cummingtonites. Maximum Mn in M4 of a cummingtonite is 1.843 in an

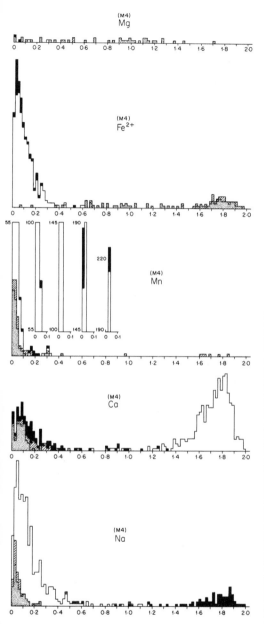

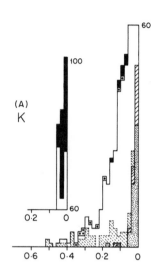

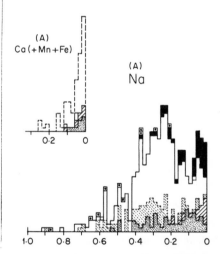

Figure 4. Histograms of inferred Mg, Fe²⁺, Mn, Ca, and Na in M4 in "accepted" wet chemical analyses of amphiboles. Stippled pattern indicates orthoamphiboles; lined pattern, cummingtonites; unpatterned, calcic amphiboles and barroisites; solid, sodic amphiboles; dotted squares for Na, richterites. Because the vertical scale was not great enough for Mn, the Mn peak has been chopped into several sections.

Figure 5. Histograms of inferred Na and K in the A-site in "accepted" wet chemical analyses of amphiboles. Also shown is the small amount of Ca (+ Mn + Fe) accepted in A in a few analyses. Stippled pattern indicates orthoamphiboles; lined pattern, cummingtonites; unpatterned, calcic amphiboles; solid, sodic amphiboles; dotted squares, richterites and arfvedsonites. Fine-dashed lined pattern indicates calcic amphiboles from charnockites and granulite facies rocks. Heavy-dashed outline indicates Ca assigned to M4 in "rejected" wet chemical analyses.

Mn-Zn cummingtonite (KL65), and the whole cummingtonite population is centered at higher Mn than the orthoamphiboles. The maximum value for calcic amphibole is 0.324 (KL12), for orthoamphibole 0.439 (KL14), and for zincian manganoan winchite is 0.301 (89407).

The distribution of Ca in M4 naturally portrays the dramatic distinction between calcic amphiboles on the one hand and Fe-Mg and sodic amphiboles on the other, with a very few assorted analyses of intermediate composition. The peak of Ca distribution is near 1.87 for calcic amphiboles and near 0.1 to 0.2 for sodic amphiboles. Most orthoamphiboles have Ca near or below 0.1, but one rather strange analysis shows 0.569 Ca (ANT-A). Cummingtonites tend to show higher Ca, in agreement with their pigeonite relatives, centered near 0.2 to 0.3, with one analysis showing 0.328 (VECU).[7]

The distribution of Na in M4 naturally separates sodic amphiboles from the calcic and Fe-Mg amphiboles. In the intermediate region, richterites are shown by dotted symbols, but there is some intermixing of amphiboles from various lists. The peak of Na for sodic amphiboles is near 1.8 to 1.9, of Na in calcic amphiboles near 0.1, of orthoamphiboles near 0.02 to 0.03, and about the same for cummingtonites. The maximum cited Na in M4 of orthoamphibole is 0.243 (DHZ-34-10, ferrogedrite, an analysis long suspected to be low in SiO_2); of cummingtonite is 0.188 (KL5B). For orthoamphiboles in plagioclase amphibolites, we find a common value of Na in M4 of about 0.08, apparently about the maximum amount of the large Na ions that can be fitted into M4 of this small-cation structure.

Assignment of Ca to the A-site is probably good grounds for rejection of an analysis. Calcic amphiboles from the Steffe list so rejected have nevertheless been plotted with dashed lines on Figure 5 to show the extent of this rejection. Also plotted are the few "accepted" other analyses requiring Ca in A. There seems little doubt that such assignments are due to analytical errors, most probably overestimation of SiO_2 or underestimation of Fe_2O_3.

The distribution of Na in the A-site is very revealing, particularly in light of the commonly cited amphibole end-members edenite, pargasite, eckermannite and richterite. The fact is that there is only a small handful of metamorphic amphiboles with Na in A greater than 0.5. On the other hand, there is a rather uniform distribution of calcic and orthorhombic amphiboles with Na in A between 0 and 0.4, with possibly a peak in the former near 0.25. Cummingtonites are clustered mainly below 0.1. The maximum values for Na in A are 0.913 in a calcic amphibole (17-495), 0.525 in an orthoamphibole (I34I), 0.188

----

[7]DHZ-36-16 shows 0.819, but Klein (1968) has proved this is an anthophyllite-tremolite mixture.

Table 2. Some extreme compositions of metamorphic amphiboles listed according to ions in various sites. The key to abbreviations is given below. DHZ-36-3 etc. refers to Deer, Howie and Zussman, Table 36, analysis 3. Asterisk indicates analysis number from Steffe (1979)

	A			M4						M1-M2-M3									T		
	K	Na	Ca	Na	Ca	Mn	Zn	Fe	Mg	Ca	Mn	Zn	Fe	Mg	Cr	Ti	Fe^{3+}	Al	Fe^{3+}	Al	Si
Calcic 14-5038	.505	.369		.475	1.524	.001					.065		2.367	.622		.206	.753	.987		2.551	5.449
Calcic Shimazaki 1	.684	.208			1.951	.038		.011					1.110	1.756		.461	.978	.695		3.487	4.513
Ortho I34I	.007	.525		.019	.042	.031		1.890					.467	3.007		.027	.133	1.364		2.047	5.953
Ortho JCS		1.000		.116	.011	.046		1.827					.036	3.053		.001	.597	1.313		2.795	5.205
Cumm DHZ-36-3		.126		.095	.151	.132		1.622					.626	3.626		.029	.052	.667		.810	7.190
Crossite DHZ-53-6	.106	.302		1.677	.323					.296	.017		1.311	1.598		.181	.953	.644		.692	7.308
Ortho FP-7		.031	.031		.067	.041		1.047	.845					4.886		.016	.098		.114	.106	7.780
Cumm DHZ-36-4	.012			.061	.300	.177		1.445					1.327	3.373		.067	.233		.147	.135	7.718
Sodic DHZ-54-14	.085			1.663	.042	.006		.202					.287	2.680			2.033		.202	.078	7.720
Calcic 16C-5319	.089	.072		.324	1.638	.009		.030					1.420	1.802		.049	.340	1.389		1.666	6.334
Calcic Doolan	.068	.206		.172	1.625	.030		.173					2.123	1.020		.022	.149	1.686		1.980	6.020
Ortho DHZ-34-10	.008	.111		.243	.005	.306		1.446					2.969	.007		.057	.261	1.706		1.953	6.047
Cumm DHZ-36-3		.126		.095	.151	.132		1.622					.626	3.626		.029	.052	.667		.810	7.190
Sodic LM-4	.011	.028		1.765	.155	.079		.079					.797	2.230		.014	.101	1.858		.264	7.736
Calcic 19B-5223	.381	.234		.208	1.609	.056		.127					1.696	1.679		.029	1.190	.406		2.061	5.939
Ortho B616	.056	.223	.006		.110	.011		1.879					.226	3.489		.092	.800	.393		1.670	6.330
Cumm DHZ-36-5	.029	.132		.042	.139	.021		1.798					1.532	3.200		.035	.233		.117	.304	7.579
Riebeckite DHZ-54-14	.085			1.663	.042	.006		.202					.287	2.680			2.033		.202	.078	7.720
Calcic 12-5132	.157	.562		.356	1.589	.001		.054					1.105	2.451		.393	.255	.772		2.247	5.753
Calcic Shimazaki 3	.705	.179			1.076	.024					.028		1.644	1.512		.520	.439	.857		3.220	4.780
Ortho R13	.045	.194		.153	.102	.022		1.723					1.515	2.798		.111	.125	.451		.882	7.118
Cumm DHZ-36-4	.012			.061	.300	.177		1.445					1.327	3.373		.067	.233		.147	.135	7.718
Arfv DHZ-57-7	.347	.573		1.827	.173					.284	.065		2.098	1.261		.234	.869	.189		.618	7.382
Calcic CRHB	.078	.890		.164	1.659	.014		.163					.117	4.041	.272	.031	.117	.422		1.675	6.325
Calcic 18-9	.021	.048		.022	1.966			.012					.030	4.920			.022	.028		.097	7.903
Ortho DHZ-34-1		.056			.496	.288			1.216					4.948			.052		.001	.105	7.894
Ortho R40		.106		.026				.626	1.348					4.940				.060		.141	7.859
Cumm YK-1	.010	.019	.010		.286	.024		1.690					.119	4.835		.008	.038		.070	.034	7.896
Rich Syn DHZ-55-1		.876		1.029	.971					.052				4.930			.018				8.033
Rich DHZ-55-2	.113	.362		.478	1.331	.191					.089			4.863			.030	.018		.042	7.958
Calcic 17-5521	.282	.414		.011	1.961	.028					.103		3.463	.828		.035	.463	.108		1.327	6.673
Ortho DHZ-34-10	.008	.111		.243	.005	.306		1.446					2.969	.007		.057	.261	1.706		1.953	6.047
Cumm DHZ-36-14	.024	.045		.049		.302		1.649					4.938	.010			.052		.036	.040	7.924
Riebeckite Hashimoto	.006			1.758	.152					.278	.102		2.595	.009		.032	1.788	.196		.117	7.883
Calcic KL-13	.057	.120		.399	1.442	.159					.376	1.049	.444	2.777			.328	.026		.132	7.868
Cumm KL-65		.023		.043	.082	1.843	.032					1.186	1.690	1.955				.169		.151	7.849
Mg-Riebeckite 89407	.054	.251		1.279	.420	.301					.223	.862	.396	2.442			1.077		.004	.102	7.894
Calcic KL-13	.057	.120		.399	1.442	.159					.376	1.049	.444	2.777			.328	.026		.132	7.868
Calcic 17-495	.045	.913		.221	1.707	.073					.201		.120	3.521		.018	.886	.254		1.912	6.088
Cumm KL-2		.017			.184	1.760					.275		.546	4.133				.046		.011	7.989
Rich DHZ-55-9	.317	.642		.931	.839	.230					.831			3.966		.011	.192		.012	.232	7.756
Calcic 14-5040	.545	.003		1.506	.494					.410	.137		1.181	.241		.190	2.387	.454		2.264	5.736
Crossite DHZ-53-6	.106	.302		1.677	.323					.296	.017		1.311	1.838		.181	.953	.644		.692	7.308
Riebeckite Hashimoto	.006			1.758	.152					.278	.102		2.595	.009		.032	1.788	.196		.117	7.883
Arfv DHZ-57-7	.347	.573		1.827	.173					.284	.065		2.098	1.261		.234	.869	.189		.618	7.382
Calcic 14-771	.020	.715		.123	1.742	.007			.127					4.019		.045	.544	.391		1.640	6.360
Calcic HBL PIRANI	.023	.144	.118		1.284	.023		.399	.294					4.825		.012	.119	.024		.590	7.410
Ortho Zotov	.027	.232		.063	.071			.164	1.702					3.829		.015	.033	1.123		1.385	6.615
Cumm KWCUM	.003	.030		.036	.232	.024		1.199	.509					4.812		.009	.002	.117		.195	7.805
Glaucophane E-2GL	.018	.007		1.726	.126	.051		.038	.059					3.121		.005	.768	1.106		.186	7.814
Calcic ESHBL	.065	.050		.086	1.298	.001		.615					.625	3.792		.061	.119	.403		.675	7.325
Ortho Ged-R1	.005	.395		.031		.017		1.952					.264	3.351		.053	.111	1.221		1.810	6.190
Cumm KL-12A		.009	.056			.039		1.961					2.126	2.833			.041		.002	.104	7.894
Riebeckite KL-13	.037	.256		.522	.891	.057		.530					.041	4.463			.496		.005	.264	7.731
Calcic KL-12	.020	.015		.114	1.562	.324					.353		.275	3.212			.168	.013		.104	7.896
Ortho KL-14				.008	.035	.439		1.140	.319					4.856			.080	.064		.018	7.982
Cumm KL-65		.023		.043	.082	1.843	.032					1.186	1.690	1.955				.169		.151	7.849
Sodic 89407	.054	.251		1.279	.420	.301					.223	.862	.396	2.442			1.077		.004	.102	7.894
Ortho Ant-A	.052	.156		.050	.569	.023		1.001	.357					4.353		.038	.122	.487		.843	7.157
Cumm VECU	.008	.042		.002	.328	.100		1.570					.417	4.271		.013	.200	.099		.371	7.629
Ortho DHZ-34-10	.008	.111		.243	.005	.306		1.446					2.969	.007		.057	.261	1.706		1.953	6.047
Cumm KL-5B		.008		.188	.154	1.658					.186		.301	4.513							8.045
Calcic 17-495	.045	.913		.221	1.707	.073					.201		.120	3.521		.018	.886	.254		1.912	6.088
Ortho I34I	.007	.525		.019	.042	.031		1.890					.467	3.007		.027	.133	1.364		2.047	5.953
Ortho JCS		1.000		.116	.011	.046		1.827					.036	3.053		.001	.597	1.313		2.795	5.205
Cumm DHZ-36-1		.181	.039		.166	.027		1.807					.216	4.445		.034	.088	.217		.629	7.371
Glaucophane 06G1		.377		1.856	.144					.030	.002		.442	2.909				1.617		.140	7.860
Rich Syn DHZ-55-1		.876		1.029	.971					.052				4.930			.018				8.033
Rich DHZ-55-9	.317	.642		.931	.839	.230					.831			3.966		.011	.192		.012	.232	7.756
Calcic 14-5374	.509	.250		.125	1.799	.013		.064					.833	2.822		.049	1.075	.222		2.029	5.971
Calcic Shimazaki 4	.746	.209			2.001					.064	.013		1.361	1.839		.405	.372	.946		3.052	4.948
Ortho FP-5	.171	.113	.019		.069	.020		.633	1.278					4.939		.016	.045		.083	.314	7.603
Ortho R19	.117	.060		.025	.187	.100		.422	1.266					4.155			.197	.648		1.001	6.999
Cumm DGCUM	.049			.026	.062	.028		1.849					.532	4.227		.038	.046	.157		.232	7.768
Riebeckite DHZ-54-9	.141	.013		1.413	.587						.018		1.361	1.908		.157	1.371		.087	.337	7.576
Arfv DHZ-57-7	.347	.573		1.827	.173					.284	.065		2.098	1.261		.234	.869	.189		.618	7.382
Calcic 17-5497	.137	.577		.175	1.779	.046					.028		3.317	.395		.136	.402	.722		1.936	6.064
Cumm YK-2	.005			.025	.179	.052		1.710					.066	4.794		.007	.133		.018	.036	7.946

14-5038*	Holm, 1971	analysis 1
Shimazaki-1	Shimazaki et al., in press	analysis 1
I34I	Robinson and Jaffe, 1969	analysis I34I
JCS	Schumacher, 1980	analysis 6F
DHZ-36-3		
DHZ-53-6		
FP-7	Fabries and Perseil, 1971	analysis 7
DHZ-36-5		
DHZ-54-14		
16C-5319*	Leake, 1971	analysis 5
Doolan	Doolan et al., 1978	Table 3, 3-1
DHZ-34-10		
DHZ-36-3		
LM-4	Makanjuola and Howie, 1972	analysis LM-4
19B-5223*	Fajklewicz, 1968	
B616	Beeson, 1978	analysis 616
DHZ-35-5		
DHZ-54-14		
12-5132*	Lovering and White, 1969	Table 11
Shimazaki-3	Shimazaki et al., in press	analysis 3
R-13	Rabbitt, 1948	analysis 13
DHZ-36-4		
DHZ-57-7		
CRHB	Varne, 1970	
18-9*	Leake, 1968	analysis 9
DHZ-34-1		
R40	Rabbitt, 1948	analysis 40
YK-1	Yakovleva and Kolesnikova, 1967	analysis 1
DHZ-55-1		
DHZ-55-2		
17-5521*	Nemec, 1970	analysis 2
DHZ-34-10		
DHZ-36-14		
Hashimoto	Hashimoto, 1973	
KL-13	Klein and Ito, 1968	Table 3 analysis 3
KL-65	Klein and Ito, 1968	analysis 89365
89407	Klein and Ito, 1968 called riebeckite by Klein	analysis 89407
KL-13	Klein and Ito, 1968	Table 3 analysis 3
17-495*	Leake, 1968	analysis 495
KL-2	Klein, 1964	Table 2 analysis 2
DHZ-55-9		
14-5040*	Holm, 1971	
DHZ-53-6		
Hashimoto	Hashimoto, 1973	
DHZ-57-7		
14-771*	Leake, 1968	analysis 771
HBL PIRANI	Pirani, 1952	
Zotov	Zotov and Sidorenko, 1967	
KWCUM	Kisch and Warnaars, 1969	
E-2GL	Ernst, 1964	
ESHBL	Eskola, 1950	
R-1	Rabbitt, 1948	analysis 1
KL-12A	Klein, 1966	analysis 12A
KL-13	Klein and Ito, 1968	analysis 3
KL-12	Klein and Ito, 1968 Ca in A includes .026 Mn, .030 Ca	analysis 2
KL-14	Klein, 1966	analysis 14
KL-65	Klein and Ito, 1968	analysis 89365
89407	Klein and Ito, 1968 called riebeckite by Klein	analysis 89407
Ant-A	Starkov, 1972	analysis A
VECU	Vernon, 1962	
DHZ-34-10		
KL-5B	Klein, 1966	analysis 5B
17-495*	Leake, 1968	analysis 495
I34I	Robinson and Jaffe, 1969	analysis I34I
JCS	Schumacher, 1980	analysis 6F
DHZ-36-1		
06G1	Dobretsov et al., 1971	
DHZ-55-1		
DHZ-55-9		
14-5374*	Serdyuchenko, 1968	analysis 4
Shimazaki-4	Shimazaki et al., in press	analysis 4
FP-5	Fabries and Perseil, 1971	analysis 5
R19	Rabbitt, 1948	analysis 19
DGCUM	DasGupta, 1972	
DHZ-54-9		
DHZ-57-7		
17-5497*	Dimanche, 1970	analysis 1
YK-2	Yakovleva and Kolesnikova, 1967	analysis 2

in a cummingtonite (KL5B), 0.876 in synthetic richterite (DHZ-55-1), and 0.642
in natural richterite (DHZ-55-9). Schumacher (1980), with corrected probe
analyses, has recently extended the range of orthoamphiboles to 1.000. Calcic
amphiboles from charnockites and granulite facies rocks (dashed pattern) show
slightly higher average Na than other calcic amphiboles.

K in the A-site is minor in most sodic amphiboles, orthoamphiboles, and
cummingtonites but can be quite important in some calcic amphiboles, richterites,
and arfvedsonites, particularly calcic amphiboles from charnockites and granulite facies rocks (dashed pattern). The maximum K values are for calcic amphibole 0.509 (14-5374), for an Mg anthophyllite in which biotite contamination
can be suspected 0.171 (FP-5), for a low Al gedrite 0.117 (R19), for cummingtonite 0.049 (DGCUM), for riebeckite 0.141 (DHZ-54-9), and for arfvedsonite
0.347 (DHZ-57-7). In recent probe analyses of unusual calcic amphiboles from
skarns in Japan, K in A extends to 0.746 (Shimazaki 4).

Composition space of metamorphic amphiboles and its population

The composition space of amphiboles has been graphically expressed in
about as many different ways as there are authors on the subject. Most of
these methods are based on the amounts of certain amphibole substitutions,
commonly plotted on orthogonal coordinates. These plots are commonly very
helpful in understanding the compositional features of the amphibole but are
very awkward for portraying other minerals with which the amphibole might be
interacting. In order to avoid this onanistic point of view, we have decided
first to portray the amphiboles in a chemical space in which all other significant phases can be plotted. This approach begins with a highly simplified
figure in which all of the chemical components can be included.

In Figure 6 all chemical components are combined into three groups, thus
making possible a two-dimensional view of the multi-dimensional amphibole composition space, as well as the compositions of any other coexisting minerals.
This is very similar to Figure 4 presented in the pyroxene volume last year
(Robinson, 1980), but differs in that the "A" apex is not $R_2^{3+}O_3$ but merely
R^{3+}. This has the double advantage of expanding the graphical extent of many
solid solutions of interest and of portraying all "tschermak's-type" solid
solution series as parallel straight lines. For this figure the "S" apex is
merely Si^{4+}. The "A" apex includes all R^{3+} ions such as Al^{3+}, Fe^{3+}, Cr^{3+},
etc. As explained last year, Ti^{4+} is also placed in the "A" apex by combining
it with an equivalent amount of R^{2+} (an ilmenite-like substitution) to produce
two "mean" R^{3+} ions. Thus, for each Ti^{4+} there are two "mean" R^{3+} ions added,
and one ion must be subtracted from the R^{2+} list. The "NCFM" apex includes all

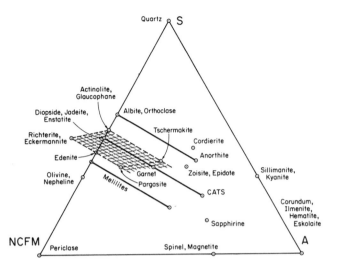

Figure 6. The field of amphibole compositions in the consolidated triangle S-A-NCFM, where S = Si, A = $Al+Fe^{3+}+2Ti-Na-K$, and NCFM = $Ca+Fe^{2+}+Mn+Mg+Zn+2Na+2K+2Li-Ti$. Before normalization to 1.00, S+A+NCFM is equal to the cation sum of the structural formula. Compositions of other minerals, mostly anhydrous, that are among the possible breakdown products of amphiboles at high metamorphic grade are also shown.

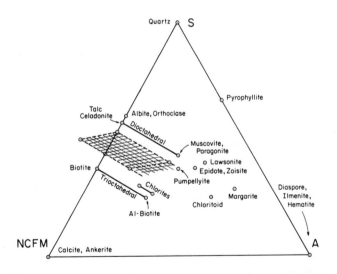

Figure 7. The field of amphibole compositions in the consolidated triangle S-A-NCFM shown with other minerals, mostly hydrous, that are among the phases that react to produce amphiboles at low metamorphic grade.

23

R^{2+} ions: Ca^{2+} (C), Fe^{2+} (F), Mg^{2+} (M), Mn^{2+}, etc. It also contains all R^{1+} ions such as Na (N), K, or Li. In this case, each R^{1+} ion is combined with an R^{3+} ion to produce two "mean" R^{2+} ions. Thus, for each R^{1+} there are two "mean" R^{2+} ions added, and one ion must be subtracted from the R^{3+} list. This scheme nicely covers the many NaAl and $NaFe^{3+}$ couples to be found in amphibole and many other minerals. In those amphiboles (richterite, eckermannite, etc.) where Na in the A-site is compensated by Na in M4, the "A" composition value becomes negative.

The complete major-element plotting parameters for Figure 6 are then as follows:

$$"S" = Si^{4+}$$

$$"A" = Al^{3+} + Fe^{3+} + Cr^{3+} + 2Ti^{4+} - Na^{1+} - K^{1+} - Li^{1+}$$

$$"NCFM" = Ca^{2+} + Fe^{2+} + Mg^{2+} + Mn^{2+} + Zn^{2+} + 2Na^{1+} + 2K^{1+} + 2Li^{1+} - Ti^{4+}\ .$$

If properly computed, the sum of S + A + NCFM should be the cation sum of the structural formula.

In Figure 6 the Si-rich edge of the amphibole field (actinolite, glaucophane, tschermakite, etc.) contains all amphiboles that have only pyroxene-like substitutions. Note that these compositions lie between the pyroxene line on Figure 6 and the talc composition in Figure 7. The Si-poor edge of the field (richterite, eckermannite, edenite, pargasite) contains all amphiboles with full A-sites and is an effective limit to amphibole compositions in this direction. The A-rich edge of the field (pargasite, tschermakite) is drawn where tetrahedral R^{3+} is equal to two, but numerous studies suggest this is not a true crystal-chemical limit. This is recognized by the dashed extensions on the A-rich corners of the field.

In Figure 6 the amphibole field is shown together with a variety of anhydrous or nearly anhydrous phases that could be among the breakdown products of amphiboles in high-grade metamorphism. In Figure 7 the amphibole field is shown together with a variety of volatile-rich minerals from which amphiboles could be produced during low-grade metamorphism.

Figure 8A is an enlarged version of the amphibole field in Figure 6 on which is plotted the entire sample of calcic amphibole analyses. Figure 8B is the same, with orthoamphiboles, cummingtonites, and sodic amphiboles.

The distribution of calcic amphibole compositions in Figure 8A is clear cut. There is a composition trend from the actinolite apex to a powerful concentration on the silica-rich side of the tschermakite-pargasite line, and with a possible further trend from there toward pargasite. Only a very few

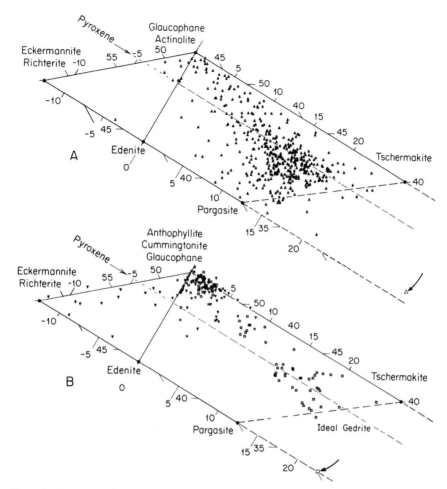

Figure 8. Population of wet chemical analyses of metamorphic amphiboles in the amphibole composition field within the condensed composition triangle S-A-NCFM (see Fig. 6). (A) Population by 434 calcic amphiboles (triangles) and sodic-calcic barroisites. Triangle with arrow at very low Si value is the most subsilicic hornblende of Shimazaki *et al.* (in press). (B) Population of 28 cummingtonites (X), 71 orthoamphiboles (squares), and 85 sodic amphiboles (inverted triangles) including sodic-calcic richterites. Square with arrow at very low Si value is the most subsilicic gedrite of J.C. Schumacher (1980 and unpublished data). For detailed comments see text.

even approach the tschermakite or pargasite apices, and the area around the edenite composition is totally devoid of analyses. This further supports the suggestions of Robinson *et al.* (1971b) that metamorphic hornblendes can be thought of, to a crude first approximation, as a solid solution between actinolite and an "ideal hornblende" composition approximately half-way between the tschermakite and pargasite apices. The extremely sub-silicic amphiboles reported by Shimazaki *et al.* (in press) seem to be a continuation of this trend. It is still not known whether this trend is related to some obscure ordering scheme in the amphibole structure, to rock bulk composition, to buffering by coexisting phases, or to some combination of all of these. It is interesting that the pyroxene line passes just on the silica-rich side of the greatest concentration, so that a sizeable fraction of calcic amphiboles show normative quartz, rather than normative olivine and nepheline.

In Figure 8B, most sodic amphiboles cluster near the "glaucophane" apex, with a very sparse scatter toward richterite-eckermannite. Cummingtonites cluster near the "actinolite" apex, indicating their very simple composition, although a few that coexist with hornblende show some solid solution in that direction. A large number of orthoamphiboles cluster near the "actinolite" apex, but there is a continuous trend from there out to an "ideal gedrite" composition halfway between the "tschermakite" and "pargasite" apices. The probe analyses of extremely subsilicic orthoamphiboles reported by Schumacher (1980) and some gedrites reported by Berg and Wiebe (1978) lie on the pargasitic side of this trend. Experience leads us to question analyses closest to the "actinolite-tschermakite" line, particularly the ferrogedrite (Seki and Yamasaki, 1957) closest to the "tschermakite" apex. It is striking that there are no analyses close to the "gedrite" end member (i.e., pure tschermakite substitution) as given in various textbooks and in the formal amphibole nomenclature (Leake, 1978).

The two-dimensional image of amphibole space in Figures 6, 7, and 8 may be expanded into three dimensions by subdividing the components of one of the apices. To establish Figure 9A, the "NCFM" apex of Figure 6 was split into "N" and "CFM" components, creating an "S-A-N-CFM" tetrahedron and turning the area of amphibole compositions into a three-dimensional volume. In Figure 9B and in an enlarged view in Figure 9C, the amphibole volume (and some related phases) is viewed in projection from the "S" apex of the tetrahedron toward the "A-N-CFM" base. The amphibole composition volume is identical, except for orientation and size, to the volume suggested by Smith (1959) and used in various studies, including the report on amphibole nomenclature by Leake (1978). In this view the top of the volume is the triangular plane actinolite-tschermakite-glaucophane. The parallel base of the volume is a four-sided plane edenite-pargasite-eckermannite-richterite. The top of the volume is connected to the base by four inclined sides, the four-sided plane actinolite-tschermakite-pargasite-edenite; the triangular plane actinolite-edenite-richterite; the four-sided plane actinolite-glaucophane-eckermannite-richterite; and the four-sided plane tschermakite-pargasite-eckermannite-glaucophane. The first three planes are true limits to amphibole compositions. As pointed out above, extra tschermak's-type substitution with more than two tetrahedral R^{3+} permits compositions to extend beyond the tschermakite-pargasite-eckermannite-glaucophane plane.

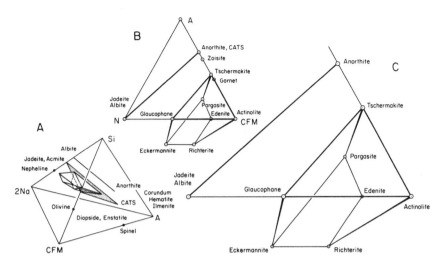

Figure 9. (A) **Expansion** of the S-A-NCFM triangle into an S-A-N-CFM tetrahedron, **showing the** volume of amphibole compositions cut by the pyroxene composition plane (stippled) and in relation to the plagioclase composition line. (B) A view of the same composition tetrahedron, amphibole composition volume, and plagioclase line from the S apex. The view in B may also be **considered as a view** of an A-N-C-FM tetrahedron viewed parallel to the C-FM axis. (C) Enlarged view of the amphibole volume.

The plotting parameters for Figure 9 are as follows:

$$"A" \quad = Al^{3+} + Fe^{3+} + Cr^{3+} + 2Ti^{4+} - Na^{1+} - K^{1+} - Li^{1+}$$

$$"CFM" = Ca^{2+} + Fe^{2+} + Mg^{2+} + Mn^{2+} + Zn^{2+} - Ti^{4+}$$

$$"N" \quad = 2Na^{1+} + 2K^{1+} + 2Li^{1+} .$$

Again, as in Figure 6, some amphibole compositions (eckermannite, richterite) have negative values of "A" and plot outside the volume of the "S-A-N-CFM" tetrahedron. Figure 10A is an enlarged view of the amphibole volume in Figure 9, in which is plotted the entire sample of calcic amphibole analyses. Figure 10B is the same with sodic and iron-magnesium amphiboles.

The picture one gets from Figure 10A is a population of calcic amphiboles close to but *not on* the actinolite-tschermakite-pargasite-edenite plane, as a result of some substitution of Na in M4 (glaucophane-like substitution). Although a few analyses lie beyond the tschermakite-pargasite-eckermannite-glaucophane plane, most lie well within it, as seen also in Figure 8A. Figure 10A again strongly emphasizes the absence of analyses approximating tschermakite in composition and analyses along the actinolite-tschermakite line.

The anthophyllite-gedrite trend is well shown in Figure 10B, as is the fact that it lies slightly closer to tschermakite than does the trend for calcic amphiboles. These analyses cannot deviate far from the actinolite-tschermakite-pargasite-edenite surface because of the inability of the orthorhombic amphibole to

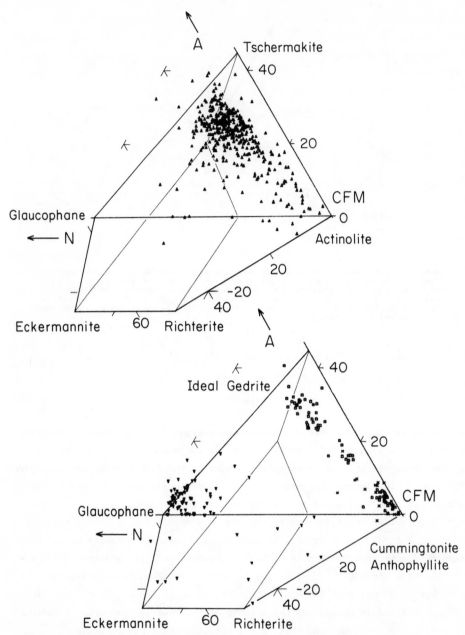

Figure 10. (A; upper) Population of wet chemical analyses of metamorphic calcic amphiboles in the amphibole composition volume in the S-A-N-CFM tetrahedron (see Fig. 9) viewed from the S apex (includes sodic-calcic barroisites). (B; lower) Population of wet chemical analyses of metamorphic cummingtonite (X), orthoamphibole (squares), and sodic amphibole (inverted triangles) in the amphibole composition volume in the S-A-N-CFM tetrahedron, viewed from the S apex (includes sodic-calcic richterites).

accommodate substantial Na in M4. The array of sodic amphiboles is concentrated close to the glaucophane apex of Figure 10B, with some substitutions toward the actinolite-tschermakite-pargasite-edenite plane. There are very few metamorphic amphiboles showing substitutions between glaucophane (riebeckite) and eckermannite (arfvedsonite) and very few metamorphic richterites.

Figure 11 is another view of the amphibole composition volume in the tetrahedron "S-A-N-CFM" of Figure 9, but rather than viewed from the "S" apex as in Figure 9B, the volume is viewed from the actinolite apex and projected onto the "S-A-N" face. This projection is topologically identical to the reciprocal square projection of Robinson *et al.* (1971b). It has the property of showing the exact coupled substitution mechanism and *direction* by which an amphibole composition differs from actinolite (or anthophyllite), although it is incapable of showing the *amount* of such substitution (the "buckshot" approach). For analyses close to the actinolite projection point, such directions are subject to random error; hence, such analyses are eliminated for plots in this projection. Those faces of the amphibole composition volume that *have actinolite as an apex* appear as lines on Figure 11, the triangular faces as the lines tschermakite-glaucophane and edenite-richterite, the four-sided faces as the lines tschermakite-pargasite-edenite, and glaucophane-eckermannite-richterite. The two four-sided faces that *do not have actinolite as an apex* appear in projections as pargasite-edenite-richterite-eckermannite, the face that describes compositions will full A-sites; and tschermakite-pargasite-eckermannite-glaucophane, the face limited either by having two octahedral Al or two tetrahedral Al. Some natural compositions pass beyond this face in the pargasite-tschermakite region.

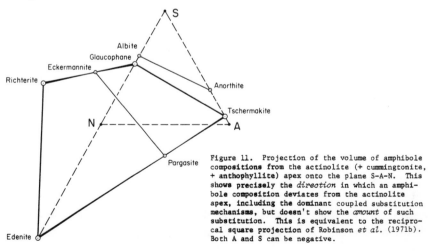

Figure 11. Projection of the volume of amphibole compositions from the actinolite (+ cummingtonite, + anthophyllite) apex onto the plane S-A-N. This shows precisely the *direction* in which an amphibole composition deviates from the actinolite apex, including the dominant coupled substitution mechanisms, but doesn't show the *amount* of such substitution. This is equivalent to the reciprocal square projection of Robinson *et al.* (1971b). Both A and S can be negative.

29

In Figure 11 values of both "A" and "S" can be negative, the latter as a result of the choice of the actinolite projection point and "S-A-N" target plane. Plotting parameters for Figure 11 are as follows:

$$S_{act} = Si - \frac{8}{7}(Ca + Fe^{2+} + Mg + Mn + Zn - Ti^{4+})$$
$$"A" = Al^{3+} + Fe^{3+} + Cr^{3+} + 2Ti^{4+} - Na^{1+} - K^{1+} - Li^{1+}$$
$$"N" = 2Na^{1+} + 2K^{1+} + 2Li^{1+} .$$

An advantage of Figure 11 over the reciprocal square projection of Robinson *et al.* (1971b) is that compositions can be plotted directly from formula ratios without going through formal site assignment. Other minerals can be shown if needed.

Figure 12A is the actinolite projection of Figure 11 with all calcic amphiboles and sodic-calcic barroisites and winchites of the representative sample plotted. Because the projection provides an end-on view of the actinolite-hornblende trend of Figure 10A, the "buckshot" approach is greatly emphasized. This figure demonstrates the elevation of most calcic amphiboles away from the actinolite-tschermakite-pargasite-edenite plane (a line in this projection) as a result of Na substitution in M4, with a mean value close to 0.2 for hornblendes that have nearly 2.0 tetrahedral Al.

In Figure 12B orthoamphiboles are seen in projection from anthophyllite along the anthophyllite-gedrite trend. This concentration of points, as expected from the discussion above, lies at lower values of Na in M4 (i.e., glaucophane component), as compared to the concentration of calcic amphiboles, and also lies slightly closer to the tschermakite apex. A few aberrant points are orthoamphiboles fairly close to the projection point with unusual (possibly erroneous) proportions of A-occupancy and tetrahedral Al. Cummingtonites, because of their proximity to the cummingtonite apex (Fig. 10B), are omitted. Sodic amphiboles have a very strong concentration close to the glaucophane (+ riebeckite) apex, with a slight trend in the general direction of the "bullseye" for calcic amphiboles of Figure 12A.

Figure 13, like Figure 9, is derived from a tetrahedral expansion of Figure 6. In this case, however, both "N" and "C" are separated from "FM" before viewing from the "S" apex. This figure is somewhat analogous to the classic ACF diagram of metamorphic petrology and effectively shows the separation between sodic and calcic and iron-magnesium amphiboles, as well as a variety of coexisting minerals including plagioclase. If a quartz projection is employed, then the triangle "A-NC-FM" can be expanded into "A-N-C-FM" or "A-NC-F-M" tetrahedra. A version of the former was effectively used by Ernst

30

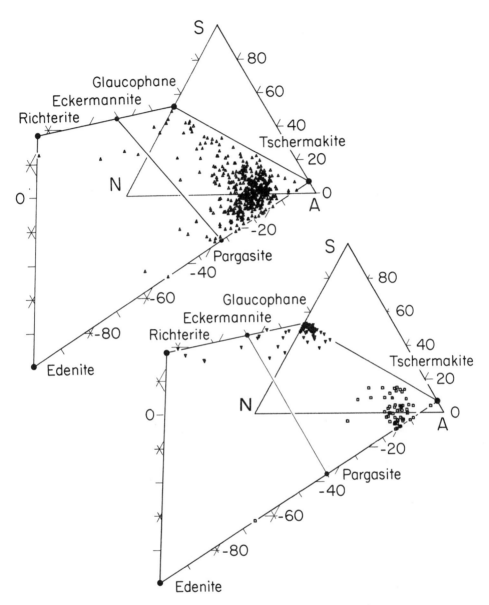

Figure 12. (A; above) The population of wet chemical analyses
of **metamorphic calcic amphiboles** in the amphibole composition
volume (see Fig. 9) as viewed in projection from the actinolite **apex** onto the S-A-N plane (also includes sodic-calcic
barroisites). Actinolites close to the projection point are
not shown. (B; to the right) The population of wet chemical
analyses of metamorphic orthoamphiboles (squares) and sodic
amphiboles and sodic-calcic richterites (inverted triangles)
in the amphibole composition volume as viewed in projection
from the actinolite (anthophyllite) apex onto the S-A-N
plane. Anthophyllites close to the projection point are not
shown.

(1963a) to explain equilibria in glaucophane schists. A plagioclase-projected modification of the latter was employed by Robinson and Jaffe (1969b) and Robinson *et al.* (1971b) to portray iron-magnesium amphibole assemblages.

In Figure 13, the calcic and sodic amphiboles form a composition poly-hedron topologically similar to the polyhedron in Figure 9. The Fe-Mg amphi-boles, on the other hand, lie very close to the surface of a plane that is topologically similar to and parallel to the plane actinolite-tschermakite-pargasite-edenite of calcic amphiboles. This is because Fe-Mg amphiboles do not normally take in significant amounts of Na in M4. The solid line in the Fe-Mg amphibole field and the dashed line in the sodic-calcic amphibole field are the anthophyllite-gedrite and actinolite-hornblende trends, respectively, of Figures 8 and 10.

Figure 14 is an enlarged view of Figure 13 in which the entire represen-tative sample is plotted. Except for the separation of the Fe-Mg amphiboles, the features of Figure 14 are fairly similar to those of Figure 10. However,

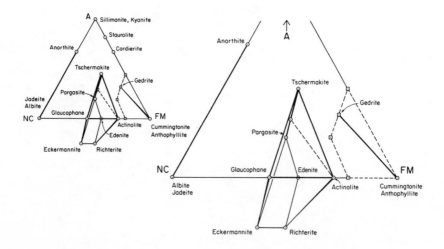

Figure 13. Expansion of S-A-NCFM triangle into an S-A-NC-FM tetrahedron. The tetrahedron is viewed from the S apex and shows the three-dimensional volume of calcic and sodic amphiboles, and the essentially planar field of cummingtonites and orthoamphiboles. A solid line shows the solid solution series from anthophyllite to gedrite, and the nearly parallel dashed line shows a similar series from actinolite to "ideal hornblende" (between tschermakite and pargasite). This may also be considered as a view of an A-N-C-FM tetrahedron viewed parallel to the N-C axis. Thus Figures 9 (top) and 13, and their analogous computer plots, Figures 10 and 14, are in a crude way "stereoscopic" pairs.

32

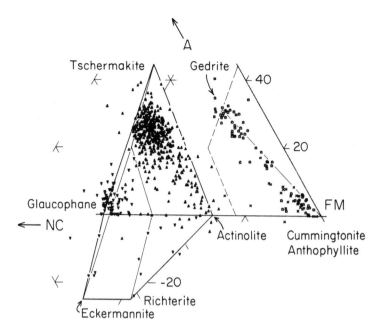

Figure 14. Population of wet chemical analyses of metamorphic
amphiboles in the S-A-NC-FM tetrahedron as viewed from the S
apex (see Fig. 13). This shows the distribution of cummingtonites (X), orthoamphiboles (squares), calcic amphiboles and
sodic calcic barroisites (triangles), and sodic amphiboles
and sodic-calcic richterites (inverted triangles).

because of the different orientation of the tschermakite-glaucophane-ecker-
mannite-pargasite plane, it is easier to see how few analyses really plot beyond it, except in the vicinity of glaucophane.

Robinson (1980) showed that all octahedral R^{3+} substitutions in pyroxenes
are compensated either by tetrahedral Al (in the "A" component) or by Na^{1+} in
M2 (in the "N" component). These two extremes were taken as opposite ends of
a triangular reciprocal prism, the edges of which were 6-coordinated Al (+ Cr),
Fe^{3+}, and $Fe^{2+}_{.5}Ti^{4+}_{.5}$ (his Fig. 13, p. 440). The same octahedral R^{3+} ions in
amphiboles in Figure 15 are compensated by the same pyroxene-like mechanisms,
the main differences being that in amphiboles the sites are differently named
and that Na^{1+} in M4 (M2 of pyroxene) may also be compensated by Na^{1+} in the A
site. In the chemographic scheme used here, amphiboles with this richterite-
like NaNa-substitution are shown with negative amounts of the "A" chemical
component expressed as a negative distance along the length of the prism
(Fig. 15).

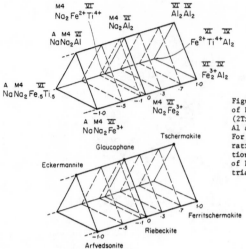

Figure 15. Composition prism showing proportions of R^{3+} octahedral ions, Al, Fe^{3+}, and $Fe^{2+}_{.5}Ti^{4+}_{.5}$ ($2Ti^{4+}$) versus the proportion between tetrahedral Al and Na in M4 compensation mechanisms ($A/2R^{3+}$). For amphiboles containing NaNa substitutions this ratio can be negative. Lower prism shows positions of some named end members. Various parts of Figure 17 represent plots of data from various triangular slices through Figure 15.

The *amount* of compensation needed for the R^{3+} ions is equal to the "A" substitution plus the "N" substitution minus that amount of "N" substitution expressed as "N" in the A-site coupled with tetrahedral Al (edenite-like substitution), or expressed as "N" in coupled NaNa-substitution (richterite-like). The amount of "N" in these substitutions is equal to two times the total amount of tetrahedral Al minus the amount of tetrahedral Al in the "A" component (which is always half the "A" component). Thus,

$$R^{3+} = \frac{\text{"A"} + \text{"N"} - 2[(8-Si) - \frac{1}{2}\text{"A"}]}{2} .$$

On the same basis the *proportion* of the "A" and "N" compensating mechanisms, which is the distance along the length of the prism, is equal to:

$$\frac{\text{"A"}}{\text{"A"} + \text{"N"} - 2[(8-Si) - \frac{1}{2}\text{"A"}]} \quad \text{or} \quad \frac{A}{2R^{3+}}$$

which can vary from 1 through 0 to $-\infty$. Because such proportions become indeterminate as R^{3+} approaches zero, and because one is not much interested in R^{3+} compensation for very low values, only analyses with R^{3+} greater than 0.2 were considered further in this respect. With this proviso, $A/2R^{3+}$ cannot go below -5.

The orthogonal axes in Figure 16 represent the *amount* of R^{3+} substitution plotted vertically and the proportion of R^{3+} compensation, the ratio $A/2R^{3+}$, plotted horizontally. For some amphibole compositions there is reason to suspect that R^{3+} is limited to 2, for example in glaucophane when all M2 sites are filled by Al. However, the inclusion of Ti^{4+} as $2R^{3+}$ ions considerably

34

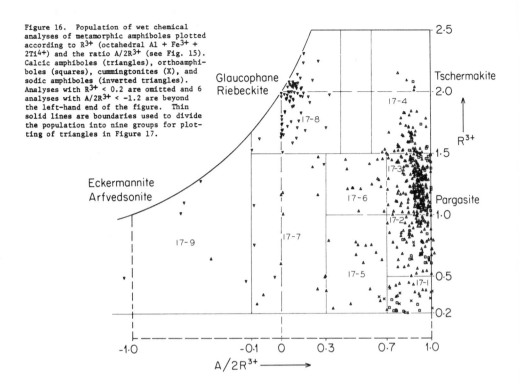

Figure 16. Population of wet chemical analyses of metamorphic amphiboles plotted according to R^{3+} (octahedral Al + Fe^{3+} + $2Ti^{4+}$) and the ratio $A/2R^{3+}$ (see Fig. 15). Calcic amphiboles (triangles), orthoamphiboles (squares), cummingtonites (X), and sodic amphiboles (inverted triangles). Analyses with $R^{3+} < 0.2$ are omitted and 6 analyses with $A/2R^{3+} < -1.2$ are beyond the left-hand end of the figure. Thin solid lines are boundaries used to divide the population into nine groups for plotting of triangles in Figure 17.

expands this limit and theoretically could lead to an R^{3+} of 4 with all M2 sites filled by Ti. The ratio $A/2R^{3+}$ is, as stated above, the distance along the length of the prism. All analyses with R^{3+} above 0.2 are shown.

The distribution of analytical points on Figure 16 should come as no surprise in light of previous figures. Most metamorphic amphiboles with substantial R^{3+} substitution are mainly compensated by tetrahedral Al, the notable exceptions being glaucophanes and riebeckites. The rest of the amphibole space of Figure 16 is sparsely populated, and there are no analyses with R^{3+} greater than 1.5 intermediate between glaucophane and tschermakite (i.e., barroisites of the formula presented by Leake, 1978).

In order to explore the proportion of different R^{3+} substitutions, i.e., 6-coordinated Al, Fe^{3+}, and $Fe^{2+}Ti^{4+}$ ($2Ti^{4+}$) in different amphibole groups, the analyses were sorted into classes. In one direction they were subdivided into the following classes of $A/2R^{3+}$, which are equivalent to thick slices of the triangular prism of Figure 15: less than -0.1, -0.1 to 0.3, +0.3 to +0.7, and +0.7 to 1.0. In the other direction they were sorted into classes according to the amount of R^{3+}: 0.2 to 0.5, 0.5 to 1.0, 1.0 to 1.5, and greater than 1.5. A ternary plot of Al (+ Cr), Fe^{3+}, and $2Ti^{4+}$ is then

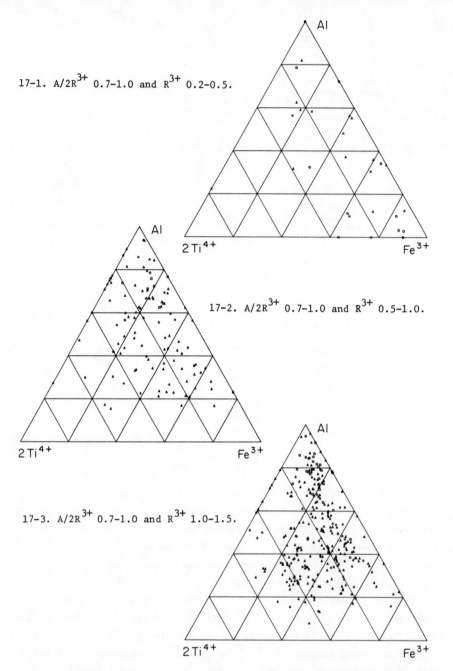

17-1. A/2R^{3+} 0.7-1.0 and R^{3+} 0.2-0.5.

17-2. A/2R^{3+} 0.7-1.0 and R^{3+} 0.5-1.0.

17-3. A/2R^{3+} 0.7-1.0 and R^{3+} 1.0-1.5.

Figure 17. Triangular plots of the proportions of octahedral Al, Fe^{3+}, and 2Ti^{4+} for each of the nine groups outlined in Figure 16. For groups 17-1, 17-2, 17-3, and 17-4, the R^{3+} substitutions are mainly compensated by tetrahedral Al as in calcic amphiboles and orthoamphiboles and a few cummingtonites. Groups 17-5 and 17-6 are calcic and sodic-calcic amphiboles and two cummingtonites with R^{3+} more or less equally compensated by tetrahedral Al and Na in M4. Groups 17-7 and 17-8 are sodic and sodic-calcic amphiboles with R^{3+} substitution mainly compensated by Na in M4. Group 17-9 includes all metamorphic amphiboles dominated by the Na in A - Na in M4 coupled substitution.

36

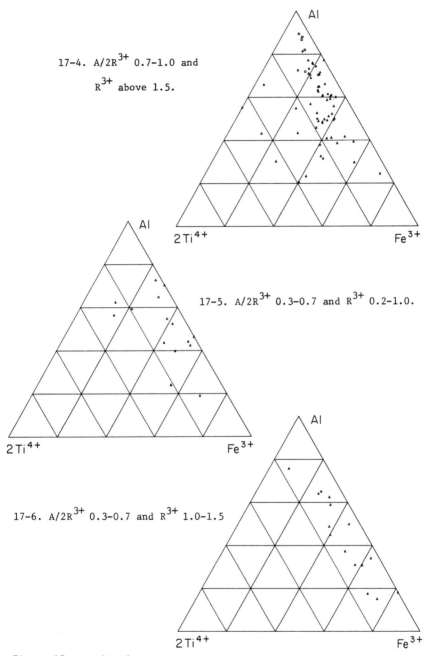

17-4. $A/2R^{3+}$ 0.7-1.0 and R^{3+} above 1.5.

17-5. $A/2R^{3+}$ 0.3-0.7 and R^{3+} 0.2-1.0.

17-6. $A/2R^{3+}$ 0.3-0.7 and R^{3+} 1.0-1.5

Figure 17, continued

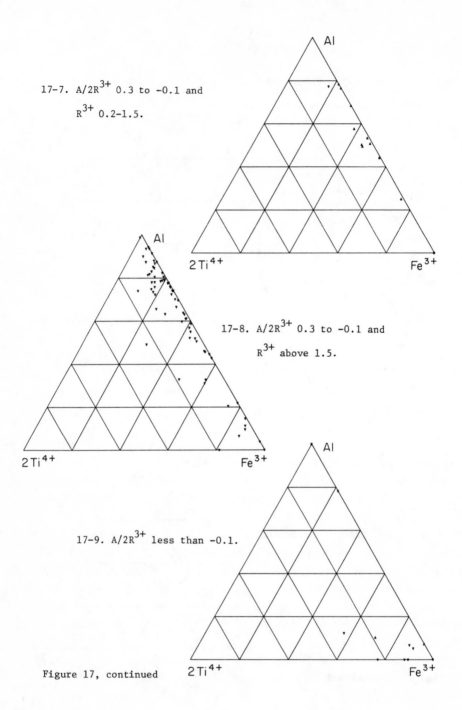

17-7. A/2R^{3+} 0.3 to -0.1 and R^{3+} 0.2-1.5.

17-8. A/2R^{3+} 0.3 to -0.1 and R^{3+} above 1.5.

17-9. A/2R^{3+} less than -0.1.

Figure 17, continued

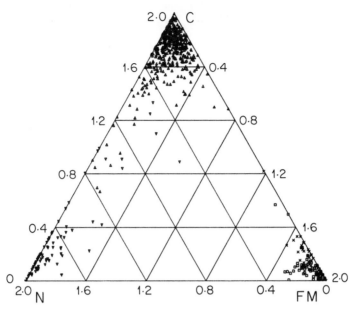

Figure 18. Population of wet chemical analyses of metamorphic amphiboles in terms of Ca (C), Na (N), and Mn + Fe + Mg (FM) in the M4 site. This separates metamorphic amphiboles into three major groups: Fe-Mg, calcic, and sodic, with a minor population of sodic-calcic amphiboles.

given in Figure 17 for all analyses present in each pigeonhole of Figure 16. These show the following significant features concerning trivalent and quadrivalent ions in octahedral sites.

In calcic amphiboles where R^{3+} substitutions are mainly compensated by tetrahedral Al (Figs. 17-1 through 17-4), Al makes up from 10 to 100% of the R^{3+}, Fe^{3+} from 0 to 80% of R^{3+}, and $2Ti^{4+}$ from 0 to 55% of R^{3+}. In ortho-amphiboles, Al makes up 40 to 100% of R^{3+}, Fe^{3+} from 0 to a maximum of 50% of R^{3+}, and $2Ti^{4+}$ from 0 to 30% of R^{3+}. The maximum of $2Ti^{4+}$ is 0.222 (see Table 2), which compares with a maximum of 0.786 for calcic amphibole. In the class of amphiboles with $A/2R^{3+} < 0.7$ (Figs. 17-5 through 17-9), few contain more than 20% $2Ti^{4+}$. Among glaucophanes and riebeckites (Figure 17-8), there is a continuous population from nearly pure Al as R^{3+} to 60% Fe^{3+}, and there are only a handful of metamorphic amphiboles more riebeckitic than this. In the extremely sodic amphiboles of group 17-9, most are dominated by Fe^{3+}.

As pointed out above, the greatest distinction among the major amphibole groups is in the occupancy of the M4 site. This is portrayed for the entire population in Figure 18, which is complementary to the histograms of Figure 4. There is a notable lack of solid solution between the Fe-Mg amphiboles and the others, whereas there is a sparse population of analyses between calcic and sodic amphiboles that can probably be explained by the behavior of miscibility gaps within this region. One cummingtonite point with extremely high Ca has

39

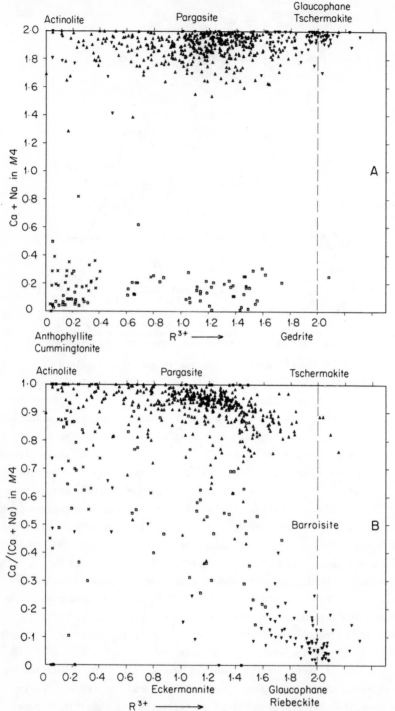

Figure 19. Population of wet chemical analyses of metamorphic amphiboles plotted according to four combinations of four different parameters. Calcic amphiboles (triangles), orthoamphiboles (squares), cummingtonites (X), and sodic amphiboles (inverted triangles). Various end members are indicated.

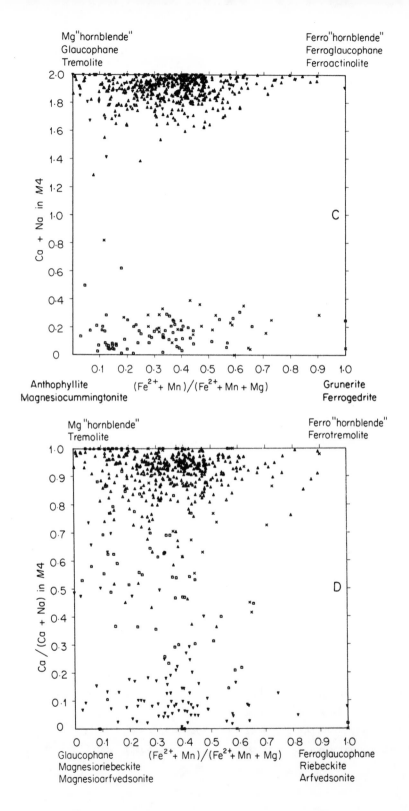

41

been proven by Klein (1968) to be a physical mixture of anthophyllite and tremolite, and should not have been included in our data. The analysis point closest to the center of the triangle is the riebeckite-tremolite from Labrador reported by Klein (1966) in which the M4 site includes 0.891 Ca, 0.530 Fe^{2+}, 0.522 Na and 0.057 Mn. Two orthoamphiboles are extremely rich in Ca. One of these (DHZ-1) is Mn-rich and may contain admixed Mn-tremolite well known from the same locality. The other (ANT-1, Starkov, 1972, see Table 2) may suffer from a similar problem. Otherwise, it can be seen that cummingtonites tend to be richer in Ca than orthoamphiboles, while the latter tend to show slightly more Na in M4.

Robinson (1980) pointed out that M2 occupancy is principally responsible for mutual solid solution in pyroxenes and for the position of analyses in the so-called "pyroxene quadrilateral." The same is true of the analogous amphibole quadrilateral. M4 occupancy can be simply expressed in two ways: (1) Ca + Na in M4; i.e., the sum of large cations versus the small cations, or (2) Ca/Ca + Na in M4, which essentially sorts out calcic and sodic amphiboles. These two simple M4 parameters can then be plotted against two other parameters, (3) the amount of R^{3+} and (4) the $(Fe^{2+} + Mn)/(Fe^{2+} + Mn + Mg)$ ratio to yield four different figures (19A, 19B, 19C, and 19D) in a sort of "magic square." Figures 19A and 19C are analogous in every respect to Figures 11 and 12 of Robinson (1980) and serve to point up interesting differences between amphiboles and pyroxenes. One obvious difference (Fig. 19A) is that orthorhombic Fe-Mg amphiboles have just as much R^{3+} substitution as calcic amphiboles, whereas orthopyroxenes do not have as much as calcic pyroxenes (compare Fig. 11, Robinson, 1980). Sodic amphiboles and sodic pyroxenes naturally show identical high R^{3+}. Cummingtonites are more like the analogous pyroxenes in having low R^{3+} values. Another difference (Fig. 19C) is that monoclinic Fe-Mg amphiboles (cummingtonites) are more abundant and cover more area in the amphibole quadrilateral than their monoclinic pyroxene relatives, the pigeonites, in the pyroxene quadrilateral. This point is strengthened by consideration of probe analyses below.

In Figure 19B (and 19D) calcic amphiboles are at the top and sodic amphiboles at the base. The calcic amphiboles show a very large range of R^{3+} values, but the bulk of the population is between 1.0 and 1.5, and there is a drastic drop in abundance above 1.5, coupled with a steady decrease in Ca/(Ca+Na). The sodic amphiboles are centered at R^{3+} = 2.0 and some show a trend of increasing Ca/(Ca+Na) and decreasing R^{3+}.

In Figure 19D the range of $(Fe^{2+} + Mn)/(Fe^{2+} + Mn + Mg)$ ratios of calcic and sodic amphiboles is seen to be comparable, but recent electron probe analyses (Black, 1973) would considerably increase the population at the Fe-rich end.

INTERNAL LIMITS IN AMPHIBOLE COMPOSITION SPACE: COEXISTING AMPHIBOLES

The investigation of miscibility gaps in amphibole solid solution series has received considerable attention in the literature. Klein (1968, 1969) has summarized early work on the compositions of coexisting amphiboles, and publications on the subject have been abundant in the last dozen years. Ghose (Chapter 7, Volume 9A) discusses microstructures arising from amphibole exsolution. Examination of amphibole miscibility gaps can provide considerable information on amphibole crystal chemistry and solid solution limits, because the amphiboles that coexist across a miscibility gap are constrained to compositions that lie on the limbs of the gap or solvus. The purpose of this section is to review the data on coexisting amphiboles that pertain to the existence of miscibility gaps and to explore the possible crystal-chemical reasons for these gaps. Strictly speaking, a miscibility gap is any compositional discontinuity in a solid solution series, whereas the term solvus is reserved for gaps in solid solution series that are isostructural.

What constitutes coexistence?

It should be noted from the outset that many occurrences of two or more amphiboles in the same sample may not be true "coexistences" in the sense that the amphiboles may not have been in equilibrium with each other. The question of equilibrium, is, of course, a common one in the interpretation of metamorphic rocks that needs to be settled by a combination of observational petrography under the optical microscope, chemical considerations involving element distributions and element mapping by electron probe, and in some cases by X-ray crystallography and electron microscopy.

The obviously ideal situation is one in which the coexisting amphiboles or other minerals formed discrete individual grains at the peak of metamorphism and then, because of kinetic factors, failed to change at all during subsequent cooling. Such a situation is, unfortunately, difficult to recognize even where it occurs. Commonly, mineral grains of complex composition show chemical zoning from the interior to the exterior, which may be used to tell the *direction* of change of composition with changing time. There are situations where such zoning reflects changes in chemical and/or physical conditions that took place with increasing temperature of metamorphism or with changing metamorphic conditions occasioned by several different metamorphisms (see the sections on metamorphism of basaltic rocks). There are other situations where mineral zoning

43

merely reflects an attempt on the part of the minerals to attain equilibrium under lower temperature conditions *after* the peak of metamorphism. Such falling temperature processes may also include internal attempts at re-equilibration that involve the production of exsolution lamellae or phase transformations from one state to another. Fortunately, the cooling range of metamorphic amphiboles is roughly two-thirds of that of pyroxenes, so that transformations tend to be simpler (see Robinson, 1980) and somewhat less difficult to interpret.

The presence of one set of amphibole lamellae in another amphibole is one of the surest and soundest pieces of evidence for a crystal-chemically controlled miscibility gap and of coexisting amphiboles. However, even this gives no assurance that phase separation has taken place on a stable equilibrium, and there are several good examples where metastable exsolution is very likely. Also, the presence of lamellae gives no assurance that there was a miscibility gap anywhere near the peak metamorphic conditions.

In some situations it is reasonably easy to recognize original "peak metamorphic" grain boundaries and to re-integrate, by graphical methods, by bulk mineral separation, or by broad beam electron probe analysis, to obtain a reasonable estimate of the primary mineral compositions. At the other extreme, there may be no trace left of primary mineral grains, and the only mineral compositions obtainable are those produced during a "retrograde" equilibrium.

Coexistence is normally envisioned as the situation where two or more distinct mineral species occurred together at a fixed set of physical conditions. However, if, in abstract amphibole space at P and T, there is a miscibility gap, and if, in a continuous metamorphic process, the equilibrium amphibole composition is changing and chances to encounter the miscibility gap, then instantaneously the early amphibole core will be in equilibrium with a later amphibole rim. Beyond this instant the early amphibole is no longer in equilibrium with the rock matrix, and the late amphibole takes over this role, but the chemically discontinuous phase boundary remains as a record of the encountered miscibility gap. Unfortunately, such reaction-encountered boundaries are not easy to prove and have resulted in much heated discussion. If such a boundary did occur, it could be subject to subsequent re-equilibration or the development of exsolution lamellae. On the other hand, it is possible that a continuously zoned mineral could encounter such a gap on cooling and generate a phase boundary. A third possibility is that such a boundary as observed optically and analytically has nothing to do with a miscibility gap but was produced by a metasomatic gradient, working inward from the exterior of a pre-existing homogeneous amphibole. Even in this situation, many would

44

suggest that amphibole crystal chemistry may play a significant role. Much of the debate in the literature over the existence or absence of miscibility gaps in systems such as actinolite-hornblende is centered around interpretations of textures such as these.

Some amphibole miscibility gaps appear to remain open under all conditions under which amphiboles are stable. Others are definitely closed within the temperature range of regional metamorphism. Thus, the *proof* of a continuous range of mineral compositions under one set of conditions in one area does not prove that there is no miscibility gap under any conditions.

Crystal-chemical principles

The possibility that two or more amphiboles can coexist together depends on the details of their internal structures (Hawthorne, Chapter 1, Volume 9A). Each amphibole structure must be sufficiently different from the other (or others) to be able to accommodate a different chemical composition. In some pairs, the structural difference is large and obvious, as between monoclinic and orthorhombic amphibole. In others, it is more subtle, a different monoclinic space group, or perhaps a different ordering scheme within a monoclinic structure. In still others, the crystal symmetry is identical and only the site dimensions and bond angles differ to permit concentration of larger and smaller ions or ions with different electron orbital structures.

As pointed out earlier, the analogies between amphibole and pyroxene structures are extremely powerful. These analogies naturally extend to miscibility gaps controlled principally by occupancy of the pyroxene-like sites, particularly M4 (M2 in pyroxene) and to a lesser extent M2 (M1 in pyroxene). For this reason, most of the crystal-chemical principles used to explain coexisting pyroxenes are needed to explain coexisting amphiboles. There are also powerful analogies between amphiboles and sheet silicates, and a few of the amphibole miscibility gaps can be best explained in terms of sheet silicate structure, particularly arrangement of Al in T1 tetrahedral sites and occupancy of the A-site. An amphibole pair that shows features of immiscibility in both pyroxene- and mica-like parts has all the more reason to be separate.

Control by M4 site in monoclinic and orthorhombic amphiboles. As a first approximation, the best way to understand "quadrilateral amphiboles" is to understand "quadrilateral pyroxenes" (see Robinson, 1980). In quadrilateral amphiboles compositional variation is mainly controlled by ions in M4 (Ross *et al*., 1968, 1969; Papike *et al*., 1969; Hawthorne, Chapter 1, Volume 9A); in quadrilateral pyroxenes by ions in M2. Robinson (1980, p. 437) and others have shown that traditional plotting of quadrilateral pyroxenes in terms of the total ratios of Ca, Mg, and Fe can give a very misleading view of pyroxene miscibility gaps when significant amounts of trivalent ions are present in M1. This misleading view is largely rectified if attention is drawn mainly to the M2 site by plotting large cations (Ca + Na) versus small cations (Mn + Fe + Mg) in the M2 site versus the Fe/(Fe + Mg) ratio to give a different version of the "pyroxene quadrilateral" (Robinson, 1980, Fig. 12). The beauty of this version is that pyroxenes with any amount of trivalent ion substitution can be plotted without devastating alteration of the position of two-pyroxene fields. An exactly identical method can be employed based on large cations versus small cations in M4 in amphiboles, with similar results (Fig. 19C).

In pyroxene terms, calcic amphiboles with $C2/m$ structure are equivalent to calcic pyroxenes (augites) with $C2/c$ structure at the tops of the quadrilaterals. The M4 site can be thought of as flexible for substitutions not only of large Na ions, but also for moderate amounts of smaller Mn, Fe^{2+}, and even Mg ions.

The orthoamphiboles with $Pnma$ structure are equivalent to orthopyroxenes with $Pbca$ structure along the bottoms of the quadrilaterals. This is the typical stable structure for small cations Mg or Fe^{2+} (or Li^{1+}), and substantial amounts of Na or Ca are not tolerated. Unlike the orthopyroxenes, the orthoamphiboles do not extend entirely across the base of the amphibole quadrilateral, exhibiting a marked intolerance for large amounts of Fe^{2+} instead of Mg in the M1,2,3 sites, unless the mean cation size can be reduced by Al substitution in M2, as in ferrogedrite (see Fig. 3, this chapter).

Cummingtonites with $C2/m$ or $P2_1/m$ structure are equivalent to pigeonites with $C2/c$ or $P2_1/c$ structure. In both amphiboles and pyroxenes, the P → C transition is a temperature-controlled displacive transformation. In most primitive pyroxenes, the transition temperature, although a function of composition, is well above room temperature. In amphiboles it is also a function of composition but in a temperature range close to room temperature (Sueno *et al.*, 1972; Prewitt *et al.*, 1970). Thus, in some outcrops it is possible to have P-amphiboles in some specimens, C-amphiboles in others, and have the proportions of C and P amphiboles depend on whether the sun is shining or not! Under metamorphic conditions it is clear that all or most cummingtonites would have $C2/m$ symmetry.

Cummingtonites, like pigeonites, are structures that tend to have ions of intermediate size in M4, particularly Fe^{2+} (1.6 to 2.0 in most; Fig. 4) and Mn (up to nearly 1.9 atoms in some samples). They tend to tolerate more Ca than orthoamphiboles but are equally intolerant of Na. They play a much more important role in the amphibole quadrilateral than do pigeonites in the pyroxene quadrilateral. This must be due to the fact that they are much more tolerant of large amounts of large Fe^{2+} ions in the M1,2,3 positions than are the orthoamphiboles. They are apparently quite intolerant of Al (and other trivalent ions) in M2,[8] which accounts for their lack of Na substitution and their surprising compositional simplicity, which still needs further crystallographic study.

The classic three-pyroxene assemblage augite-orthopyroxene-pigeonite of the pyroxene quadrilateral in igneous rocks (Huebner, 1980, Fig. 5) is exactly mimicked by the assemblage hornblende-anthophyllite-cummingtonite of metamorphic rocks, although the latter, because of a narrower temperature range, extends over a narrower composition range than do the igneous assemblages.

In those chemically unusual situations where it is possible to have coexisting sodic amphibole and cummingtonite, the miscibility gap is clearly also mainly influenced by the sizes of ions in the M4 sites.

Coupled M4-M2 relation. In pyroxenes, there seem to be no examples on a macroscopic or microscopic scale of coexisting calcic and sodic pyroxenes; however, on a submicroscopic scale (Carpenter, 1980) there is abundant evidence of exsolution between diopside-rich and jadeite-rich solid solutions, with a further complication in the center of the series where an ordered intermediate phase, primitive omphacite (Buseck *et al.*, 1980) occurs.

The principal feature of primitive omphacite is the ordering of Al and Mg in alternate M1 positions in the octahedral strip, coupled with partial ordering of Na and Ca in adjacent M2 sites, thus destroying the *c*-glide. Although an amphibole analog of such an ordered structure has not been definitely recognized, the possibility of the occurrence of such an "omphibole" might be considered. Most significant, however, in this series is the coupled substitution relationship between CaMg and NaAl, which is probably most important in controlling miscibility gaps between calcic or sodic-calcic and sodic amphiboles, rather than the size differences between the Ca and Na ions in M4. It is also worth mentioning that patterns of exsolution such as are found in the "quadrilateral" amphiboles have not been observed in calcic-sodic pairs, perhaps pointing up the differences in crystal-chemical control.

The overall crystal-chemical control on amphibole miscibility gaps by ions in M4 is shown in a very generalized way in Figure 20. All of the plotted analysis points come from amphibole pairs. Because of space limitations, only a few of the tie lines are shown.

----

[8]This has an exact parallel also in pyroxenes, where orthopyroxenes are much more tolerant of Al in M1 than are pigeonites.

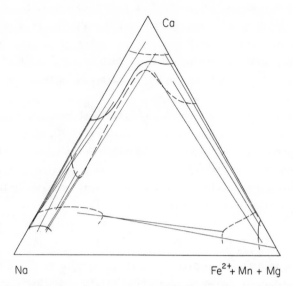

Figure 20. Triangle showing schematically the occupancy of M4 by Ca, Na,
and Fe^{2+} + Mn + Mg in coexisting amphiboles. A few representative tie
lines are shown, including the only two pairs of coexisting Na and Fe-Mg
amphiboles (see Table 3). Widths of miscibility gaps as shown are a function of temperature, of compositional factors not shown by this triangle,
of quality of mineral separations and of quality of analyses. The greatest compositional range seems to be in calcic or calcic-sodic amphiboles
coexisting with sodic amphiboles. Here the solid field boundary includes
probe analyses from the highest grade pairs from New Caledonia reported
by Black (1973), whereas the dashed boundary includes wet analyses
reported by Dobretsov *et al.* (1971).

Tetrahedral Al and A-occupancy. In the trioctahedral mica-like portion
of amphibole structures there is the possibility of having a completely empty
A-site and no tetrahedral Al, or of having significant A-site occupancy which
may or may not be coupled with significant Al in the Tl tetrahedral site. If
A-occupancy is not coupled with tetrahedral Al, then it is coupled with Na in
M4 in the uniquely "amphibole" coupled substitution of richterites and ecker-
mannites. When A-occupancy is coupled with tetrahedral Al, then the difference
between an empty A (MTA) amphibole and a filled A (SOLE) amphibole may be
likened to the difference between talc (MTA) and Na biotite (SOLE). Note
that the additional $R^{3+VI}Al^{IV}$ substitution to be found in the amphiboles may
also be found in the comparable sheet silicates, though usually to a lesser
extent, and that in both examples the MTA (empty A) analogue has much less
extra octahedral substitution than the coexisting SOLE (fillet) analogue.
Similarly in both examples, the "filled A" example in each mineral group is
likely to actually have some A-site vacancies, though there are generally more
vacancies in the amphibole than in the sheet silicate. Further, although com-

plete solubility at high temperature between talc and biotite cannot be found,[9] complete solid solution is well demonstrated in the amphibole analogues at temperatures above about 600°C. In summary, the differences between talc-like and biotite-like I-beam segments, like the differences between talc and Na-biotite, appear to be the controlling influences on miscibility gaps that can develop between amphiboles with very small and large A-site occupancies, i.e., actinolite-hornblende and anthophyllite-gedrite. The different patterns of grain contact in coexisting actinolite-hornblende and anthophyllite-gedrite and patterns of exsolution lamellae in the coexisting orthoamphiboles, as compared to the coexisting "quadrilateral" amphiboles, emphasize this different crystal-chemical basis.

Miscibility gaps and substitution mechanisms. A convenient way to describe miscibility gaps in amphiboles is in terms of the major substitution mechanisms that can be employed to describe the solid solution behavior. Most amphiboles from igneous and metamorphic environments can be described in terms of the chemical system $SiO_2-Al_2O_3-Fe_2O_3-TiO_2-MgO-FeO-CaO-Na_2O-H_2O$. Taking tremolite ($\square Ca_2Mg_5Si_8O_{22}(OH)_2$) as a base, where $\square$ = vacancy in the A-site, the major chemical variations in amphiboles can be described in terms of the following set of linearly independent exchange components: $Fe = Mg$; $Na^A Al^{IV} = \square Si$ (edenite); $Al^{VI} Al^{IV} = MgSi$ (tschermakite); $Fe^{3+VI} Al^{IV} = MgSi$ (ferri-tschermakite); $Na^{M4} Al^{VI} = Ca^{M4} Mg$ (glaucophane); $TiAl_2^{IV} = MgSi_2$ (Ti-tschermakite); $Mg^{M4} = Ca^{M4}$ (cummingtonite). Application of an exchange component to the tremolite formula will yield a particular amphibole end-member formula. Other exchange components and hence other end-member formulae can be derived from linear combinations of these components. For example, the pargasite substitution ($Na^A Al^{VI} Al_2^{IV} = \square MgSi_2$) is a linear combination of the edenite and tschermakite substitutions (e.g., Ed+Ts); and the plagioclase substitution, $Ca^{M4} Al^{IV} = Na^{M4} Si$, is a linear combination of the glaucophane and tschermakite substitutions (e.g., Gl-Ts). It should be noted that these exchange components do not account for certain types of substitutions in the amphibole formula such as Fe^{3+} in the tetrahedral site, nor do they permit any vacancies in the structure except in the A-site.

Formulated in this way, miscibility gaps in amphiboles can be divided into three groups. (1) Gaps in the amount of edenite + tschermakite (i.e., pargasite)

----

[9] Note, however, that wonesite (Spear *et al.*, 1981) is a highly sodic cation-deficient analogue of biotite coexisting with K-biotite and talc that actually has its A-sites less than half filled on the average, and is hence comparable in this respect to gedrites coexisting with anthophyllites.

substitution. Examples of this gap are in the gedrite-anthophyllite and horn-
blende-actinolite series. (2) Gaps in the amount of cummingtonite substitution,
for example, actinolite-cummingtonite and hornblende-cummingtonite. (3) Gaps
in the amount of glaucophane or plagioclase substitution, for example, actino-
lite-glaucophane and hornblende-glaucophane. Each gap can be explained, at
least to a first approximation, by consideration of size differences in the
species that are substituting for one another, as discussed above.

Electron probe analyses of coexisting amphiboles

As presented in the following sections, numerous electron probe analyses
of coexisting amphiboles were selected from the literature, and their formulae
were established on the basis of the chemical and crystal-chemical limits
discussed earlier in this chapter. Formulae for cummingtonites, orthoamphiboles,
sodic amphiboles, and calcic amphiboles were most satisfactory using the following assumptions. *Cummingtonites*: All FeO or 15 cations excluding Na,K.
Orthoamphiboles: All FeO, 15 cations excluding Na,K or 14.92 cations excluding
Na,K (0.08 Na in M4). *Sodic amphiboles*: 13 cations excluding Ca,Na,K except
when, after this correction, octahedral $Al + Fe^{3+} + Ti > 2$. If > 2, then
another correction was done by setting $Na(M4) = [Na^{M4}$ for 13 eCNK] $- [(Al +
Fe^{3+} + Ti) - 2]$, which sets octahedral $Al + Fe^{3+} + Ti$ less than 2. *Calcic
amphiboles*: All FeO, 13 cations excluding Ca,Na,K, or by specifying various
values of Na^{M4}, usually near 0.2.

Calcic amphiboles and cummingtonites[10]

Chemographic relations. The miscibility gap between calcic and Fe-Mg
monoclinic amphiboles is essentially a compositional discontinuity in the
occupancy of the M4 site brought about because of size differences between Ca
and Fe or Mg. It is similar in many respects to the gap between calcic and
Fe-Mg pyroxenes. The miscibility gap can be visualized in the three schematic
diagrams shown in Figure 21. Cummingtonite can coexist with calcic amphiboles
ranging from actinolites to hornblendes (Fig. 21A). The most aluminous cummingtonites will be those that coexist with a more aluminous phase (e.g.,
chlorite or gedrite) irrespective of the Al-content of the coexisting calcic
amphibole. It is possible for cummingtonite of a single Fe/Mg to coexist with

----

[10] In this discussion, the name cummingtonite will be used to refer to any monoclinic Fe-Mg amphibole, even though the name grunerite is reserved for amphiboles with $Fe/(Fe+Mg) > 0.7$ and magnesiocummingtonite is the proper name for
species with $Fe/(Fe+Mg) < 0.3$.

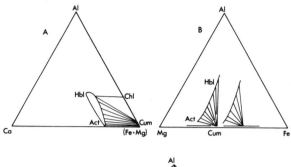

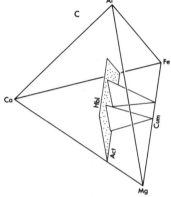

Figure 21. Schematic composition diagrams depicting the miscibility gap between Fe-Mg clinoamphibole (cummingtonite = Cum) and calcic amphibole (actinolite = Act and hornblende = Hbl). Chlorite = Chl. (A) Ca-Al-(Fe+Mg) plot and (B) Al-Fe-Mg plot showing cummingtonites coexisting with calcic amphiboles with a range of Fe/Mg and Al contents. (C) Al-Ca-Fe-Mg plot showing cummingtonite coexisting with actinolite + hornblende.

calcic amphibole with a range of Al contents and Fe/Mg (Fig. 21B). Furthermore, it is possible, under appropriate conditions, for cummingtonite to coexist with both actinolite and hornblende over a range of Fe/Mg (Fig. 21A,B,C).

The compositions of pairs of coexisting calcic amphiboles and cummingtonites are plotted in Figure 22. Figure 22B is part of a modified amphibole quadrilateral with Ca + Na in M4 plotted against $(Fe^{2+} + Mn)/(Fe^{2+} + Mn + Mg)$. Like the corresponding augite-pigeonite pairs of igneous rocks, this field begins near the 30% Fe ratio, but extends from there continuously toward the Fe-rich edge of the quadrilateral, without obvious evidence of closure of the miscibility gap, such as is shown by corresponding pyroxenes. There are several possible explanations for this, including the lower temperature of formation of the amphiboles. Another possibility has to do with the size of exsolution lamellae and its effect on resultant probe analyses. Jaffe *et al.* (1968), for example, indicate that exsolution lamellae are coarser and more abundant in Fe-rich pairs, consistent with greater mutual solubility before exsolution. Probe analyses, however, would tend to include very fine lamellae of more Mg-rich pairs and to exclude coarse lamellae of more Fe-rich pairs, resulting in the same or an even wider apparent miscibility gap for the Fe-rich pairs. Thus, there is much room for quantitative study of such matters. Ross *et al.*

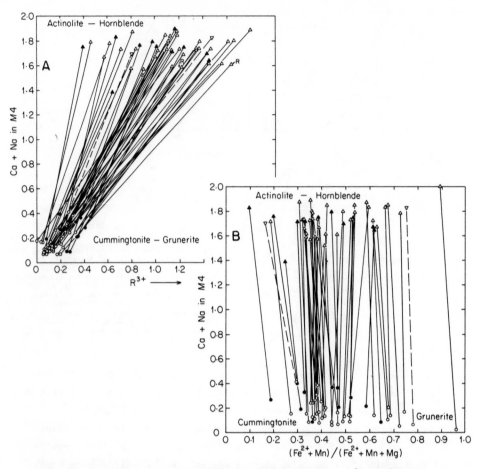

Figure 22. (A; left) Plot of Ca + Na in M4 versus R^{3+} (octahedral Al + Fe^{3+} + $2Ti^{4+}$) for coexisting calcic amphiboles (triangles) and monoclinic Fe-Mg amphiboles (circles). Closed symbols represent wet analyses; open symbols represent microprobe analyses. R indicates amphibole pairs considered to be a retrograde assemblage. Dashed tie lines connect two pairs of coexisting sodic amphibole (inverted triangles) and Fe-Mg amphibole. Wet analyses from Klein (1968), Robinson *et al.* (1971a), Eskola (1950), Haslam and Walker (1971), DasGupta (1972), Kisch and Waarnars (1969), Robinson and Jaffe (1969b), and Vernon (1971) and probe analyses from Klein (1968), James *et al.* (1978), Clark (1978), Stephenson and Hensel (1979), Spear (1980), Black (1970), Immega and Klein (1976), and Schumacher (unpublished data). (B; right) Plot of Ca+Na in M4 versus $(Fe^{2+}+Mn)/(Fe^{2+}+Mn+Mg)$ for coexisting calcic amphiboles (triangles) and monoclinic Fe-Mg amphiboles (circles). Dashed tie lines connect coexisting monoclinic Fe-Mg amphiboles and sodic amphiboles (inverted triangles). Sources for analyses and closed and open symbols same as in Figure 22A.

(1969) illustrate coexisting actinolite and cummingtonite from the Ruby Mountains, Montana, which appear to have been almost but not quite "hypersolvus" compositions before exsolution (unfortunately, they give only partial probe analyses). Although the calcic amphiboles of Mg-rich pairs have lower Fe

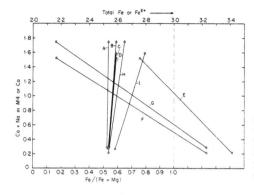

Figure 23. Diagram illustrating various ways of displaying the difference in Fe ratio between coexisting hornblende and cummingtonite. All tie lines are based on the same analyzed pair 7A8BX reported by Robinson and Jaffe (1969b). For explanation of various examples A, B, etc., see text.

ratios than the coexisting cummingtonites, the situation is clearly reversed for many Fe-rich pairs. The reasons for this will be discussed below.

The same pairs are plotted with Ca+Na in M4 versus R^{3+} in octahedral positions in Figure 22A. The contrast between the high and variable R^{3+} of the hornblendes and the low and limited R^{3+} of the cummingtonites is striking and illustrates the basic simplicity of the cummingtonites, in parallel with the low R^{3+} of their pyroxene analogues, the pigeonites. In rocks where hornblende appears to have been retrograded in equilibrium with plagioclase and cummingtonite (note R in Fig. 22A), the hornblende is enriched in R^{3+}. Thus, the slope of tie lines in Figure 22A seems to have a relation to metamorphic grade.

There are several problems in trying to evaluate coexisting amphiboles in terms of their $Fe^{2+}/(Fe^{2+}+Mg)$ ratios, not the least of which is the lack of direct determination of Fe^{3+} in probe analyses. These problems are illustrated by wet chemical analyses of coexisting hornblende and cummingtonite in Figure 23. The vertical axis is the familiar quantity Ca+Na in M4. The horizontal axis includes two different scales on which various values are plotted. In tie line A the analyses are plotted exactly as in Figure 22B, according to the ratio $(Fe^{2+}+Mn)/(Fe^{2+}+Mn+Mg)$ with Fe^{3+} not included. The two minerals have very nearly the same Fe ratio. In B, the Fe^{3+} is added to Fe^{2+}, although the formula is not recalculated. Because hornblende has more Fe^{3+} than cummingtonite, its Fe ratio is now increased substantially. However, if we treat all Fe as FeO, as if we had a probe analysis, then the formula calculation would be different, and this would give different values for Ca+Na in M4, as shown with pair C. This last variation could be partially ironed over by merely treating Ca in M4, as in line D.

One of the obvious problems in comparing cummingtonite and hornblende analyses is that the hornblendes have much greater and much more variable

53

amounts of R^{3+} ions in M2. X-ray crystallographic studies (Hawthorne, Chapter 1, Volume 9A) have shown that Mg is very strongly ordered into M2, provided it is not already occupied by Al, Fe^{3+}, or Ti^{4+}. Thus, in hornblendes rich in R^{3+} substitution, Mg tends to be partially excluded from the M2 site and tends to occur instead in M2 of the cummingtonite, thus causing the hornblende to have a higher Fe ratio. In other words, the tschermak substitution in calcic amphibole is dominantly a substitution of $Al^{VI}Al^{IV}$ for MgSi, not FeSi; hence, the Fe/Mg ratio of calcic amphibole displays a first-order dependence on the Al^{VI} content. One way to equalize the effect of this Mg exclusion by R^{3+} ions is to ignore Mg completely and consider Fe^{2+} or total Fe only. In this way, the distribution of Ca between the two amphiboles can be examined as a function of Fe/Mg, without interference related to Al^{VI} content in the calcic amphibole. In tie line E this has been done for total Fe and Ca per formula unit based on the all FeO assumption. In tie line F this has been done for Fe^{2+} and Ca per formula unit, and in line G for Fe^{2+} and Ca+Na per formula unit. It should be recalled that line E, although it excludes Mg, does include the Fe^{3+} that is fairly certainly in the M2 site excluding Mg. In both cases by overriding the "unfair" advantage that cummingtonite has for Mg in M2, the calcic amphibole comes out with a lower Fe amount than the cummingtonite, and thus the slopes of the lines in the "pure" Ca-Mg-Fe quadrilateral are imitated.

The slopes of tie lines in the "pure" quadrilateral are themselves, however, dependent on another exclusion principle (also well known in pyroxenes), namely the exclusion of Fe^{2+} (strongly ordered over Mg in M4) from M4 when that site is occupied by Ca and Na. This exclusion is the one that gives "pure quadrilateral" calcic amphiboles lower Fe ratios than coexisting cummingtonites. In amphiboles this effect can also be overridden by ignoring the M4 site and dealing exclusively with Mg and Fe^{2+} in the M1 and M3 sites. Fortunately, a very high proportion of amphiboles appear to contain M1 and M3 sites exclusively occupied by Mg and Fe^{2+}, so that the calculated ratio for these sites, assuming perfect ordering of Mg into M2 and Fe^{2+} into M4, is likely to be close to the real ratio under most circumstances. Line H shows the analysis plotted for Ca+Na in M4 and the ratio $Fe^{2+}/(Fe^{2+}+Mg)$ of the M1 and M3 sites. Line I shows the analysis calculated for FeO only, for Ca in M4 and for Fe/(Fe+Mg) in M1 and M3. In these cases, by overriding the "unfair" effect of Ca and Na on Fe^{2+} in M4, we see that the calcic amphibole has an Fe ratio in M1 and M3 consistently *higher* than the coexisting cummingtonite. It makes much crystal-chemical sense for a small-cation amphibole such as cummingtonite to have smaller mean cations in M1 and M3 than coexisting large-cation calcic amphibole.

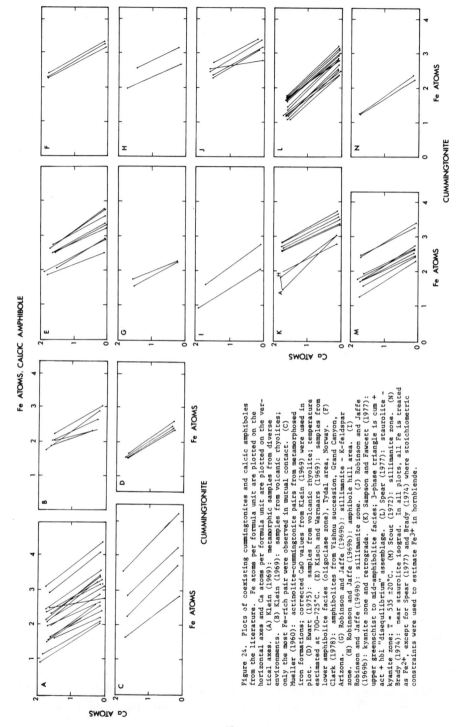

Figure 24. Plots of coexisting cummingtonites and calcic amphiboles from the literature. Fe atoms per formula unit are plotted on the horizontal axes and Ca atoms per formula unit are plotted on the vertical axes. (A) Klein (1969): metamorphic samples from diverse environments. (B) Klein (1969): samples from volcanic rhyolites; only the most Fe-rich pair were observed in mutual contact. (C) Mueller (1960): actinolite-cummingtonite pairs from metamorphosed iron formations; corrected CaO values from Klein (1969) were used in plot. (D) Ewart (1975): samples from volcanic rhyolite; temperature estimated at 700-725°C. (E) Kisch and Warnaars (1969): samples from lower amphibolite facies (oligoclase zone), Tydal area, Norway. (F) Clark (1978): amphibolites from Vishnu succession, Grand Canyon, Arizona. (G) Robinson and Jaffe (1969b): sillimanite - K-feldspar zone. (H) Robinson and Jaffe (1969b): amphibole hill area. (I) Robinson and Jaffe (1969b): sillimanite zone. (J) Robinson and Jaffe (1969b): kyanite zone and retrograde. (K) Sampson and Fawcett (1977): upper greenschist to mid-amphibolite facies; 3-phase triangle is cum + act + hbl "disequilibrium" assemblage. (L) Spear (1977): staurolite - kyanite zone; T = 535 ±20°C. (M) Stout (1972): sillimanite zone. (N) Brady (1974): near staurolite isograd. In all plots, all Fe is treated as Fe²⁺, except for Spear (1977) and Brady (1974) where stoichiometric constraints were used to estimate Fe³⁺ in hornblende.

Figure 24 shows calcic amphibole-cummingtonite pairs from a variety of geologic settings plotted in terms of Ca and total Fe as in line E of Figure 23. Cummingtonite coexists with either actinolite or hornblende, depending on the bulk composition and metamorphic grade, and commonly both. Cummingtonite-calcic amphibole pairs are observed in rocks from the epidote amphibolite facies through the granulite facies, as well as in some igneous environments. As can be seen from the plots, cummingtonites always have more Fe than coexisting calcic amphiboles, be they actinolites or hornblendes. This reflects the fact that the M4 site in amphiboles strongly prefers Fe over Mg, and thus the substitution is dominantly Ca = Fe (not Mg). As mentioned above, Fe/Mg ratios in calcic amphiboles depend strongly on Al^{VI} content, but in general, the Fe/Mg distribution between these phases is nearly equal, or favors a higher Fe/Mg in cummingtonite. Three studies have addressed the thermodynamics of Fe-Mg partitioning between cummingtonite and calcic amphibole (Mueller, 1960, 1961; Kisch and Warnaars, 1969; Powell, 1975).

Samples collected from a single metamorphic grade generally show a systematic distribution of Ca between coexisting amphiboles, although cummingtonite is apparently more regular in Ca content than the calcic amphibole. Moreover, there is a general decrease in the size of the gap with increasing temperature, although the temperature dependence is not great. Samples collected from the epidote amphibolite facies (Fig. 24E,K,N) contain cummingtonites with 0.05-0.15 Ca per formula unit and calcic amphiboles with 1.5-1.9 Ca. Samples from the amphibolite facies (Fig. 24F,H,I,L,M) contain cummingtonites with up to 0.2 Ca, and samples from volcanic rhyolites (T $\simeq$ 725-750°C) (Fig. 24B,D) contain cummingtonites with up to 0.3 Ca. The reason for the irregular Ca content of the calcic amphiboles is not known, but both hornblende and cummingtonite typically contain exsolution lamellae of one in the other, so that part of the scatter may reflect the abundance of exsolution lamellae in the sample. It also appears that there is no systematic change in the size or shape of the solvus with changes in Fe/Mg.

In Figure 25 most of the amphibole population of Figures 22B and 27B is plotted with Ca+Na in M4 versus $Fe^{2+}/(Fe^{2+}+Mg)$ in M1 and M3. The inset in the upper left explains the rationale for the scheme. The vertical scale is Ca+Na in M4 and ranges from 0 to 2. For tremolite, where Ca = 2, all Fe and Mg are excluded from M4. Exclusion of Mg (and Fe^{2+}) from M2 is controlled by the amount of substitution of $Al + Fe^{3+} + Ti^{4+}$, which is usually greater in calcic and sodic amphiboles, though not necessarily when the Fe-Mg amphiboles are gedrites. In the plotting ratio, the denominator is always Mn+Fe+Mg in M1+M3, which is nearly always 3. In unusually Fe-rich amphiboles it is possible to

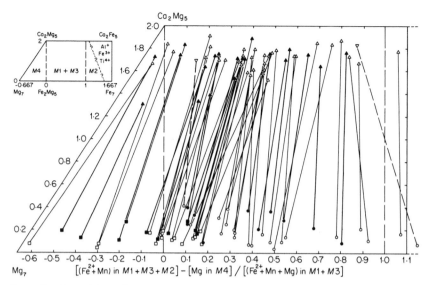

Figure 25. Compositions of coexisting calcic amphiboles (triangles) and Fe-Mg amphiboles (orthoamphiboles, squares; cummingtonites, circles) plotted in terms of Ca+Na in M4 (vertical axis) and the ratio $(Fe^{2+}+Mn)/(Fe^{2+}+Mn+Mg)$ as assigned to the M1+M3 sites (see text).

assign Fe to M2, and this added to the numerator permits plotting ratios as high as 1.667 for theoretical pure ferroactinolite (Ca_2Fe_5) or grunerite (Fe_7). In unusually Mg-rich amphiboles, where Mg must be assigned to M4, the amount is subtracted from the numerator, thus making possible negative plotting ratios as low as -0.667 for pure Mg cummingtonite or anthophyllite. It is notable in this light that only one cummingtonite barely plots in this negative class, while there are numerous anthophyllites.

The plotting ratio used in Figure 25 is very sensitive to the ferric corrections used on microprobe analyses, because correcting Fe^{3+} into M2 both increases Mg and decreases Fe^{2+} in M1 and M3. The similarity of tie-line orientations for both "wet" (heavy tie lines and filled symbols) and corrected probe analyses of amphibole pairs in Figure 25 supports the validity of the correction procedures. In addition, the systematic distribution of tie lines appears to provide a useful criterion for judging the quality of analyses of amphibole pairs.

Exsolution lamellae. When two amphiboles that crystallized together at moderate to high temperature are permitted to cool gradually, they commonly exsolve lamellae of each other, or of related compositions, as a result of decreased mutual solubility at lower temperature. Such exsolution features vary in scale from rather coarse lamellae that are easily observed at low power

under the petrographic microscope, to very fine features barely observed at
high power, to submicroscopic lamellae detectable only by X-ray crystallography
or electron microscopy (Ghose, Chapter 7 in Vol. 9A; Ross *et al.*, 1968;
Gittos *et al.*, 1976). Careful petrographic interpretation of such features
is crucial to understanding the cooling history of a rock and also to
understanding the meaning of wet chemical and electron probe analyses. For
example, do the analyses indicate the compositions of host grains and exsolution lamellae representative of equilibrium at the temperature of exsolution,
or are the analyses a composite of host grains and fine lamellae representative
of equilibrium above the temperature of exsolution? Other features to be considered include oriented (epitaxial) intergrowths of two or more amphiboles
formed during metamorphic crystallization that have a completely different
significance. Patterns of exsolution lamellae may also be confused by recrys-
tallization subsequent to exsolution or by exsolution from metamorphic grains
with primary compositional gradients.

Exsolution lamellae are most obvious in rocks of the high amphibolite
facies and low granulite facies, but they can be seen with careful search under
high power in a few lower grade rocks. Exsolution lamellae are to be found,
for the most part, in rocks containing two or more amphiboles, but there are
examples of rocks with a single amphibole containing exsolution lamellae of
another amphibole. Wolff (1978), for example, described fine cummingtonite
lamellae in magnesian hornblende in olivine-orthopyroxene hornblendite, where
the orthopyroxene has the effect of saturating the hornblende with cummingtonite component, even though cummingtonite is not one of the primary phases
in the rock (see the section on metamorphosed ultramafic rocks).

Analogies between coexisting pyroxenes and coexisting amphiboles extend
even to their exsolution lamellae, although there are some important differences.
Exsolution lamellae in coexisting augite and pigeonite have been described in
many papers (see detailed summary, Robinson, 1980). On cooling, augite ex-
solves two sets of pigeonite lamellae and vice-versa. One set of lamellae
forms on planes within a few degrees of (001) of augite and pigeonite hosts.
The other set forms on planes within a few degrees of (100) of augite and
pigeonite hosts. The reason that the lamellae are not usually exactly parallel
to (001) and (100) is that the two monoclinic lattices *do not* fit along (001)
and (100) but they *do* fit along irrational planes[11] termed "exact phase

----

[11]Such irrational planes near (001) and (100) are termed "001" and "100"
(Robinson *et al.*, 1971a).

boundaries" that are a function of the lattice parameters of the two monoclinic structures under the pressure and temperature conditions when exsolution was initiated (Robinson *et al.*, 1977). It is extremely important in this connection to note that although the *phase boundaries* are not usually parallel to (001) and (100), when the *lattice orientations* are examined in X-ray single crystal photographs, the host and lamellae do come within a fraction of a degree of sharing (001) or (100) in most examples. In addition, the augite hosts commonly produce exsolution lamellae of orthopyroxene exactly parallel to (100), and as cooling proceeds the pigeonite may develop stacking faults parallel to (100) that appear to be a first step in the process of inversion to orthopyroxene.

To understand the analogies between augite-pigeonite and calcic amphibole-cummingtonite exsolution, it is necessary to understand what these minerals have in common in their internal structures. In Figure 26 (lower left part) is an image of the octahedral-tetrahedral structure of diopside, viewed as if cut by a plane parallel to (010), and with the axes of the tetrahedral chains and octahedral strips parallel to the c crystallographic axis oriented vertically. If monoclinic amphibole structures are cut in the same way parallel to (010), provided the cut is through the pyroxene-like part of the structure, the view will not be greatly different, except for minor details of angular relationships. For all such monoclinic structures there are two alternative ways to define the unit cell, as shown by the pairs in the upper left part of Figure 26. In each pair one alternative is end-centered, C, and the other body-centered, I. Due to the different geometries of the central parts of pyroxene and amphibole I-beams, the C-cell structural arrangement for pyroxene as viewed on (010) is identical to the I-cell arrangement for amphibole and vice-versa. According to the formal rules for space group assignment, when there is a choice between C and I cells in the monoclinic system, the C-cell is usually chosen. As a result, the identical structural plane described as (001) in $C2/c$ pyroxene is formally described as ($\bar{1}$01) in $C2/m$ amphibole. Similarly, exsolution lamellae described as near (001) in clinopyroxene are described as near ($\bar{1}$01) in amphibole, even though the two planes are absolutely identical with respect to the internal structures. One way to avoid this confusion, which helps in comparative studies of exsolution in the two mineral groups, as well as in comparisons of structural behavior at temperature, is to use the I-cell to describe the amphibole (see, for example, Cameron *et al.*, 1973).

The right-hand part of Figure 26 shows exsolved grains of cummingtonite and hornblende intergrown along a common irrational plane nearly parallel to

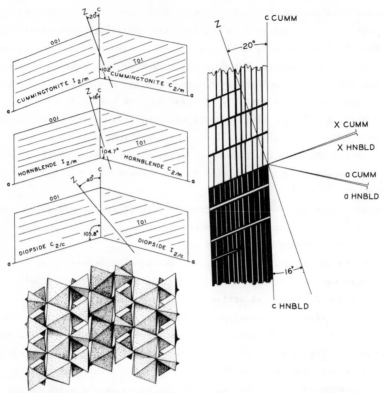

Figure 26. Oriented diagram showing the relationships between the internal structures, alternative unit cells, exsolution lamellae, and optical vibration directions of clinopyroxenes and clinoamphiboles (from Jaffe, Robinson, and Klein, 1968). Lower left: View of the internal structure of diopside cut parallel to (010). Upper left: alternative ways of describing the unit cells of clinopyroxenes and clinoamphiboles, and of describing the exsolution lamellae. Right: Drawing of grains of cummingtonite (white) and hornblende (black) of specimen 7A8BX (Robinson and Jaffe, 1969) in contact along a common "$\bar{1}01$" (or "001") plane and showing the correct optical vibration directions with respect to unit cells and internal structure. The "001" lamellae lie at about 4° to the a-crystallographic axes (I-cell) and the "100" hornblende lamellae lie at about 2° to c of the cummingtonite host in accordance with the exact phase boundary theory (Robinson *et al.*, 1971; 1977).

($\bar{1}01$) (C-cell). Both host minerals contain exsolution lamellae of the other: a set of "100" lamellae essentially parallel to (100), and a set of "$\bar{1}01$" lamellae about 4° from ($\bar{1}01$). Although not anticipated when this figure was published in 1968, this 4° discrepancy in a cummingtonite-hornblende pair from southwestern New Hampshire led to further observations of exsolution lamellae in coexisting cummingtonite-magnesioarfvedsonite (see Fig. 35) and pyroxenes, and to the development of the theory for such irrational "exact phase boundaries." Similar angular observations were made in coexisting cummingtonite-hornblende from Italy by Callegari (1966). The thermal implications of the "exact phase boundary" theory as outlined for pyroxenes (see Robinson, 1980) appear to be less useful for amphiboles, partly because the cooling range of

60

amphiboles is far less than that of pyroxenes, and partly because the amphibole structures do not change angular relationships so drastically with changing temperature. Although Fe-rich cummingtonites are C-centered at room temperature, whereas more Mg-rich cummingtonites are primitive, it appears (see Hawthorne, Chapter 1, Volume 9A) that most were C-centered under the temperature conditions of exsolution.

Despite the similarity of patterns of monoclinic lamellae in augite-pigeonite and calcic amphibole-cummingtonite pairs, there is one striking difference. In the clinoamphiboles we know of no examples of (100) lamellae of orthoamphiboles analogous to the ubiquitous (100) lamellae of orthopyroxene common in calcic clinopyroxenes.

When viewed parallel to the c-axis, exsolved calcic amphiboles and cummingtonites show a common pattern with fine "100" lamellae running parallel to the long diagonal of the diamond-shaped section and bisecting the *acute* angle between the (110) cleavage planes. These lamellae are parallel to (100) twin planes that show up under crossed nicols, and they can serve as a useful petrographic tool for distinguishing cummingtonite and orthoamphibole where both coexist with calcic amphibole.

Another result of the ambiguity of choice of C- and I-cells for amphiboles is confusion in the literature concerning the orientation of optical vibration directions Z and X with respect to the internal structure. Exsolution lamellae have permitted clarification of this question, and correct orientations are shown on Figure 26. In older sources of optical data, orientations are commonly shown with respect to the I lattice orientation. Many newer sources give the same orientation diagram together with lattice parameters for the C-cell.

Calcic amphiboles and orthoamphiboles

Chemographic relations. Pairs of coexisting calcic amphiboles and orthoamphiboles are plotted in Figure 27. Figure 27B is part of a modified amphibole quadrilateral in which the proportion of large cations (Ca+Na) in M4 is plotted against the ratio $(Fe^{2+} + Mn)/(Fe^{2+} + Mn + Mg)$. Like the corresponding augite-orthopyroxene pairs of igneous rocks, calcic amphibole-orthoamphibole pairs are restricted to fairly Mg-rich compositions, and the orthorhombic phase usually has a higher Fe ratio.

In Figure 27A the same pairs are plotted with Ca+Na in M4 versus $Al + Fe^{3+} + 2Ti/(R^{3+})$ in octahedral positions. This shows the departures of these amphiboles from the "quadrilateral" defined in the narrowest sense. In each pair the calcic amphibole contains a higher proportion of R^{3+} substitution than does the orthoamphibole, perhaps reflecting the greater "flexibility" of the large

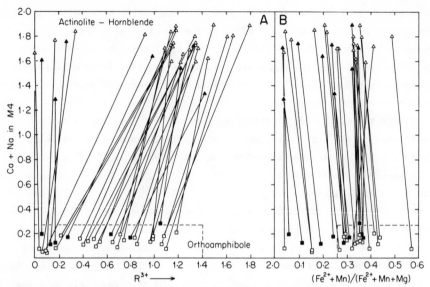

Figure 27. Compositions of coexisting calcic amphiboles (triangles) and orthoamphiboles (squares). Open symbols, probe analyses; closed symbols, wet analyses. Vertical axis is Ca+Na in M4 for both A and B. (A) Horizontal axis is R^{3+} (octahedral $Al+Fe^{3+}+2Ti^{4+}$). (B) Horizontal axis is $(Fe^{2+}+Mn)/(Fe^{2+}+Mn+Mg)$. Dashed rectangles in A and B are the spaces occupied by A and B of Figure 28. Probe analyses are from Wolff (1978), Schumacher (unpublished), Spear (1980), Hawthorne *et al.* (1980), Klein (1968), James *et al.* (1978), and Stout (1972). Wet analyses are from Robinson and Jaffe (1969b), Tiba *et al.* (1970), Soen (1968), and Klein (1968).

cation calcic amphibole structure in this competitive situation, although in assemblages without calcic amphibole, orthorhombic amphiboles (gedrites) can have much higher R^{3+} contents (see Fig. 19A). This exactly imitates the situation in all natural calcic pyroxene-orthopyroxene pairs, although Perkins and Newton (1981) show that in a synthetic system with Al as the only R^{3+} ion and no Na (a strictly $Al^{VI}Al^{IV}$ substitution) the orthopyroxene shows slightly *higher* R^{3+}. Most typically in a metamorphic rock of basaltic composition, the hornblende has R^{3+} of 1.2 to 1.4 and the anthophyllite 0.4 to 1.0.

The details of Figure 27A also hint at complexities to be discussed below. For example, in the actinolite-hornblende series there is a large gap in analyses with R^{3+} between 0.35 and 0.90, suggesting the possibility that the actinolite-hornblende miscibility gap plays some role here. Does the abundance of hornblende analyses coexisting with cummingtonite (Fig. 22A) within this range suggest that high Mg content might favor opening of the actinolite-hornblende gap? The tie lines from hornblende to orthoamphibole lie at various angles, which reflect the appearance of a miscibility gap in that series at low to moderate metamorphic temperatures (see below).

Exsolution lamellae. In coexisting augite and orthopyroxene from igneous and metamorphic rocks it is common for the augite to contain "001" and "100" exsolution lamellae of pigeonite, as well as (100) exsolution lamellae of orthopyroxene (see under Calcic Amphiboles and Cummingtonite, this paper; also Robinson, 1980). The coexisting orthopyroxene commonly contains exsolution lamellae of augite parallel to (100). In the analogous calcic amphibole-ortho-amphibole pairs, the calcic amphibole commonly contains "$\bar{1}01$" and "100" exsolution lamellae of cummingtonite, but lamellae of orthoamphibole parallel to (100) have never been reported. Similarly, no lamellae of calcic amphibole have been reported parallel to (100) of an orthoamphibole, if one excludes the common epitaxial intergrowths of several grains (Robinson *et al.*, 1969, Fig. 3c). These differences may perhaps be due to the smaller cooling range of the amphiboles, to the reduced mutual solubility, especially of the orthoamphibole and calcic amphibole as compared to orthopyroxene and augite, and to the different amphibole structure.

The only kind of exsolution to be found in the orthoamphibole is when it is breaking down to a two-phase mixture of anthophyllite and gedrite (see below). In fact, the absence of exsolution lamellae in orthoamphibole serves as a useful petrographic tool. When viewed in end section, hornblende coexisting with orthoamphibole or cummingtonite coexisting with hornblende usually show fine "100" exsolution lamellae parallel to the long diagonal of the diamond-shaped end section (Robinson *et al.*, 1969, Fig. 3). Because most calcic amphibole-orthoamphibole pairs are relatively magnesian, the cummingtonite exsolution lamellae in the former usually are primitive cummingtonite at room temperature (Ross *et al.*, 1968).

Cummingtonite and orthoamphibole

Chemographic relations. Cummingtonite and anthophyllite have in the past seemed to provide a classical example of amphibole polymorphism. However, like the pair pigeonite-orthopyroxene, when coexisting minerals are compared in detail, there are usually subtle chemical differences. Among the suggested possibilities that will be examined in detail are the following:

(1)   cummingtonite is richer in Fe^{2+} than orthoamphibole;

(2)   cummingtonite is richer in Ca than orthoamphibole;

(3)   cummingtonite is poorer in Al and Fe^{3+} than orthoamphibole;

(4)   cummingtonite is poorer in Na than orthoamphibole.

Analyses of coexisting cummingtonites and orthoamphiboles (in a few examples both anthophyllite and gedrite) are plotted in Figure 28. Figure 28B has the coordinates of the modified quadrilateral, but with both horizontal and vertical axes exaggerated. The space occupied by this figure relative to previous figures is shown by the dashed inset in Figure 27B. Figure 28A has the same coordinates as Figure 27A, but the vertical axis is greatly exaggerated.

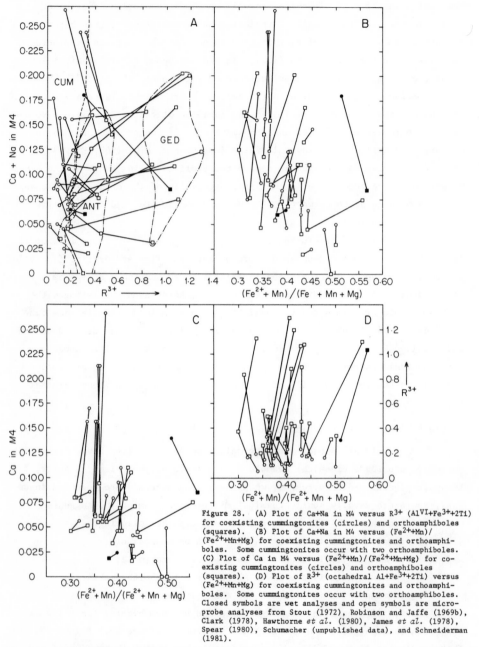

Figure 28. (A) Plot of Ca+Na in M4 versus R^{3+} ($Al^{VI}+Fe^{3+}+2Ti$) for coexisting cummingtonites (circles) and orthoamphiboles (squares). (B) Plot of Ca+Na in M4 versus ($Fe^{2+}+Mn$)/ ($Fe^{2+}+Mn+Mg$) for coexisting cummingtonites and orthoamphiboles. Some cummingtonites occur with two orthoamphiboles. (C) Plot of Ca in M4 versus ($Fe^{2+}+Mn$)/($Fe^{2+}+Mn+Mg$) for coexisting cummingtonites (circles) and orthoamphiboles (squares). (D) Plot of R^{3+} (octahedral $Al+Fe^{3+}+2Ti$) versus ($Fe^{2+}+Mn+Mg$) for coexisting cummingtonites and orthoamphiboles. Some cummingtonites occur with two orthoamphiboles. Closed symbols are wet analyses and open symbols are microprobe analyses from Stout (1972), Robinson and Jaffe (1969b), Clark (1978), Hawthorne *et al.* (1980), James *et al.* (1978), Spear (1980), Schumacher (unpublished data), and Schneiderman (1981).

The space occupied by Figure 28A in a more normal format is shown in a dashed inset in Figure 27A.

In terms of the quantity Ca+Na in M4 (see Fig. 28B), i.e., the substitution toward calcic-sodic amphibole, there is little to choose between cummingtonites and orthoamphiboles. In terms of Fe ratio, the cummingtonites are usually slightly more Fe-rich than coexisting anthophyllites, but if the ortho-amphibole is gedrite, the orthoamphibole is more Fe-rich. This can be understood as due to the exclusion of Mg from M2 in the more aluminous phase. All of these pairs fall in a rather narrow range of Fe ratios.

When the coexisting amphiboles are plotted according to Ca+Na in M4 versus R^{3+}, there is a rather neat separation into fields of cummingtonite, antho-phyllite, and gedrite, although tie-line orientations are chaotic. There is no doubt that part of this chaos is due to increasing solubility of hornblende component in cummingtonite with increasing metamorphic grade. The three cum-mingtonite points highest on the diagram are from the highest grade rocks.

Robinson and Jaffe (1969b, Fig. 8) showed that when Na_2O and CaO are plotted against $MgO + FeO + MnO$, there is an absolute separation of anthophyllites into Na-rich ratios and cummingtonites into Ca-rich ratios. However, this included total Na, not just Na in M4. Nevertheless, compared on the basis of Ca alone in M4, the cummingtonites (Fig. 28C) consistently show higher Ca than coexisting anthophyllites, and only lose out to a few coexisting gedrites with relatively large amounts of tetrahedral and octahedral Al.

As expected, coexisting anthophyllites, as well as gedrites, are always higher in R^{3+} than coexisting cummingtonites (Fig. 28D). Where the orthoamphi-bole is anthophyllite, it is more Mg-rich than cummingtonite. When it is gedrite it is less Mg-rich than cummingtonite. For most cummingtonite-anthophyllite-gedrite assemblages this situation creates typical dog-leg patterns of tie lines from cummingtonite to anthophyllite to gedrite.

Exsolution lamellae. In examples where cummingtonite coexists with ortho-amphibole and the rock contains no other amphibole, exsolution lamellae are un-usual. It is common for the two Fe-Mg amphiboles to show intimate homoaxial intergrowths and for the cummingtonite to show intense polysynthetic twinning on (100),[12] which helps, along with inclined extinction, to distinguish it from orthoamphibole. Where calcic amphibole is also present, the cummingtonite usually contains distinctive "$\bar{1}$01" and "100" exsolution lamellae and, for reasons not yet understood, usually has only subordinate (100) twinning. The orthoamphibole may be in the process of separating into two coexisting orthoamphiboles (see below), but lamellae are usually on a submicroscopic or very fine microscopic scale.

----

[12]An extremely skilled thin-section technician at Amherst College some years ago managed to grind down cummingtonite until it could be mistaken for twinned plagioclase! The scarcity of such talent prevents this from becoming a major problem!

Coexisting orthorhombic amphiboles

Chemographic relations. A well documented miscibility gap exists in the anthophyllite-gedrite series. Robinson *et al.* (1969, 1970, 1971b) and Ross *et al.* (1969) observed exsolution lamellae in intermediate compositions of the solid solution series and noted that there should be a solvus between antho-phyllite and gedrite at appropriate temperatures and pressures. Stout (1969, 1970, 1971, 1972), Spear (1977, 1980), Stoddard and Miller (1979), and Crowley and Spear (1981) have described coexisting, sub-solvus orthoamphiboles. The compositions of coexisting orthoamphiboles from Stout (1972), Spear (1980), and Schumacher (unpublished data) are shown in Figure 29. The data of Spear are from an essentially isothermal, isobaric suite of samples (T = 535 $\pm$ 20°C, P = 4-6 kb); the data of Stout (1972) come from three locations in the silli-manite zone, 10-15 km apart; and the data of Schumacher come from two localities in central Massachusetts, one in the kyanite zone and one just within the staurolite-sillimanite zone.

The data shown in Figure 29 reveal that gedrite is always enriched in A-site occupancy, Al^{VI}, and Al^{IV} relative to coexisting anthophyllite (i.e., the tschermakite and pargasite substitutions), as well as Fe/Mg. The higher Fe-Mg in gedrite can be explained because the M2 site in orthoamphibole favors Mg over Fe, and substitution of Al^{VI} into the M2 site via the tschermak exchange exor-cises Mg preferentially over Fe. Thus, coexisting anthophyllite and gedrite have relatively similar total Fe contents, but gedrite has less total Mg and, hence, a higher Fe/(Fe+Mg). This is tantamount to saying that the tschermak exchange in orthoamphiboles is dominantly $Al^{VI}Al^{IV}$ = MgSi and not $Al^{VI}Al^{IV}$ = FeSi, as has been pointed out by Papike and Ross (1970), Robinson *et al.* (1971b), Stout (1972), Abraham and Schreyer (1973), Kamineni (1975), and Spear (1980).

Also apparent in Figure 29 is the dependence of the size and shape of the miscibility gap on Fe/Mg, most notable with respect to A-site occupancy. Why the gap should be narrower in Mg-rich compositions is not clear, but it has been suggested by Crowley and Spear (1981) that the Mg-tschermak substitution may be more nearly ideal than Fe-tschermak; in Fe-rich compositions some Fe^{2+} is par-titioned into the M2 site and the greater nonideality of Fe-tschermak results in a wider gap. If this suggestion is correct, it would imply that the solvus would close off in Mg-rich bulk compositions at a lower temperature than in Fe-rich compositions, and the critical composition would sweep across the Mg-Fe join with the increasing T. The data of Stoddard and Miller (1979, pers. comm.) may be an example of complete miscibility in a magnesian composition with a sizeable gap still present in Fe-rich compositions.

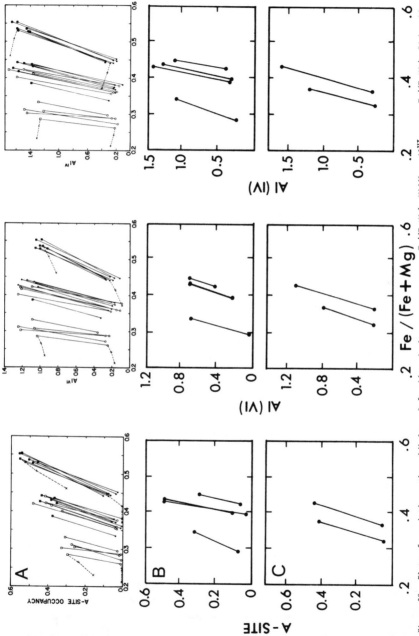

Figure 29. Plots of coexisting orthoamphiboles. Left side: A-site occupancy versus Fe/(Fe+Mg); Middle: AlVI versus Fe/(Fe+Mg); Right side: AlVI versus Fe/(Fe+Mg). (A) Data from Spear (1980), Post Pond Volcanics, Mt. Cube Quadrangle, VT., Staurolite-kyanite grade. Filled symbols are hornblende-bearing, open symbols are hornblende-absent. (B) Data from Stout (1972), Telemark, Norway, sillimanite zone. (C) Data from Schumacher (pers. comm.), Ammonoosuc Volcanics, central Massachusetts, kyanite zone and lower sillimanite-staurolite zone. The gedrites are consistently higher than the anthophyllites in A-site occupancy, AlVI, AlIV, and Fe/(Fe+Mg).

67

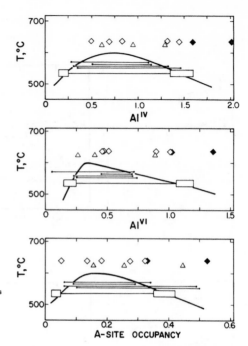

Figure 30. T-X diagrams depicting the orthoamphibole solvus, taken from Spear (1980).
Diamonds and triangles are supersolvus orthoamphiboles from Robinson *et al.* (1971) and James
et al. (1978), respectively. Dots are from
Stout (1972) and open boxes from the Post Pond
Volcanics (Spear, 1980).

Spear (1980) estimated that the crest of the solvus should lie at approximately 600°C in samples with a bulk Fe/(Fe+Mg) of approximately 0.4 (see Fig.
30). Samples from Robinson *et al.* (1971b) and James *et al.* (1978) contain
orthoamphiboles with compositions that completely span the miscibility gap and
must therefore be supersolvus. Samples from Stout probably crystallized at
$560 \pm 25°C$ and generally show a narrower gap than samples from the Post Pond
Volcanics (T = $535 \pm 20°C$). Temperature estimates from Stoddard and Miller (1979)
indicate a temperature of $560 \pm 25°C$, and these orthoamphibole pairs show a smaller
gap than those from the Post Pond Volcanics. Pressure dependence of the solvus
is not well established, but Crowley and Spear (1981) have suggested that the
critical curve has a positive dP/dT slope.

It is also apparent that the solvus is probably asymmetric with respect to
the tschermak and edenite substitutions, as indicated in Figure 30. Exsolution
lamellae of anthophyllite in gedrite are always coarser than those of gedrite
in anthophyllite; thus, the solvus should be steeper on the anthophyllite limb.

Exsolution lamellae. Evidence for exsolution in orthoamphibole was first
seen by K. L. Giesecke, who collected specimens of what he called "labradori-
serende hornblende," at Avisisarfik, on his open-boat trip along the west Greenland coast in 1810. These specimens were later studied and analyzed by Bøggild
(1905, 1924) in connection with his study of iridescence in plagioclase.

68

Bøggild determined by reflection goniometry that the plane of iridescence is (010). Robinson and Jaffe saw iridescence in gedrite rocks in southwestern New Hampshire in 1967, but dismissed it as probably due to labradorite, until X-ray single crystal photographs by Ross *et al.* (1968) showed that many of the orthoamphiboles from Massachusetts and southwestern New Hampshire are actually two-phase mixtures of anthophyllite and gedrite with different *b*-crystallographic dimensions. High power optical examination of two of these specimens by Robinson and Jaffe (1969b) showed very fine visible lamellae parallel to (010), and subsequent electron microscopic studies (Gittos *et al.*, 1976) showed that the iridescent orthoamphiboles are *submicroscopic* intergrowths of anthophyllite and gedrite. A few months after the discovery of the New Hampshire intergrowths, Stout (1969) reported on a rock from Norway with two coexisting orthoamphiboles. All of these eventualities were predicted by J. B. Thompson (pers. comm., 1968) on the basis of the structural analogy between anthophyllite-gedrite and the then-documented coexistence of actinolite and hornblende (Shido and Miyashiro, 1959).

In view of the history of discovery, it is interesting that the pattern of (010) lamellae, either in optical micrographs or electron micrographs, very closely resembles the pattern in electron micrographs of labradorite (Ribbe, 1975) and in orthoclase cryptoperthite (Yund, 1975). In the last two examples, the exsolution texture is thought to be typical of the process of spinodal decomposition. Another interesting observation is that lamellae are coarser in gedrite hosts than anthophyllite hosts. This may be explained by a gentler gedrite limb of the solvus, or by the greater ease of Al-ordering in an Al-rich as compared to an Al-poor composition.

The electron optical studies of Gittos *et al.* (1976) turned up another style of exsolution in orthoamphiboles. These are lamellae approximately parallel to (120) that are approximately perpendicular to the (210) cleavage of the orthorhombic cell (see Ghose, Volume 9A, Fig. 21). Such (120) patterns, along with (010) lamellae, have also been seen in the optically visible range by Hawthorne *et al.* (1980) and by Spear (1980, Figs. 2 and 3) at the boundaries between gedrite cores and anthophyllite rims (Fig. 31). Another feature in the Gittos *et al.* (1976) electron micrographs are extremely thin lamellae, no more than one or two unit cells thick, of monoclinic amphibole, apparently cummingtonite, parallel to (100). These are the only examples known to the authors of clinoamphibole lamellae in an orthoamphibole.

Coexisting calcic amphiboles

There have been a great number of reported occurrences of the two-amphibole association actinolite + hornblende in rocks from both low-pressure (andalusite-

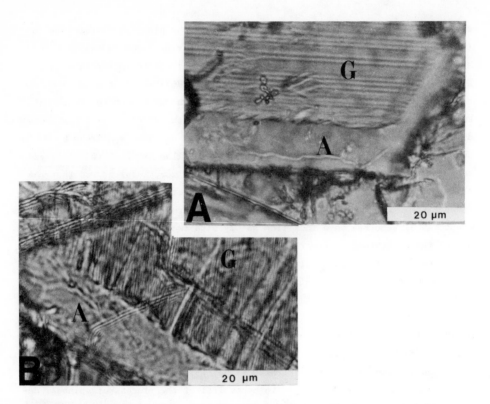

Figure 31. Photomicrographs showing exsolution features in gedrite (G) rimmed by anthophyllite (A) from the Post Pond Volcanics, Vermont (Spear, 1980). (A) (010) (east-west) and scarce (120) (diamond pattern) anthophyllite lamellae in a gedrite host surrounded by optically homogeneous anthophyllite. (B) Gedrite containing (120) lamellar features adjacent to an anthophyllite contact. These features appear to be cut by finer and very typical (010) lamellae.

sillimanite) and intermediate-pressure (kyanite–sillimanite) facies series (e.g., Sundius, 1946; Compton, 1958; Klein, 1969; Choudhuri, 1974; Doolan *et al.*, 1973; Miyashiro, 1958; Shido, 1958; Shido and Miyashiro, 1959; Cooper and Lovering, 1970; Cooper, 1972; Tagiri, 1977; Brady, 1974; Sampson and Fawcett, 1977; Graham, 1974; Grapes, 1975; Hietanen, 1974; Sugi, 1931; Wiseman, 1934; Allen and Goldie, 1978). In spite of the large number of occurrences, or perhaps because of it, there has been considerable debate in the literature over whether or not a miscibility gap exists in the actinolite–hornblende series. The essential arguments in favor of a gap are the presence of sharp optical and chemical discontinuities and the systematics of element partitioning between the coexisting amphiboles (e.g., Miyashiro, 1958; Shido, 1958; Shido and Miyashiro, 1959; Cooper and Lovering, 1970; Klein, 1969; Choudhuri, 1974; Brady, 1974; Tagiri, 1977). Arguments against the existence of a gap focus on the absence of sharp chemical and optical boundaries, the abundance of core-rim relations and the continuous gradation of composition between actinolite and hornblende with increasing metamorphic grade in some occurrences (e.g., Ernst, 1972a; Sampson and Fawcett, 1977; Grapes, 1975; Graham, 1974; Grapes and Graham, 1978). In these reports, coexistence of actinolite and hornblende has been assumed to represent disequilibrium.

The only experimental work that pertains to the actinolite-hornblende miscibility gap is the work of Oba (1980), who studied phase relations along the tremolite-pargasite join. Oba found there to be a well defined miscibility gap between tremolite and pargasite up to temperatures of approximately 825°C at 1 kbar PH_2O, where the amphiboles begin to break down. At 5 kbar, he observed complete miscibility between tremolite and pargasite at temperatures above 800°C; experiments below 800°C were not successful, but if a gap exists, the crest of the solvus must be below 800°C.

The most compelling evidence for the existence of a solvus, the presence of exsolution lamellae of hornblende in actinolite, or vice versa, has not been conclusively demonstrated. Cooper and Lovering (1970) described the existence of such lamellae, but these were later found to be twin lamellae (Cooper, 1972).

Plots of coexisting actinolite and hornblende compositions from selected literature sources are shown in Figure 32. An attempt has been made to present each data set in a consistent fashion similar to the plots of anthophyllite-gedrite. In the case of actinolite-hornblende, Fe^{3+} in hornblende can be considerable, and the amount of ferric iron will strongly affect A-site occupancy and Fe^{2+}/Mg. No attempt has been made to resolve this uncertainty, however, and all data have been plotted as they appear in the literature (i.e., using the author's estimate of Fe^{3+}).

The plots in Figure 32 show that there is a relatively consistent gap between actinolite and hornblende from diverse geologic environments. Hornblende always has a higher Fe/Mg and is enriched in Al and Na over coexisting actinolite. The higher Fe/Mg in hornblende arises largely because octahedral aluminum displaces Mg from the M2 site (thus hornblende has less total Mg than actinolite) and also because hornblende has a somewhat higher total Fe content than coexisting actinolite.

If a solvus does exist, there should be a relationship between the compositions of phases coexisting across the solvus and metamorphic grade. Misch and Rice (1975) have presented analyses of amphiboles ranging in composition from actinolite to hornblende that show no apparent compositional break (Fig. 32F) and have concluded that these amphiboles equilibrated above the crest of the solvus (T ≃ 600°C, 5±1 kbar). A distinct gap in composition is found in samples that crystallized at 500-525°C, 5±1 kbar, and Misch and Rice have postulated a maximum possible size for the gap at these conditions (Fig. 32E),

71

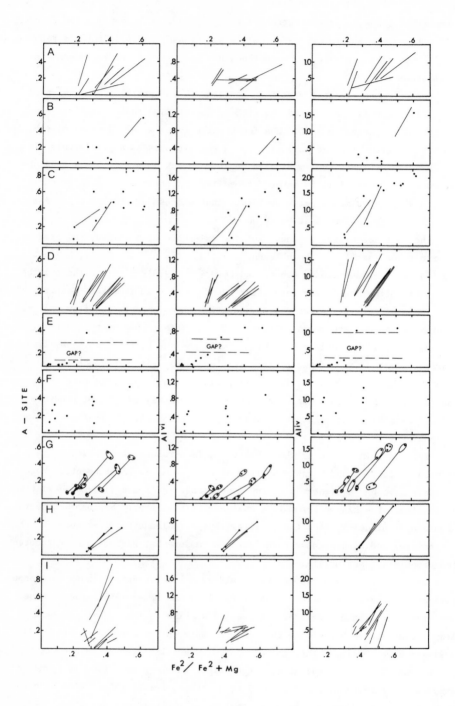

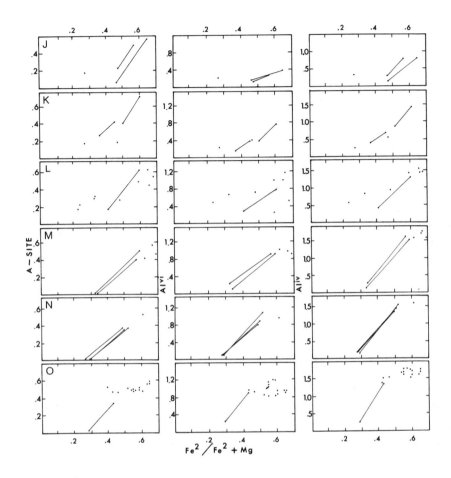

Figure 32. Plots of coexisting calcic amphibole compositions from numerous literature sources. Left column is A-site occupancy versus Fe/(Fe+Mg); middle column is octahedral Al versus Fe/(Fe+Mg); Right column is tetrahedral Al versus Fe/(Fe+Mg). (A) Klein (1969) - various metamorphic grades; (B) Cooper and Lovering (1970) - chlorite-biotite zone; (C) Cooper and Lovering (1970) - garnet-oligoclase zone; (D) Brady (1974) - lower staurolite zone; (E) Misch and Rice (1975) - low grade (∿500-525°C), postulated miscibility gap indicated by dashed lines; (F) Misch and Rice (1975) - high grade (∿600°, 4-6kbar) super solvus conditions; (G) Tagiri (1977) - upper greenschist to epidote-amphibolite facies; (H) Choudhuri (1974) - upper greenschist facies; (I) Grapes (1975) - greenschist to amphibolite facies; (J) Graham (1974) and Harte and Graham (1975) - lower chlorite zone; (K) Graham (1974) and Harte and Graham (1975) - biotite zone; (L) Graham (1974) and Harte and Graham (1975) - garnet zone; (M) Sampson and Fawcett (1977) - greenschist-lower amphibolite facies (albite zone); (N) Sampson and Fawcett (1977) - lower amphibolite facies (oligoclase zone); (O) Sampson and Fawcett (1977) - amphibolite facies (andesine zone).

although no two-amphibole assemblages were found. A well defined gap is present in the data of Brady (1974), Tagiri (1977) and Choudhuri (1974) (Fig. 32D,G,H), but estimates of metamorphic conditions from these three studies are not well enough known to permit comparison of the sizes of the different gaps. The data of Cooper and Lovering (1970) (Fig. 32B,C) and Sampson and Fawcett (1977) (Fig. 32D,M,N) have been separated with respect to the metamorphic zones from which the samples were collected. The gap of Cooper and Lovering shows little or no decrease in size with increasing grade (in fact, relative to A-site occupancy and Al^{VI} the gap appears to be larger at higher grade). The gap of Sampson and Fawcett does show a slight contraction with increasing grade, but it should be mentioned that these authors did not interpret the coexisting actinolite and hornblende from this area as equilibrium pairs. The coexisting pairs from Klein (1969) (Fig. 32A) are from three different localities; one pair displays rather aberrant behavior with respect to A-site occupancy and Al^{IV}, and two pairs do so with respect to Al^{VI}. The data of Grapes (1975) (Fig. 32I) is clearly the least consistent and it is understandable that Grapes interpreted these coexisting amphiboles as nonequilibrium pairs.

The shape of the solvus was discussed by Tagiri (1977), who noted that in his samples (Fig. 32G), Fe-rich compositions showed a wider gap than Mg-rich compositions. A similar Fe/Mg dependence is present in the anthophyllite-gedrite system. The gap of Brady (1974) may also show a slight tendency towards decreasing size in Mg-rich rocks, especially with respect to A-site occupancy, but the trend is not so pronounced as in the data of Tagiri (1977).

In attempting to reconcile the diversity of actinolite-hornblende associations, as well as the diversity of interpretations of these associations, two factors should be discussed: the textures of the coexisting amphiboles and the reactions producing them. Core-rim relations where actinolite is mantled by hornblende are common (e.g., Cooper and Lovering, 1970; Graham, 1974), as are patchy intergrowths of actinolite and hornblende (e.g., Klein, 1969; Tagiri, 1977; Choudhuri, 1974). In most of these occurrences there is a sharp optical and compositional boundary between the hornblende and actinolite. A notable exception is Grapes (1975), who observed a gradational contact in some grains. Klein (1969) reported discrete coexisting grains of hornblende and actinolite from a location in Madagascar. Brady (1974) described discrete coexisting grains and intergrowths with sharp, but irregular boundaries. The core-rim relations and patchy intergrowths have been interpreted by some authors as evidence for disequilibrium (e.g., Grapes, 1975; Graham, 1974; Grapes and Graham, 1978). Others have interpreted the patchy intergrowths as equilibrium textures (e.g., Klein, 1969; Choudhuri, 1974; Tagiri, 1977; Brady, 1974). Brady has pointed

74

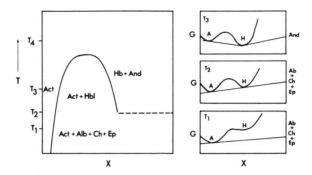

Figure 33. Schematic T-X and G-X sections showing a possible configuration of the actinolite-hornblende solvus for the greenschist-amphibolite facies transition. The X compositional variable is a projection onto the actinolite-hornblende join. See text for discussion.

out that the commonly observed patchy intergrowth cannot represent a minimum potential energy configuration of the interface. He suggests that the potential energy of the actinolite-hornblende interface may be very low (both phases have the same structure and similar cell dimensions), and there may not be a significant thermodynamic potential for achieving a more regular geometry.

The reactions that produce actinolite-hornblende associations occur in the greenschist to amphibolite facies transition zone. Metamorphosed mafic rocks of the greenschist facies typically consist of assemblages such as actinolite + albite + chlorite + epidote $\pm$ quartz $\pm$ sphene $\pm$ carbonates. With increasing grade, albite, chlorite, epidote, and actinolite break down to produce pargasitic hornblende + andesine, which is the typical assemblage of the amphibolite facies. Several schematic reactions have been postulated, such as:

tremolite + albite = edenite + quartz;

chlorite + actinolite + epidote + quartz = tschermakite + H_2O;

chlorite + epidote + quartz = tschermakite + anorthite + H_2O.

Schematic T-X and G-X diagrams depicting a possible configuration for the actinolite-hornblende solvus are shown in Figure 33 (taken, in part, from Tagiri, 1977, and Misch and Rice, 1975). In the greenschist facies (T1), hornblende is metastable relative to actinolite + chlorite + albite + epidote. At some temperature (T2) the G-X curve for hornblende intersects this join, and hornblende begins to form at the expense of these phases. In the middle amphibolite facies (T3), hornblende + andesine is the stable association found in most common metamorphosed volcanic rock types, but a solvus relation may still be present between hornblende and actinolite. At some higher temperature (T4), continuous solid solution between hornblende and actinolite is observed. Eventually, actinolite should break down to phases such as clinopyroxene and cummingtonite, as suggested by Tagiri (1977).

If the cartoon shown in Figure 33 is even approximately correct, it can be used to explain the diversity of actinolite-hornblende associations. First, depending on the bulk composition (especially Fe/Mg) and the specific P-T path a rock experiences, the solvus may be intersected at different temperatures giving rise to gaps of different sizes. Second, rocks with aluminous compositions (i.e., to the right of hornblende on the G-X diagram in Fig. 33) will tend to show hornblende rimming actinolite, whereas rocks low in Al (i.e., between hornblende and actinolite) will show stable two-amphibole associations.

Considering the possible metamorphic scenarios for producing actinolite-hornblende pairs, it is not surprising that a wide diversity of interpretations has been put forth. As pointed out above, one of the principal arguments against the existence of a gap is that in some environments a continuous gradation in composition between actinolite and hornblende is observed with increasing metamorphic grade. However, as Misch and Rice (1975, p. 3) have pointed out: ". . . continuous compositional change of calcic amphiboles with changing grade in rocks of similar overall compositions constitutes a type of evidence quite different from a continuous solid solution series observed at one grade in rocks of dissimilar bulk compositions." If complete ranges of bulk compositions were available at every outcrop, a much more consistent picture would certainly emerge; however, metamorphosed volcanic rocks are typically quite restricted in their compositions.

Considering the bulk of the available data, it is reasonable to conclude that a solvus relation does exist between actinolite and hornblende, if for no other reason than the difficulty in explaining the abundances of optically and chemically distinct pairs by any other mechanism. However, it is also reasonable to conclude that not every association of actinolite with hornblende is an equilibrium manifestation of the solvus. There is certainly room for additional research in this area.

Assemblages of three or more amphiboles

The recognition of different amphibole pairs and their positions in chemical space naturally led to a search for rocks containing three or more amphiboles, particularly with the classic three-pyroxene assemblage augite-orthopyroxene-pigeonite in mind. Such an assemblage should consist of three or more discrete host amphiboles that coexisted in equilibrium, whatever later amphiboles may have developed from them by exsolution or retrograde reaction processes.

Robinson (1963) found several rocks containing hornblende-anthophyllite-cummingtonite but had doubts based on textures or abundance of secondary chlorite that all three amphiboles coexisted in equilibrium. The chemography of amphibole pairs in the kyanite and sillimanite zones of central Massachusetts and south-western New Hampshire (Klein, 1968; Robinson and Jaffe, 1969b) suggested that the three-amphibole assemblage should occur in rocks with a bulk $Fe^{2+}/(Fe^{2+}+Mg)$ ratio centered on 0.39. Eventually, a suitable sample was found for study in the sillimanite-orthoclase zone of central Massachusetts, where the three-amphibole assemblage has a bulk $Fe^{2+}/(Fe^{2+}+Mg)$ ratio of 0.35 (Robinson *et al.*, 1969). In this rock the three amphiboles are a magnesian hornblende with fine cummingtonite exsolution lamellae, a primitive cummingtonite host (the first such primitive host found in Massachusetts) with fine hornblende lamellae, and an anthophyllite that contains about 20% of submicroscopic gedrite lamellae.

Two sets of three analyses from different spots in this rock are plotted in Figure 34A (2A and 2B), together with a similar assemblage (W-4) from high grade rocks reported by James *et al.* (1978). In two out of the three assemblages (Fig. 34A-right) the cummingtonite is more Fe-rich than the coexisting antho-phyllite and lies on the Fe-rich side of the anthophyllite-hornblende tie line, imitating the analogous three-pyroxene assemblage, but with an extremely slim three-phase field. Detailed reexamination of set 2A suggests it may have under-gone retrograde re-equilibration, and that the hornblende in particular seems to have increased in Al and decreased in Mg by reaction with matrix plagioclase. In Figure 34A-left, the cummingtonite has consistently higher Ca+Na in M4 (0.2-0.25, hornblende component) than the anthophyllite (0.1-0.18), whereas the latter has consistently higher R^{3+} (near 0.5) compared to 0.2-0.3 for cum-mingtonite. The orthoamphibole is thus well within the low-temperature limbs of the anthophyllite-gedrite solvus (see above). The hornblendes are modestly "cummingtonitic," with Ca+Na in M4 of 1.6-1.7, and have R^{3+} of 1.1-1.3, much higher than the other amphiboles.

Shortly after the Massachusetts findings, Stout (1969, 1970) found similar but lower grade rocks in central Telemark, Norway, containing cummingtonite-hornblende and *two* orthoamphiboles, anthophyllite and gedrite; and subsequent work in a number of areas revealed multiple amphibole assemblages complicated by the anthophyllite-gedrite gap.

Figure 34B shows similar plots of five multiple amphibole assemblages from low in the sillimanite zone; 2R6E and OS5 are from unpublished data of Schumacher from central Massachusetts; GAB1 and 101A are from the Telemark area, Norway; and 1317 (Hawthorne *et al.*, 1980) is from the Canadian Shield. These assem-blages show the effect of an emerging anthophyllite-gedrite solvus and of lower temperature. 2R6E and GAB1 are anthophyllite assemblages, 1317 and OS5 are gedrite assemblages, and 101A is an assemblage with four amphiboles.

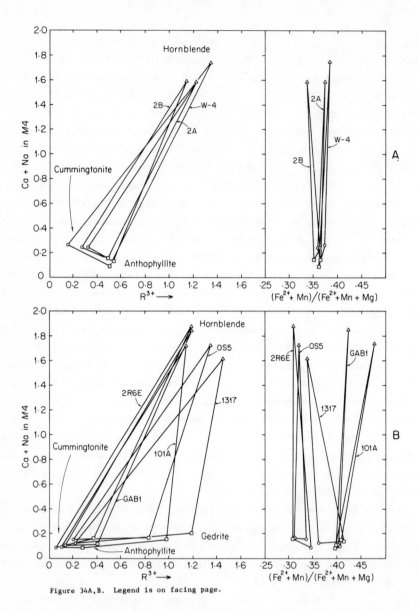

Figure 34A,B. Legend is on facing page.

In the three cummingtonite-anthophyllite pairs, and even in one of the cummingtonite-gedrite pairs (Fig. 34B-right), the cummingtonite is consistently more Fe^{2+}-rich than the coexisting orthoamphibole, and, in fact, some of the three-phase fields appear to be more open than in the higher grade assemblages of Figure 34A. On the other hand, the two more R^{3+}-rich gedrites (1317 and 101A), because of R^{3+} exclusion of Mg in M2, are more Fe-rich than coexisting cumming-

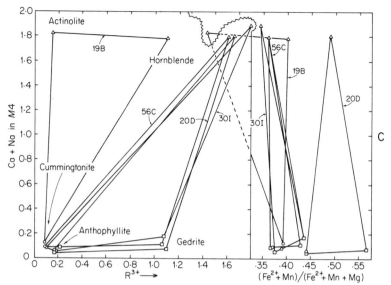

Figure 34. Compositions from probe analyses in assemblages with three or four coexisting amphiboles. Triangles, hornblendes; circles, cummingtonites; squares, anthophyllites and gedrites. In each figure the vertical axis is Ca + Na in M4. The horizontal axis on the left is R^{3+} (octahedral Al + Fe^{3+} + $2Ti^{4+}$), the horizontal axis on the right is $(Fe^{2+}+Mn)/(Fe^{2+}+Mn+Mg)$. (A) Assemblages from high in the sillimanite zone reported by Robinson *et al.* (1969, 2A, 2B) and James (1978; W-4). (B) Assemblages from low in the sillimanite zone reported by Stout (1972; GAB1, 101A), Hawthorne *et al.* (1980; 1317), and J.C. Schumacher (unpublished data, 2R6E, OS5). (C) Assemblages from the kyanite-staurolite zone reported by Spear (1980; 56C, 20D, 30I) and Spear (unpublished data; 19B). Two parts of figure overlap along jagged line.

tonites, and in the four-amphibole assemblage cummingtonite is intermediate between anthophyllite and gedrite.

In terms of Ca+Na in M4 and R^{3+} in these low-sillimanite-zone assemblages, the cummingtonites have the same or lower Ca+Na (0.15-0.18), consistent with a much lower hornblende substitution, than in Figure 34A. R^{3+} of cummingtonite is also less, at 0.2 or less, as is R^{3+} of anthophyllite (0.2-0.3), consistent with opening of the anthophyllite-gedrite solvus. Gedrites coexisting with less aluminous amphibole extend between 0.8 and 1.2 and tend to have a slightly higher Ca+Na (hornblende) component. As compared to higher grade rocks (Fig. 34A), the hornblendes tend toward higher Ca+Na in M4 (1.6-1.9), i.e., a lower cummingtonite component with about the same R^{3+} of 1.1-1.4.

The lowest grade multiple-amphibole assemblages, all with four amphiboles, come from low in the staurolite-kyanite zone of Vermont (Spear, 1980) and are shown in Figure 34C-right. Here the anthophyllite-gedrite solvus is still more open. Cummingtonites are consistently more Fe-rich or the same as coexisting anthophyllites, whereas they are consistently much less Fe-rich than the gedrites. The high Fe ratios of the gedrites thus provide a very wide three-phase triangle in this view. In Figure 34C-left these cummingtonites have still lower Ca+Na

79

in M4 (0.10 or less) and R^{3+} (0.18-0.10), consistent with less hornblende component at lower temperature. The anthophyllites show lower R^{3+} near 0.2, and
the gedrites show higher R^{3+} near 1.1, consistent with a wider orthoamphibole
solvus. In these rocks the hornblendes have higher Ca+Na in M4 of 1.8-1.9,
consistent with a lower cummingtonite component, and also show a much higher
R^{3+} of 1.6-1.8 that may be consistent with a lower temperature of equilibration.

In the same area in Vermont, Spear (unpublished data) has located a specimen which appears to contain coexisting cummingtonite, actinolite, and hornblende.
This assemblage seems to be consistent with the inferred conditions of formation
of these Vermont rocks, and the composition triangle neatly fills a large vacant
area in Figure 34C-left. In Figure 34C-right the cummingtonite-hornblende pair
shows similar Fe ratios to other pairs, whereas the coexisting actinolite,
as predicted above, is much more magnesian $[(Fe^{2+}+Mn)/(Fe^{2+}+Mn+Mg) = 0.23]$.
In Figure 34C-left the cummingtonite has the highest Ca+Na of any at that grade
(highest actinolite component). The actinolite and hornblende have similar Ca+Na
in M4 of 1.8 (i.e., similar cummingtonite component) but vastly different R^{3+}
of 0.15 and 1.1. A similar assemblage of anthophyllite-actinolite-hornblende
seems likely to be found, particularly in light of the chemographic relations
shown here and in Figure 27A. If this is also possible, then the next tar-
getted four-amphibole assemblage should be anthophyllite-cummingtonite-actino-
lite-hornblende.

Since Stout's discoveries in 1969, the search for five coexisting amphiboles as well as other four-amphibole assemblages has gone on without success.
The addition of lithium amphibole to a list of four others is possible but improbable, because holmquistites seem to be confined to lithium-rich pegmatites.
Another possibility is to have an actinolite-hornblende pair along with cummingtonite and two orthoamphiboles. However, since low-grade calcic amphiboles
coexisting with gedrite (Fig. 34C) seem to have very high Al contents, it may
be impossible to have calcic amphibole of the requisite low Al composition
range required for coexisting actinolite-hornblende.

Cummingtonites and sodic amphiboles

The combination of Fe-Mg amphibole and sodic amphibole represents one of
the three possible combinations along the edges of Figure 20. We have found
only two analyzed pairs of such occurrences, both from metamorphosed chemical
sedimentary rocks of unusual composition from Labrador (Klein, 1966, 1968, with
formulae recast by Robinson *et al.*, 1971a) and from New Caledonia (Black, 1973).
In both cases the Fe-Mg amphibole is a cummingtonite and the sodic amphibole is
rich in Fe^{3+}. In other respects they are very different. Both pairs are

plotted with special symbols on Figure 22A,B and Figure 25, and corrected
formulae are given in Table 3. On Figure 22 (dashed tie lines) these pairs
are not distinguishable from cummingtonite-calcic amphibole pairs, but in Figure
25 their tie lines consistently cut across the tie lines for cummingtonite-
calcic amphibole pairs. This difference may tie in with the different way in
which R^{3+} substitution is valence-compensated in the sodic as compared to the
calcic amphiboles (see Fig. 16).

Table 3. Compositions of coexisting Fe-Mg amphiboles and sodic amphiboles from Klein (1966, 1968)
[left] and Black (1973) [right] based on electron
probe analyses. The left-hand pair is also based
on wet chemical analysis of an impure separate showing no FeO.

	Cummingtonite	Magnesio-Arfvedsonite	Grunerite	Riebeckite
Si	8.000	7.890	7.930	7.961
Al		.016	.007	.039
Fe^{3+}		.094	.063	
	8.000	8.000	8.000	8.000
Si	.010			
Al	.016			.279
Fe^{3+}	.252	.804	.055	1.189
Ti				
Mg	4.450	3.770	1.495	.917
Fe^{2+}		.426	3.450	2.615
Mn	.272			
	5.000	5.000	5.000	5.000
Fe^{2+}			1.163	.045
Mn	1.589	.305	.772	.127
Ca	.108	.354	.067	.329
Na	.303	1.341		1.499
	2.000	2.000	2.002	2.000
Na	.002	.246	.015	.070
K	.017	.404		
	.019	.650	.015	.070

In the Labrador pair, a wet chemical analysis of a partially purified
separate indicates that all Fe is Fe_2O_3. The cummingtonite has Mn assigned
both to M4 and M1,2,3 and has an unusually large amount of Ca and Na assigned
to M4, as well as an unusually large amount of Fe^{3+}. The sodic amphibole has
Na_B of 1.341, barely out of the sodic-calcic class, but has nearly as much Mn
as Ca in M4. It is an arfvedsonite with A-occupancy of 0.650 and more K than
Na in the A-site.

In the New Caledonia pair, the Fe-Mg amphibole is grunerite with little
Fe^{3+} and surprisingly little Na, but with substantial Mn in M4. The sodic
amphibole is again not far above Na_B of 1.34, but it has very low A occupancy
and can be thought of as about three-fourths of the distance from tremolite
(+ Mn cummingtonite) to riebeckite.

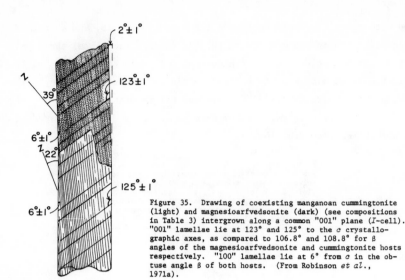

Figure 35. Drawing of coexisting manganoan cummingtonite (light) and magnesioarfvedsonite (dark) (see compositions in Table 3) intergrown along a common "001" plane (*I*-cell). "001" lamellae lie at 123° and 125° to the *c* crystallographic axes, as compared to 106.8° and 108.8° for β angles of the magnesioarfvedsonite and cummingtonite hosts respectively. "100" lamellae lie at 6° from *c* in the obtuse angle β of both hosts. (From Robinson *et al.*, 1971a).

The Labrador pair is of particular interest because of the unusual pattern of exsolution lamellae (Fig. 35). This pattern is, of course, due to the unusual combination of lattice parameters in this mineral pair, and provided a key theoretical test in the evolution of the theory of "exact phase boundaries" (Robinson *et al.*, 1971a, 1977).

Calcic amphiboles and sodic amphiboles

The miscibility gap between calcic and sodic amphiboles involves a discontinuity in the occupancy of the M4 site: in sodic amphiboles the dominant cation is Na, whereas in calcic amphiboles the dominant cation is Ca. Coexisting sodic amphibole + actinolite and sodic amphibole + hornblende have both been reported in the literature. Papers addressing the chemistry of coexisting sodic and calcic amphiboles include Coleman and Papike (1968), Himmelberg and Papike (1969), Klein (1969), Black (1970, 1973), Ernst *et al.* (1970), Ernst and Dal Piaz (1978), Ernst (1979), and Triboulet (1978).

The miscibility gap between the sodic and calcic amphiboles can be visualized in the square pyramid in Figure 36. Sodic amphiboles are predominantly solid solutions between glaucophane [$Na_2Mg_3Al_2Si_8O_{22}(OH)_2$] and magnesioriebeckite [$Na_2Mg_3Fe_2^{3+}Si_8O_{22}(OH)_2$], in addition to Fe:Mg solid solution (i.e., ferroglaucophane and riebeckite). Complete miscibility between glaucophane and magnesioriebeckite in blueschist facies amphibolites has been demonstrated by Miyashiro (1957), Borg (1967), and Coleman and Papike (1968). Thus, there is complete

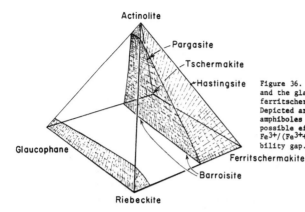

Figure 36. Pyramid with actinolite at the apex and the glaucophane-riebeckite-tschermakite-ferritschermakite reciprocal square at the base. Depicted are fields for calcic to calcic-sodic amphiboles and for sodic amphiboles, and the possible effects of Na in M4, total R^{3+}, and $Fe^{3+}/(Fe^{3+}+Al)$ ratio on the width of the miscibility gap.

substitution between Al^{VI} and Fe^{3+} in the M2 site. Calcic amphiboles coexisting with sodic amphiboles are considerably more complicated. They can range from actinolites at the apex of the pyramid through various degrees of substitution of Al and Fe^{3+} in M2. When such substitution is compensated *only* by tetrahedral Al, this can lead to pargasite and hastingsite, each with one R^{3+} ion in M2, or to tschermakite or ferritschermakite, each theoretically with two R^{3+} ions in M2. In natural hornblendes, of course, it is usual for there to be Na in A, which *also* must be compensated by tetrahedral Al. This A-site substitution is not illustrated in Figure 36. In natural aluminous calcic amphiboles coexisting with sodic amphiboles, a substantial part of the octahedral R^{3+} substitution is compensated by Na in M4, in effect a "glaucophane-riebeckite substitution." All of the data we have examined shows that this glaucophane substitution is much more important in what appear to be high-temperature hornblendes than it is in low-temperature actinolites.

Under appropriate conditions, a miscibility gap may also be present in the actinolite-hornblende series; thus, it is conceivable that two calcic and one sodic amphiboles might coexist stably at some metamorphic grade, although an equilibrium coexistence of this three-amphibole association has not been reported. Black (1970) has reported on coexisting glaucophane and riebeckite-arfvedsonite from New Caledonia. Both amphiboles have similar values of Ca/(Ca+Na) in M4, the major difference being the larger A-site occupancy of the riebeckite-arfvedsonite. If this represents an equilibrium pair, it may be similar to the miscibility gap between actinolite-hornblende (i.e., a gap in

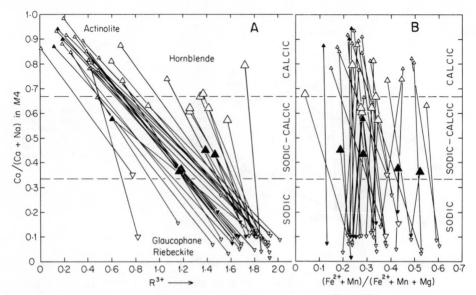

Figure 37. (A) Plot of Ca/(Ca+Na) in M4 versus R^{3+} (octahedral Al + Fe^{3+} + $2Ti^{4+}$) for coexisting calcic amphiboles (triangles) and sodic amphiboles (inverted triangles).
(B) Plot of Ca/(Ca+Na) in M4 versus the $(Fe^{2+}+Mn)/(Fe^{2+}+Mn+Mg)$ ratio for coexisting calcic amphiboles and sodic amphiboles. Large triangles and small inverted triangles represent $R^3 > 1.1$; medium triangles and medium inverted triangles represent $0.5 < R^{3+} < 1.1$; small triangles represent $R^{3+} < 0.5$. Closed symbols are wet analyses and open symbols are microprobe analyses. Probe analyses from Ernst *et al.* (1970), Klein (1969), Immega and Klein (1976), and Black (1973). Wet analyses from Coleman and Papike (1968) and Dobretsov *et al.* (1971).

the amount of A-site Na, tetrahedral Al, and octahedral R^{3+} substitution), but manifested in the sodic amphibole solid solution series. Coleman and Papike (1968) and Himmbelberg and Papike (1969) have determined that all of the alkali amphiboles found coexisting with calcic amphiboles belong to the *C2/m* space group. Therefore, the miscibility gap can be considered to be a true solvus.

Coexisting sodic and calcic amphiboles show very different compositional variability when Ca/(Ca+Na) in M4 is plotted against R^{3+} in Figure 37A. Figure 37A may be thought of, in part, as a collapsed side view of the pyramid in Figure 36, in which the Al = Fe^{3+} substitution is not seen. The sodic amphiboles have R^{3+} values mostly between 1.4 and 2.0 and Ca/(Ca+Na) ratios mostly less than 0.2 (Fig. 37A). Low R^{3+} values in sodic amphiboles with low Ca/(Ca+Na) ratios can be attributed either to a cummingtonite component or to an eckermannite-arfvedsonite component with substantial A-site occupancy. The calcic amphiboles show large variations in R^{3+} and Ca/(Ca+Na). As R^{3+} increases, both Na in M4 (glaucophane substitution) *and* tetrahedral Al (tschermakite substitution) increase, causing the calcic amphiboles to approach barroisite composition. The limited compositional variability of the sodic amphiboles

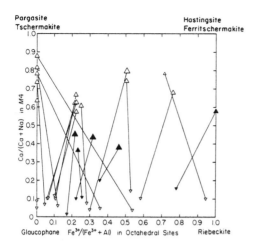

Figure 38. Plot of Ca/(Ca+Na) in M4 versus $Fe^{3+}/(Fe^{3+}+Al)$ in M2 for coexisting calcic amphiboles (triangles) and sodic amphiboles (inverted triangles). With one exception, the only pairs plotted were those in which the calcic amphibole contains $R^{3+} > 0.5$. Large triangles and small inverted triangles represent $R^{3+} > 1.1$; medium triangles and medium inverted triangles represent $0.5 < R^{3+} < 1.1$; small triangle represents $R^{3+} < 0.5$. Closed symbols represent wet analyses and open symbols represent microprobe analyses.

suggests that the sodic limb of the solvus is steep. The more extensive compositional variability exhibited by the calcic amphiboles suggests that the calcic limb of the solvus is gentler and governed by a more complex substitution mechanism.

As shown in Figure 37B, the ratio of $(Fe^{2+}+Mn)/(Fe^{2+}+Mn+Mg)$ for coexisting sodic and calcic amphiboles is very similar for both members of the pairs and varies from about 0.1 to 0.6, with the bulk of the values lying between 0.2 and 0.35. In most of the pairs, the sodic amphibole shows slight enrichment in Fe^{2+} relative to the calcic amphibole. This most likely results from the exclusion of Mg from the M2 site due to the higher R^{3+} contents in the sodic amphiboles. It is tempting to speculate that the more ferrous calcic and sodic-calcic amphiboles show slightly more solid solution toward the sodic amphiboles than do the magnesian ones.

Another important way to compare coexisting sodic and calcic amphiboles is in terms of their relative $Fe^{3+}/(Fe^{3+}+Al)$ ratios. This may be done by dropping all analysis points found in the pyramid onto the square base, which represents a ternary reciprocal system, as in Figure 38. Here, the vertical axis Ca/(Ca+Na) in M4 represents the proportion of calcic to sodic amphibole, whereas the horizontal axis represents the $Fe^{3+}/(Fe^{3+}+Al)$ ratio. It needs to be pointed out that the latter ratio for probe analyses is extremely susceptible to ferric correction procedures and analytical errors. Needless to say, for analyses with low R^{3+} substitutions, the ratio is meaningless. With these facts in mind it is interesting that most of the wet analyses and what appear to be the better probe analyses (particularly those of Black, 1973) show a consistent fractionation, with the calcic amphibole containing a higher ferric ratio than the

85

coexisting sodic amphibole. Possibly this fractionation has petrologic significance.

Figure 39A-J are plots of coexisting sodic and calcic amphiboles from selected literature sources. An attempt has been made to group coexisting pairs according to environment of formation, so that the effect of P and T on shape and size of the solvus can be deduced. As with all electron microprobe analyses of amphiboles, uncertainties in the estimate of ferric iron can greatly influence the calculated site occupancies; this is especially true of sodic amphiboles, in which large amounts of Fe^{3+} can be present in the M2 site. In the plots of Figure 39, site occupancies have been calculated assuming an Fe^{3+} content that is an average of the maximum and minimum values calculated from stoichiometric constraints. In some cases (especially with low-Al calcic amphiboles), the range of acceptable Fe^{3+} contents is small, but often it is quite large, resulting in large uncertainties in the plotting positions. Estimated conditions of crystallization of the amphibole pairs are taken from Triboulet (1978) and Ernst (1979). The reader is referred to these papers for additional discussion of coexisting sodic and calcic amphiboles.

The effect of metamorphic grade on the size and shape of the sodic-calcic amphibole solvus can be seen by comparing the different plots in Figure 39. In general, an increase in metamorphic grade in a particular terrane results in a shrinking of the miscibility gap with respect to Ca/(Ca+Na) in M4. This can best be seen by comparing Figure 39A and B, which are plots of type II and type IV blueschists from Cazadero, California, and Figure 39I and J, which are plots of lawsonite and epidote zone blueschists, respectively, from New Caledonia. Moreover, the increase in miscibility of the sodic amphibole component in the calcic amphibole is always greater than the increase in the miscibility of the calcic component in the sodic amphibole with increasing grade (i.e., the solvus is asymmetric). This results in the formation of intermediate sodic-calcic amphiboles (barroisities) in high-grade blueschists. Another change with increasing metamorphic grade is the shift in the calcic amphibole from actinolite in low-grade blueschists to hornblende (or barroisite) in high-grade blueschists. This can be seen in the plots of R^{3+} versus Ca/(Ca+Na) in M4 and is especially evident in the data of Black (1973; Fig. 39I and J). Thus, in high-grade blueschists, the sodic and calcic amphiboles have rather similar R^{3+}.

Black (1973) has enumerated other changes in amphibole chemistry with increasing metamorphic grade in the New Caledonian blueschists. Glaucophane shows an increase in Mg/(Mg+Fe) and A-site occupancy with increasing grade;

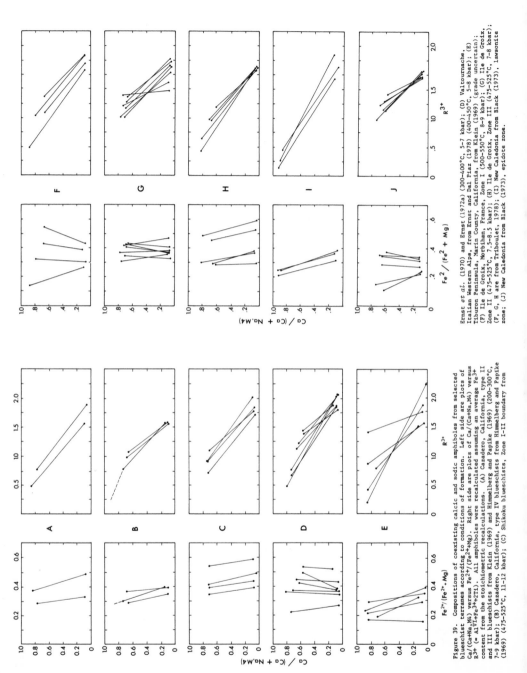

Figure 39. Compositions of coexisting calcic and sodic amphiboles from selected blueschist terranes according to conditions of formation. Left side are plots of $Ca/(Ca+Na,M4)$ versus $Fe^{2+}/(Fe^{2+}+Mg)$. Right side are plots of $Ca/(Ca+Na,M4)$ versus R^{3+} ($= Al^{VI}+Fe^{3+}+Ti$). All amphiboles were recalculated assuming an average Fe^{2+}/Fe^{3+} ratio from stoichiometric calculations. (A) Cazadero, California, Type II and III blueschists from Klein (1969) and Himmelberg and Papike (1969) (200–300°C, 7 kbar); (B) Cazadero, California, Type IV blueschists from Himmelberg and Papike (1969) (475–525°C, 11–12 kbar); (C) Shikoku blueschists, Zone I–II boundary from

Ernst et al. (1970) and Ernst (1972a) (300–400°C, 5–7 kbar); (D) Valtournanche, Italian Western Alps, from Ernst and Dal Piaz (1978) (400–450°C, 8–10 kbar;(E) Tiburon Peninsula, Marin County, California from Klein (1969) (grade uncertain); (F) Ile de Groix, Morbihan, France, Zone I (500–550°C, 8–9 kbar); (G) Ile de Groix, Zone II (475–525°C, 7.5–8.5 kbar); (H) Ile de Groix, Zone III (475–525°C, 7–8 kbar); Zone III blueschists from Triboulet, 1978); (I) New Caledonia from Black (1973), lawsonite zone; (J) New Caledonia from Black (1973), epidote zone.

87

coexisting calcic amphiboles show an increase in total Al, total Na, Na/Ca, and A-site occupancy.

Whether it is T or P that has the greater influence on the size and shape of the solvus can also be ascertained from Figure 39. Samples from the Cazadero type IV blueschists (Fig. 39B), Ile de Groix (Fig. 39F,G,H) and Valtournache (Fig. 39D) crystallized at approximately the same temperature, 400-500°C, but the type IV blueschists are considerably higher pressure (10-12 kbar as opposed to 5-9 kbar). No systematic differences with pressure can be observed among these suites. An increase in T at approximately constant P can be seen between the Cazadero type II and III (Fig. 39A) and the New Caledonia lawsonite zone blueschists (Fig. 39F,I), both of which are relatively low temperature, and the Shikoku (Fig. 39C), Valtournache (Fig. 39D), and Ile de Groix (Fig. 39F,G,H) blueschists. Calcic amphiboles from the high-temperature terranes are all more barroisitic than those from the low-temperature terranes; thus, it appears that temperature has the larger influence on the size of the solvus.

It should be noted that no evidence for closure of the solvus under blue-schist facies conditions was reported from any of these studies, although Ernst (1979) has argued that barroisitic amphiboles from the high-grade Shiritaki district do bridge the gap. His plots show total Na, however, rather than Na in M4; thus, the high-Na barroisites may simply have large A-site occupancies.

AMPHIBOLES IN IRON-FORMATIONS

Most of the amphiboles in Precambrian[13] banded iron-formations tend to be restricted to relatively simple compositional series because the bulk chemical compositions of Precambrian iron-formations show low contents and small ranges for some of the pertinent oxide components, such as Al_2O_3 and Na_2O. Iron-formation bulk chemistries range widely in MgO, FeO, and CaO contents, which accounts for the common metamorphic occurrence of members of the cummingtonite-grunerite and tremolite-ferroactinolite series. Anthophyllite is found locally and hornblende compositions are not uncommon. Riebeckite-tremolite solid solutions and magnesio-riebeckite may also be part of some metamorphic iron-formation assemblages. Riebeckite and its fibrous variety crocidolite can be very abundant as late diagenetic minerals in essentially unmetamorphosed iron-formations.

----

[13]This treatment relates mainly to the mineralogy of Precambrian iron-formations, although some data from a Devonian iron-rich lithology are also considered (Huntington, 1975).

Cummingtonite-grunerite series

The most common amphiboles in metamorphic iron-formations are the light brown members of the monoclinic cummingtonite-grunerite series, which range from approximately $Fe_2Mg_5Si_8O_{22}(OH)_2$ to $Fe_7Si_8O_{22}(OH)_2$. *Amosite* is a rare asbestiform variety of grunerite which occurs in metamorphosed iron-formation in the Transvaal Province of South Africa (Peacock, 1928; du Toit, 1945; Vermaas, 1952; Hutchison *et al.*, 1975; Ross, Chapter 6, Volume 9A).

James (1955) has correlated the first occurrence of grunerite with the garnet and staurolite zones of pelitic schists in the iron-formation districts of northern Michigan. Klein (1978) notes the first occurrence of Mg-Fe clinoamphiboles at the onset of the biotite zone for iron-formations in central Labrador, Canada. Haase (1981) infers the transition from his zone I (stilpnomelane-minnesotaite-rich) to his zone II (grunerite-rich) in the Negaunee Iron Formation in northern Michigan in a region that is fairly close to the biotite isograd as mapped by James (1955). It appears therefore that Mg-Fe clinoamphiboles in metamorphosed banded iron-formations are stable from the biotite isograd on, through the garnet and staurolite isograds of pelitic schists. The extensive iron ore deposits of the Labrador City (Klein, 1966) and Mount Wright (Mueller, 1960) areas contain abundant coarse-grained amphibole assemblages, and these deposits are located within the kyanite-staurolite zone of metamorphic conditions.

The amount of solid solution of cations other than Fe^{2+} and Mg in the cummingtonite-grunerite series is generally very limited, except for Mn^{2+}. Table 4 lists the maxima observed for several lesser oxide components in cummingtonites and grunerites from metamorphic iron-formation assemblages. The maxima listed in this table tend to be lower than those reported in other assemblages (e.g., Klein, 1968), which may contain plagioclase as a Ca-Na-Al saturating phase, or may be of higher temperature (even volcanic) origin. In other words, the majority of analyses of cummingtonite and/or grunerite in metamorphic iron-formations consist of quadrilateral (anthophyllite-grunerite-tremolite-ferroactinolite) components in excess of ∿95%.

MnO can show very wide ranges in these amphiboles, mainly in Mn-rich bulk chemistries. Manganese-rich members of the cummingtonite-grunerite series with formulas very closely approaching $Mn_2Mg_5Si_8O_{22}(OH)_2$ have been reported by Klein (1964) from metamorphic Mn-rich iron-formation (see Fig. 40). Jaffe *et al.* (1961) reported an almost identical species from a metamorphosed manganese carbonate occurrence. Such amphiboles were originally referred to as manganoan cummingtonite but are now classified as tirodite (Leake, 1978). The compositional

Table 4. Weight percentages for some minor oxide components in cummingtonite-grunerite from iron formations.

Wt %	1	2	3	4
TiO_2	0.05	0.10	0.03	0.11
Al_2O_3	0.39	1.60	1.44	0.73
Fe_2O_3	0	2.10*	1.8*	0.77*
CaO	0.97	3.19	1.30	1.41
Na_2O	0.12	0.22	0.20	0.21

*recalculated from total Fe.
1) *Wet chemical analyses of six members of the series ranging from 59.2 to 88.8 atomic percent Fe^{2+} (Klein, 1964).*
2) *Electron probe analyses from the Gunflint Iron Formation by Floran and Papike (1978).*
3) *Electron probe analyses from several Archean iron-formations (Gole, 1979).*
4) *Electron probe analyses from the Negaunee Iron Formation (Haase, 1979).*

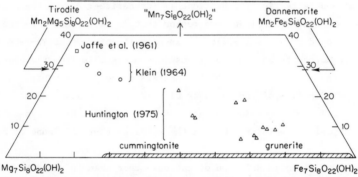

Figure 40. Compositional range of the cummingtonite-grunerite series and manganoan clinoamphiboles in terms of molecular percentages of MgO, FeO, and MnO. The extent of the Mg-Fe clinoamphiboles in Precambrian iron-formations is based on data from Bonnichsen (1969), Gole (1979), Floran and Papike (1978), Haase (1981), and Klein (1964). Tirodite from Jaffe *et al.* (1961) is from a metamorphosed manganese carbonate formation, whereas the tirodites from Klein (1964) are from manganese-rich, Precambrian iron-formation. The data points of Huntington (1975) are from iron-rich lenses in the Devonian Littleton Formation, Massachusetts.

extent of Mg-Fe-Mn clinoamphiboles in metamorphic iron-formations is shown in Figure 40. The common occurrence of members of the cummingtonite-grunerite series with a calcic amphibole is shown in Figure 41 for several metamorphic iron-formations.

The types of reactions that give rise to members of the cummingtonite-grunerite series are as follows (Klein, 1973):

$$7Ca(Fe,Mg)(CO_3)_2 + 8SiO_2 + H_2O \rightarrow (Fe,Mg)_7Si_8O_{22}(OH)_2 + 7CaCO_3 + 7CO_2 ;$$
ferrodolomite   quartz   grunerite   calcite

$$7(Fe,Mg)CO_3 + 8SiO_2 + H_2O \rightarrow (Fe,Mg)_7Si_8O_{22}(OH)_2 + 7CO_2 ; \text{ and}$$
siderite   quartz   grunerite

$$7Fe_3Si_4O_{10}(OH)_2 \rightarrow 3Fe_7Si_8O_{22}(OH)_2 + 4SiO_2 + 4H_2O .$$
minnesotaite   grunerite   quartz

The first two reactions have been documented texturally in several studies of metamorphic iron-formations (e.g., French, 1968; Floran and Papike, 1978; Gole, 1979; Klein, 1973, 1978). The third reaction, the conversion of minnesotatite to grunerite, however, has been documented texturally only twice, by Gair (1975) and Gole (1979, 1980). The formation of grunerite at the expense of preexisting minnesotatite reported by Gair is the result of contact metamorphism of iron-formation by a diabase in the Marquette district of Michigan. The same reaction, as documented by Gole, is the result of prograde regional metamorphism of Archean iron-formations in the Yilgarn Block of Western Australia.

A systematic study of the chemistry and physical properties of members of the cummingtonite-grunerite-tirodite series in medium-grade metamorphic iron-formation is given by Klein (1964); X-ray parameters for this same series are given in Klein and Waldbaum (1967).

Anthophyllite

Anthophyllite is not common in metamorphic iron-formations and tends to be restricted to hematite (or specularite)-rich assemblages with high $Fe^{3+}/(Fe^{2+} + Fe^{3+})$ ratios in the bulk composition. If such Fe^{3+}-rich bulk compositions are essentially devoid of Na_2O, Fe^{3+} is accommodated mainly in the hematite structure (minor magnetite may be present as well) but cannot be incorporated in the associated silicates and carbonates, and therefore Mg-rich members of the Mg-Fe amphibole series occur. The most common assemblages are: quartz-specularite (or hematite)-anthophyllite, and quartz-hematite-anthophyllite-tremolite with minor magnetite (Haase, 1981; Klein, 1966, 1978). See Figure 41.

Tremolite-ferroactinolite series

Calcium clinoamphiboles are less abundant than Mg-Fe clinoamphiboles in metamorphosed iron-formation assemblages, and their chemical compositions are generally very close to the Al-free, tremolite-ferroactinolite join, because bulk compositions of iron-formations tend to be low in Al_2O_3 as well as Na_2O. Gole and Klein (1981a) report a maximum Al_2O_3 average of 1.80 wt %, and a maximum total range of 0 to 7.54 wt % Al_2O_3 in their chemical compilation of many iron-formations. The maximum average value for Na_2O is 0.50 wt %, with a maximum range for Na_2O reported as 0 to 4.97 wt %. (The preceding values are for analyses recalculated to 100% on an H_2O- and CO_2-free basis). *Hornblende* compositions are by no means absent from metamorphic iron-formations, but they appear to be much less common than those of the Al-poor tremolite-ferroactinolite series. Mueller (1960) and Klein(1966) report mainly Al-poor Ca-clinoamphiboles (maximum Al_2O_3 content 1.2 wt % in an actinolite analysis of Mueller,

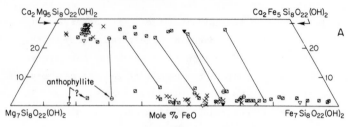

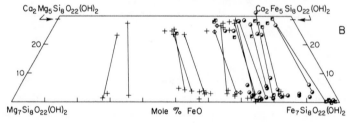

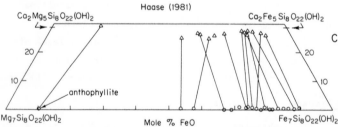

Figure 41A,B,C. Legend is on facing page.

1960), but Floran and Papike (1978), Gole (1979), and Haase (1981) list a considerable number of hornblende-like compositions. Floran and Papike (1978) report that a ferrotschermakite component ($Ca_2Fe_3^{2+}Al_2Si_6Al_2O_{22}(OH)_2$, the Al analog of actinolite) is the most common nonquadrilateral component, although a hastingsite component ($NaCa_2Fe_4^{2+}Fe^{3+}Si_6Al_2O_{22}(OH)_2$) may also be present.

Assemblages with tremolite-cummingtonite or actinolite-grunerite pairs are common (see Fig. 41). Such coexistences are the result of the following type of reaction (Klein, 1966):

$$14Ca(Mg_{0.5}Fe_{0.5})(CO_3)_2 + 16SiO_2 + 2H_2O = Ca_2Mg_5Si_8O_{22}(OH)_2 +$$

$$\textit{ferrodomomite} \qquad \textit{quartz} \qquad\qquad \textit{tremolite}$$

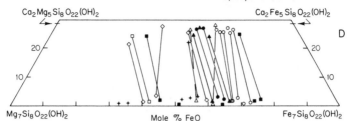

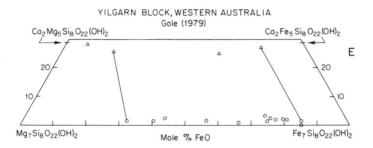

Figure 41. Compositional ranges and element fractionation data for amphiboles from several major Precambrian iron-formation occurrences in terms of molecular percentages of MgO, FeO and CaO. A, B and D are from Immega and Klein (1976).

$$+ \; Fe_7Si_8O_{22}(OH)_2 \; + \; 14(Ca_{0.857}Mg_{0.143})CO_3 \; + \; 14CO_2 \; .$$
     grunerite   *calcite*

The amphibole pairs commonly show well developed exsolution textures, as described by Bonnichsen (1969), Ross *et al.* (1969), and Immega and Klein (1976). An example of such exsolution is shown in Figure 42.

Riebeckite

This blue alkali amphibole, or its fibrous variety *crocidolite*, may be a major constituent of some late diagenetic to very low-grade metamorphic iron-formations, such as the Marra Mamba and Brockman Iron Formations of Western Australia (Trendall and Blockley, 1970; Klein and Gole, 1981) and the Griqualand Group of the Transvaal Supergroup of South Africa (Beukes, 1973). (See also Ross, Chapter 6, Volume 9A.) These enormous iron-formation sequences contain large amounts of riebeckite and crocidolite. The Brockman Iron Formation in Western Australia probably contains the largest mass of alkali amphibole on earth. Trendall and Blockley (1970) estimated the total reserves and resources of crocidolite (excluding nonfibrous riebeckite) to be approximately 2,410,000 tons. The fibrous crocidolite, as compared to massive riebeckite,

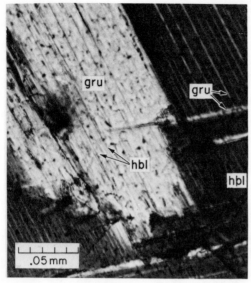

Figure 42. Exsolution relationships between grunerite and hastingsitic hornblende. Both minerals act as hosts with exsolution lamellae along "$\bar{1}01$" and "100." The grunerite host contains about 10 volume % hornblende lamellae, and the hornblende contains about 15-20 volume % grunerite lamellae. Plane polarized light. From a Precambrian iron-formation in southwestern Montana (Immega and Klein, 1976).

makes up only a few percent of the total amount of alkali amphibole in the Brockman Iron Formation. In most other late diagenetic to very low-grade metamorphic banded iron-formations, riebeckite is only a very minor and sporadic constituent (e.g., the Sokoman Iron Formation: Dimroth and Chauvel, 1973; Zajac, 1974; Klein, 1974; the Negaunee Iron Formation: Haase, 1981). Magnesioarfvedsonites occur in the Green River Formation of Eocene soda lake beds (Milton and Eugster, 1959; Milton et $al.$, 1974), where they appear to have formed at or near room temperature. Although riebeckite has a large temperature stability field (Ernst, 1968) it appears also to have formed as an authigenic mineral in many iron-formations.

The composition of riebeckite in iron-formations is not greatly variable. Table 5 compares several representative riebeckite and crocidolite analyses with the composition of end-member riebeckite, $Na_2Fe_3^{2+}Fe_2^{3+}Si_8O_{22}(OH)_2$. The major variation is in the partial substitution of Mg for Fe^{2+}, with MgO (wt %) values ranging from 1.37 to 7.71 (equivalent to 0.31 and 1.74 Mg atoms per formula unit).

Riebeckite, or crocidolite, in iron-formations occurs in close association with chert (or quartz), magnetite, hematite, stilpnomelane, and carbonates such as members of the dolomite-ankerite series, calcite, and siderite (Trendall and Blockley, 1970; Klein and Gole, 1981).

$Riebeckite$-$tremolite$ and $magnesioarfvedsonite$ have been reported in some relatively Na_2O-rich assemblages in the metamorphic iron-formation of the Labrador City region, Newfoundland, by Klein (1966) and Robinson et $al.$ (1971a).

Table 5. Representative analyses of riebeckite and crocidolite from iron formations compared with the compositon of end-member riebeckite, $Na_2Fe_3^{+2}Fe_2^{+3}Si_8O_{22}(OH)_2$.

Wt %	1	2	3	4	5	6
SiO_2	51.94	53.10	53.52	54.14	52.90	51.36
TiO_2	–	–	n.d.*	0.07	0.16	
Al_2O_3	0.20	0.88	0.41	0.26	0.04	
Fe_2O_3	18.64	16.95	17.72	21.07		17.06
FeO	19.39	17.54	16.26	9.27	26.29[1]	23.03
MnO	–	–	0.01	0.06	0.01	
MgO	1.37	3.13	3.63	7.39	7.71	
CaO	0.19	0.52	0.08	0.11	0.29	
Na_2O	6.07	6.21	5.57	5.1	7.30	6.62
K_2O	0.04	0.14	0.05	0.00	0.04	
$H_2O(+)$	2.58	}1.66	2.63	2.02		1.93
$H_2O(-)$	0.31		0.32	0.02		
F	–	–	–	0.09		
Total	100.73	100.13	100.20	99.60	94.74	100.00
Total iron as FeO	36.18	32.18	32.22	28.25	26.29	38.40

n.d.* = none detected; [1] total Fe as FeO only.
1) Crocidolite from Kliphuis, South Africa (Peacock, 1928).
2) Crocidolite, Brockman Iron Formation, Western Australia (Trendall and Blockley, 1970).
3) Massive riebeckite, Dales Gorge Member, Western Australia (Trendall and Blockley, 1970).
4) Crocidolite, Sokoman Iron Formation, Canada (Zajac, 1972).
5) Riebeckite, Marra Mamba Iron Formation, Western Australia (Klein and Gole, 1981).
6) Recalculated weight percentages for end-member riebeckite.

Diagenetic and metamorphic conditions of amphibole formation

Riebeckite has a very large stability field ranging from late diagenetic to medium-grade metamorphic conditions. Its possible range of temperature and pressure conditions of formation in the Marra Mamba Iron Formation of the Hamersley Basin in Western Australia has been evaluated by Klein and Gole (1981) on the basis of zeolite facies isograds delineated by Smith *et al.* (1981) in the underlying volcanic sequences of the Fortescue Group. It appears from such studies that the Marra Mamba Iron Formation was subjected, during burial, to temperatures of 200 to 300°C and pressures of about 1.2 kbar. Oxygen isotope temperature estimates (Becker and Clayton, 1976) on the overlying Dales Gorge Member and Wittenoom Dolomite indicate temperatures of burial for those formations of 270 to 310°C.

Anthophyllite, members of the cummingtonite-grunerite and tremolite-ferroactinolite series, and hornblende occur in metamorphic iron-formations that range from the biotite grade through the staurolite-kyanite grade as defined on the basis of pelitic schists. Several investigators of the metamorphism of iron-formations have evaluated temperature and pressure of formation of the assemblages and the role of a possible fluid phase. James (1955) estimates that the first appearance of members of the cummingtonite-grunerite series is reflective of garnet isograd conditions which, between 2 to 5 kbar pressures, would suggest a temperature range of 450 to 500°C (Winkler, 1979). Klein (1978)

notes that Fe–Mg clinoamphiboles appear very close to the biotite isograd in
the south–central part of the Labrador Trough. This would imply temperatures
somewhat lower than 450°C for the onset of Fe–Mg clinoamphibole formation. The
upper limit for *abundant* amphibole stability is probably close to the high temperature part of the kyanite–staurolite zone. On the basis of the staurolite-
kyanite gneisses associated with the iron–formation in the Labrador City region,
Newfoundland, Klein (1966) concludes that the maximum temperature of metamorphism was below 600°C and the pressure was between 6 and 10 kbar. Haase (1981)
estimates maximum metamorphic temperatures of about 500°C for his amphibole–rich
but pyroxene–free zone (his zone 3A) in the Negaunee Iron Formation, on the
basis of garnet–biotite geothermometry. He also reports oxygen isotopic temperatures of about 400°C for this same zone. These temperatures are based on
isotopic data by James and Clayton (1962) and have been calculated with the
quartz–magnetite fractionation curve of Becker and Clayton (1976). Haase (1981)
concludes that the pressure conditions in this zone appear to have been between
2 and 3 kbar. The amphibole–rich assemblages that are diagnostic of medium-
grade metamorphism must have originated under high P_{H_2O} conditions. Haase (1979)
suggests that, with further increasing metamorphic grade of the Negaunee Iron
Formation, the X_{CO_2} of the fluid phase increased considerably.

At metamorphic grades that straddle the sillimanite zone of pelitic rocks
(ranging from upper amphibolite to granulite facies), the hydrous amphiboles
and associated minerals react to form anydrous assemblages rich in ortho- and
clinopyroxenes, and locally fayalite.

Examples of the types of reactions that occur are as follows (Klein, 1973):

$$Ca(Fe,Mg)(CO_3)_2 + 2SiO_2 \rightarrow Ca(Fe,Mg)Si_2O_6 + 2CO_2 ;$$
      ankerite   *clinopyroxene*

$$(Fe,Mg)CO_3 + SiO_2 \rightarrow (Fe,Mg)SiO_3 + CO_2 ; \text{ and}$$
      siderite   *orthopyroxene*

$$Fe_7Si_8O_{22}(OH)_2 \rightarrow 7FeSiO_3 + SiO_2 + H_2O .$$
   grunerite   *orthopyroxene*

More complex reactions are given in French (1968) and Floran and Papike (1978).
Huntington (1975) reports numerous grunerite–olivine–magnetite–graphite assemblages in Devonian iron–rich beds more Mn–rich than most Precambrian iron–formations and one assemblage where these appear to be reacting to form orthopyroxene.
Conditions of regional metamorphism are in the sillimanite–muscovite–staurolite
zone at estimated temperatures of 600–630°C and pressures around 6 kbar (Tracy
et al., 1976). The ranges of pyroxene compositions in several major, high–grade
metamorphic iron–formations are shown in Figure 43. Fayalite may also be pro-

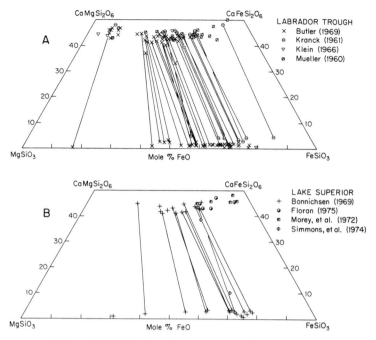

Figure 43. Compilation of compositional ranges and major element fractionation data for pyroxenes from some high grade metamorphic iron-formations (Immega and Klein, 1976).

duced at the highest metamorphic grade, in contact-metamorphosed as well as regionally-metamorphosed iron-rich bulk compositions. Figure 44 shows fayalite compositions in pyroxene-rich iron-formation assemblages.

The highest metamorphic temperatures have been recorded from the contact metamorphosed Biwabik (French, 1968; Bonnichsen, 1969) and Gunflint Iron Formations (Simmons *et al.*, 1974; Floran and Papike, 1978) and an iron-formation that was contact metamorphosed by the Stillwater Igneous Complex (Vaniman *et al.*, 1980). Such temperature estimates range from about 740 to 825°C at pressure ranges from 0.5 to 2 kbar.

Regional, high-grade metamorphosed terrains which tend to be ortho- and clinopyroxene rich but which may also contain fayalite-bearing assemblages (Gole and Klein, 1981b) suggest somewhat lower temperatures but higher pressure ranges than the contact-metamorphosed occurrences. Temperature estimates range from 600 to ~750°C and pressures from 3 to 11 kbar in the highest grades of regionally-metamorphosed iron-formations (Butler, 1969; Immega and Klein, 1976; Klein, 1978; Dahl, 1979; Gole and Klein, 1981b). Figure 45 shows the relative stabilities of minerals in iron-formations ranging from diagenetic to high-grade metamorphic conditions.

97

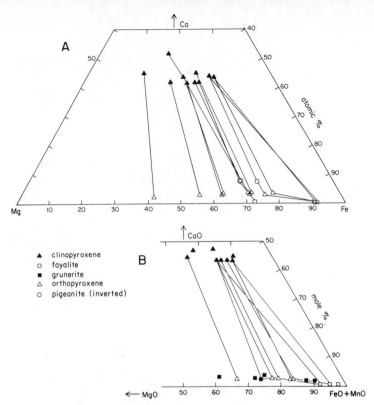

Figure 44. Examples of the compositional ranges of ortho-
pyroxene, clinopyroxene and fayalite (and lesser grunerite)
in some high-grade metamorphic iron-formation occurrences.
(A) Assemblages in the highest-grade metamorphic zone of the
Biwabik Iron Formation. From Bonnichsen (1969). (B) Mineral
compositions and assemblages from high-grade metamorphic
Archean iron-formations in the Yilgarn Block of Western
Australia. From Gole and Klein (1981).

AMPHIBOLES IN METAMORPHOSED ULTRAMAFIC ROCKS

Phase relations in recrystallized ultramafic rocks have been successfully
modelled theoretically and experimentally in systems composed of MgO, SiO_2, CaO,
Al_2O_3, and H_2O. Calcic and magnesian amphiboles have been shown to be stable
over a range of P-T conditions in model ultramafic rock compositions. Nearly all
natural amphiboles in ultramafic rocks, however, contain in excess of 0.1 atoms
per formula unit of Fe, and, in many cases, similarly significant amounts of
Na, Cr, Ti, and K. Magnesium/iron ratios are consistently high, of course, with
the result that colors in thin section are pale or absent.

For the treatment of amphibole compositions and phase relations, the author
has found it useful to distinguish rocks formed *metasomatically* from those recrystallized *largely isochemically*. The former tend to be mono- or bimineralic,
that is, possess high variance, so that amphibole compositions reflect the influence of the chemical potentials of species in the fluid phase rather than P

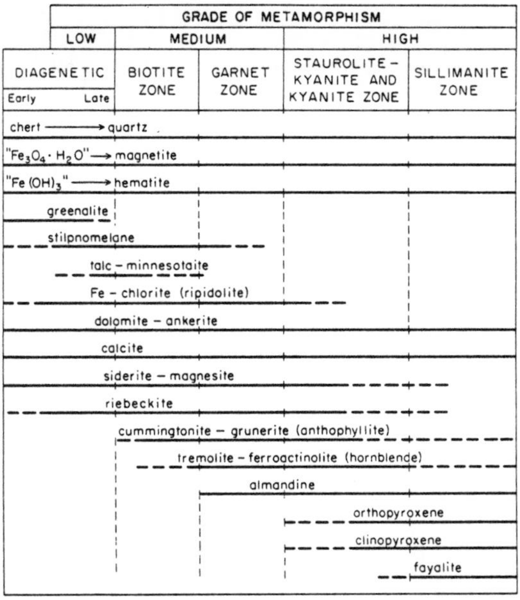

GRADE OF METAMORPHISM

	LOW	MEDIUM		HIGH	
	DIAGENETIC (Early — Late)	BIOTITE ZONE	GARNET ZONE	STAUROLITE – KYANITE AND KYANITE ZONE	SILLIMANITE ZONE

chert ⟶ quartz

"Fe₃O₄·H₂O" ⟶ magnetite

"Fe(OH)₃" ⟶ hematite

greenalite

stilpnomelane

talc – minnesotaite

Fe – chlorite (ripidolite)

dolomite – ankerite

calcite

siderite – magnesite

riebeckite

cummingtonite – grunerite (anthophyllite)

tremolite – ferroactinolite (hornblende)

almandine

orthopyroxene

clinopyroxene

fayalite

Figure 45. Relative stabilities of minerals in metamorphosed iron-formations as a function of metamorphic zone. Data compiled from James (1955), Floran and Papike (1978), French (1968), Klein (1978) and Gole and Klein (1981).

and T. The latter are multiphase, low-variance rocks and usually contain olivine (except at lowest metamorphic grades), an additional Mg-silicate mineral (one of serpentine, talc, magnesian amphibole, and orthopyroxene), an aluminous phase (chlorite, MgAl-spinel, pyropic garnet, or anorthitic plagioclase), and a calcic phase (calcic amphibole and/or clinopyroxene); the distribution and basic chemical composition of amphibole in these isochemically-formed rocks are determined by metamorphic grade. Some metasomatic introduction may have taken place (e.g., of K into some ultramafic xenoliths), but not enough to have eliminated the key minerals.

Isochemical rocks

Although some parageneses under certain physical conditions contain both calcic clinopyroxene and calcic amphibole, the widespread tremolites, magnesio-hornblendes, and pargasites of isochemically-metamorphosed ultramafic rocks can be regarded, to a first approximation, as substituting for the clinopyroxene of the protolith. Similarly, anthophyllite and magnesio-cummingtonite may be regarded as representing the protolith orthopyroxene. Textural evidence for the direct replacement of pyroxene by amphibole is much more likely to be found in ultramafic rocks subjected to retrograde rather than prograde metamorphism. Since this review attempts to summarize *stable* amphibole phase relations and compositions, progressively metamorphosed rocks have been used, as much as possible, as a source of information.

99

Table 6. Calcic amphibole in metamorphic ultramafic rocks: Relation to metamorphic facies, critical mineral parageneses, aluminum phase, and typical Si-content of calcic amphibole.

Facies	Critical Paragenesis	Al-phase	Si Content
prehnite-pumpellyite	chrys + talc + tremolite	chlorite	
pumpellyite-actinolite	chrys + antig + tremolite	chlorite	8.0 to 7.9
	chrys + antig + diopside	chlorite	
greenschist and	brucite + antig + diopside	chlorite	
blueschist	olivine + antig + diopside	chlorite	
amphibolite and	olivine + antig + tremolite	chlorite	
hornblende hornfels	olivine + talc + tremolite	chlorite	
	olivine + Mg-amph + tremolite	chlorite/chromite	8.0 to 7.8
	olivine + opx* + tremolite	chlorite/chromite	7.9 to 7.5
	olivine + opx* + {tremolitic hornblende, Mg-hornblende}	spinel	7.6 to 6.5
granulite	olivine + opx** + cpx {edenitic hornblende,	spinel	6.6 to 5.9
pyroxene hornfels	olivine + opx** + cpx + {pargasitic hornblende,	plagioclase	
eclogite (garnet lherzolite)	olivine + opx** + cpx {or pargasite	garnet	

*CaO in opx: <0.20 wt.%; ** CaO in opx: 0.1 to 0.7 wt.%

Calcic amphibole. Calcic amphibole is stable in metamorphic ultramafic rocks in several of the metamorphic facies (Table 6). Not surprisingly, it figures most prominently in the amphibolite and hornblende-hornfels facies. The occurrence of tremolite in serpentinites, vis-a-vis diopside, is a function of the relative proportions of CaO, MgO, and SiO_2 in the rock and location relative to reaction (1) (Oterdoom, 1978) and reaction (2) (Trommsdorff and Evans, 1972):

$$\text{chrysotile} + \text{tremolite} = \text{antigorite} + \text{diopside} + H_2O \quad (1)$$

$$\text{antigorite} + \text{diopside} = \text{tremolite} + \text{forsterite} + H_2O . \quad (2)$$

In the N-S profile Totalp-Oberhalbstein-Engadine in eastern Switzerland, tremolite occurs in serpentinites in the prehnite-pumpellyite and pumpellyite-actinolite facies, diopside in the high pumpellyite-actinolite and greenschist facies, and tremolite in the amphibolite facies. The occurrence of tremolite in many incompletely recrystallized serpentinites appears non-systematic and probably reflects kinetic factors and local equilibrium.

At the other end of the temperature scale, calcic amphibole (pargasite) occurs persistently, although in small amounts, in olivine + two-pyroxene parageneses in alpine-type peridotites and ultramafic xenoliths. Some of these examples are undeniably fragments of upper mantle. Based on pyroxene and other geothermometry, these amphiboles formed at temperatures above the upper limit of tremolite in peridotites (700 to 800°C, Evans, 1977), which is determined by the reaction:

$$\text{tremolite} + \text{forsterite} = 5 \text{ enstatite} + 2 \text{ diopside} + H_2O . \quad (3)$$

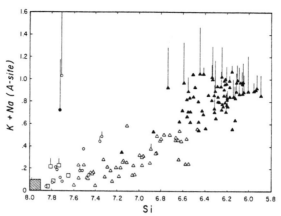

Figure 46. Compositions of ultramafic calcic amphiboles in parageneses buffering the tschermakite content, in terms of K + Na in the A-site and Si atoms per formula unit. Length of vertical bar indicates calculated occupancy of M4 by Na. Box (ruled) at bottom left includes all antigorite-olivine and talc-olivine parageneses, and some Mg-amphibole-olivine parageneses. Filled circle: antigorite-olivine paragenesis; squares: Mg-amphibole-olivine parageneses; circles: orthopyroxene-olivine-chlorite-Cr spinel parageneses; open triangles: orthopyroxene-olivine-Al spinel ± chlorite parageneses; filled triangles: orthopyroxene-clinopyroxene-olivine ± Al spinel ± pyropic garnet ± plagioclase parageneses. (Sources of data: Pfeifer, 1979; Misch and Rice, 1975; Vance and Dungan, 1977; Springer, 1974; Frost, 1975, 1976, unpublished; Trommsdorff and Evans, 1972; Ehrenberg, 1975; Pinsent and Hirst, 1977; Rice *et al.*, 1974; Garrison, 1981; Reamsbottom, 1974; Ernst, 1978; Medaris, 1980, unpublished; Leake, 1968, Deere *et al.*, 1963; Smith, 1979; Aoki, 1970, 1971, 1975; Desmarais, 1981; Wolff, 1978; Cawthorn, 1975; Best, 1970, 1974, 1975; Evans and Trommsdorff, 1974, 1978; Francis, 1976, 1977; Boyd, 1971; Green, 1964; Varne, 1970; Frey and Green, 1974; Griffin, 1973; Obata, 1980; Savage and Sills, 1980; Hunter and Smith, 1981; Vinx and Jung, 1977; Leavy and Hermes, 1979; Bussod, 1981; Wilshire and Trask, 1971).

Clearly, natural calcic amphibole, in agreement with the experimental evidence (Gilbert *et al.*, Chapter 2, this volume), is stablized beyond the limit provided by reaction (3) through its uptake of other amphibole components, notably pargasite.

Chemical analyses (largely by microprobe) of 215 calcic amphiboles in rocks containing olivine, an additional Mg-silicate mineral, and an aluminous mineral, have been gathered from the literature (cited in caption to Fig. 46), and recast on an anhydrous basis of 23 oxygens. Some published analyses were excluded because they were incomplete, represented impure separates, or were of amphibole whose paragenesis was not given or was ambiguous (mostly on account of a retrograde metamorphic history). In these low-iron amphiboles, calculation of ferric/ferrous iron ratios, using any of the common stoichiometric assumptions, was believed inappropriate. Thus, throughout this review, the cation contents of amphiboles refer to 23 anhydrous oxygens and FeO = total iron. Tetrahedral aluminum $Al^{IV} = 8.0 - Si$, "Mg"(M4) = $Al^{VI} + Ti + Cr + Fe + Mg + Mn + Ni - 5.0$,[14] and Na(M4) = 2.0 - Ca - "Mg"(M4). Undeniably, a large uncertainty attaches to

---

[14]"Mg"(M4) is, in effect, the sum of the small cations $Fe^{2+} + Mg + Mn$ assigned to the M4 site, normally *in that order of abundance* (except in the most extreme magnesian amphiboles) based on the site assignment scheme described earlier (see The Amphibole Formula, The Composition Range of Metamorphic Amphiboles, this chapter).

both M4 estimates; this procedure maximizes the "Mg"(M4) values and minimizes Na(M4).

A description of the compositional variability of calcic amphibole in ultramafic rocks is given below, first major elements and then minor elements, with particular reference to metamorphic grade. Then follows an attempt to provide some sort of theoretical explanation for most of the observations.

The *progressive* metamorphism of ultramafic rock produces a continuous although not particularly binary trend from tremolite, through tremolitic hornblende, magnesiohornblende and pargasitic hornblende, to pargasite (Fig. 46). The composition of calcic amphibole correlates well with metamorphic grade, as indicated by the mineral paragenesis of the rock and, in general, by parageneses in associated lithologies. The *Si-content* of the formula unit appears to be the compositional parameter most sensitive to metamorphic grade (Table 6, Fig. 46). There are also correlations of varying quality among Si, Al^{VI}, Na+K, "Mg"(M4), Fe/Mg, Cr, Ti, and metamorphic grade.

The gradual change in Si-content from 8.0 (tremolite) to 6.0 (pargasite) is accompanied by a change in habit from thin prisms, with excellent development of {110} prism faces, to stout prisms or equidimensional grains with poor development of prism faces. At the same time, color in thin section changes from colorless to pale green or brown, and there is an increase in refractive indices.

The composition of calcic amphibole remains close to that of the tremolite end member until conditions high in the amphibolite facies are reached, corresponding to the first appearance of aluminous spinel in ultramafic rocks (beyond the first occurrence of orthopyroxene) and sillimanite + garnet + biotite in associated pelitic rocks. This is in marked contrast to the behavior of calcic amphibole in metabasaltic and aluminous rocks, in which common hornblendes occur throughout the amphibolite facies. Thus, it is incorrect to conclude that the pair tremolite + chlorite is necessarily indicative of greenschist facies conditions in ultramafic rocks; they overlap the stability field of orthopyroxene.

The prograde trend of increasing alkalis in the A-site (mostly *sodium*) appears to be slightly curvilinear, the ratio $(K+Na)A/Al^{IV}$ changing from <1:3 at the tremolite end to 1:2 at the pargasite end (Fig. 46). The scatter of analysis points indicates a lack of correlation between the amounts of the pargasite and tschermakite end members. The correlation is much closer, however, when samples from only one area are considered (e.g., Frost, 1976, Fig. 7). Although compositional gaps may be found in calcic amphibole in retrograded high-temperature ultramafic rocks (e.g., Steele *et al.*, 1977), the tremolite to magnesiohornblende range is continuous in prograde metamorphosed ultramafic rocks (e.g., Misch and Rice, 1975). This is not surprising in light of the

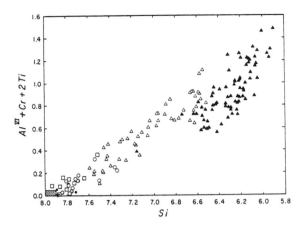

Figure 47. Plot of R^{3+} and R^{4+} cations, excluding unknown F^{3+}, in octahedral sites against Si in calcic amphibole in ultramafic parageneses buffering the tschermakite content. Symbols as in Figure 46; filled circles: antigorite + olivine parageneses; cross: talc + olivine parageneses. Diagram includes some analyses not plotted in Figure 46 because Na was not analyzed. Sources of data as in Figure 46.

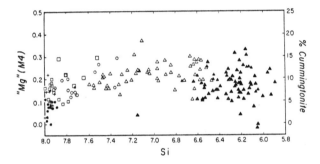

Figure 48. Calculated occupancy of M4 by Mg or Fe or Mn (labelled "Mg") plotted against Si in calcic amphibole in ultramafic parageneses buffering the tschermakite content. Symbols as in Figures 46 and 47. There is a tendency for the average % cummingtonite component to increase with temperature, flatten out, and possibly decline slightly. Sources of data as in Figure 46.

estimated equilibrium temperatures of 600–700°C for olivine + opx + chlorite/ spinel rocks with calcic amphibole in the range 7.9 > Si > 6.5 (see the section "Coexisting calcic amphiboles").

The calculated occupancy of the M4-site by Na is zero (90% of the analyses) or less than 0.07, except for two analyses of richteritic tremolites from kimberlitic xenoliths (Fig. 46, upper left), and, more importantly, many of the calcic amphiboles in granulite-facies parageneses (filled triangles in Fig. 46), that is, most ultramafic xenoliths and some alpine-type peridotites [e.g., Ronda (Obata, 1980) and Balmuccia (Ernst, 1978)]. The entry of Na into M4 in the richteritic tremolites is charge balanced not by extra octahedral R^{3+} (Fig. 47), but by extra Na and K in the A-site (Fig. 46), indicative of the

103

"richterite" substitution $Na(A)Na(M4)Ca(M4)_{-1}$, or, more accurately, a trend
towards magnesio-katophorite and magnesio-taramite. In the granulite facies
parageneses, the entry of Na into M4 takes place in amphiboles with large
tschermakite (Fig. 48) and pargasite (Fig. 47) substitutions, i.e., Na+K in A,
octahedral Al, and tetrahedral Al. The modest Na(M4) (glaucophane or riebeckite-
like substitution) is a usual feature of such amphiboles (see Figs. 10A and 12A,
this chapter). Parageneses representing high P relative to T, such as the garnet
lherzolites, have no greater amounts of Na in M4, possible glaucophane substitution, than spinel and plagioclase lherzolites. In fact, the majority of garnet
lherzolites [e.g., Arami (Ernst, 1978), Almklovdalen (Medaris, 1980, unpublished)]have no calculated Na(M4)--assuming all iron is FeO.

There are at least two factors contributing to departure from the 1:2
proportions of Al^{VI} to Al^{IV} called for by a simple binary solid solution of
tremolite and pargasite. These are variations in content of the tschermakite
end member and, notably in granulite facies parageneses, high contents of Cr
and Ti (see below). The plot of $Al^{VI} + Cr + 2Ti$ versus Si (Fig. 47) shows much
less scatter than that of Al^{VI} versus Al^{IV} (not shown here). The data from
calcic amphibole in ultramafic parageneses lend no support to the idea that
either the ratio Al^{VI}/Al^{IV}, or the Al^{VI} content alone, is any sort of pressure
indicator.

By analogy with coexisting calcic and magnesian pyroxenes, the occupancy
of the M4-site by Mg and Fe (*cummingtonite* solid solution) might be expected to
show an increase with temperature. Figure 48 shows that this is true for parageneses in which the calcic amphibole is in the tremolite compositional range,
but the trend flattens out at around Si = 7.0, and thereafter the average "Mg"
(M4) declines slightly. In terms of paragenesis, the average "Mg" in M4 is as
follows: olivine + antigorite, 0.07; olivine + talc, 0.12; olivine + magnesian
amphibole, 0.18; olivine + opx (cpx-free), 0.21; olivine + opx + cpx, 0.18. The
percentage of the cummingtonite component is, of course, equal to half these
numbers × 100. It should be stressed that actual values of "Mg"(M4) are highly
dependent on analytical accuracy. Nevertheless, the existence of a maximum in
the content of cummingtonite component is believed real (see below).

Iron/magnesium ratios are systematically higher in the more aluminous
calcic amphiboles. This trend, which has been known for calcic amphiboles in
general for quite some time (e.g., Leake, 1968, p. 26), is not caused by a change
in the amounts of Fe and Mg available in the rock, but by a change in partitioning
relative to coexisting minerals. For example, the K_D (Fe-Mg) relative to olivine
increases continuously from 0.4 (± 0.1) for tremolite to 1.2 (± 0.1) for pargasite
with Si = 6.0 (Fig. 49). Since Fe^{3+} is less than Fe^{2+} in classical analyses of

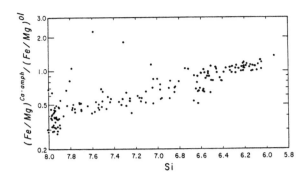

Figure 49. Plot of K_D = (Fe/Mg in Ca-amphibole)/(Fe/Mg in olivine) against Si-content of amphibole. The samples plotting above the principal trend contain forsterite-rich olivine (Fo % > 95); these may not be in equilibrium.

calcic amphiboles from ultramafic metamorphic rocks, failure to separate the Fe^{3+} from the Fe^{2+} could account for only a small part of the increase in K_D. If the change in K_D were simply due to the temperature increase from the tremolite to the pargasite parageneses, it would imply an unusually large difference between $\Delta H°$ ($\sim$10 Kcal) and $\Delta G°$ (<1.6 Kcal) for the exchange reaction. It is likely, therefore, that the major influence on the K_D is the pargasite content of the amphibole.[15] Since the K_D for olivine-orthopyroxene pairs is close to unity, the K_D plot for calcic amphibole and orthopyroxene is similar to Figure 49, including the change in sign of log K_D at approximately Si = 6.4. A similar dependence of K_D upon Al-content of calcic amphibole has been shown by Fleet and Barnett (1978) for hornblende. Talc and chlorite are always more Mg rich, however, and garnet and Cr-spinel more Fe rich than coexisting calcic amphibole in ultramafic rocks.

   Chromium contents of tremolite in antigorite + olivine and talc + olivine parageneses are less than 0.02 atoms; in these rocks, Cr is mostly contained in chlorite and chrome-magnetite (or ferri-chromite). As the coexisting spinel changes into chromite (Evans and Frost, 1975), chromium in calcic amphibole rises to roughly 0.1 atoms; the paragenesis is now olivine + orthopyroxene + chlorite + chromite. Little change in the Cr content of calcic amphibole, perhaps even a decline, takes place as the spinel changes from red Cr-spinel, through red-brown Cr-Al spinel, to green Al-spinel. However, the entry of clinopyroxene signals a sudden increase in the possible range of Cr-contents of calcic amphibole, up to 0.35 atoms/formula unit (Fig. 50). Whereas the pargasites in garnet lherzolites contain between 0.08 and 0.21 atoms Cr, those in spinel lherzolites cover a much wider range, from 0.01 to 0.35 atoms Cr.

----

[15] See text explanation of Figure 23, this chapter, concerning the effect of Al on Fe/Mg ratio.

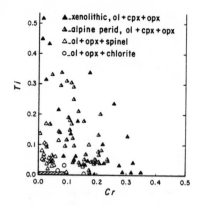

Figure 50. Plot to show negative correlation between Ti and Cr contents of calcic amphibole in buffered ultramafic parageneses. Box at bottom left (ruled) includes all other, mostly lower grade, parageneses.

The behavior of *titanium* shows some parallels with Cr; a threshold level of 0.01 atoms is generally exceeded only in high-grade rocks, namely spinel + opx + olivine and spinel + opx + cpx + olivine parageneses. Figure 50 shows that both titanium and chromium are highest in calcic amphibole in granulite-facies parageneses, there being little overlap with lower-grade parageneses when these elements are considered jointly. The negative correlation between Cr and Ti (Fig. 50) emerges more clearly when calcic amphiboles from individual complexes are plotted [e.g., Ronda (Obata, 1980); Finero (Cawthorn, 1975; Ernst, 1978; Medaris, unpublished)]. The most titaniferous (kaersutitic) pargasites are from peridotite xenoliths, variably described as interstitial, intercumulus, poikilitic, and veining. Some of these amphiboles may be igneous rather than metamorphic in origin, and some may not be in equilibrium with the other minerals. Titanium in pargasite in some of the alpine-type peridotites [e.g., Balmuccia (Ernst, 1978); Ronda (Obata, 1980)] is also quite high (> 0.3 atoms Ti).

The *potassium* content of ultramafic Ca-amphiboles shows a correlation with metamorphic grade, in that the pargasitic amphiboles contain up to 0.3 atoms K per formula unit, and the tremolites ordinarily contain less than 0.05 atoms K. The K-bearing pargasites in xenoliths typically also have 0.05 to 0.4 atoms Na in the M4-site. The richteritic tremolite (Si 7.72, Al^{VI} = 0.0, Ca = 1.37, K = 0.15, Na(A) = 0.57, Na(M4) = 0.46) analyzed by Smith (1979) and the potassic richterite (Si 7.71 Al^{VI} = 0.0, Ca = 1.08, K = 0.92, Na(A) = 0.11, Na(M4) = 0.79) of Aoki (1975), both from kimberlitic xenoliths, are more extreme examples of the association of K with substitution of Na in M4, although both are from lower-grade parageneses (Fig. 46). However, K in the low-Si calcic amphiboles in alpine-type peridotites, with the exception of the Balmuccia body, is associated with the edenitic substitution $(Na(A)Al^{IV}Si_{-1})$. For example, while

106

Na(M4) = 0, K in calcic amphibole in 16 samples of the Finero peridotite, which carries phlogopite in places, averages 0.12 atoms (highest K = 0.23 atoms, 1.26 wt % K_2O). Most alpine-type and other metamorphic, isofacial peridotites have much less potassic calcic amphibole, although in some of the low-Na magnesio-hornblendes from plagioclase-peridotite hornfelses from Icicle Canyon, Washington (Frost, 1976), K is greatly in excess of Na.

Manganese and *nickel*, both present in amounts less than 0.03 atoms/formula unit, show no noteworthy variation as a function of paragenesis.

Fluorine and *chlorine* have unfortunately seldom been analyzed in amphiboles of ultramafic rocks. A study of the halogen contents of calcic amphibole, particularly in granulite-facies parageneses, might be rewarding.

Controls on the chemical composition of calcic amphibole in "isochemically" metamorphosed ultramafic rock are complex and varied. Some are directly related to metamorphic grade (T, P, P_{H_2O}) by virtue of equilibria existing among mineral components in the rocks. For example, the increasing tschermakite content of calcic amphibole in ultramafic parageneses (the substitution $Al^{VI}Al^{IV}Mg_{-1}Si_{-1}$) is related to the following equilibria (μ = chemical potential):

$$\mu_{tsch} = \mu_{trem} + \mu_{chlorite} + 4/5\mu_{talc} - 9/5\mu_{forst} - 16/5\mu_{H_2O} \qquad (4a)$$

$$\mu_{tsch} = \mu_{trem} + \mu_{chlorite} - 4/9\mu_{Mg-amph} - 13/9\mu_{forst} - 13/9\mu_{H_2O} \qquad (4b)$$

$$\mu_{tsch} = \mu_{trem} + \mu_{chlorite} - 4\mu_{enstatite} - \mu_{forst} - 4\mu_{H_2O} \qquad (4c)$$

$$\mu_{tsch} = \mu_{trem} + \mu_{spinel} - 2\mu_{enstatite} \qquad (4d)$$

A chlorite composition of $Mg_5Al_2Si_3O_{10}(OH)_8$ has been adopted in all these equations. Equilibria 4a, b and c show that the tschermakite component is favored by increasing dehydration, i.e., increasing T. At any value of P and T, the value of μ_{tsch} in these equilibria is considerably less than its value in parageneses with cordierite, aluminosilicate, garnet, plagioclase, or epidote. The chemography of calcic amphibole in an ACF-diagram for the amphibolite facies shows these differences clearly (see Fig. 98A). It should also be kept in mind (Fig. 46) that *substantial* tschermakite substitution does not take place in the absence of Na that will permit a pargasite component in addition.

Similarly, the cummingtonite component in calcic amphibole (the substitution $Mg(M4)Ca(M4)_{-1}$) is controlled by T, P, P_{H_2O}, and the coexisting olivine, Mg-silicate, and fluid, by virtue of the equilibria

$$\mu_{cumm}(Ca-amph) = 9\mu_{serp} - 10\mu_{forsterite} - 17\mu_{H_2O} \qquad (5a)$$

$$\mu_{cumm}(Ca-amph) = 9/5\mu_{talc} + 4/5\mu_{forsterite} - 4/5\mu_{H_2O} \qquad (5b)$$

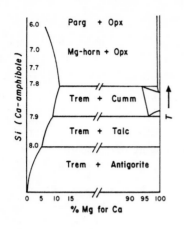

Figure 51. The pseudobinary join tremolite-cummingtonite, showing schematically the extent of cummingtonite solid solution in calcic amphibole in ultramafic rocks as a function of paragenesis, Si-content of Ca-amphibole, and temperature.

$$\mu_{cumm}(Ca\text{-}amph) = \mu_{cumm}(Mg\text{-}amph) \qquad (5c)$$

$$\mu_{cumm}(Ca\text{-}amph) = 9\mu_{enst} - \mu_{forsterite} + \mu_{H_2O} \qquad (5d)$$

The change in sign of μ_{H_2O} here explains why, when orthopyroxene takes the place of Mg-amphibole in the ultramafic paragenesis, the content of cummingtonite in the calcic amphibole no longer continues to increase with temperature (Fig. 51). These relations are similar to those controlling the paragonite content of muscovite in pelitic schists, where the Na-content of muscovite begins to decrease with temperature, after the limit of stability of paragonite + quartz has been reached (Evans and Guidotti, 1966).

Although Figure 46 demonstrates a broad correlation between the pargasite and tschermakite contents of calcic amphibole, it seems unwise to attribute this to energetic requirements intrinsic to the amphibole. The scatter of analysis points is real and not an artifact of the method of recasting the analyses. Except in plagioclase peridotites, there is usually no other Na-bearing mineral, so that the chemical potential of albite in a possible equilibrium such as

$$\mu_{edenite} = \mu_{tremolite} + \mu_{albite} + 4\mu_{forsterite} - 8\mu_{enstatite} \qquad (6)$$

cannot be specified. It was clearly very low in the anorthite-bearing ultramafic hornfelses of Icicle Canyon, Washington (Frost, 1976), where magnesio-hornblende has Si = 6.6 and Na+K = 0.25, and in the anorthite-bearing xenolith from Itinome-gata, Japan (Aoki, 1971), where pargasite has Si = 6.15 and Na+K = 0.55 (Fig. 46). The fact that trends in Figure 46 from specific areas are less scattered than the whole data set suggests that there ordinarily are some constraints (presumably bulk composition) on the variability in effective chemical potential of albite in ultramafic rocks as a whole. In terms of the edenite/

tschermakite correlation, it is perhaps significant that both edenite and tschermakite components face tremolite on the other side of the equilibria.

In addition to entering calcic amphibole, chromium is contained in existing chlorite, spinel, garnet, and pyroxene. Thus, many Cr-Al exchange equilibria could be written to illustrate the control of Cr-substitution in the amphibole. The ratio Cr/Al of the rock is determined in the first place, in "isochemical" samples, by the degree of depletion or fractionation of the protolith. The Cr-content of calcic amphibole is therefore controlled by many factors, not the least of which are the modal amounts of the minerals among which Cr and Al are distributed. Titanium and potassium (in addition to sodium) in most instances are contained only in the calcic amphibole. Thus, the amounts of these elements are a function of rock composition and the modal amount of amphibole. The reason that Cr, Ti, and K are high in calcic amphibole in granulite-facies parageneses may be the generally very small amounts of amphibole in these rocks. The inverse correlation of Cr and Ti is no doubt largely a reflection of the degree of depletion or fractionation of the protolith (harzburgitic versus lherzolitic versus wehrlitic versus pyroxenitic). In the absence of an internally-controlling equilibrium in ultramafic metamorphic rocks, there is no theoretical basis for the use of the Ti content as a geothermometer. The high K in calcic amphibole in some of the xenoliths is possibly related to a metasomatic event in the mantle; there is in some cases abundant accompanying phlogopite. However, in the rocks here taken to be "isochemical," the number of mobile components was not sufficient to reduce the number of phases below that required for buffering according to equilibria such as 4d.

Magnesian amphibole. Anthophyllite and magnesio-cummingtonite are the species found in isochemically metamorphosed ultramafic rocks (viz. in the parmagenesis olivine + Mg-amphibole + chlorite $\pm$ Cr-spinel $\pm$ tremolite). The occurrence of magnesian amphibole in olivine-bearing rocks is much more restricted than that of calcic amphibole. This fact is consistent with the narrow temperature range indicated for olivine + Mg-amphibole in the experimentally determined phase diagram (Gilbert *et al.*, Chapter 9, this volume). The actual temperatures required for this pair are, of course, a function of solid and H_2O pressure. The many instances of magnesite in anthophyllite-bearing rocks indicate that equilibrium temperatures and H_2O-pressures have been lowered by the presence of CO_2 in the fluid phase. In the progressive contact metamorphism of serpentinized peridotite, where H_2O-pressure is presumably maintained at high values, a narrow anthophyllite ($\pm$ magnesio-cummingtonite) + olivine zone usually intervenes between a broad talc + olivine zone and an orthopyroxene + olivine zone closer to the intrusive contact (Trommsdorff and Evans, 1972; Springer,

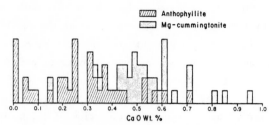

Figure 52. Histogram of CaO-contents of anthophyllite (not including gedrite) and magnesio-cummingtonite in ultramafic rocks, isochemical and metasomatic, as analyzed by microprobe. Includes samples with and without coexisting tremolite. (Sources of data: Springer, 1974; Garrison, 1981; Frost, 1975; Arai, 1975; Trommsdorff and Evans, 1972; Pfeifer, 1979; Pinsent and Hirst, 1977; Reamsbottom, 1974; Wolff, 1978; Desmarais, pers. comm.; Evans and Trommsdorff, 1974; Klein, 1968; Kisch, 1969; Ehrenberg, 1975; Rice *et al.*, 1974.)

1974; Arai, 1975), although there is commonly overlap in the distribution of anthophyllite and orthopyroxene (Frost, 1975). Obviously, there is little scope for systematic compositional variation of magnesian amphibole as a function of metamorphic grade.

Although their optical distinction is straightforward unless very finely fibrous (viz. anthophyllite, parallel extinction; Mg-cummingtonite, Z:c ≈ 15°, 2V(+) ≈ 70°), compositionally the dimorphs differ only slightly in CaO-content. Most anthophyllites (but not gedrites) contain less than 0.45% CaO (0.07 atoms per formula unit), whereas most magnesio-cummingtonites possess between 0.4 and 0.7% CaO (0.06 to 0.10 atoms); see Figure 52 and caption for sources of analyses. The greater amounts of CaO in many classical analyses of anthophyllite can in most instances be ascribed to contamination by tremolite. In some cases, analyzed magnesio-cummingtonites have been misidentified as anthophyllite. In rocks containing both anthophyllite and magnesio-cummingtonite, the mole fraction of Mg in the former is greater than in the latter by a barely detectable amount (Pfeifer, 1979).

With only one exception known to the writer, the anthophyllites and magnesio-cummingtonites in *isochemical* ultramafic rocks are, like the tremolites they coexist with, rich in SiO_2 and poor in Al_2O_3 and Na_2O. The exception is sample 6-18 (Frost, 1975), an aluminous anthophyllite (Si = 7.06, Na = 0.33, Al^{VI} = 0.60) from a chlorite-forsterite-enstatite-spinel assemblage developed in metamorphosed blackwall. Otherwise, the limits of the composition of anthophyllite, per formula unit, calculated on the 23 anhydrous oxygens and zero Fe^{3+} basis, appear to be Si 8.0 to 7.8, Al^{VI} 0.0 to 0.23, Na 0.00 to 0.1. The corresponding ranges for magnesio-cummingtonite are Si 8.0 to 7.87, Al^{VI} 0.0 to 0.07, Na 0.00 to 0.07; Mg/(Mg+Fe) values rise at least as high as 0.9. For reasons unknown, a good proportion of the microprobe analyses of these amphiboles contains insufficient Al to bring the tetrahedral cations to 8.0.

Analogous to equilibrium 4b, governing tschermakite component in calcic amphibole, the constraint on the Al-content of Mg-amphibole is potentially the equilibrium

$$\mu_{Mg\text{-}gedrite}^{16} = 5/9\mu_{anthoph} + 2\mu_{chlorite} - 40/9\mu_{forsterite} - 68/9\mu_{H_2O} \quad (7)$$

The upper limit on Al^{IV} in calcic amphibole coexisting with Mg-amphibole in olivine-bearing rocks is 0.35 or less (Fig. 46; Table 6), and, in coexisting calcic and magnesian amphiboles, the former are more aluminous (Robinson et al., 1971b). Unfortunately, the limit of Al^{IV} in anthophyllite at around 0.2 (Si = 7.8) also corresponds to the limb of the anthophyllite-gedrite solvus (Robinson et al., 1971b, Fig. 15). Thus, it is not possible to decide whether the limit on the gedrite content of anthophyllite is being determined by the solvus or the dehydration equilibrium 7. Obviously, equilibrium 7 is a stable one only within the limits of stability of anthophyllite + olivine, which are certainly narrow. The writer has no good explanation for the exceptional Al-anthophyllite paragenesis of Frost; it is no richer in FeO than many low-Al anthophyllites in ultramafic rocks.

Fe/Mg in anthophyllite and magnesio-cummingtonite are greater than Fe/Mg in coexisting olivine, orthopyroxene, tremolite, talc, and chlorite. Relative to total octahedral cations, Mn is partitioned as follows: cumm or anth = opx > tremolite, olivine > chlorite, and Ni: olivine > chlorite > tremolite > cumm or anth > opx.

Magnesio-cummingtonite generally occurs in tremolite-bearing rocks, in many cases as a prismatic homoaxial overgrowth on, or replacement of, tremolite (Rice et al., 1974). Anthophyllite, invariably as very thin needles, commonly occurs without tremolite, whereas cummingtonite rarely does. Thus, saturation in the tremolite component provides a chemical environment favorable for mag-nesio-cummingtonite. The phase relations of orthorhombic and monoclinic Mg-amphiboles are likely to be analogous to those of orthopyroxene and pigeonite. There appear to be as yet few field data relevant to this subject. Possibly, tremolite-anthophyllite pairs represent equilibration at temperatures below those of the inversion of anthophyllite to magnesio-cummingtonite with increasing temperature.

Metasomatic rocks

Calcic amphibole. Calcic amphibole of metasomatic origin is commonly found at contacts between ultramafic and country rock, usually on the ultramafic side

---

[16] Here, "Mg-gedrite" is taken as the pure AlAl gedrite, not the Na-substituted version used elsewhere in this paper.

of a blackwall zone of chlorite and/or biotite. The amphibole zone may be monomineralic, or there may be in addition one or more of many other minerals (e.g.,
Mg-amphibole, talc, chlorite, diopside, phlogopite, spinel, garnet, plagioclase).
Compositionally, the amphibole has ultramafic affinities (i.e., $Mg/(Mg+Fe) \sim 0.9$)
on the ultramafic side of the zone, but over several centimeters, it becomes
gradually richer in Fe, Al, Na, K and Ti and poorer in Mg and Si in the direction of the country rock, due to diffusion processes. Thus, compositions may
be more aluminous than calcic amphibole in isochemical (olivine-containing) rocks
at the same metamorphic grade. This is because the constraints imposed on the
chemical potential of the tschermakite component (equilibria 4a-c), as well as
the pargasite component, are not present in the metasomatic occurrences.

The pattern of overall compositional variation of these amphiboles, from
Si = 8.0 to Si = 6.0, is similar to that in the isochemical amphiboles (Fig. 46),
although the A-site versus Si trend (not figured here) appears straighter and
heads for the composition $Na_{0.6}Ca_2(Mg,Fe)_{3.6}(Al,Fe^{3+})_{1.4}Al_2Si_6O_{22}(OH)_2$, a hornblende end composition suggested by Robinson *et al.* (1971b). This could make it
appear as though there were, after all, an intrinsic rather than extrinsic energy
control on the edenite (or pargasite)/tschermakite ratio of these amphiboles.
However, the writer admits his compilation of reliable analyses of metasomatic
ultramafic amphiboles is very incomplete. It is clear, though, that the trend
of decreasing Si, as in the isochemical calcic amphiboles, is accompanied by
generally increasing contents of Fe, Na, Al^{IV}, Al^{VI}, Cr, and Ti. Some samples
have unusually high contents of Cr, Mn, or Na.

Magnesian amphibole. The Mg-amphibole in contact reaction zones between
ultramafic and country rock, or introduced magmatic rock, is almost invariably
orthorhombic, either anthophyllite or gedrite. Like the metasomatic Ca-amphiboles, their compositions are not constrained by an equilibrium with olivine,
chlorite, and fluid. Furthermore, the upper temperature limit on anthophyllite
alone is on the order of 100°C higher than that of olivine + anthophyllite
(Gilbert *et al.*, Chapter 9, this volume). Thus, ultramafic Mg-amphiboles in
monomineralic, high-variance assemblages can extend well into the gedrite range
(Si < 7.0).

An example is provided by sample K34A, a pargasite-gedrite (Si = 6.97)-
garnet-anorthite rock of "hybrid" origin from Petersham, Massachusetts (Wolff,
1978). Based upon satisfactory classical analyses listed by Rabbitt (1948) and
Deer *et al.* (1963), and more recent microprobe analyses (references cited in
caption to Fig. 52), it is clear that the majority of metasomatic Mg-amphiboles
are anthophyllite with Si in the range 7.7 to 8.05, Na < 0.2, and Al^{VI} < 0.2.

They are not compositionally distinguishable from anthophyllite in isochemical olivine-bearing rocks. There is a hiatus in the composition range from Si = 7.7 to 7.1, possibly reflective of the anthophyllite-gedrite solvus characterized by Robinson *et al.* (1971b), Stout (1972), and Spear (1981).

The high-Si anthophyllites are in many cases asbestiform or nephritic, or cross-fiber when vein-filling (Zoltai, Ch. 5, Ross, Ch. 6, Vol. 9A). Metasomatic anthophyllites, for example those of Chester, Vermont, are those which on cooling have tended to alter to the wide-chain silicates chesterite and jimthompsonite (Veblen, Volume 9A). Possibly, the presence of olivine in isochemical samples, by maintaining a lower activity of SiO_2 in the fluid than in olivine-free rocks, hinders the formation of the higher-SiO_2 wide chain silicates, which are compositionally intermediate between anthophyllite and talc.

AMPHIBOLES IN METAMORPHOSED BASALTIC ROCKS: GREENSCHIST FACIES TO AMPHIBOLITE FACIES

"Die Amphibole scheinen sehr empfindliche Indikatoren der Temperatur zu sein, und wenn sie aus verschiedenen Faziestypen genügend eingehend untersucht worden sind, wird man sie als zuverlässige geologische Thermometer anwenden können."

Eskola in *Die Entstehung der Gesteine* (1939, p. 357).

Summaries of typical occurrences of greenschist to low-grade amphibolite are presented by Turner (1968), Miyashiro (1973), and Dobretsov *et al.* (1973). Miyashiro (1973, Chapters 8A and 8B; 1968) gives a particularly good summary of the systematic mineral composition and modal variations observed. A representative but certainly not exhaustive list of the literature follows:

Scottish Highlands:

>   Phillips (1930), van de Kamp (1970) - Caledonian metamorphism of pyroclastic deposits (Green Beds). Medium-P facies series (Med-P) (using the terminology of Miyashiro, 1961).

>   Wiseman (1934), Graham (1974) - Caledonian metamorphism of diabasic intrusions (epidiorites). Med-P.

North America:

>   James (1955) - Precambrian metamorphism of extrusive and intrusive basaltic composition rocks (sills and dikes) in northern Michigan. Low-pressure facies series (Low-P).

>   Billings and White (1950) - Devonian metamorphism of mafic dikes in Vermont and New Hampshire. Med-P.

>   Laird (1977, 1980), Laird and Albee (1981b) - Ordovician and Devonian metamorphism of pyroclastic deposits with varying amounts of sedimentary detritus, minor lava flows, and perhaps some minor intrusions in Vermont. Med-P and low-P regional.

>   Kuniyoshi and Liou (1976) - (Probable) Jurassic metamorphism of basaltic flows, pillows, and aquagene tuffs on Vancouver Island, British Columbia. Low-P contact.

>   Hietanen (1974) - Cretaceous metamorphism of intermediate and mafic volcanic and intrusive rocks from northern Sierra Nevada, California. Low-P contact.

Japan:

> Miyashiro (1958), Shido (1958), Shido and Miyashiro (1959) - Cretaceous metamorphism of pyroclastic material and mafic sills and dikes from the Abukuma Plateau. Low-P regional and contact.

New Zealand:

> Brown (1967) - Cretaceous metamorphism of water-laid tuffs with varying amounts of sandy detritus in eastern Otago. Med-P.

> Cooper and Lovering (1970), Cooper (1972) - Cretaceous metamorphism of volcanogenic sediments, lava flows, and minor intrusions in the Haast Schist Group. Med-P.

Europe:

> Wenk and Keller (1969), Wenk (1970), Wenk *et al.* (1974) - Tertiary metamorphism of mafic rocks from the Central Alps. Med-P. See also Frey *et al.* (1974) and the references therein for discussions of Alpine metamorphism in mafic schist from the Western, Central, and Eastern Alps and Ernst (1973) for his interpretation of the data.

Definition of greenschist and amphibolite

Mafic rock that is the typical light-green color of *greenschist* and is intercalated with chlorite- or biotite-grade pelitic schist *is commonly* actinolite + chlorite + epidote + albite + quartz + sphene + magnetite or hematite ± phengitic muscovite, green or brown biotite, calcite, stilpnomelane, apatite, tourmaline, pyrite or pyrrhotite, and chalcopyrite schist (Turner, 1968, pp. 268-277; Miyashiro, 1973, pp. 67, 304; Dobretsov *et al.*, 1973, pp. 171, 189; Winkler, 1979, pp. 75, 173). Actinolite is not present in all greenschists and, in the chlorite grade of associated pelitic schist, is removed from common mafic schist compositions by the reaction actinolite + epidote → chlorite + calcite + quartz as X_{CO_2} increases (Billings and White, 1950, p. 640; see also T-X_{CO_2} grids of Harte and Graham, 1975, and Sivaprakash, 1981).

Eskola (1920, 1939) defined the amphibolite facies by the assemblage hornblende + anorthitic plagioclase. In his later work (pp. 355-357) he added an epidote-amphibolite facies transitional between the amphibolite and the greenschist facies. He did not include amphibole in the greenschist facies but rather divided the transitional facies into a lower-grade subfacies containing actinolite + chlorite + epidote + albite and a higher-grade subfacies containing hornblende + chlorite + epidote + albite. Now, however, actinolite is generally included in the greenschist facies because it is so common in world-wide occurrences of low-grade, light-green-colored mafic schists of various protoliths and metamorphic ages.

Many have kept the distinction of a separate facies between greenschist and amphibolite to cover mafic schist with hornblende coexisting with albite ± oligoclase (rather than with more calcic plagioclase) and either have kept

Eskola's name of epidote-amphibolite facies (Miyashiro, 1973, pp. 67-68, 305) or have used the term greenschist-amphibolite transition facies (Turner, 1968, pp. 303-307) to avoid the problem that epidote also occurs with amphibole in the greenschist facies and in the low-grade part of the amphibolite facies.

Without agonizing over nomenclature problems, the common actinolite-bearing greenschist assemblage listed above will be examined in terms of variations in mode and mineral composition accompanying medium- and low-P progressive metamorphism into the amphibolite facies. For historical reasons the term *epidote-amphibolite facies* will be used for hornblende + albite $\pm$ oligoclase mafic schist, while the term *amphibolite facies* will be used for assemblages with hornblende + oligoclase or more calcic plagioclase.

Modal variations, the common assemblage

The major changes accompanying progressive metamorphism of mafic schist are presented in the pioneering work of Phillips (1930), Wiseman (1934), Miyashiro (1958), and Shido (1958). More recent studies (see list of representative references above) have reconfirmed these conclusions.

During medium-pressure facies series metamorphism, almandine garnet occurs only in the epidote-amphibolite and amphibolite facies and in general appears at about the garnet isograd in associated pelitic schist, while stilpnomelane occurs only in the greenschist facies. Both minerals are confined to assemblages relatively rich in Fe^{2+}. Neither mineral is particularly common in low-pressure facies series.

The distinctive change in color between light-green greenschist and dark-green to gray epidote-amphibolite and amphibolite is a manifestation of the increase in modal amphibole, which becomes darker blue green, green, and then brown green in color, and the simultaneous decrease in modal chlorite and epidote. The relative decrease of chlorite and epidote depends on rock composition as well as metamorphic grade and facies series. For example, in the Scottish Highlands, chlorite may or may not occur in epidote-amphibolite and amphibolite in the garnet zone, while epidote remains until the sillimanite zone (Wiseman, 1934, pp. 390-394). Chlorite also breaks down before epidote in the Central Alps (Wenk and Keller, 1969, Table 4), while both remain stable into the staurolite-kyanite zone of Vermont (Laird and Albee, 1981b, Table 1). In low-pressure facies series in Japan, chlorite and epidote are stable up through the low-grade part of the amphibolite facies and break down below the garnet isograd (Miyashiro, 1958, pp. 229, 234).

Clinopyroxene and Fe-Mg-Mn amphiboles are uncommon in medium-P facies series mafic schist until high-grade amphibolite to granulite facies. Wiseman

(1934, p. 395) and Wenk (1970, Fig. 3, p. 40) find that clinopyroxene first forms in the sillimanite zone of associated pelitic schist. Neither report the Fe-Mg-Mn amphiboles coexisting with clinopyroxene in high-grade amphibolites. In low-P facies series, however, clinopyroxene and Fe-Mg-Mn amphiboles tend to form at somewhat lower parts of the amphibolite facies, about at the breakdown of epidote and chlorite and the beginning of the garnet zone in associated pelitic rocks.

Sphene, which is common in greenschist and epidote-amphibolite, is less common in amphibolite, both in medium- and low-P facies series. It may be replaced by rutile or ilmenite, and more Ti may be incorporated into hornblende and biotite (reflected in the color change of both). It has been suggested that muscovite is absent in mafic schist above the greenschist facies (Miyashiro, 1973, p. 258). However, van de Kamp (1970, Table 2), Billings and White (1950, p. 633), and Laird and Albee (1981b, Table 1) show that muscovite does occur in epidote-amphibolite and amphibolite, if the rocks, are, presumably, rich enough in K_2O and Al_2O_3. Biotite and calcite may occur in mafic schist throughout the greenschist, epidote-amphibolite, and amphibolite facies during both medium- and low-P facies series metamorphism. If X_{CO_2} is high enough, dolomite/ankerite may occur, locally in equilibrium with calcite.

Accessory apatite is typical and tourmaline is less common throughout the sequence. Little work has been published on the relative abundances of magnetite, hematite and ilmenite, and of pyrite, pyrrhotite and chalcopyrite in mafic schist as a function of f_{O_2}, P_{solid}, and T. Shido (1958, p. 193) notes that magnetite and ilmenite are common in both greenschist and amphibolite, whereas hematite occurs in the lower-grade rocks only, suggesting reduction with low-P facies series metamorphism. Although magnetite tends to be more common in greenschists and epidote-amphibolite from Vermont and hematite tends to be more common in amphibolite, suggesting perhaps oxidation with medium-P metamorphism, hematite occurs in some greenschists instead of magnetite, and both magnetite and hematite occur in some epidote-amphibolite and amphibolite (see Laird and Albee, 1981b, Table 1).

In summary then, very little change in mineral assemblage occurs from greenschist to amphibolite below the disappearance of epidote and chlorite and the formation of clinopyroxene and Fe-Mg-Mn amphiboles. The *common assemblage* is amphibole (AMP) + chlorite (CHL) + epidote (EPI) + plagioclase (PLG) + quartz (QTZ) $\pm$ sphene (SPN) or rutile (RUT) or ilmenite (ILM), magnetite (MGT) or hematite (HEM), muscovite (MUS) or biotite (BIO), calcite (CAL) or dolomite (DOL)/ankerite (ANK), apatite (APT), tourmaline (TRM), pyrite (PYT)/pyrrhotite (PYH), chalcopyrite (CPY). Fe^{2+}/Mg-rich assemblages in which stilpnomelane

(STP; greenschist facies) or garnet (GAR; epidote-amphibolite and amphibolite facies) occur will be considered below, but to minimize the problem of mistaking variations due to rock composition for those due to metamorphic grade and facies series changes, the primary focus will be the progressive metamorphism of the common assemblage. Epidote- and chlorite-absent and Fe-Mg-Mn amphibole and clinopyroxene assemblages are considered elsewhere in this paper.

As cited above, many papers have discussed modal (as well as mineral compositional) variations in mafic schist as a function of metamorphic grade and facies series. This procedure is "legitimate" in invariant assemblages and appears to yield systematic results for the common assemblage because it has low variance. Ten to 15 system components are needed if the minor component MnO and the trace constituents Cr, Ba, Zn, F, and Cl are eliminated: SiO_2, Al_2O_3, Fe_2O_3, TiO_2, MgO, FeO, CaO, Na_2O, K_2O, $H_2O \pm CO_2$, P_2O_5, B_2O_3, S, and Cu. The common assemblage is univariant at constant P, T, and μH_2O if one Fe^{3+} oxide (MGT, HEM), one major TiO_2 mineral (SPN, RUT, ILM), and one major K_2O mineral (MUS, BIO) occur and if one or none each of CAL or DOL/ANK, APT, TRM, PYT/PYH, and CPY occur. The assemblage is invariant if either stilpnomelane or garnet is also present.

Liou *et al.* (1974) and Moody *et al.* (in preparation) provide experimental verification that increasing metamorphic temperature at constant rock composition causes common greenschist to change to amphibolite by decreasing modal CHL, EPI, and SPN and by increasing modal AMP and ILM to accommodate changing mineral compositions. As shown in Table 7, mass-balance calculations (Laird, 1980) also indicate that these general modal variations occur in basaltic compositions open only to H_2O and CO_2 and are relatively insensitive to small compositional differences in mafic rock, which accounts for the presence or absence of various Ti-, Fe^{3+}-oxide-, K-, and CO_2-rich phases, and even of stilpnomelane or garnet.

Mineral compositional variation

Wiseman (1934, pp. 368, 369, 382-385) showed that the change in color of amphibole from light green in the greenschist facies to dark blue green to green in the epidote-amphibolite and low-grade amphibolite facies is due to an increase in atomic Al^{IV}, Al^{VI}, Ti, Fe^{3+}, Na, K, and Fe^{2+}/Mg, with a concomitant decrease in Si, $(Fe^{2+} + Mg + Mn)$, and Ca. These compositional relationships (many of which are implicit in the facies definitions, because actinolite is characteristic of greenschist and hornblende is characteristic of higher grades) have been confirmed by later studies of natural occurrences. (See data from

Table 7   Variation in mode with medium-pressure facies series metamorphism of common mafic schist from Vermont*

Facies & Sample / Mineral**	Greenschist LA426	Epidote-Amphibolite V340B	Greenschist V14J	Epidote-Amphibolite V94A	Amphibolite V1180
AMP	15 (25)	28 (25)	36 (30)	44 (15)	51 (55)
CHL	31 (20)	25 (5)	15 (<1)	14 (20)	10 (2)
EPI	24 (10)	15 (5)	30 (10)	13 (25)	8 (20)
PLG	21 (35) An 0.2	16 (25) An 1	18 (50) An 1	16 (20) An 0.4	15 (10) An 24
QTZ	5 (<1)	10 (3)	0.2 (0)	6 (10)	10 (10)
SPN	3 (5)		3 (2)	2 (2)	
ILM		2 (2)			2 (2)
CAL	0 (5)	2 (15)	0 (3)	4 (2)	4 (<1)
DOL		1 (5)			
BIO	2 (<1)	1 (15)	2 (tr)	1 (5)	
MGT			0 (5)	0 (1)	
Other	PYT, CPY	APT, PYT	PYT	CPY	PYT, CPY

*Weight percentages from the mass-balance calculations of Laird (1977, p. 170) who modeled coexisting mineral compositions in LA426 and V340B to the same basaltic rock composition and of Laird (1980, p. 18) who modeled V14J, V94A, and V1180 to another basaltic composition. Numbers in parenthesis are visual estimates of mode in each sample and reflect rock composition as well as metamorphic grade variation.

**See text for abbreviations. Molecular percent anorthite compositions are from electron microprobe analyses.

Laird and Albee, 1981b, as illustrated in Figure 53,[17] and other representative references listed above.) Further support is provided by the hydrothermal experiments of Liou *et al*. (1974) and Moody *et al*. (in preparation), who find that Al, Ti, Na, and Fe/Mg in common greenschist amphiboles increase with increasing temperature.

The compositional variation in common mafic schist amphibole shown in Figure 53 and Table 8 can be explained by compositional and modal variations in other minerals in a system open only to H_2O and CO_2 (Laird, 1980). During medium-P facies series metamorphism, AMP changes more in composition between the greenschist and epidote-amphibolite facies than between the latter and the amphibolite facies, although in general the trends are the same. Using the

---

[17]A complete set of representative analyses for coexisting minerals in biotite-to sillimanite-grade mafic schist from Vermont appears in NAPS Document No. 03800 as appendices to Laird and Albee (1981b) and may be obtained from ASIS/ NAPS, c/o Microfiche Publications, P. O. Box 3513, Grand Central Station, New York, NY, 10163, remitting $3.00 for microfiche or $21.50 for photocopies. Checks are to be made payable to "Microfiche Publications." Outside the U. S. and Canada, add postage of $4.50 for photocopy and $1.00 for microfiche.

Table 8. Variation in amphibole composition with medium-pressure facies series metamorphism of common mafic schist from Vermont

Facies*	Grade of associated pelitic schists	Amphibole formula**
Greenschist (LA426)	Biotite	K$_{.01}$(Ca$_{1.85}$Na$^{M4}_{.14}$Fe$^{2+}_{1.48}$Mg$_{3.16}$Mn$_{.04}$Al$^{VI}_{.03}$Fe$^{3+}_{.29}$Ti$_{.005}$)(Si$_{7.80}$Al$^{IV}_{.20}$)O$_{22}$(OH)$_2$
Epidote-amphibolite (V340B)	Garnet	(Na$^A_{.25}$K$_{.08}$)(Ca$_{1.72}$Na$^{M4}_{.28}$)(Fe$^{2+}_{1.52}$Mg$_{1.88}$Mn$_{.01}$Al$^{VI}_{.80}$Fe$^{3+}_{.75}$Ti$_{.04}$)(Si$_{6.32}$Al$^{IV}_{1.68}$)O$_{22}$(OH)$_{1.91}$F$_{.09}$
Greenschist (V14J)	Biotite	(Na$^A_{.04}$K$_{.02}$)(Ca$_{1.78}$Na$^{M4}_{.22}$)(Fe$^{2+}_{1.33}$Mg$_{3.07}$Mn$_{.05}$Al$^{VI}_{.13}$Fe$^{3+}_{.41}$Ti$_{.002}$)(Si$_{7.61}$Al$^{IV}_{.39}$)O$_{22}$(OH)$_{1.99}$F$_{.01}$
Epidote-amphibolite (V94A)	Low Garnet	(Na$^A_{.21}$K$_{.06}$)(Ca$_{1.65}$Na$^{M4}_{.35}$)Fe$^{2+}_{1.07}$Mg$_{2.43}$Mn$_{.03}$Al$^{VI}_{.56}$Fe$^{3+}_{.87}$Ti$_{.04}$)(Si$_{6.57}$Al$^{IV}_{1.43}$)O$_{22}$(OH)$_{1.97}$F$_{.03}$
Amphibolite (V1180)	High Garnet	(Na$^A_{.27}$K$_{.07}$)(Ca$_{1.65}$Na$^{M4}_{.35}$)(Fe$^{2+}_{1.19}$Mg$_{2.11}$Mn$_{.04}$Al$^{VI}_{.81}$Fe$^{3+}_{.80}$Ti$_{.04}$)(Si$_{6.30}$Al$^{IV}_{1.70}$)O$_{22}$(OH)$_{1.99}$F$_{.01}$

*Sample numbers listed in parenthesis all contain the common mafic schist assemblage (See Table 1).

**Each of these electron microprobe analyses was obtained and normalized to a structural formula as described in Laird and Albee (1981a, p. 122-123; see also section on GENERAL REVIEW OF METAMORPHIC AMPHIBOLE COMPOSITIONS). Essentially each was normalized to total cations-(Na + K + Ca) = 13 with the constraint that if the resulting formula had (Ca + Na^{M4}) > 2.0, the analysis was normalized to total cations-(K) = 15. Site population and Fe^{3+} versus Fe^{2+} were estimated assuming stoichiometry. The analyses are tabulated in Laird and Albee (1981b, appendix available through NAPS) and are representative (compare with Laird, 1980, Table 3) of the averaged analyses used in the mass-balance calculations reported in Table 7.

terminology of Thompson (Chapter 3, Volume 9A), the following coupled substitutions (proceeding along the exchange vector as written and condensed from the simple substitutions KNa$_{-1}$, FeAl$_{-1}$, TiFe$_{-1}$, FeMg$_{-1}$, and MnFe$_{-1}$) describe chemical changes in AMP during the greenschist to amphibolite transition: NaAlSi$_{-1}$, NaSiCa$_{-1}$Al$_{-1}$, and Al$_2$Mg$_{-1}$Si$_{-1}$.

Wiseman's (1934) suggestion that (Fe^{2+}/Mg)$_{AMP}$ increases with metamorphic grade does appear to be true in rocks of the same composition (Table 9). In support of this statement, grains zoned from actinolite to hornblende compositions show concomitant increase in Fe^{2+}/Mg (Fig. 54). Furthermore, the Fe^{2+}Mg$_{-1}$ distribution between AMP and coexisting CHL is such that actinolite is distinctly more Mg-rich than coexisting CHL, but hornblende and CHL have about the same X$_{Mg}$ (Fig. 55).[18] For each metamorphic grade, the Fe^{2+}Mg$_{-1}$ distribution between AMP and CHL is about the same for a variety of rock compositions, providing further support for comparing compositions of individual minerals in the common assemblage as a function of grade and facies series.

The compositional variations noted above also appear to be true in general for low-P metamorphism. In contact metamorphosed rocks, NaAlSi$_{-1}$ and Al$_2$Mg$_{-1}$Si$_{-1}$ in AMP both increase between the greenschist and amphibolite facies (Hietanen, 1974; Kuniyoshi and Liou, 1976). Similar variations are inferred from the occurrences of actinolite in greenschist and hornblende in amphibolite from the Abukuma Plateau. Hietanen (1974) finds no systematic variations in Mg/Fe or

---

[18] An explanation of this phenomenon is the progressive exclusion of Mg from M2 of amphibole as the Al + Fe^{3+} + Ti increases (see Fig. 23 and accompanying text).

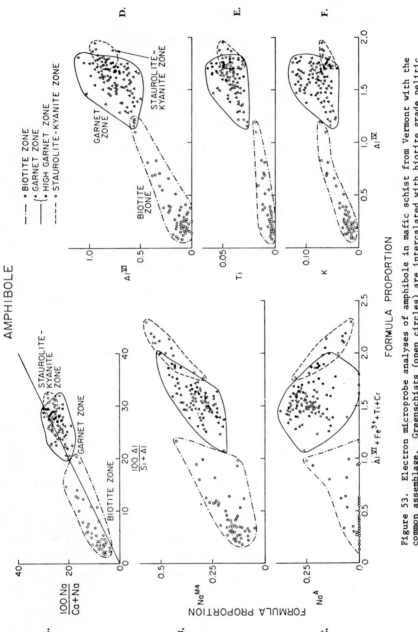

Figure 53. Electron microprobe analyses of amphibole in mafic schist from Vermont with the common assemblage. Greenschists (open circles) are intercalated with biotite grade pelitic schists, epidote-amphibolites (triangles) with low garnet grade pelitic schists, and amphibolites (triangles, filled circles, and diamonds) with garnet and staurolite-kyanite grade pelitic schists. (Laird and Albee, 1981b, Fig. 2.)

120

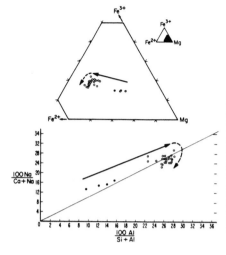

Figure 54. Electron microprobe analyses of zoned amphibole in AMP + CHL + EPI + albite + oligoclase + QTZ + SPN + CAL + BIO + HEM + APT + CPY (see text for abbreviations) schist from Vermont (Pinney Hollow Formation, Saxtons River quadrangle, garnet zone of associated pelitic schists). Many porphyroblasts are optically discontinuous (see Plate 2B, Laird and Albee, 1981b), with colorless to pale green pleochroic cores (filled circles) and darker blue-green rims (open circles). Smaller grains are also darker colored and shown on the figure by open circles. Solid arrows show discontinuous zoning from core to rim. Continuous compositional zoning within the rims of a few grains is indicated by dashed arrows. (Laird, 1977, Fig. IV-66.)

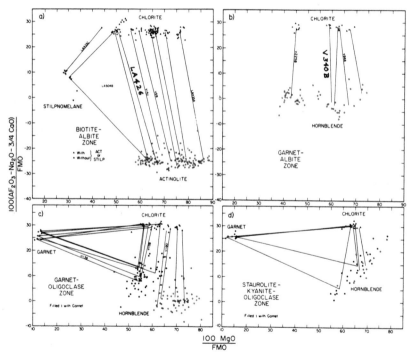

Figure 55. Electron microprobe analyses of mafic minerals in greenschist (a), epidote-amphibolite (b), and amphibolite (c,d) from Vermont, projected from quartz, albite, epidote, and H_2O. Tie lines connect average compositions of coexisting phases. Samples in Tables 7-9 are indicated. Metamorphic grades of associated pelitic schists and plagioclase compositions of the mafic schists are indicated. $AF_2O_3 = Al_2O_3 + Fe_2O_3$, $FMO = FeO + MgO + MnO$, mol % units. From Laird (1980, Fig. 4).

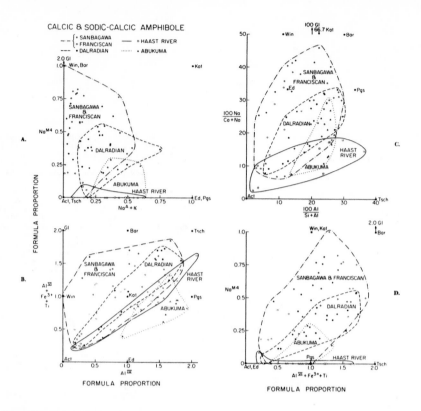

Figure 56. Wet chemical and electron microprobe analyses of amphibole from various world-wide occurrences of mafic schist. Envelopes delimit analyses from (1) high-P facies series terranes in Japan (Iwasaki, 1963; Banno, 1964; Ernst *et al.*, 1970) and California (Ernst *et al.*, 1970) [Sanbagawa and Franciscan, respectively], (2) medium-P terranes in Scotland (Graham, 1974) and New Zealand (Cooper and Lovering, 1970) [Dalradian and Haast River, respectively], and (3) the low-P, Abukuma terrane in Japan (Shido, 1958; Shido and Miyashiro, 1959). End-member compositions are indicated for actinolite, barroisite, edenite, glaucophane, katophorite, pargasite, tschermakite, and winchite. From Laird and Albee (1981b, Fig. 8).

Ti that are independent of rock composition and f_{O_2}, but Kuniyoshi and Liou (1976) report that TiO_2 and FeO/MgO (wt % units) increase with temperature of metamorphism.

Amphibole composition appears to be dependent upon facies series as well as metamorphic grade (Fig. 56). Compared to low-P terranes, AMP from higher P facies series has greater $(Al^{VI} + Fe^{3+} + Ti)$ for a given value of Al^{IV} and greater Na^{M4} for given values of $(Na^A + K)$ and $(Al^{VI} + Fe^{3+} + Ti)$. Using many of these same data, Graham (1974) and Brown (1977) reached similar conclusions. Even in assemblages other than the common one in greenschist to low-grade amphibolite, Na, Al, and Ti in AMP appear to be correlated positively with increasing pressure and temperature (Shido, 1958; Shido and Miyashiro, 1959; Leake, 1965; Kostyuk and Sobolev, 1969; Raase, 1974).

Interpretation of compositional variations in calcic amphibole is complicated by the possibility of immiscibility and of zoning due to disequilibrium.
However, the variations noted above are observed in world-wide occurrences of
common mafic schist and do not appear to be due to serendipity. By considering
only rim compositions (as in Fig. 55), mineral zoning complications with respect
to correlations of AMP chemistry and the physical conditions of metamorphism
can be lessened. Furthermore, if these correlations are understood, zoning
relationships can be very useful in deciphering polymetamorphic history (Laird
and Albee, 1981b). Miscibility gaps are treated in an earlier section, "Coexisting calcic amphiboles."

A major distinction between medium-P and low-P facies series metamorphism
of common mafic schist is made very clear by Miyashiro (1973, p. 250) and is
reaffirmed by later work. During medium-P metamorphism, the change in AMP
composition from actinolite to hornblende occurs in the garnet zone of associated pelitic rocks, while the coexisting plagioclase is albite. In contrast,
at low-P PLG changes from albite across the peristerite gap to oligoclase in
the biotite or lower metamorphic grades of associated pelitic rocks *before* AMP
becomes hornblende. These relationships are demonstrated by the substitution
of Na for Ca (Fig. 57) and also by noting in Figure 58 that progressive metamorphism results in a general change in AMP composition from the lower left to
the upper right of each diagram and that medium-P amphiboles plot above low-P
ones. Therefore, in medium-P facies series metamorphism, AMP composition
"crosses" the garnet isograd in associated pelitic schist before the oligoclase
isograd in the mafic schist (correlative with the oligoclase isograd in associated pelitic schist for the medium-P rocks shown in Fig. 58). However, it
"crosses" the oligoclase isograd before the garnet isograd in low-P facies
series metamorphism. Whereas the epidote-amphibolite facies is usually encountered in medium-P metamorphism, it is commonly absent in low-P metamorphism.

PLG continues to become more anorthitic past the peristerite gap, reaching
An_{30} in common mafic schist from the staurolite-kyanite zone in Vermont, An_{38}
in hornblende + PLG + QTZ schist from the staurolite- to silimanite-grade of
Scotland (van de Kamp, 1970, Table 2, #49), about An_{43} in common mafic schist
above the oligoclase isograd in New Zealand (Cooper, 1972, Fig. 10), and An_{30}
in common mafic schist and An_{50} in hornblende + BIO + EPI + PLG schist below
the incoming of clinopyroxene in the Central Alps (Wenk and Keller, 1969, p.
166-167). For low-P facies series, very anorthitic PLG is recorded below the
grade at which Fe-Mg-Mn AMP and clinopyroxene are stable: An_{65} in EPI + hornblende + PLG schist from the Abukuma Plateau (Miyashiro, 1958, p. 235, #3) and

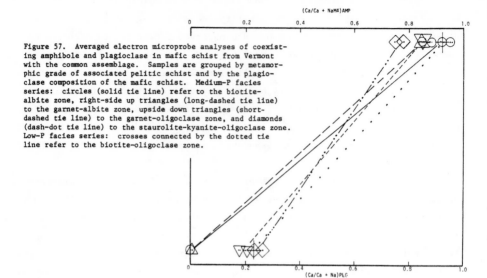

Figure 57. Averaged electron microprobe analyses of coexisting amphibole and plagioclase in mafic schist from Vermont with the common assemblage. Samples are grouped by metamorphic grade of associated pelitic schist and by the plagioclase composition of the mafic schist. Medium-P facies series: circles (solid tie line) refer to the biotite-albite zone, right-side up triangles (long-dashed tie line) to the garnet-albite zone, upside down triangles (short-dashed tie line) to the garnet-oligoclase zone, and diamonds (dash-dot tie line) to the staurolite-kyanite-oligoclase zone. Low-P facies series: crosses connected by the dotted tie line refer to the biotite-oligoclase zone.

Table 9. Variation in biotite and chlorite composition with medium-pressure facies series metamorphism of common mafic schist from Vermont

Facies*	Biotite formula**
Greenschist	$(K_{.91}Na_{.02}Ca_{.01})(Mg_{1.27}Fe^{2+}_{1.37}Mn_{.02}Al^{VI}_{.27}Ti_{.06})(Si_{2.92}Al^{IV}_{1.08})O_{10}(OH)_{1.96}F_{.04}$
Epidote-amphibolite	$(K_{.88}Na_{.03}Ca_{.01})(Mg_{1.40}Fe^{2+}_{1.22}Mn_{.01}Al^{VI}_{.27}Ti_{.11})(Si_{2.81}Al^{IV}_{1.19})O_{10}(OH)_{1.87}F_{.13}$

	Chlorite formula**
Greenschist	$(Mg_{2.42}Fe^{2+}_{2.26}Mn_{.04}Zn_{.01}Al^{VI}_{1.15}Fe^{3+}_{.11})(Si_{2.73}Al^{IV}_{1.27})O_{10}(OH)_{7.98}F_{.01}Cl_{.01}$
Epidote-amphibolite	$(Mg_{2.67}Fe^{2+}_{1.96}Zn_{.01}Al^{VI}_{1.27}Fe^{3+}_{.07}Ti_{.01})(Si_{2.64}Al^{IV}_{1.36})O_{10}(OH)_{8}$

*The greenschist sample (LA426) and the epidote-amphibolite sample (V340B) both contain the common mafic schist assemblage (see Table 7).

**Electron microprobe analyses are tabulated in Laird and Albee (1981b, appendix available through NAPS) and are representative of the average analyses used in the mass-balance calculations reported in Table 7. Biotite is normalized to total cations-(K + Na + Ca) = 7 and chlorite is normalized to total cations = 10. Site population and Fe^{3+} versus Fe^{2+} were estimated assuming stoichiometry (see Laird and Albee, 1981b, p. 132 and 1981a, p. 124 for details).

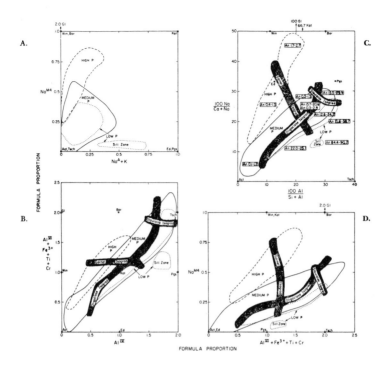

Figure 58. Range of electron microprobe analyses of amphibole in mafic schist with the common assemblage from Vermont. Envelopes surround the data (presented by Laird and Albee, 1981b, Figs. 9-11) for high-P (dashed lines), medium-P (solid lines), and low-P (dotted lines) facies series samples. Broad bands show the range over which intercalated pelitic schists change from biotite to garnet and from garnet to staurolite-kyanite grade. The oligoclase isograd shows the AMP compositions at which coexisting PLG "jumps" from albite (upper side of isograd) to oligoclase. The compositional range for PLG coexisting with AMP is indicated (mol % anorthite, diagram c) for each facies series and grade. End member amphibole compositions are shown as in Figure 56. From Laird and Albee (1981b, Fig. 12).

An_{70} (Kuniyoshi and Liou, 1976, hornblende + PLG schist) to An_{94} (Hietanan, 1974, common assemblage) in contact metamorphic rocks.

In some areas, medium-P metamorphism of common mafic schist also appears to result in a minor increase in $Al_2Mg_{-1}Si_{-1}$ in BIO, CHL, and MUS (Laird and Albee, 1981b, Figs. 3, 4, and 13). With respect to BIO and CHL, this general result may be seen by comparing rocks with overlapping compositional volumes (Table 9), and it is not dependent upon the $Fe^{2+}Mg_{-1}$ distribution between AMP and CHL (Fig. 55, excluding GAR-bearing assemblages). Contact metamorphism may also result in increasing Al in CHL (Hietanen, 1974, p. 37).

Many studies (e.g., Phillips, 1930; Wiseman, 1934; Miyashiro, 1958; Laird and Albee, 1981b) have noted that biotite in medium- and low-P facies series greenschist is commonly (but not invariably) green. With increasing metamorphic grade it becomes brown. This color change may be due to increasing Ti, as shown by the optical absorption studies of Robbins and Strens (1972).

Cooper (1972, p. 467) showed that epidote composition in mafic schist is dependent on f_{O_2} and bulk composition but fairly insensitive to metamorphic grade. However, taking into consideration the effects of f_{O_2}, Raith (1976) found that in both oxidized, hematite-bearing, and reduced, sulfide-bearing assemblages epidote becomes poorer in Fe^{3+} as greenschist changes to amphibolite. Laird and Albee (1981b, Fig. 7) also reported a decrease in Fe^{3+} in EPI with progressive, medium-P facies series metamorphism of sulfide-bearing common mafic schist, and Kuniyoshi and Liou (1976) and Hietanen (1974) reported a slight decrease in Fe^{3+}_{EPI} with progressive, contact metamorphism of the common assemblage. Complications due to possible immiscibility (see Raith, 1976 and references therein) and to mineral zoning resulting from polymetamorphism and disequilibrium also encumber our understanding of epidote in natural assemblages.

Chemical reactions

Following the practice of Harte and Graham (1975), Holland and Richardson (1979), and Thompson *et al.* (in press), we shall concentrate on reactions among AMP, CHL, EPI, PLG, and QTZ to explain the greenschist-amphibolite transition. This simplification of the common assemblage is justified in that usually only one or zero each of a Ti-rich mineral, a K-mica, a carbonate, an iron sulfide, an Fe^{3+} oxide, apatite, and tourmaline occurs, and the five major minerals are the ones showing systematic chemical and modal variations in world-wide occurrences of common mafic schist. Furthermore, during metamorphism of a system open only to H_2O and CO_2, modal variations of these five minerals "absorb" almost completely the compositional variations in all minerals of the assemblage (Laird, 1980).

If μ_{H_2O} is externally controlled and quartz is ubiquitous (but not necessarily modally large), compositional variation in the five-phase assemblage can be illustrated graphically by combining crystallographically compatible cations (Figs. 59 and 60). Combining $Fe^{2+} + Mg + Mn$ is "legitimate" to a certain extent because the $Fe^{2+}Mg_{-1}$ distribution between amphibole and chlorite is not particularly sensitive to rock composition (Fig. 55).

Figures 59 and 60 show that as AMP changes from actinolite to hornblende during the greenschist-amphibolite transition, the rock composition range in which the five-phase assemblage can be stable is reduced. AMP composition approaches that of the rock composition, explaining why it is observed that modal AMP increases and modal EPI and CHL decrease. These modal and mineral compositional variations are expressed in the following end-member reaction

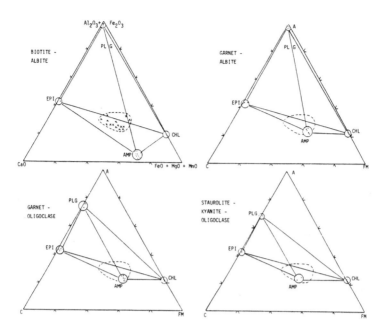

Figure 59. Mol % Al_2O_3 + Fe_2O_3 (A) versus CaO (C) versus FeO + MgO + MnO (FM) diagrams for averaged compositions of coexisting minerals in medium-P facies series mafic schist with the common assemblage from Vermont, projected from quartz and H_2O. Note that this is not an Eskola (ACF) diagram because plagioclase variation is shown. Dashed envelope encompasses the range of bulk analyses tabulated by Cady (1969, Table 4) for the mafic units from which the samples come. (See Laird, 1980, Fig. 3, for Na_2O variation as well and for the actual electron microprobe analyses.) Samples are grouped by metamorphic grade of the associated pelitic schist and by the anorthite content of plagioclase in the mafic schist. See text for abbreviations.

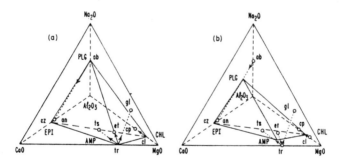

Figure 60. Compositional variation within coexisting AMPhibole, CHLorite, EPIdote, PLAGioclase, and quartz shown in the subsystem NCMASH (mol units), as projected through SiO_2 and H_2O. The space may also be regarded as a condensation of a more generalized composition space by projection along exchange vectors such as $FeMg_{-1}$, $FeAl_{-1}$, etc. Arrows indicate changes observed in mineral composition between the greenschist (a) and amphibolite facies (b). The change in AMP composition from tremolite (tr) is a combination of advancement along $Al_2Mg_{-1}Si_{-1}$ to tschermakite (ts), $NaAlSi_{-1}$ to edenite (et), and $NaSiCa_{-1}Al_{-1}$ + $Al_2Mg_{-1}Si_{-1}(NaAlCa_{-1}Mg_{-1})$ to glaucophane (gl). CHL changes along $Al_2Mg_{-1}Si_{-1}$ from clinochlore (cl) to corundophyllite (cp), and PLG changes along $NaSiCa_{-1}Al_{-1}$ from albite (ab) to anorthite (an). EPI is clinozoisite (cz) in this subspace. From Thompson *et al.* (in press; Fig. 3).

127

written by many (Shido, 1958, p. 180, #5; Miyashiro, 1958, p. 235; Cooper, 1972, p. 461, #c; Graham, 1974, p. 183, #2; Kuniyoshi and Liou, 1976, p. 91, #9; Holland and Richardson, 1979, Table 2 (GL,ED)):

$$Ca_2Mg_5Si_8O_{22}(OH)_2 + 14Mg_5Al_2Si_3O_{10}(OH)_8 + 24Ca_2Al_3Si_3O_{12}(OH) + 28SiO_2 =$$
$$\quad\text{[AMP]}\qquad\qquad\text{[CHL]}\qquad\qquad\quad\text{[EPI]}\qquad\qquad\quad\text{[QTZ]}$$

$$25Ca_2Mg_3Al_4Si_6O_{22}(OH)_2 + 44H_2O \qquad\qquad (1a)$$
$$\text{[AMP]}\qquad\qquad\quad\text{[ENV]}$$

where ENV refers to the H_2O lost to the environment during dehydration. Using the shorthand of Thompson (Chapter 3, Volume 9A) for writing mineral compositions as one end member plus the necessary simple and coupled substitutions (expressed as exchange vectors), and choosing tremolite and clinochlore as the AMP and CHL end members (for convenience because they most closely represent greenschist AMP and CHL in the system $CaO-MgO-Al_2O_3-SiO_2-H_2O$), reaction (1a) becomes

$$7Mg_5Al_2Si_3O_{10}(OH)_8 + 12Ca_2Al_3Si_3O_{12}(OH) + 14SiO_2 =$$
$$\text{[CHL]}\qquad\qquad\quad\text{[EPI]}\qquad\qquad\quad\text{[QTZ]}$$

$$12Ca_2Mg_5Si_8O_{22}(OH)_2 + 25Al_2Mg_{-1}Si_{-1} + 22H_2O \; . \qquad (1)$$
$$\text{[AMP]}\qquad\qquad\quad\text{[AMP]}\qquad\quad\text{[ENV]}$$

Reaction (1) neatly separates modal from mineral compositional variation and illustrates exactly what is observed in natural occurrences of common mafic schist during progressive metamorphism: modal CHL, EPI, and QTZ decrease, modal AMP increases, dehydration occurs, and $Al_2Mg_{-1}Si_{-1}$ increases in AMP (see above and Table 7). By adding as required the exchange reaction

$$Al_2Mg_{-1}Si_{-1}[AMP] = Al_2Mg_{-1}Si_{-1}[CHL] \qquad\qquad (2)$$

or in the more conventional form

$$Ca_2Mg_3Al_4Si_6O_{22}(OH)_2 + 2Mg_5Al_2Si_3O_{10}(OH)_8 =$$
$$\text{[AMP]}\qquad\qquad\qquad\text{[CHL]}$$

$$Ca_2Mg_5Si_8O_{22}(OH)_2 + 2Mg_4Al_4Si_2O_{10}(OH)_8 \; , \qquad\qquad (2a)$$
$$\text{[AMP]}\qquad\qquad\quad\text{[CHL]}$$

reaction (1) also explains the observation that CHL becomes richer in $Al_2Mg_{-1}Si_{-1}$ with increasing metamorphic grade.

Reaction (1) reduces the rock composition range in which the five-phase assemblage can form, as does the reaction

$$NaAlSi_3O_8 = 4SiO_2 + NaAlSi_{-1} \qquad\qquad (3)$$
$$\text{[PLG]}\qquad\text{[QTZ]}\quad\text{[AMP]}$$

(Shido, 1958, p. 179, #1; Cooper, 1972, p. 461, #c; Graham, 1974, p. 183, #1; Kuniyoshi and Liou, 1976, p. 91, #1; Holland and Richardson, 1979, Table 2 (GL,TS); see also Thompson's treatment of this reaction in Chapter 3 of Vol. 9A). Reaction (3) proceeds from left to right with progressive metamorphism, because $NaAlSi_{-1}$ [AMP] is known to increase (see above and Fig. 60) and explains why modal plagioclase decreases in some bulk compositions (Cooper, 1972, p. 462; Laird, 1980, Figs. 9 and 10) between the greenschist and epidote-amphibolite facies.

If anorthitic plagioclase is closer to the rock composition than albite (Figs. 59 and 60), however, modal plagioclase may increase abruptly across the oligoclase isograd (e.g., Wenk *et al.*, 1974, p. 118). The following reaction written by Miyashiro (1958, p. 235; Cooper, 1972, p. 461, #a; Graham, 1974, p. 183, #3; Kuniyoshi and Liou, 1976, p. 91, #7) would then be important:

$$3Mg_5Al_2Si_3O_{10}(OH)_8 + 6Ca_2Al_3Si_3O_{12}(OH) + 7SiO_2 =$$
$$\quad\quad [CHL] \quad\quad\quad\quad\quad [EPI] \quad\quad\quad\quad\quad [QTZ]$$

$$5Ca_2Mg_5Si_8O_{22}(OH)_2 + 10Al_2Mg_{-1}Si_{-1} + 2NaAlSi_3O_8 + 2CaAlNa_{-1}Si_{-1} + 10H_2O \ . \ (4)$$
$$\quad [AMP] \quad\quad\quad\quad\quad [AMP] \quad\quad\quad\quad [PLG] \quad\quad\quad [PLG] \quad\quad\quad [ENV]$$

Variation in $NaSiCa_{-1}Al_{-1}$ [AMP] may be incorporated by adding as appropriate the exchange reaction

$$NaSiCa_{-1}Al_{-1}[AMP] = NaSiCa_{-1}Al_{-1}[PLG] \quad\quad\quad\quad\quad\quad\quad\quad (5)$$

(with reference to (4), $CaAlNa_{-1}Si_{-1}$ clearly equals $-NaSiCa_{-1}Al_{-1}$). Written from left to right with dehydration, reaction (4) also illustrates the modal variation in CHL, EPI, QTZ, and AMP noted to be distinctive of the greenschist-amphibolite transition. Using the method of Thompson for determining an independent set of heterogeneous reactions (see Chapter 3, Volume 9A), Thompson *et al.* (in press) show that in the subsystem $Na_2O-CaO-MgO-Al_2O_3-SiO_2-H_2O$ (NCMASH) open only to H_2O there are two exchange reactions and three independent net-transfer reactions (as defined by Thompson and Thompson, 1976, p. 255) necessary and sufficient to describe all the mineral compositional and modal variations in AMP + CHL + EPI + PLG + QTZ schist. The exchange reactions are (2) and (5).

To express modal change in this five-phase assemblage, Thompson *et al.* (in press) chose independent net-transfer reactions (1), (3), and:

$$22NaAlSi_3O_8 + 2Mg_5Al_2Si_3O_{10}(OH)_8 = 5Ca_2Mg_5Si_8O_{22}(OH)_2$$

[PLG]   [CHL]   [AMP]

$$+ 15Al_2Mg_{-1}Si_{-1} + 22NaSiCa_{-1}Al_{-1} + 6Ca_2Al_3Si_3O_{12}(OH) + 7SiO_2 . \qquad (6)[19]$$

[AMP,CHL]   [AMP,PLG]   [EPI]   [QTZ]

This is not a unique set of nondependent reactions, but it is convenient in that all are written among end members closely approximating the compositions of these phases in greenschist (in NCMASH) and can be readily visualized (e.g., in Fig. 60) as expressing modal and mineral compositional variation observed during the transition to amphibolite. Furthermore, reactions (3) and (6) do not involve H_2O and are therefore independent of a_{H_2O} and a function of P and T alone. That is why reaction (6) and not reaction (4) was chosen to illustrate $NaSiCa_{-1}Al_{-1}$ [AMP,PLG] variation. Reaction (6) also has the advantage that it very nearly represents the greenschist-glaucophane schist transition in the five-phase assemblage (see Blueschist-Greenschist-Eclogite Relations, this chapter).

FeO, MnO, Fe_2O_3, Cr_2O_3, TiO_2, and K_2O may also be involved in mineral compositional variation within this five-phase assemblage. Addition of these components to the subsystem NCMASH will not change the number of independent net-transfer reactions among AMP, CHL, EPI, PLG, and QTZ (see Thompson *et al.*, in press, for justification) but will add seven independent exchange reactions:

$$FeMg_{-1}[AMP] = FeMg_{-1}[CHL] \qquad\qquad (7)$$

$$MnFe_{-1}[AMP] = MnFe_{-1}[CHL] \qquad\qquad (8)$$

$$FeAl_{-1}[AMP] = FeAl_{-1}[CHL] = FeAl_{-1}[EPI] \qquad (9),(10)$$

$$CrFe_{-1}[AMP] = CrFe_{-1}[CHL] \qquad\qquad (11)$$

$$TiFe_{-1}[AMP] = TiFe_{-1}[CHL] \qquad\qquad (12)$$

$$KNa_{-1}[PLG] = KNa_{-1}[AMP] . \qquad\qquad (13)$$

Any end-member or whole-rock reaction (including all phases) written to explain modal and mineral compositional variation within the five-phase assemblage is a linear combination of reactions (1) through (3) and (5) through (13). Only independent net-transfer reactions (1), (3), and (6) change the mode appreciably, and they can be portrayed in three dimensions (Fig. 61). In such a "reaction space" (conceived by Thompson, and described by Thompson *et al.*, in press), one can visualize for a particular rock composition the degree of

---

[19] Reaction (6) may be obtained by combining two dehydration reactions, the choice of which is non-unique, so as to eliminate H_2O; for example, 5 × reaction (1) - 1 × reaction (4), both written from left to right.

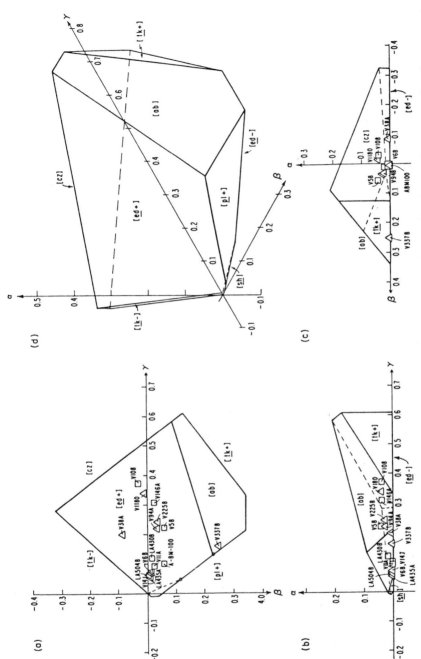

Figure 61. Reaction polyhedron for a quartz tholeiite composition corresponding to degrees of advancement on net-transfer reactions (3), (6), and (1), respectively. Coordinate axes α, β, and γ correspond to degrees of advancement on net-transfer reactions (3), (6), and (1), respectively. Faces of the polyhedron correspond to elimination of epidote [cz] or plagioclase [ab] from the assemblage AMP + CHL + EPI + PLG + QTZ, or to loss of exchange capacity (see text). Plotted points show how far each sample has advanced from the origin (representing ideal greenschist, see text) along each net-transfer reaction. Mineral compositions used are representative ones from mafic schist in Vermont with the 5-phase assemblage, as reported by Laird (1980), triangles, and Laird and Albee (1981a,b), squares. They have been condensed along FeMg₋₁, MnFe₋₁, FeAl₋₁, CrFe₋₁, TiFe₋₁, and (for the Al-site in AMP) KNa₋₁. Points are labeled by sample number. V38A is from the low-P facies series biotite-oligoclase zone and V337B is glaucophane schist. Medium-P facies series samples are: greenschist - V14J, LA504B, V6B, LA435A, LA430B; epidote-amphibolite - V94A, V225B; amphibolite - V146A, V118O, V108. V11A, A-BM-100, and V5B contain calcic to sodic-calcic amphiboles. From Thompson et al. (in press; Fig. 7).

131

advancement along each net-transfer reaction and its proportion in any whole-rock reaction proceeding during greenschist-amphibolite (or glaucophane schist) transition.

Starting at a convenient reference point or origin, which in the case of Figure 61 is taken as *ideal greenschist* in NCMASH (tremolite + clinochlore + clinozoisite + albite + quartz), reactions (1), (3), and (6) will proceed with progressive metamorphism in a particular proportion dependent on P, T, a_{H_2O} (reaction (1) only), and rock composition. Only mode (but not mineral assemblage) and mineral composition will change until one of two things happen:

(1) The whole-rock reaction (linear combination of net-transfer reactions in this condensed composition space) proceeds to a point where one of the phases of the five-phase assemblage is eliminated. In other words, a particular rock composition may be "removed" from the volume defined by AMP + CHL + EPI + PLG + QTZ (see Fig. 60) as the volume changes shape in response to variations in coexisting mineral compositions.

(2) The reaction proceeds to a point where a mineral can no longer change composition along a particular exchange vector, i.e., it has reached its limit of exchange capacity (see Thompson, Chapter 3, Volume 9A; also Thompson *et al.*, in press, for discussion of limits of exchange capacity).

Figure 61 shows the reaction polyhedron for a typical basaltic composition. Progressive metamorphism of ideal greenschist will proceed until EPI or PLG are completely consumed or until one of the following limits of exchange capacity is reached. [Refer to Fig. 60 herein and to Fig. 10 of Thompson (Chapter 3, Volume 9A) to visualize these limits of exchange capacity.]

[ed-] AMP has advanced no $NaAlSi_{-1}$ from end-member tremolite.

[ed+] AMP has advanced one $NaAlSi_{-1}$ (mol units).

[tk-] AMP has advanced no $Al_2Mg_{-1}Si_{-1}$ from tremolite and CHL has advanced no $Al_2Mg_{-1}Si_{-1}$ from clinochlore.

[tk+] AMP has advanced two $Al_2Mg_{-1}Si_{-1}$ and CHL one $Al_2Mg_{-1}Si_{-1}$.

[pl+] AMP has advanced two $NaSiCa_{-1}Al_{-1}$ from tremolite, and PLG is pure albite.

[sh] AMP composition is on the shaded plane in Figure 10 of Thompson (Chapter 3, Volume 9A) that separates compositions not accessible to AMP from those that are accessible.

Using coexisting mineral compositions in mafic schist from Vermont as an example and balancing on the number of oxygen equivalents transferred, because the mode of each phase is very nearly proportional to the number of oxygen units in its end-member component (see Thompson *et al.*, in press, for specific details), gives Figure 61. Samples showing medium-P facies series metamorphism (all but V38A, V337B, A-BM-100, and V5B) plot along reaction (1), γ on Figure 61, and this reaction is the most important. Greenschist samples are next to the ideal greenschist origin. Epidote-amphibolite and amphibolite show increasingly greater advancement along reaction (1), and corresponding, but less, advancement along reaction (3), α on the figure. Advancement along reaction (6), β on the figure, is discontinuous. The major change in mineral composition in the greenschist to epidote-amphibolite transition is in AMP, from actinolite to hornblende, so that reaction (6) proceeds in a positive direction (from left to right as written) as $NaSiCa_{-1}Al_{-1}$[AMP] increases (from the origin to V94A, V225B, Fig. 61a). $NaSiCa_{-1}Al_{-1}$[AMP] may show a minor increase between the epidote-amphibolite and amphibolite facies, but the major mineral compositional variation is in PLG, which jumps from albite across the peristerite gap to oligoclase, causing reaction (6) to proceed in the opposite (negative) direction (from V94A to V108, Fig. 61a).

In the specific case of the bulk composition used for Figure 61, EPI should be consumed first by continued reaction along the trend observed. However, in other bulk compositions a similar linear combination of reactions (1), (3), and (6) may result in elimination of CHL first (e.g., Fig. 62; also Fig. 6, Thompson *et al.*, in press), explaining the variation in relative order of EPI and CHL loss observed in the medium-P terranes of Scotland, the European Alps, and Vermont (see above).

Trajectories for whole-rock reactions in low-P facies series metamorphism are distinct from those for medium-P terranes in that reaction (6) is more important (origin to V38A, Fig. 61), consistent with the observation that greenschist passes nearly directly into the amphibolite facies in low-P metamorphism and does not go through the epidote-amphibolite facies as in medium-P metamorphism. PLG changes from albite to oligoclase and becomes more calcic "quicker" with respect to the change in AMP composition from actinolite to hornblende.

Reactions involving other phases

Whole-rock reactions written to express modal and mineral compositional variations in greenschist, epidote-amphibolite, and amphibolite (e.g., Brown, 1971, 1975; Laird, 1980) include varying amounts of other phases in the common

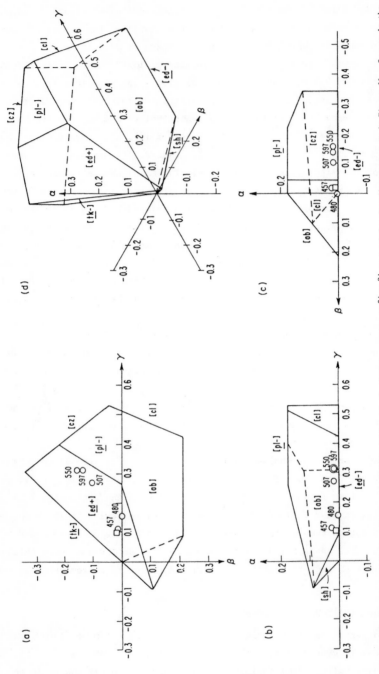

Figure 62. Reaction polyhedron for sample K1060 of Liou et al. (1974) assuming $Fe^{3+}:Fe^{2+}$ to be 3:7. Coordinate axes as in Figure 61. Square is the original rock, which shows some advancement from the ideal greenschist origin. Circles are experimental runs at temperatures (°C) indicated, all at 2 kbar. The bulk composition of K1060 is distinct from that for the reaction polyhedron in Figure 61, in that progressive metamorphism may also cause chlorite [cl] to be eliminated from the 5-phase assemblage, and the limits of exchange capacity [tk+] and [pl+] are not attainable (see text) but [pl−] (no advancement from tremolite along $NaSiCa-1Al-1$, plagioclase is anorthite), is attainable. From Thompson et al. (in press; Fig. 8).

assemblage and also stilpnomelane, garnet, and K-feldspar. For each additional
phase one independent net-transfer reaction will be added (as long as AMP, CHL,
EPI, PLG, and QTZ are still present), and other exchange reactions may be added
to the independent set. Reaction polyhedra may be conceived if not illustrated
(due to reaction space being greater than three dimensions) for each set of
independent reactions. Observed mineral compositional and modal variations
will suggest which of the reactions are more important in the greenschist-
amphibolite transition, as will factoring the whole-rock reactions.

Adding clinopyroxene and Fe-Mg-Mn amphiboles to the system gives net-
transfer reactions pertinent to continued progressive metamorphism of mafic
schist from amphibolite to granulite. Some of these reactions are presented
by Thompson et $al.$ (in press).

Dependence of reactions on T and P

"Dirty rock" experiments such as those of Liou et $al.$ (1974) and Moody
et $al.$ (in preparation) may be used to calibrate a set of independent net-
transfer reactions. A reaction polyhedron for a specific bulk composition may
be constructed, and from coexisting mineral compositions or modes of the charge
at various P and T, it may be determined how far each run has progressed along
each independent reaction. For example, data of Liou et $al.$ (1974) at P_T =
P_{fluid} = 2 kbar are illustrated in Figure 62 with reference to reactions (1),
(3), and (6) (see Thompson et $al.$, in press, for details). That the dominant
reactions are (6), β proceeding in a negative direction to cause increasing
$CaAlNa_{-1}Si_{-1}$[PLG] (or decreasing $NaSiCa_{-1}Al_{-1}$), and (1), γ, proceeding in a
positive direction to cause increasing $Al_2Mg_{-1}Si_{-1}$[AMP,CHL], is consistent
with results for low-P versus medium-P metamorphism in Vermont (Fig. 61).

Exchange equilibria (2), (5), and (7) through (13) offer possible geothermometers if they can be calibrated. Figures 55 and 63 show that in the
common assemblage, $FeMg_{-1}$ distribution between AMP and CHL changes from the
greenschist facies, where CHL is relatively more Fe^{2+}-rich, to the epidote-
amphibolite and amphibolite facies, where AMP and CHL have about the same Fe^{2+}/
Mg (similar relationships are shown by Cooper, 1972, p. 488, and Harte and
Graham, 1975, p. 355, although they consider total $Fe(Fe^{2+}+Fe^{3+})$ and show that
Fe/Mg in hornblende is greater than that in CHL). Although systematic, there
appears to be only a weak temperature dependence of this exchange, so that it
is probably not very useful for geothermometry.

A greater temperature dependence is shown by $Al_2Mg_{-1}Si_{-1}$ distribution
between AMP and CHL and by $NaSiCa_{-1}Al_{-1}$ distribution between AMP and PLG (Figs.
64 and 65), so that experimental studies may be worthwhile. However, cross

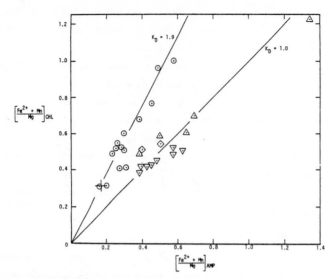

Figure 63. $Fe^{2+}Mg_{-1}$ distribution (atom units) between chlorite and amphibole in mafic schist from Vermont. K_D is X_{Mg} [AMP] divided by X_{Mg} [CHL]. Each point is representative of coexisting compositions in a sample of mafic schist with the common assemblage from Vermont (data in Laird and Albee, 1981b, Appendix in NAPS). Medium-P facies series: circles, biotite-albite zone; triangles, garnet-albite zone; inverted triangles, garnet-oligoclase zone; diamonds, staurolite-kyanite- oligoclase zone. Low-P facies series: cross, biotite-oligoclase zone.

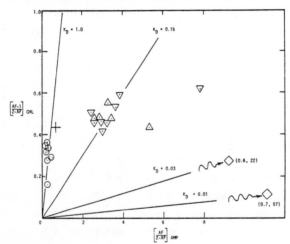

Figure 64. $Al_2Mg_{-1}Si_{-1}$ distribution (atom units) between chlorite and amphibole. K_D is X_{AF} [CHL] divided by X_{AF} [AMP], where $AF = Al^{VI}+Fe^{3+}+Cr+2Ti$. CHL is assumed to show displacement along this exchange from clinochlore to corundophyllite and AMP from tremolite to tschermakite. It is assumed in AMP that this exchange involves only the M2 site. Data and symbols as in Figure 63.

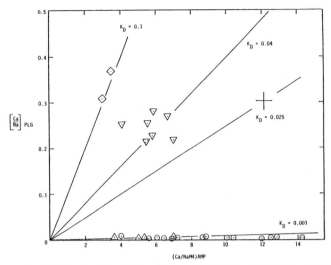

Figure 65. NaSiCa$_{-1}$Al$_{-1}$ distribution (atom units) between plagioclase and amphibole. K$_D$ is X$_{Ca}$ [PLG] divided by X$_{Ca}$ [AMP]. Data and symbols as in Figure 63.

effects resulting because NaAlSi$_{-1}$, Al$_2$Mg$_{-1}$Si$_{-1}$, and NaSiCa$_{-1}$Al$_{-1}$ all involve tetrahedral replacement, may prevent these from being practical geothermometers.

Reactions (3) and (6) do not involve H$_2$O and are therefore independent of a$_{H_2O}$; they may thus be useful as geothermometers or geobarometers. Reaction (3) has been studied experimentally by Best (1978) and Greenwood (1979). Neither study resulted in a calibration of this reaction, in part because of problems in synthesizing pure edenite, but both studies indicate that reaction (3) is quite sensitive to T. Reaction (6) appears to be more dependent on P, as indicated from simple thermodynamic calculations (Laird et $al.$, 1978). If T and P can be determined from exchange equilibria and H$_2$O-conserving reactions, then one net-transfer reaction open to H$_2$O [(1), (4), others] is sufficient to determine a$_{H_2O}$[ENV].

Although involving significant cumulative errors, empirical evaluation of the P-T dependence of NaSiCa$_{-1}$Al$_{-1}$ in AMP and in PLG, of Al$_2$Mg$_{-1}$Si$_{-1}$ in AMP and in CHL, and of NaAlSi$_{-1}$ in AMP may be made for the common assemblage, if T and P are known independently, by contouring changes in coexisting mineral compositions (Laird et $al.$, 1979; see also Brown, 1977, for an empirical evaluation of Na^{M4} in AMP).

The task of determining the T-P dependence of reactions in mafic schist remains a difficult one, because of problems due to crystallographic complexity of the phases involved, especially AMP. However, it is clear that modal and mineral compositional variations in common mafic schist are systematic and (quoting from Alexander Pope) "Hope springs eternal in the human breast."

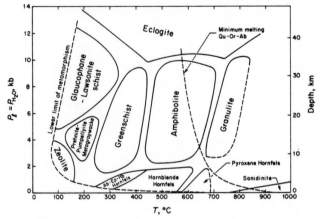

Figure 66. Tentative scheme of metamorphic facies after Turner (1968, Fig. 8-6). All boundaries are gradational.

AMPHIBOLES IN METAMORPHOSED BASALTIC ROCKS: BLUESCHIST-GREENSCHIST-ECLOGITE RELATIONS

Eskola (1939, pp. 345, 363-368) defined two facies which he considered to represent pressures of metamorphism greater than the greenschist-amphibolite transition. He listed the minerals glaucophane, lawsonite, and pumpellyite as critical to the glaucophane schist facies and omphacite + eclogitic garnet (usually almandine-rich with rarely more than 30 mol % pyrope and 12% grossular) as diagnostic of the eclogite facies. Because of problems in defining these facies, their stability in P-T-a_{H_2O}-composition space, and their geologic conditions of formation, questions arose as to the validity of each as a metamorphic facies, but many now agree with Eskola that glaucophane schists and eclogites represent high-P facies series of metamorphism as defined by Miyashiro (1961). Figure 66 shows Turner's (1968) diagrammatic scheme for these metamorphic facies. This is very similar both to Eskola's diagram (1939, p. 345; see also Table 5-1 in Turner, 1968, p. 184, for his version of Eskola's diagram in English) and to those of other current metamorphic petrology textbooks (Miyashiro, 1973, p. 90, Fig. 3-12; Dobretsov et al., 1972, p. 199, Fig. 76; Ernst, 1976, p. 251, Fig. 6.46).

Earlier it was thought that glaucophane schists were primarily formed metasomatically, so that a separate metamorphic facies for these rocks should be abolished (see Miyashiro, 1973, pp. 436-437, and Dobretsov et al., 1973, p. 84, for historical discussions of the birth, death, and rebirth of the glaucophane schist facies). Small-scale metasomatism does appear to occur and some spilitization of ocean floor basalt protoliths before or during metamorphism seems probable for some mafic schists. However, the rather large amount of data now accumulated shows that basalts, eclogites, mafic glaucophane schists, greenschists, and epidote amphibolites all have similar bulk compositions (Ernst, 1971, and references therein; Dobretsov et al., 1975, pp. 102-107). Consequently, glaucophane schists in general are not formed purely by metasomatism, and their parageneses must be distinct from greenschists and epidote amphibolites because they were formed at different P-T-a_{H_2O} conditions.

Experimental data (to be discussed below) have shown that glaucophane schist assemblages have rather high-P stability fields, and the glaucophane schist facies has been reinstated. Bailey et al. (1964, p. 91) proposed to rename this the blueschist facies because (1) other blue amphiboles are also characteristic, (2) other minerals (lawsonite, aragonite, jadeitic pyroxene) are critical, and (3) glaucophane is neither restricted to nor required in rocks of the facies. The terms blueschist and glaucophane schist are now pretty much used synonymously, although some clearly prefer one over the other. At times, blueschists is a misnomer, as some glaucophane schists are not very blue. Glaucophane close to its end-member composition is colorless to pale lavender, owing to its small Fe content.[20] The term blueschist is also problematical in that the blue amphiboles riebeckite and arfvedsonite are common in alkalic igneous rocks. Furthermore, reactions forming glaucophane with increasing P will be moved to lower P as the amount of Fe^{2+} or Fe^{3+} substitution in glaucophane increases. Consequently, interpretation of blue amphiboles as being indicative of high P can be erroneous, as recently noted, for example, by Munhá (1979) who argued that blue amphiboles in southern Portugal were formed during extensional tectonics, rather than in a subduction zone as had been proposed previously.

Following the definitions of Eskola (1939, pp. 366-367), Coleman et al. (1965) have defined three groups of eclogites and have characterized each by the pyrope content of the garnet coexisting with omphacite:

Group A (Eskola's types 1 and 2) - Inclusions in kimberlites, basalts, or layers in ultramafic rocks. >55% pyrope.

Group B (Eskola's type 3) - Bands or lenses within migmatite gneissic terrains. Surrounded by amphibolite and show retrograde metamorphism. 30-55% pyrope.

Group C (Eskola's type 4) - Bands or lenses within the metamorphic rocks of alpine-type orogenic zones, locally forming isolated blocks when

---

[20]Bancroft and Burns (1969, pp. 145-146) show that the blue color of alkali amphiboles is due to electron transfer between neighboring Fe^{3+} and Fe^{2+}.

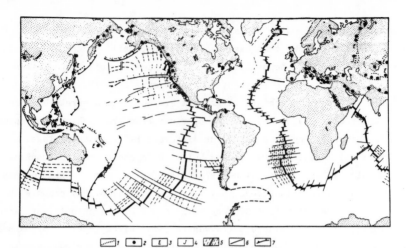

Figure 67. Map of world distribution of glaucophane schists and associated eclogites after Coleman (1972) with additions by N.L. Dobretsov. The glaucophane schist and eclogite locality in northern Vermont (Laird and Albee, 1981a) has been added. Symbols: (1) "ophiolite belts," (2) glaucophane schists, (3) Type C eclogites, (4) jadeite bodies in serpentinites, (5) mid-ocean ridges and associated magnetic anomalies, (6) transform faults, (7) subduction zones. From Dobretsov *et al.* (1975; Fig. 26).

associated with glaucophane schists. <30% pyrope.

Because different types of eclogites have different coexisting minerals and therefore different P-T-a_{H_2O} stabilities, Coleman *et al.* (1965) suggested that eclogite no longer satisfied the definition of a metamorphic facies and should not be considered as such. Nevertheless, the various eclogite groups are well defined, and if the P-T-a_{H_2O} stabilities of each can be determined, each will satisfy Eskola's concept of facies.

Although petrologically very important, we shall not consider types A or B eclogites below for time and space reasons, but will concentrate on group C.

Glaucophane schists and group C eclogites in space and time.

Figure 67 shows the world distribution of glaucophane schists and associated eclogites after Coleman (1972) and Dobretsov *et al.* (1975), with one new occurrence. Ernst (1972b, Table 1) and Dobretsov *et al.* (1975) have done an excellent job of compiling references on glaucophane schist localities. Summaries of these occurrences are presented, for example, in recent metamorphic petrology textbooks (Turner, 1968; Miyashiro, 1973; Dobretsov *et al.*, 1975, which gives particularly extensive summaries and includes details of the glaucophane schist belts of the Ural Mountains published in Russian elsewhere), in two accumulations of pertinent papers edited by Ernst (1975a,b), and in Ernst (1977). More recent papers include studies in New Caledonia (Black, 1977, and her earlier papers referenced therein); Taiwan (Liou *et al.*, 1975); Turkey (Okay, 1980a); the

140

Aegean orogenic belt (Seidel and Okrusch, 1976; Okrusch *et al.*, 1978; Schliestedt, 1980; Kornprobst *et al.*, 1979); southern Italy (de Roever *et al.*, 1976);
the Western and Ligurian Alps (Desmons, 1977, and her other papers referenced
therein; Goffe, 1977; Compagnoni, 1977; Desmons and Ghent, 1977; Gosso, 1977;
Lombardo *et al.*, 1977; Reinsch, 1977, 1979; Ernst, 1981, and his other papers
referenced therein); Ile de Groix, France (Triboulet, 1974, 1978); the Coast
Ranges of Oregon and California (Ghent and Coleman, 1973; Brown and Bradshaw,
1979; Moore and Liou, 1979); and in northern Venezuela (Morgan, 1970; Blackburn
and Navarro, 1977; Maresch and Abraham, 1977).

Many have noted that glaucophane schists are more common in post-Paleozoic
than in pre-Mesozoic orogenic belts. To explain this apparent relationship
de Roever (1956) and Ernst (1972b), for example, have suggested that the Earth's
geothermal gradient has become more gradual with time. Dobretsov *et al.* (1975,
p. 111) strongly disagree. They argue (1) that glaucophane schists occur in
orogenic belts of any age, beginning at least with latest Precambrian time
(Riphean) and (2) that their relative rarity in pre-Mesozoic rocks is due to
poor preservation. Statement (2) above is supported by the computer modeling
of England and Richardson (1977, pp. 206-207), who suggest that the probability
of a glaucophane schist surviving erosion decreases significantly after the
rock is 100 Ma old and goes to zero by 500 Ma. Dobretsov *et al.* (1975) support
their first statement by describing upper Precambrian and Paleozoic glaucophane
schists in various parts of the Pacific Ocean margin, in the Ural Mountains, and
in the Mediterranean region.

Another Paleozoic glaucophane schist locality has been added to the compilation in Figure 15. Laird and Albee (1981a) report glaucophane (as defined
by the I.M.A.; Leake (1978)--see Hawthorne, Chapter 1, Volume 9A) and omphacite + quartz-bearing mafic schist from a locality in northern Vermont. Compositions of coexisting garnet and omphacite in eclogite indicate the rocks
are group C eclogites of Coleman *et al.* (1965) and are the high-P metamorphic
type of Miyashiro (1973, p. 318, Fig. 12-5). Glaucophane has also been reported
in New Brunswick, Canada (Trzcienski, 1979). These two localities are isolated.
There is not a major glaucophane schist unit in the northern Appalachian Mountains, but the reasonably widespread occurrence of sodic-calcic amphiboles in
northern Vermont and Southern Quebec (Laird and Albee, 1981b) and of crossite
in Quebec and Newfoundland (Trzcienski, 1976; Jamieson, 1977) suggest that a
somewhat higher than "normal" medium-P Ordovician metamorphic event is preserved in part. Perhaps it would be possible to correlate these rocks to the
British Caledonides and the recently reported Dalradian crossite- and barroisite-bearing mafic schists (Gray and Yardley, 1979).

The transition from greenschist to glaucophane schist

Glaucophane schist is distinct from greenschist in that it contains glauco-
phane-crossite and may contain lawsonite, pumpellyite, aragonite, and jadeite
or omphacite. Also, biotite is absent. However, their assemblages are similar
in that sphene also occurs in glaucophane schist, as may Ca-rich clinoamphibole,
chlorite, albite, epidote, quartz, phengitic muscovite, paragonite, stilpnomelane,
calcite, dolomite, hematite, magnetite, apatite, tourmaline, and sulfide (see
previous section on basaltic rocks for typical greenschist assemblages).

To support his argument that the concept of a glaucophane schist facies is
valid, de Roever (1955, p. 241) noted that glaucophane may form by the reaction

$$10NaAlSi_3O_8 + 2Mg_5Al_2Si_3O_{10}(OH)_8 + Ca_2Mg_5Si_8O_{22}(OH)_2 =$$
$$[PLG] \qquad\qquad [CHL] \qquad\qquad\qquad [AMP]$$

$$5Na_2Mg_3Al_2Si_8O_{22}(OH)_2 + 2CaAl_2Si_2O_8 \cdot 2H_2O \tag{14}$$
$$[AMP] \qquad\qquad\qquad [LAW]$$

where PLG, CHL, AMP, and LAW refer to plagioclase, chlorite, clinoamphibole,
and lawsonite, respectively. This reaction, he suggested, would account for the
common occurrence of glaucophane and lawsonite in the Franciscan Complex of the
California Coast Ranges and the absence of this assemblage in greenschists.
Furthermore, it shows that glaucophane + lawsonite may be formed isochemically
from greenschist without gain or loss of H_2O and should represent the higher
pressure assemblage, because the molar volume of the right-hand side of
reaction (14) is less than that of the left-hand side. This reaction has been
written by others (e.g., Coleman and Lee, 1963, p. 286; Ernst, 1963a, p. 23 #III;
Thompson *et al.*, in press, #28) and interpreted similarly.

De Roever (1955) wrote another reaction:

$$10NaAlSi_3O_8 + 3Mg_5Al_2Si_3O_{10}(OH)_8 + 6Ca_2Al_3Si_3O_{12}(OH) + 7SiO_2 + 14H_2O =$$
$$[PLG] \qquad\qquad [CHL] \qquad\qquad\qquad [EPI] \qquad\qquad [QTZ] \quad [ENV]$$

$$5Na_2Mg_3Al_2Si_8O_{22}(OH)_2 + 12CaAl_2Si_2O_8 \cdot 2H_2O \tag{15}$$
$$[AMP] \qquad\qquad\qquad [LAW]$$

where EPI refers to epidote and ENV to H_2O lost to the environment. Miyashiro
and Banno (1958, p. 101) also wrote (15) and the following other reaction to
express the greenschist-glaucophane schist transition:

$$50NaAlSi_3O_8 + 9Mg_5Al_2Si_3O_{10}(OH)_8 + 6Ca_2Mg_5Si_8O_{22}(OH)_2 =$$
$$[PLG] \qquad\qquad [CHL] \qquad\qquad\qquad [AMP]$$

$$25Na_2Mg_3Al_2Si_8O_{22}(OH)_2 + 6Ca_2Al_3Si_3O_{12}(OH) + 7SiO_2 + 14H_2O \tag{16}$$
$$[AMP] \qquad\qquad\qquad [EPI] \qquad\qquad [QTZ] \quad [ENV]$$

which is a linear combination of the other two [6 × reaction (14) - reaction (15) = reaction (16)].

If reaction (16) is combined with reaction (1) of the last section ("Amphiboles in basaltic rocks - greenschist facies to amphibolite facies") to eliminate H_2O, the following reaction is obtained:

$$22NaAlSi_3O_8 + 2Mg_5Al_2Si_3O_{10}(OH)_8 + 6Ca_2Mg_5Si_8O_{22}(OH)_2 + 7Al_2Mg_{-1}Si_{-1} =$$
[PLG]   [CHL]   [AMP]   [AMP,CHL]

$$11Na_2Mg_3Al_2Si_8O_{22}(OH)_2 + 6Ca_2Al_3Si_3O_{12}(OH) + 7SiO_2 .$$ (6a)
     [AMP]   [EPI]   [QTZ]

Reaction (6a) may be visualized easily on Figure 68. It may also be seen that while actinolite + chlorite + epidote + albite (+ quartz) is commonly observed in greenschist, actinolite to winchite + chlorite + glaucophane + epidote and albite + epidote + glaucophane + chlorite are common in glaucophane schists (see also Fig. 3 in Ernst, 1963a, which is similar to Fig. 68). It should be remembered, however, that reaction (6a) is continuous (as are the other net-transfer reactions written above and in the last section) and is not really a discontinuity. Even though the Fe^{2+}/Mg is similar in coexisting AMP and CHL in some glaucophane schists (Fig. 69), actinolite to winchite, chlorite, glaucophane, epidote, albite, and quartz may all coexist in part of Na_2O-CaO-MgO-FeO-Al_2O_3-SiO_2-H_2O space (see "Coexisting calcic amphiboles and sodic amphiboles," this chapter).

Brown (1974) and Laird (1980) wrote whole-rock reactions between samples of greenschist and blueschist to determine which phases were primarily involved in this transition. Laird's reaction (no. 7, see also her Table 9) is very nearly the same as reaction (6a) and indicates that the primary modal and mineral compositional variations in this transition involve AMP, CHL, EPI, PLG, and QTZ. Phengite, sphene, magnetite, and paragonite are not significantly involved in the reaction. Brown obtained a similar, but somewhat different, reaction

crossite + epidote = albite + actinolite + iron oxide + H_2O , (17)

indicating that iron oxide may be more important in greenschist to crossite-bearing schist than in greenschist to glaucophane schist reactions, although Fe^{3+} oxides are not uncommon in both greenschists and blueschists. Brown also showed that muscovite and sphene are not appreciably involved in this transition (see his Table 6), supporting the validity of simplifying the system to the five phases (above) commonly found in mafic schist. As discussed by Thompson *et al.* (in press), (6a) may be converted to reaction (6) in the last section simply by subtracting $6Ca_2Mg_5Si_8O_{22}(OH)_2$[AMP] and $7Al_2Mg_{-1}Si_{-1}$[AMP,CHL] from both sides

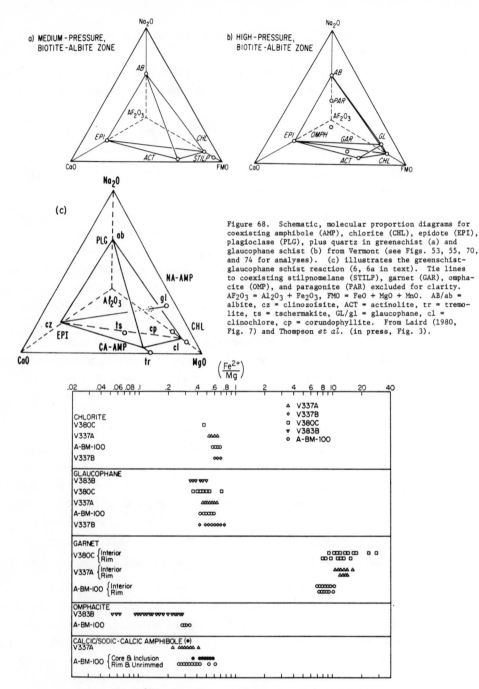

Figure 68. Schematic, molecular proportion diagrams for coexisting amphibole (AMP), chlorite (CHL), epidote (EPI), plagioclase (PLG), plus quartz in greenschist (a) and glaucophane schist (b) from Vermont (see Figs. 53, 55, 70, and 74 for analyses). (c) illustrates the greenschist-glaucophane schist reaction (6, 6a in text). Tie lines to coexisting stilpnomelane (STILP), garnet (GAR), omphacite (OMP), and paragonite (PAR) excluded for clarity. $AF_2O_3 = Al_2O_3 + Fe_2O_3$, FMO = FeO + MgO + MnO. AB/ab = albite, cz = clinozoisite, ACT = actinolite, tr = tremolite, ts = tschermakite, GL/gl = glaucophane, cl = clinochlore, cp = corundophyllite. From Laird (1980, Fig. 7) and Thompson *et al.* (in press, Fig. 3).

Figure 69. $Fe^{2+}Mg_{-1}$ distribution for mafic minerals in high-P facies series mafic schist from Vermont. Same data as in Figures 70 and 74. From Laird and Albee (1981a, Fig. 15).

144

and noting that glaucophane is tremolite $+2Al_2Mg_{-1}Si_{-1} + 2NaSiCa_{-1}Al_{-1}$ (see Fig. 10 of Thompson, Volume 9A). Consequently, (6), as one of the three net-transfer reactions of the independent set of heterogeneous reactions necessary and sufficient to describe all modal and mineral compositional variations during metamorphism of AMP + CHL + EPI + PLG + QTZ schist, describes a transition from greenschist to glaucophane (+ epidote) schist! Furthermore, this transition, like that to glaucophane (+ lawsonite) schist (reaction 14) involves no gain or loss of H_2O. It is therefore not surprising that the glaucophane schist sample shown in Figure 61 (V337B, also used for the mass-balance calculations of Laird, 1980, Model D) shows significant advancement along reaction (6) and plots very near the limit of exchange capacity of AMP and PLG for $NaSiCa_{-1}Al_{-1}$.

Reaction (6/6a) predicts that PLG should show a major decrease in mode as AMP increases in mode and becomes more glaucophane-rich. This is indeed observed in whole-rock reactions where bulk composition remains constant (Laird, 1980, Fig. 12) and explains why albite is nearly ubiquitous in greenschist but is less common in glaucophane schist. Another reaction which will decrease modal PLG has been written by Ernst (1963a, p. 23, #I) for the formation of glaucophane:

$$13NaAlSi_3O_8 + 3Mg_5Al_2Si_3O_{10}(OH)_8 + SiO_2 =$$
$$[PLG] \qquad\qquad [CHL] \qquad\qquad\quad [QTZ]$$

$$5Na_2Mg_3Al_2Si_8O_{22}(OH)_2 + 3NaAl_3Si_3O_{10}(OH)_2 + 4H_2O \qquad\qquad (18)$$
$$[AMP] \qquad\qquad\qquad\quad [PAR]$$

where PAR refers to paragonite. Reaction (18) may be visualized on Figure 70, which illustrates coexisting mineral compositions in several samples from the glaucophane schist and eclogite locality in northern Vermont.[21] This reaction may be factored into the following continuous, net-transfer reactions (in the subspace NMASH) so that control of the three-phase assemblages (plus QTZ as necessary) NaAMP, CHL, PLG and CHL, PAR, PLG on $Al_2Mg_{-1}Si_{-1}$ [AMP,CHL] may be visualized:

$$Mg_5Al_2Si_3O_{10}(OH)_8 + 4NaAlSi_3O_8 = 2Na_2Mg_3Al_2Si_8O_{22}(OH)_2 + Al_2Mg_{-1}Si_{-1} + 2H_2O \quad (19)$$
$$[CHL] \qquad\qquad\quad [PLG] \qquad\qquad [AMP] \qquad\qquad [AMP,CHL] \quad [ENV]$$

and:
$$6NaAl_3Si_3O_{10}(OH)_2 =$$
$$[PAR]$$

$$Mg_5Al_2Si_3O_{10}(OH)_8 + 5Al_2Mg_{-1}Si_{-1} + 6NaAlSi_3O_8 + 2SiO_2 + 2H_2O \qquad (20)$$
$$[CHL] \qquad\qquad\quad [AMP,CHL] \qquad\quad [PLG] \qquad [QTZ] \quad [ENV]$$

----

[21] Representative mineral analyses and structural formulas for these data are found in NAPS document No. 03800. Order as indicated in Footnote 17.

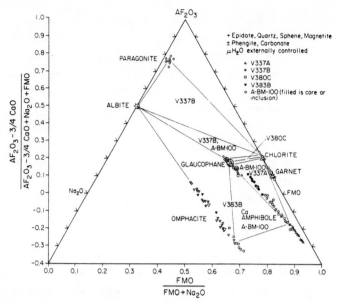

Figure 70. Epidote + quartz + sphene + magnetite ± phengetic muscovite ± calcite or dolomite projection of electron microprobe analyses of minerals from high-P facies series mafic schist from Vermont. Tie lines connect inferred coexisting compositions, but those to garnet are omitted for clarity. All 3-phase and 2-phase assemblages (plus minerals from which diagram is projected) may also include garnet if the bulk composition is Fe-rich. $AF_2O_3 = Al_2O_3 + Fe_2O_3$, FMO = FeO + MgO + MnO (mole %). Pure jadeite projects at albite. From Laird and Albee (1981a, Fig. 14).

Reactions (19) and (20) both imply that dehydration is accompanied by increasing $Al_2Mg_{-1}Si_{-1}$ [AMP,CHL], the distribution between AMP and CHL being controlled by exchange reaction (2) in the last section. Modal CHL and PLG decrease in (19) and increase in (20) with dehydration. Combining reactions (19) and (20) so as to eliminate $Al_2Mg_{-1}Si_{-1}$ results in reaction (18).

Another glaucophane-producing reaction written by Ernst (1963a, p. 23, #II) is

$$4NaAlSi_3O_8 + 3Ca_2Mg_5Si_8O_{22}(OH)_2 + 6NaAl_3Si_3O_{10}(OH)_2 + 8H_2O =$$
[PLG]   [AMP]   [PAR]   [ENV]

$$6CaAl_2Si_2O_8 \cdot 2H_2O + 5Na_2Mg_3Al_2Si_8O_{22}(OH)_2 + 2SiO_2 . \qquad (21)$$
[LAW]   [AMP]   [QTZ]

Reaction (21) may be obtained from reactions (14) and (18) by eliminating CHL; hence, it is not independent. From the last section we know that there are three independent net-transfer reactions among AMP, CHL, EPI, PLG, and QTZ. Adding LAW and PAR to this five-phase assemblage adds two more independent net-transfer reactions plus the various independent exchange reactions. Consequently, (1), (3), (6), (14), and (18) define a reaction space for this seven-phase assemblage.

	Type II	Type III	Type IV
Glaucophane			
Lawsonite			- -
Pumpellyite			- -
Clinozoisite			
Epidote		- -	
Jadeitic pyroxene	70–80% Jd	70–80% Jd	30–40% Jd
Muscovite	1M	$2M_1$	$2M_1$
Chlorite			
Aragonite	- -		- -
Calcite	- -		- -
Sphene			-
Rutile			
Garnet	?	Al–Gr–Sp	Al–Gr
Apatite	?		
Pyrite	-		
Texture	non-foliated	foliated	gneissic
Average Density	2·88	3·05	3·20
H_tO^+ (wt.% average)	4·0	3·1	1·5

Figure 71. Summary of mineral parageneses of glaucophane-bearing metabasalt types II, III, and IV from the Franciscan Formation, California. Jd = jadeite, Al = almandine, Gr = grossular, Sp = spessartine. ? indicates that the mineral has not been observed but may be present in small amounts. See Coleman and Lee (1963, Table 1).

Progressive metamorphism

Because many glaucophane schists are polymetamorphic and may be retrograded to greenschist (e.g., Compagnoni, 1977; Ernst, 1977), it is commonly difficult to determine equilibrium assemblages. Furthermore, outcrops are often in tectonic contact, and it has proven very difficult to locate layers with similar bulk compositions that can be traced through a progressive change in metamorphic grade. Consequently, the progressive metamorphism of glaucophane schist is not so well understood as the greenschist to amphibolite transition.

From detailed field and petrologic work, Coleman and Lee (1963) recognized three different grades of glaucophane schist facies in the Franciscan Complex in the Cazadero area, northern California. Figure 71 is their summary of mineral parageneses in metabasalts. They note that in pillow basalts which occur in Type II rocks, hydrous minerals are modally less abundant in the cores than the rims of the pillows, and that jadeitic pyroxene is confined to the cores of the pillows and to interbedded pyroclastic rocks. Grain size and development of foliation increase from Type II to IV. Type IV rocks are distinct in that they occur as isolated tectonic blocks. Because the assemblage epidote/clinozoisite + rutile occurs in Type IV rocks and lawsonite + pumpellyite + sphene occurs in Types II and III, Coleman and Lee (1963, p. 286) suggested that II and III are related to IV by the reactions

$$\text{pumpellyite} + \text{lawsonite} + \text{sphene} = \text{epidote} + \text{rutile} + \text{quartz} + H_2O \quad (22)$$

$$\text{and } 3CaAl_2Si_2O_8 \cdot 2H_2O + CaTiSiO_5 = 2Ca_2Al_3Si_3O_{12}(OH) + TiO_2 + SiO_2 + 5H_2O . \quad (23)$$
$$\quad [LAW] \qquad\qquad [SPN] \qquad\qquad [EPI] \qquad\qquad [RUT] \quad [QTZ] \quad [ENV]$$

In their study of Types II through IV glaucophane schists in the Cazadero and other areas of the Franciscan Complex, Brown and Bradshaw (1979) wrote the following generalized, whole-rock reactions between Types II and IV:

147

pumpellyite + chlorite + $Al_2Mg_{-1}Si_{-1}$ [CHL] + omphacite + quartz =
garnet + sodic amphibole + epidote + H_2O (24)

and

lawsonite + chlorite + $Al_2Mg_{-1}Si_{-1}$ [CHL] + omphacite + quartz =
garnet + sodic amphibole + epidote + H_2O .   (25)

Reaction (25) may be expressed in terms of five independent net-transfer reactions, three involving AMP, CHL, EPI, QTZ, and LAW, plus two more, one to control modal clinopyroxene (CPX) and one to control modal garnet. An obvious choice for the former would be

$$NaAlSi_3O_8 = NaAlSi_2O_6 + SiO_2 .$$
  [PLG]   [CPX]   [QTZ]   (26)

Thompson *et al.* [in press, reactions (34) to (36)] list three from among many petrologically informative reactions which control garnet mode and composition (see also Thompson, Volume 9A). An independent net-transfer reaction controlling modal pumpellyite would also be needed to define a reaction space for assemblages related by reaction (24).

New Caledonia is one of the few places where progressive metamorphism of glaucophane schist to eclogite can be studied without complications of intense tectonism or polymetamorphism. Black (1977 and references therein) has mapped a series of isograds in metamorphosed mafic igneous rocks. With increasing grade, the pumpellyite, Na-amphibole, omphacite, epidote, almandine, and hornblende isograds are encountered. Pumpellyite and lawsonite go "out" about where epidote and almandine, respectively, come "in." Figures 72 and 73 illustrate the variation in mineral assemblages with progressive metamorphism.

Black notes that whereas paragonite does not occur in mafic assemblages in low grades, it is stabilized in less aluminous rocks at higher grades by the formation of omphacite + paragonite between the mid-lawsonite and low-epidote zone and by the stability of calcic amphibole + paragonite in the high-grade epidote zone. Concomitantly calcic amphibole changes from actinolite to barroisitic hornblende.

As noted by Coleman (1967) and as may be seen by comparing Figures 71 and 72, low-grade samples in both California and New Caledonia contain pumpellyite, lawsonite, and sphene, while higher-grade samples contain epidote and rutile. Phengitic muscovite, chlorite, and locally stilpnomelane occur in both areas. [Although not shown in Fig. 71, stilpnomelane does occur in Type III metabasalts (Coleman and Lee, 1963, p. 275). Brown and Bradshaw (1979, p. 70) also find that stilpnomelane occurs in Type II samples with high FeO/MgO.] The two terranes are distinct, however, in that calcic amphibole, albite, and paragonite

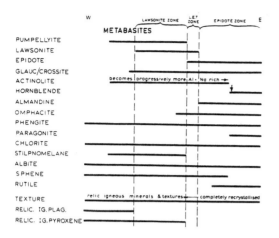

Figure 72. Summary of mineral parageneses and textures in metamorphosed mafic rock from the Ouégoa district, New Caledonia. Weakly metamorphosed rocks crop out in the west (W). Metamorphic grade increases eastward through the lawsonite and lawsonite-epidote transitional (L.E.T.) zones into the epidote zone. From Black (1977, Fig. 2).

occur in the Ouégoa district but not in the Franciscan Complex. Omphacite and aragonite do not occur in the lower-grade glaucophane schists of New Caledonia but are found in California. Aragonite does occur, however, with lawsonite + albite in New Caledonia at a grade lower than where glaucophane is stable (Brothers, 1970).

Oxygen isotope data unquestionably show that metamorphic temperature increases between Types II and IV metabasalt from the Franciscan Formation and from the lawsonite to the epidote zone in New Caledonia. The pioneering work of Taylor and Coleman (1968) yields the following metamorphic temperatures: 170°C for Type II, 270° to 315°C for Type III, and 410° to 535°C for Type IV rocks in California; 165°C and 240°C for lowest-grade rocks in New Caledonia and 410° to 580°C for the highest-grade samples. Black (1974) reports similar temperatures for the Ouégoa district in New Caledonia: 240° to 280°C for weakly metamorphosed sediments, 260° to 340°C in the lawsonite zones, 390°C in the lawsonite-epidote transitional zone, and 410° to 550°C in the epidote zone.

Although the metamorphic temperatures in these two areas are the same, Coleman (1967, p. 486) suggests that the differences in mineral assemblage indicate higher-pressure metamorphism in California than in New Caledonia, and that the low-grade rocks from the latter area may indicate metamorphism transitional between the greenschist and glaucophane schist facies. Pressure estimates made for each area using different criteria are somewhat conflicting (e.g., compare the estimates of Ernst, 1977, Fig. 13b, and Brown and Bradshaw, 1979, Fig. 6, with Ghent and Coleman, 1973). Nevertheless, Coleman (1967, p. 490, Fig. 4) shows that metabasalts in the Franciscan Complex have compositions similar to those in New Caledonia. Therefore, except for temperature, the two areas must

149

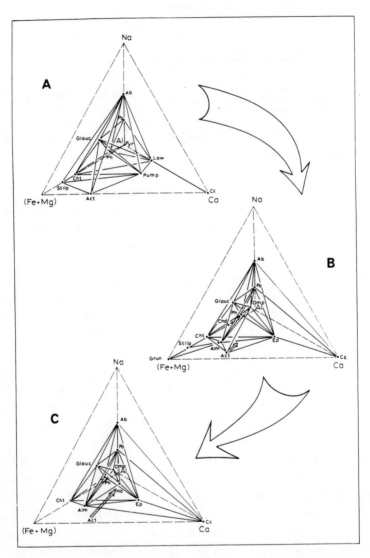

Figure 73. Schematic representation of mineral assemblages, Ouégoa district, New Caledonia. A: mid-lawsonite zone, B: low-grade epidote zone, C: highest grade part of the epidote zone past (East of) the hornblende isograd. Within the epidote zone, calcic amphibole changes from actinolite (B) to hornblende (C). Ab = albite, Act = actinolite, Alm = almandine, Cc = calcite, Cht = chlorite, Chd = chloritoid, Ep = epidote, Glauc = sodic amphibole, Grun = grunerite, Ho = hornblende, Law = lawsonite, Omp = omphacite, Pa = paragonite, Ph = phengite, Pump = pumpellyite, Pyr = pyrophyllite. From Black (1977, Fig. 6).

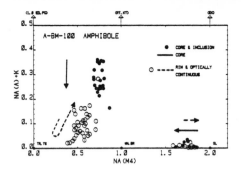

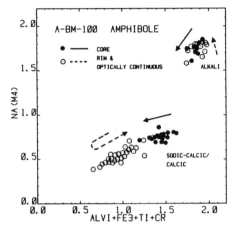

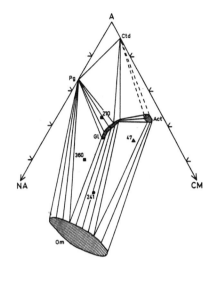

Figure 74. Formula proportion diagrams for sodic-calcic and calcic amphiboles in high-P facies series mafic schist from Vermont. Also included in the assemblage are glaucophane, chlorite, epidote, albite, garnet, omphacite, calcite, phengite, sphene, magnetite, apatite, chalcopyrite, and pyrite. Zoning trends toward grain exteriors are delineated by arrows. From Laird and Albee (1981a, Figs. 3 and 4).

Figure 75. Coexisting mineral compositions (tie lines somewhat schematic) in glaucophane schists and eclogites from the Island of Sifnos, Greece, projected from epidote and garnet onto $Al+Fe^{3+}$ (A); $Na-(Al+Fe^{3+})$ (NA); $Ca+Mg$ (CM). All assemblages contain phengite, quartz, rutile, sphene, apatite, and calcite. Pg = paragonite, Gl = glaucophane, Om = omphacite, Act = actinolite, Ctd = chloritoid. Numbers refer to samples. The only assemblage not observed is Act + Ctd. Tick marks are every 20 atom %. From Schliestedt (1980, Fig. 54).

have formed under different metamorphic conditions to show different mineral assemblages.

De Roever (1955) and many others (e.g., Ernst, 1963a and his later papers; Seki, 1972; Liou *et al.*, 1975) note that lawsonite and epidote are often mutually exclusive in glaucophane schist terranes. As noted above, progressive metamorphism in the Franciscan Complex and New Caledonia has caused lawsonite-bearing assemblages to be replaced by epidote-bearing assemblages at higher temperatures. Pseudomorphs of epidote + white mica $\pm$ quartz after lawsonite in glaucophane-bearing eclogites from Greece (Okrusch *et al.*, 1978) and the Western Alps of Europe (Compagnoni, 1977) support this conclusion.

Black (1977) found that calcic amphibole changes progressively from actinolite to barroisitic hornblende with increasing metamorphic grade. This indicates that, as for medium-P facies series metamorphism (see last section),

151

$NaSiCa_{-1}Al_{-1}$, $NaAlSi_{-1}$, and $Al_2Mg_{-1}Si_{-1}$ [Ca AMP] also increase with T during high-P facies series metamorphism. Consistent with this conclusion is the continuous and discontinuous zoning between actinolite and barroisite in glaucophane schist and glaucophane-bearing eclogite from northern Vermont (Fig. 74).

Chloritoid-bearing glaucophane + epidote schists occur in the Western Alps (Compagnoni, 1977; Desmons, 1977) and in Greece (Schliestedt, 1980). Figure 75 shows the coexisting mineral compositions found in high-P facies series mafic schist from the Greek island of Sifnos.

Estimates of P, T, f_{O_2}, X_{CO_2}, and a_{H_2O}

Delineation of the stability field of glaucophane has historically been a controversial subject. Maresch (1977) reviewed the experimental data and concluded that no one had been able to synthesize pure glaucophane. The suggestion of a polymorphic transition between a glaucophane I at low P and a glaucophane II at higher P (Ernst, 1963b) has not been substantiated (see Thompson, Volume 9A). The two phases produced were different compositions. Glaucophane I was ecker-mannite-"magnesiorichterite"; glaucophane II may have been close to $Na_2Mg_3Al_2Si_8O_{22}(OH)_2$ (Maresch, 1977, p. 118). Maresch's experiments on the maximum stability limits of a natural glaucophane with some $FeMg_{-1}$ and $FeAl_{-1}$ substitution (Fig. 76) indicate that somewhat lower than "normal" geothermal gradients are required to form glaucophane. However, sodic amphiboles richer in Fe^{2+} and Fe^{3+} are stable to low pressures, emphasizing that by themselves, sodic amphiboles other than glaucophane do not indicate high-P facies series metamorphism.

The thermodynamic calculations of Muir Wood (1980) give the P-T grid of Figure 77 for the stability of glaucophane + quartz relative to jadeite, talc, antigorite, and albite. (See also Thompson, Volume 9A, for a discussion of phase relations in $Na_2O-MgO-Al_2O_3-SiO_2-H_2O$ space which are pertinent to glauco-phane schist-eclogite metamorphism.) Muir Wood concluded that glaucophane is stable only at high pressure. From petrologic examination of various glaucophane schists and eclogites, he suggested that in the glaucophane schist facies, magnesioriebeckite is replaced by aegirine + talc, that deerite occurs rather than riebeckite, and that except at low T, almandine occurs instead of ferro-glaucophane.

A summary of other experimental data pertinent to glaucophane schists and eclogites is presented by Ernst (1977). Newton and Fyfe (1976) give an excellent evaluation of these data. Figure 78 shows the experimental results they selected. Recent experimental work and thermodynamic calculations by Holland (1979a), pertinent at higher temperatures, are summarized in Figure 79.

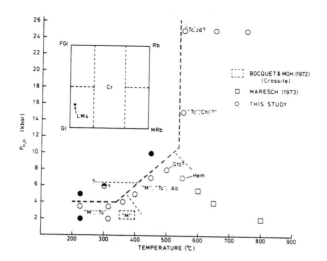

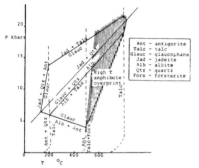

Figure 76 (above). Experimental data on natural glaucophane from Ile de Groix, France. Box inset shows composition of the glauco-phane in terms of the end members glaucophane (Gl), ferroglauco-phane (FGl), riebeckite (Rb), and magnesioriebeckite (MRb). Cr = crossite. Hachured, dashed line indicates maximum possible sta-bility limit of this amphibole. Open symbols = glaucophane breakdown, filled symbols = no change observed, half-fill symbol = equivocal result. Ab = albite, Hem = hematite, Qtz = quartz, "M" = 12.5 or 15 Å layer silicate, "Tc" = 9.4 Å layer silicate, "Chl" = 7 Å layer silicate. From Maresch (1977, Fig. 5).

Figure 77 (to the left). Reaction grid for glaucophane formation calculated from thermodynamic data and placed in P-T space relative to experimentally studied reactions (dashed, dehydration curves; albite = jadeite + quartz). From Muir Wood (1980, Fig. 4).

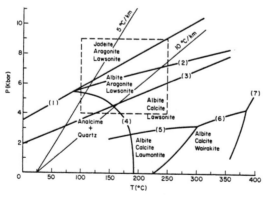

Figure 78. Selected experimental data on reactions pertinent to glaucophane schist metamor-phism. Fields of compatibility of some diagnostic assemblages shown for quartz-excess systems under conditions of $P_{H_2O} = P_{total}$. (1) albite = jadeite + quartz, nearly ordered albite, from Newton and Smith (1967), Hlabse and Kleppa (1968), and Johannes et $al.$ (1971). (2) analcime = jadeite + H_2O from Manghnani (1970). (3) calcite = aragonite from Johannes and Puhan (1971). (4) analcime + quartz = albite + H_2O from Thompson (1971). (5) and (6) laumontite = lawsonite + quartz + H_2O and wairakite = lawsonite + quartz + H_2O respectively, from Liou (1970). (7) dehydration limit of lawsonite after Newton and Kennedy (1963), Crawford and Fyfe (1965), and Nitsch (1972). Suggested P-T conditions for blueschist metamorphism which are compatible with experimental curves and oxygen isotope data delimited by dashed area. From Newton and Fyfe (1976, Fig. 22).

153

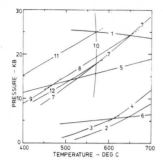

Figure 79. Equilibria in the system Na$_2$O-Al$_2$O$_3$-CaO-FeO-SiO$_2$-H$_2$O involving the **phases paragonite (pg)**, jadeite (jd), kyanite (ky), albite (ab), quartz (qz), **andalusite (an)**, lawsonite (lw), zoisite (zo), **chloritoid (ct)**, almandine (al), corundum (cd), and H$_2$O (v), **from experimental** data and thermodynamic calculations. (1) pg = jd + ky + v, (2) pg = ab + cd + v, (3) pg = ab + an + v, (4) pg + qz = ab + ky + v, (5) jd + qz = ab, (6) ky = an, (7) 4 lw = 2 zo + ky + qz + 7 v, (8) 4 lw + jd = 2 zo + pg + qz + 6 v, (9) 4 lw + ab = 2 zo + pg + 2 qz + 6 v, (10) 3 ct + 2 qz = al + 2 ky + 3 v, (11) 3 ct + 2 jd + 2 qz = al + 2 pg + v, and (12) 8 lw + al = 4 zo + 3 ct + 4 qz + 11 v. From Holland (1979a, Fig. 2).

An early and continuingly important clue that high-P metamorphism is recorded in the Franciscan Complex is that aragonite is widespread. Although experimental data on the calcite-aragonite transition are in some disagreement and Newton and Fyfe (1976, p. 120) feel that all experiments in this system may have had problems in attaining equilibrium, there is at least some convergence in the data of Jamieson (1953), Clark (1957), Crawford and Fyfe (1964), Boettcher and Wyllie (1967, 1968), and Johannes and Puhan (1971). (See Figs. 7 and 8, Newton and Fyfe, 1976, pp. 117, 119, or Fig. 7 in Ernst, 1977, p. 205, for a comparison of the data.) The phase boundary of Johannes and Puhan is in the middle of the data and is shown on Figure 78.

Metamorphic aragonite is not widespread in high-P facies series terranes except in California. However, it does occur with glaucophane, lawsonite, and jadeite-rich pyroxene in southern Italy (de Roever *et al.*, 1976), in lawsonite + albite schist from New Caledonia (Brothers, 1970), and in glaucophane + lawsonite + pumpellyite + chlorite + albite metabasalts from Crete (Seidel and Okrusch, 1976). Calcite occurs in many high-P facies series terranes, some of which may have reached P,T conditions above the calcite to aragonite transition. If ever formed in these areas, aragonite may not have been preserved, as it inverts to calcite at temperatures at about 400°C in only about 100 years (Brown *et al.*, 1962). Only if temperatures decrease rapidly to 200-300°C after formation will it be preserved. Alternatively, aragonite may have inverted to calcite by metamorphism with increasing T (e.g., Brothers, 1970, Fig. 4, p. 199).

Calibration of the stability of jadeite + quartz [reaction (26) above] provides important information on the P,T conditions of glaucophane schists and eclogites. Experimental and calculated curves for this reaction show reasonably good agreement (Fig. 20 in Newton and Fyfe, 1976, p. 20). Recent experimental data of Holland (1980) extend the curve to 1200°C. Isopleths for the omphacite content of the clinopyroxene have been determined experimentally by Kushiro (1969) at high temperatures (1050-1400°C). Holland (1980) does not find a change in

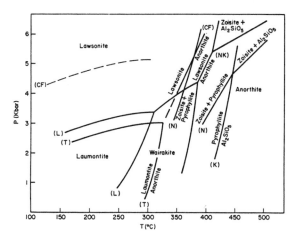

Figure 80. Experimentally determined stability curves of Ca-Al silicate minerals in quartz-excess systems under conditions of $P_{H_2O} = P_{total}$. CF = Crawford and Fyfe (1965), K = Kerrick (1968), L = Liou (1970), N = Nitsch (1971, 1972), NK = Newton and Kennedy (1963), T = Thompson (1970). From Newton and Fyfe (1976, Fig. 15).

slope for the end-member reaction between 600° and 1200°C, and perhaps it is not unreasonable to extrapolate Kushiro's data to lower T, but. . . . Thermodynamic models (Ganguly, 1973) have also been used to estimate isopleths on reaction (26), both on omphacite content and plagioclase content, i.e., along $(CaAlNa_{-1}Si_{-1} + MgSiAl_{-2})$ [CPX] and $CaAlNa_{-1}Si_{-1}$ [PLG].

Although there is a certain amount of disparity among the experimental data (Fig. 80), maximum (or minimum) T estimates may be made for assemblages with (or without) lawsonite using experimental data for the breakdown of lawsonite to anorthite + H_2O or, at higher P, to zoisite + kyanite + quartz + H_2O. Epidote and/or zoisite + paragonite occurs in glaucophane schist and eclogite in New Caledonia (Black, 1977), the Western Alps (Compagnoni, 1977; Reinsch, 1979), Greece (Okrusch et al., 1978; Schliestedt, 1980), and northern Vermont (Laird and Albee, 1981a). Therefore, the reactions

$$4CaAl_2Si_2O_8 \cdot 2H_2O + NaAlSi_3O_8 =$$
$$\text{[LAW]} \qquad\qquad \text{[PLG]}$$

$$2Ca_2Al_3Si_3O_{12}(OH) + NaAl_3Si_3O_{10}(OH)_2 + 2SiO_2 + 6H_2O \qquad\qquad (27)$$
$$\text{[EPI]} \qquad\qquad \text{[PAR]} \qquad\qquad \text{[QTZ]} \quad \text{[ENV]}$$

and
$$4CaAl_2Si_2O_8 \cdot 2H_2O + NaAlSi_2O_6 =$$
$$\text{[LAW]} \qquad\qquad \text{[CPX]}$$

$$2CaAl_3Si_3O_{12}(OH) + NaAl_3Si_3O_{10}(OH)_2 + SiO_2 + 6H_2O \ , \qquad\qquad (28)$$
$$\text{[EPI]} \qquad\qquad \text{[PAR]} \qquad\qquad \text{[QTZ]} \quad \text{[ENV]}$$

which have been calibrated by Holland (1979a) and Franz and Althaus (1977) (see Fig. 79), are helpful in limiting the P and T at which these rocks formed.

155

Oxygen isotope studies have proved very helpful in estimating metamorphic temperatures of high-P facies series metamorphism (as well as medium- and low-P). As discussed above, Taylor and Coleman (1968) and Black (1974) have obtained temperatures between 170° and 340°C for Type II and III glaucophane schists in California and weakly metamorphosed, lawsonite zone, and lawsonite-epidote transitional zones in New Caledonia. These data indicate that the maximum T estimated by Newton and Fyfe (1976) for glaucophane schist metamorphism (Fig. 78) is perhaps 50° to 100°C too low, but this is somewhat of a semantic problem. Oxygen isotope data on Type C eclogites in the Alps and in Venezuela are reported by Vogel and Garlick (1970) and Desmons and O'Neil (1978).

Temperatures may also be estimated from several exchange equilibria which have been calibrated. Råheim and Green (1974) and Ellis and Green (1979) have calibrated experimentally the $FeMg_{-1}$ distribution between garnet and omphacite. Unfortunately, from the point of view of a metamorphic petrologist, these experiments were at high P and T (20 to 40 kbar, 600° to 1500°C, and 24 to 30 kbar, 750° to 1300°C, respectively), and such long, linear extrapolations to temperatures realized in glaucophane schist and Type C eclogite terranes are clearly fraught with danger. (It should be noted that Carpenter (1978, 1979) has discovered omphacites in blueschist from Greece, Turkey, and Guatemala that are not fully ordered and may be metastable.) A thermodynamic model for this exchange equilibrium, useful at P-T conditions more pertinent to glaucophane schists and related eclogites, is presented by Ganguly (1979).

Krogh and Råheim (1978) propose a garnet-phengite geothermometer which is based on phengite compositions in the experimental runs of Råheim and Green (1974) and in a natural sample for which T and P had been estimated independently. Their calculations assumed all Fe was ferrous and thus may be subject to significant error if used for phengites rich in Fe^{3+}.

Muscovite and paragonite may coexist in high-P facies series mafic schist, so that the geothermometer calibrated by Eugster *et al.* (1972) is potentially applicable. One problem is that their thermodynamic calculations were for the end-member compositions and did not consider phengite substitution ($MgSiAl_{-2}$), which is significant in K white mica but not in paragonite from high-P terranes, or $CaAlNa_{-1}Si_{-1}$ substitution, which is greater in paragonite but small in both phases. This may explain why this calibration has yielded geologically unreasonable results for some natural samples (Eugster *et al.*, 1972; Feininger, 1980; Laird and Albee, 1981a). Another geothermometer which may be useful is calcite-dolomite (Bickel and Powell, 1977; Rice, 1977; references therein).

Reactions written earlier (22 and 23) to express the observation that lawsonite, sphene, and pumpellyite break down to epidote, rutile, quartz, and H_2O

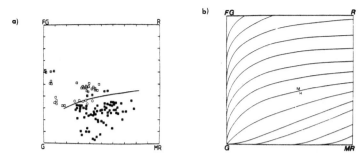

Figure 81. (a) Compositions of sodic amphiboles from glaucophane + lawsonite schist from northwest Turkey, coexisting with hematite (filled squares), hematite and magnetite (open circles), and magnetite (open squares and open squares with dots). (b) Set of oxygen fugacity contours for P-T conditions of these rocks based on determining the hematite (H)/magnetite (M) buffer from (a) and assuming that end member glaucophane (G) is stable over the whole range of f_{O_2}, that ferroglaucophane (FG) and magnesioriebeckite (MR) are stable over a limited range of f_{O_2}, and that an average composition of naturally occurring sodic amphiboles is stable at one f_{O_2}. R = riebeckite. From Okay (1980b, Figs. 3 and 4).

with progressive metamorphism are quite dependent on f_{O_2}, because both LAW and EPI show $FeAl_{-1}$ substitution. Liou *et al.* (1975, p. 106) suggest that high values of f_{O_2} would favor the epidote-bearing assemblage and thus shift any generalized reaction:

$$\text{lawsonite + iron-bearing phase + sphene =}$$
$$\text{epidote + rutile + quartz + H}_2\text{O} \tag{29}$$

to lower T. Ghent and Coleman (1973, see Table 7, #6 and Fig. 3) calculate the following equilibrium constant for reaction (23):

$$5 \log f_{H_2O} = \frac{-16,330}{T} + 38.36 + \frac{0.236(P-1)}{T} . \tag{30}$$

Relative oxygen fugacity may be empirically evaluated in a blueschist terrane at constant T and P (Okay, 1980b) by contouring compositions of sodic amphiboles coexisting with hematite, hematite + magnetite, or magnetite (Fig. 81). Okay (1980b) suggests that the wide variation in sodic amphibole compositions in an area mean f_{O_2} was internally controlled, but that mineral zoning across f_{O_2} contours is due to change during metamorphism. However, other minerals besides sodic amphiboles may be zoned in glaucophane schists, for example, calcic or sodic-calcic amphiboles and epidote. Consequently, $FeAl_{-1}$ and $FeMg_{-1}$ exchange equilibria among these minerals, which are dependent primarily on T, control the zoning. Compositional changes of one mineral may be "absorbed" by others.

X_{CO_2} of the fluid may be evaluated from experimental data on the reaction

$$\text{rutile + calcite + quartz = sphene + CO}_2 \tag{31}$$

(Fig. 82). Relatively low values of X_{CO_2} are implied by the common occurrence of sphene in low-grade glaucophane schists (and in greenschists). Increasing

b)

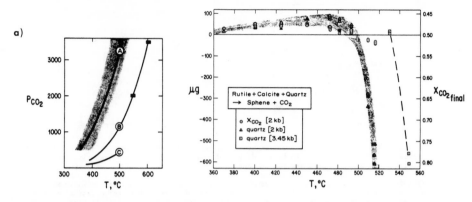

Figure 82. (a) Comparison of data for the reaction rutile + calcite + quartz = sphene + CO_2.
A: Calculated from thermodynamic data. Shaded area represents error bracket. B: Experimental
data from Hunt and Kerrick (1977) extrapolated to X_{CO_2} = 1. C: Experimental data from Schuiling
and Vink (1967). (b) Experimental data from Hunt and Kerrick (1977) showing weight changes (left-
hand scale) of quartz at 2 kbar (points within shaded area) and 3.45 kbar (points connected by
dashed line). Circles refer to the final X_{CO_2} for the 2 kbar runs. From Hunt and Kerrick (1977,
Figs. 1 and 3).

X_{CO_2} may explain the replacement of sphene by rutile observed with progressive
metamorphism of glaucophane schists (and greenschists). Alternatively, because
increasing P_{fluid} stabilizes rutile to lower values of X_{CO_2} and even higher values
of T, rutile may be formed without changing X_{CO_2} by increasing P_{fluid}. Low X_{CO_2}
is further indicated by the experimental work of Nitsch (1972) and Storre and
Nitsch (1972) who show that lawsonite and zoisite are stable with H_2O-rich and
CO_2-poor fluids.

The estimation of a_{H_2O} is a rather "volatile" subject, especially in connection with the formation of Type C eclogites. Omphacite + garnet + quartz
assemblages with hydrous minerals (amphiboles, lawsonite, epidote, chlorite,
white mica) occur. These assemblages appear to be in equilibrium, with different
assemblages being explained by small differences in rock composition (Figs. 70
and 75). Fry and Fyfe (1971; see also Newton and Fyfe, 1976) and Ghent and
Coleman (1973) point out that hydrous minerals in a rock need not imply high
P_{H_2O}. Fry and Fyfe (1971) suggest that NaCl- and KCl-rich fluids may have been
present during metamorphism of glaucophane schist, so that a_{H_2O} was low. Black
(1977) concluded that the fluid phase was diluted with CO_2 during high-P facies
series metamorphism in New Caledonia. However, fluid inclusion studies on Type
B eclogites from the Tauern Window, Austria (Holland, 1979b, p. 21) imply
salinities less than 2 wt % NaCl equivalent and H_2O-rich fluids with X_{CO_2} less
than 0.1. Others (e.g., Brown and Bradshaw, 1979; Schliestedt, 1980) have
appealed to high values of a_{H_2O} during metamorphism of glaucophane-bearing
schists and eclogites.

There commonly are many potentially useful geothermometers, geobarometers, and geohygrometers in glaucophane schists and eclogites, but because rocks have a habit of being "dirty," different criteria for estimating T and P have commonly given conflicting results and lead to different geological interpretations. P_{total} estimates are typically well below lithostatic pressures estimated from density and thickness data (Coleman, 1967, p. 495; Black, 1974, 1977, p. 101). Thus, the geological problems of forming and exhuming glaucophane schists and related eclogites will long survive this review.

ORTHOAMPHIBOLE AND CUMMINGTONITE AMPHIBOLITES

Introduction

Since Eskola's classic study of the Orijärvi region of southwestern Finland (Eskola, 1914), there have been a great number of studies of the phase relations and mineral chemistry of low-Ca amphibolites. Low-Ca amphibolites, as used in this paper, are rocks that are characterized by the presence of orthoamphiboles (one or two) or cummingtonite coexisting with phases such as cordierite, garnet, staurolite, aluminosilicate, talc, chlorite, spinel, orthopyroxene, hornblende, plagioclase, or quartz. Thus, these rocks are distinct from more typical meta-morphosed basalts, which contain abundant calcic phases such as carbonates or epidote, or iron formations, which are typically very low in Al and do not contain orthoamphiboles or other aluminous phases (see previous sections of this chapter).

One of the motivations for studying these rocks, in addition to an inherent proclivity among petrologists to study exotic mineral assemblages, is that the thermodynamic variance of mineral assemblages found in low-Ca amphibolites is typically much lower than the variance of mineral assemblages from normal meta-morphosed basalts. Hence, orthoamphibole- and cummingtonite-bearing rocks can yield considerable information about conditions of metamorphism and are poten-tially quite useful for the delineation of metamorphic facies.

This report will cover theories for the origin of these rocks, techniques for graphical analysis, phase relations of selected occurrences, and petrogenetic grids. Significant references on the phase relations of low-Ca amphibolites include Robinson and Jaffe (1969a,b), Robinson *et al.* (1969), Tilley (1937, 1939), Stout (1971, 1972), Sampson and Fawcett (1977), James *et al.* (1978), Clark (1978), Gable and Sims (1970), Beeson (1978), Savolahti (1966), Goroshnikov and Yur'yev (1965), Lal and Moorhouse (1968), Kamineni (1975), Hietanen (1959), Lal (1969), Abraham and Schreyer (1973), and Froese (1969).

Origin of cordierite-anthophyllite rocks

The origin of rocks containing dominantly cordierite + anthophyllite has been the subject of considerable discussion in the literature (e.g., Eskola, 1914; Tilley and Flett, 1929; Wegmann and Kranck, 1931; Tilley, 1935; Tuominen and Mikkola, 1950; Seki, 1957; Floyd, 1965; Vallance, 1967; Chinner and Fox, 1974). The debate centers around an observation succinctly phrased by Seki (1957, p. 336): "Chemically similar rocks are not known among igneous, sedimentary, or metamorphic types." This statement of Seki could be modified in light of the interpretation made by Schreyer and Abraham (1976) and Schreyer (1977) that "whiteschists" from Afghanistan, which are characteristically low in Fe and include orthoamphibole rocks, are metamorphosed evaporite deposits. Comparison of whole-rock analyses of evaporitic mudstones to those of the "whiteschists" show that both rocks possess similar Mg- and Al-rich bulk chemistries. Because most orthoamphibole rocks are more Fe-rich than the "whiteschists," such an evaporite protolith could explain the origin of only a small number of orthoamphibole occurrences.

Anthophyllite-cordierite rocks are characterized by a pronounced depletion in Ca and alkalis (notably K) and an enrichment in mafic components (notably Mg relative to Al). Hypotheses as to the origin of these rocks fall into three main categories:

(1) Metasomatic alteration during metamorphism. This hypothesis can be subdivided into

    (a) introduction of Fe, Mg, and Al and/or loss of complementary elements (e.g., Ca). This model has had particular appeal in contact metamorphic environments, where the metasomatism may originate from a nearby granite.

    (b) metasomatic redistribution of Fe, Mg, Ca (and Al?) during metamorphism via an unknown mechanism.

(2) Metamorphism of rocks that already reached appropriate composition prior to metamorphism by a variety of processes. These may include original igneous rocks or sedimentary rocks derived by weathering, erosion, and redeposition of volcanic material (Robinson and Jaffe, 1969a). The processes involved may include:

    (a) sub-aerial weathering;

    (b) deuteric alteration by late-stage magmatic fluids;

    (c) hydrothermal alteration by seawater.

(3) Residuum of a partial melt.

It should be emphasized from the outset that no one hypothesis can account for all of the occurrences of cordierite. However, similarity of bulk rock

compositions from widely dispersed areas and the common stratigraphic environment
(i.e., interbedded with amphibolites of primary basaltic composition) suggests
that many occurrences may have a similar origin. Pros and cons of the different
models are discussed below.

The metasomatic origin was first postulated by Eskola (1914), who envisioned
introduction of Fe and Mg in the contact aureole of Orijärvi. Tilley (1935)
favored metasomatic removal of Ca, but in earlier work (Tilley and Flett, 1929)
postulated a premetamorphic atmospheric weathering of original mafic and ultramafic rocks. The principal reason for Tilley's change of view was the absence of
any known weathering phenomenon that would produce the necessary chemical alteration. Four problems are associated with the metasomatism hypothesis: (1) Field
relations are generally inconsistent with metasomatism from a single source. In
many occurrences, unaltered rocks are interbedded (on a scale of tens of meters)
with altered rocks; (2) metasomatism typically results in high variance, dimineralic
assemblages (e.g., Thompson, 1970), and cordierite-anthophyllite rocks typically
contain quartz, cummingtonite, plagioclase, spinel, chlorite, Fe-Ti oxides,
biotite, or talc, in assemblages that are often rather low variance; (3) typical
late-stage deuteric fluids from granitic intrusions are not known to be enriched
in Mg and Fe; and (4) cordierite-anthophyllite rocks are commonly found in
regionally metamorphosed terrains where no obvious source of metasomatising fluids
is evident. Based on these observations, it is clear that synmetamorphic metasomatism cannot account for a large number of occurrences of cordierite-anthophyllite rocks, although metasomatism may have affected chemical compositions
locally.

A pre-metamorphic origin for bulk compositions giving rise to cordierite-
anthophyllite rocks has been proposed by Tilley and Flett (1929), Vallance (1967),
and Chinner and Fox (1974). As mentioned above, Tilley and Flett's notion of
sub-aerial weathering was abandoned, owing to lack of a known mechanism. Vallance
(1967) pointed out the chemical equivalence of the assemblage of chlorite + quartz
clots in altered basalt to the higher-grade assemblage cordierite + anthophyllite
and demonstrated a thermal metamorphic change from chlorite + quartz clots in
altered basaltic rocks to aggregates of cordierite + anthophyllite. Vallance
also compared major element chemistry of altered mafic volcanic rocks to bulk
compositions of cordierite-anthophyllite rocks and found that the range of bulk
compositions common to cordierite-anthophyllite rocks could indeed be produced
by such hydrothermal alteration. Froese (1969) thinks that chloritic alteration
of mafic rocks provides a suitable protolith for cordierite-anthophyllite rocks
found at the Coronation Mine, Saskatchewan, and suggests that because these rocks

are spatially related to the ore body, alteration probably accompanied minerali-zation that occurred prior to metamorphism. Chinner and Fox (1974) noted the diversity of mineral assemblages found in cordierite + anthophyllite rocks from the Land's End aureole, and especially the fact that some rocks are silica under-saturated (i.e., spinel- and corundum-bearing) and some are silica saturated (quartz-bearing). They concluded that the rocks could not have attained their bulk composition from synmetamorphic metasomatism and concurred with the model of Vallance of a low-temperature hydrothermal origin.

The bulk of the field and chemical data indicate that most cordierite-anthophyllite rocks attained their bulk composition prior to metamorphism. One mechanism, similar to that proposed by Vallance, is that of hydrothermal altera-tion by seawater. It is now well established that in oceanic ridge and island arc environments, large-scale hydrothermal circulation cells involving seawater occur. The limited amount of experimental data on basalt-seawater interaction involving major element chemical changes in basalt indicates that when large seawater/basalt ratios are employed, the basalt is readily depleted in Ca and K and enriched in Mg (e.g., Humphris and Thompson, 1978). Na may also be enriched in the basalt. Moreover, studies such as those of Mottl (1976), Humphris and Thompson (1978), and Rona *et al.* (1980) demonstrate similar changes in dredged basalts that have undergone seawater alteration. The extent of alteration should depend entirely on the local access of seawater, which is probably dominated by the local fracture density. In this way, altered volcanics could easily be interbedded with unaltered rock, consistent with many field observations.

Whole-rock analyses of amphibolites of basaltic composition, orthoamphi-bolites, and cordierite-staurolite-gedrite rocks from central Massachusetts and southwestern New Hampshire (Schumacher, 1981a) show that rocks containing the "aluminous" assemblages are depleted in Ca and enriched to various degrees in Mg relative to rocks with "primary" basaltic chemistries. Al in all the rock types shows little variability. With respect to these elements, the chemistry of orthoamphibole rocks from these localities behaves like that of the hydrothermally altered basalts studied by Humphris and Thompson (1978).

The seawater alteration hypothesis is attractive, but it has not yet been proved. If true, it might be possible to map the distribution of fossil hydro-thermal systems based on the occurrence of cordierite-anthophyllite rocks. This might have important consequences with respect to prospecting for massive sulfide deposits that are believed to be intimately associated with hydrothermal cells involving seawater (e.g., Galapagos rift, 22°N, Dymond *et al.*, 1976).

Grant (1968) and Hoffer and Grant (1980) have suggested that bulk composi-tions similar to the bulk compositions of some cordierite-anthophyllite rocks could be residua of partial melts. This hypothesis could be attractive in certain multiply metamorphosed terranes, but most orthoamphibole-cordierite localities show little compelling evidence that P-T conditions sufficient to initiate partial melting and form the residua existed prior to orthoamphibole formation.

<u>Graphical analysis of low-Ca amphibolites</u>

The major element chemistry of many orthoamphibole-bearing rocks can be described by the system $SiO_2-Al_2O_3-TiO_2-Fe_2O_3-MgO-FeO-CaO-Na_2O-K_2O-H_2O$. If certain assumptions are made, this system can be reduced to a tractable number of components amenable to graphical analysis.

Biotite is the only phase present in the rocks that contains appreciable K_2O, and potassium can be omitted from the list by assuming that all available K_2O will be used to form this mica. Similarly, TiO_2 forms Fe-Ti oxide phases (rutile in Mg-rich bulk compositions and ilmenite in Fe-rich compositions). TiO_2 does enter orthoamphiboles to a limited degree, but to a first approximation can be omitted from the list. Fe_2O_3 can enter gedrite in appreciable quantities (e.g., Lal and Morehouse, 1968, report a gedrite with 6.5 wt % Fe_2O_3), but many orthoamphiboles contain limited amounts of ferric iron (less than 10% of the total iron) and Fe_2O_3 can be omitted to a first approximation. This leaves SiO_2-Al_2O_3-MgO-FeO-CaO-Na_2O-H_2O as a model chemical system to describe orthoamphibole-bearing rocks.

Many such rocks are quartz-bearing and, in this case, projection from SiO_2 may be employed. In silica-undersaturated situations (e.g., spinel-bearing or corundum-bearing) SiO_2 must be retained as a component. CaO and Na_2O pose special problems. Many orthoamphibole-bearing rocks contain very low bulk CaO-contents, and in some cases CaO can be omitted from the list. However, Spear (1977, 1980) and Schumacher (1981b) have found that the bulk CaO/Na_2O ratio can drastically influence the observed phase relations. Specifically, when sufficient CaO is present, hornblende + plagioclase may be stable with orthoamphiboles. In rocks with little CaO, plagioclase (oligoclase or andesine) may or may not be present. It is prudent to consider carefully the phases present in each assemblage before resorting to graphical analysis. Several procedures have been presented in the literature.

Robinson and Jaffe (1969b) and Stout (1972) have utilized a projection through plagioclase, quartz, and H_2O onto a plane with the coordinates A = Al_2O_3 - Na_2O - CaO; F = FeO + MnO; and M = MgO (Fig. 83). This diagram can be expanded to account for Fe_2O_3 and TiO_2 by using the coordinates A = Al_2O_3 + Fe_2O_3 + $2TiO_2$ - Na_2O - CaO; F = FeO + MnO - TiO_2; M = MgO. This projection adequately describes

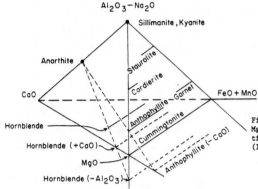

Figure 83. The tetrahedron (Al$_2$O$_3$–Na$_2$O), CaO, MgO, (FeO+MnO) depicting the plagioclase projection of Robinson and Jaffe (1969b) and Stout (1972). Taken from Robinson and Jaffe (1969b).

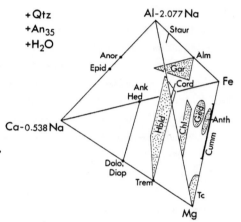

Figure 84. The tetrahedron Ca'-Al'-Fe'-Mg' showing the plagioclase (An$_{35}$) projection of Spear (1977). Qtz = quartz, An$_{35}$ = plagioclase, Anor = anorthite, Epid = epidote, Staur = staurolite, Alm = almandine, Gar = garnet, Ank = ankerite, Hed = hedenbergite, Dolo = dolomite, Diop = diopside, Cord = cordierite, Chl = chlorite, Hbld = hornblende, Ged = gedrite, Anth = anthophyllite, Cumm = cummingtonite, Trem = tremolite, and Tc = talc.

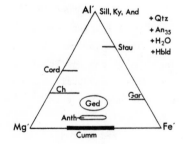

Figure 85. Plotting positions of minerals projected from quartz, plagioclase (An$_{35}$), hornblende, and H$_2$O. Note that anorthite projects through infinity. Epidote (not shown) also projects through infinity and would plot just above anorthite. Abbreviations as in Figure 85, except Ch = chlorite, Stau = staurolite, Sill, Ky, And = aluminosilicates.

164

phase assemblages in quartz-plagioclase-bearing rocks, so long as hornblende is not found coexisting with highly aluminous phases such as staurolite, cordierite, or aluminosilicate. The effect of projecting onto Al_2O_3 - $(CaO + Na_2O)$ is to lump $CaO + Na_2O$ as a single component and thus obscure the important effect of variable CaO/Na_2O on the phase relations. Spear (1977) has suggested an alternative projection for similar rocks from plagioclase (andesine), quartz, and H_2O into the tetrahedron $CaO-Al_2O_3-FeO-MgO$ (Fig. 84). This projection can be thought of as an A-C-F diagram in which Fe and Mg are expanded into two components, with the understanding that andesine does not plot on the diagram. In rocks where two plagioclase feldspars coexist (e.g., Spear, 1977), the high-An feldspars will plot on the diagram. The plotting coordinates for minerals on this diagram (projected from An_{35}) are Fe' = Fe, Mg' = Mg, Al' = Al - 2.077 Na, and Ca' = Ca - 0.538Na. Thus, phases that have a Ca/Na less than 0.538 (such as gedrite) will plot negatively with respect to Ca'.

From Figure 84 it is seen that in rocks with sufficient CaO, hornblende may coexist with cummingtonite, anthophyllite, gedrite, or more aluminous phases such as staurolite, cordierite, or aluminosilicate. For the special case of hornblende-bearing rocks, phases that plot near the A-F-M face of the tetrahedron can be thought of as being saturated with Ca/Na (that is, they contain the maximum Ca/Na at that particular metamorphic grade). For such rocks, a projection through an "average" hornblende composition can be employed, resulting in an A-F-M triangle similar to Figure 85, but with the understanding that hornblende is present in all assemblages (see Fig. 84). For rocks that do not contain hornblende, the Ca/Na ratio is not constrained, and phase relations must be considered in the tetrahedron Ca'-Al'-Fe'-Mg' or, alternatively, Na'-Al'-Fe'-Mg' (projected from plagioclase + quartz + H_2O).

If it is desired to examine the relationship between plagioclase composition and coexisting silicates, quartz-bearing samples can be represented in the tetrahedron Al-Ca-Na-(Fe+Mg). This representation obscures the important effect of Fe-Mg solid solution, but inasmuch as many reactions in these rocks involve plagioclase, this diagram is useful for visualizing such reactions.

Quartz-absent assemblages can be represented by projection from plagioclase into the tetrahedron Si-Al-(Ca or Na)-(Fe+Mg) or, as has been done by Robinson and Jaffe (1969a), represented in the plane $SiO_2-(MgO+FeO)-Al_2O_3$ or projected from aluminosilicate onto the plane $SiO_2-FeO-MgO$ in the tetrahedron $Al_2O_3-SiO_2-FeO-MgO$.

Petrogenetic grids

Three petrogenetic grids for orthoamphibole-bearing assemblages have been presented in the literature (Robinson and Jaffe, 1969b; Spear, 1978; Percival and Helmstaedt, 1979; see also Froese, 1969; Trzcienski, 1971; Carmichael *et al.*, 1978). The third reference has been published only in abstract form. Grant (1973) also discusses some reactions involving orthoamphiboles. Each of these studies displays certain features of orthoamphibole paragenesis, but each is incomplete in some way. Two complicating factors are (1) the rocks under consideration are not easily amenable to graphical analysis, and (2) many of the reactions encountered in this system are continuous reactions. Both factors complicate any attempt at Schreinemakers' analysis.

The grid of Robinson and Jaffe (1969b) considers quartz-saturated phase relations in the system $SiO_2-Al_2O_3-FeO-MgO-H_2O$. Phases considered include sillimanite, kyanite, staurolite, cordierite, garnet, aluminous anthophyllite, and cummingtonite. The orthoamphibole was considered to be supersolvus, and no reactions involving plagioclase, chlorite, or hornblende were considered. The grid of Spear (1977) for rocks containing quartz, plagioclase, and hornblende in the system $SiO_2-Al_2O_3-MgO-FeO-CaO-Na_2O-H_2O$ includes the phases kyanite, staurolite, cordierite, garnet, chlorite, gedrite, anthophyllite, and cummingtonite. Orthoamphiboles were treated as two phases, and no supersolvus reactions were considered. The grid of Grant (1973) is principally concerned with pelitic assemblages, and the grid of Percival and Helmstaedt (1979) is derived for low-potash pelites.

Although different in many respects, all of these grids do show some features in common. If democracy has any relevance to scientific truth, then we may take these features as representing, at least to a first approximation, a reasonable guess at the correct answer. Specifically, all of these grids show orthoamphibole + aluminosilicate to be a relatively high-pressure occurrence, the equivalent low-pressure assemblage being staurolite + cordierite + orthoamphibole at low temperatures and garnet + cordierite + orthoamphibole at higher temperatures. This rudimentary demarcation enables relative evaluation of the P-T conditions of several common assemblages. The staurolite + cordierite + gedrite assemblage of Spear (1977) must have formed at lower temperatures than the cordierite + garnet + gedrite assemblage of Stout (1972). Similarly, the staurolite + gedrite + kyanite + sillimanite assemblage from the "Amphibole Hill" area (Robinson and Jaffe, 1969a,b) must have formed at higher pressures than either of these other assemblages. Another assemblage thought to form at low pressure is cummingtonite + cordierite ± anthophyllite ± gedrite, as reported by Eskola (1914) and

Schneiderman (1981) at Orijärvi and by Tella and Eade (1978) in the Churchill
Province, District of Keewatin.

Considerably more work needs to be done towards deriving a valid petrogenetic
grid for orthoamphibole-bearing rocks. Such a grid should incorporate details
of the orthoamphibole solvus, as well as reactions that form and destroy orthoamphiboles.

Phase relations

This section covers some of the features of the phase relations and progressive metamorphism of the orthoamphibole-bearing rocks. Rather than attempting
to reconcile the large number of reported assemblages, a few well characterized
areas are discussed in detail, specifically those reported by Robinson and Jaffe
(1969a,b), Stout (1972), Spear (1977, 1978), and Schumacher (unpublished data).

Low-grade assemblages and orthoamphibole-forming reactions. Amphibolites
of the greenschist facies do not typically contain orthoamphiboles; these minerals
first appear in the lower amphibolite facies.

In the Post Pond Volcanics, west-central New Hampshire, orthoamphiboles
first appear at conditions just below the staurolite isograd. Low-grade (bio-
tite-zone) assemblages are typically chlorite + epidote + albite + actinolite
(or hornblende) + quartz $\pm$ carbonates. This assemblage is shown in a series of
three diagrams in Figure 86A. The large volume occupied by the assemblage
chlorite + epidote + actinolite + albite can be seen in Figure 86A1; hence, most
typical metamorphosed basalts will contain this assemblage at low grades.
Another assemblage, chlorite + albite + actinolite + cummingtonite, is possible
in Al- and Ca-poor rocks, but it has not as yet been reported. The disposition
of these two assemblages with respect to Fe/Mg can be seen in Figure 86A2, which
is a projection from albite into the tetrahedron Fe-Mg-Ca-Al. Both assemblages
should span a range of Fe/Mg. Figure 86A3 is a projection from Ca-amphibole
onto the triangle Fe-Mg-Al. Note that epidote projects negatively. Fe-rich
amphibolites may contain stilpnomelane, but a question mark has been shown in
Figure 86A3 (see Harte and Graham, 1975). From these three diagrams it can be
seen that the mineralogy of most greenschist facies amphibolites should be rather
simple.

At the slightly higher grade of the garnet-oligoclase zone, phase relations
of the Post Pond Volcanics are shown in Figure 86B. It is significant that the
plagioclase coexisting with chlorite + Ca-amphibole (now hornblende) is oligo-
clase/andesine, rather than albite. Moreover, garnet is now present, resulting
in the assemblage chlorite + garnet + cummingtonite + hornblende + oligoclase.
Garnet has been omitted from Figure 86B1 for clarity, but this assemblage can be

167

seen as a tetrahedral volume in Figure 86B2 and as the three-phase triangle in Figure 86B3. The assemblages chlorite + hornblende + epidote and chlorite + hornblende + cummingtonite are still present in magnesian rocks.

The composition fields for gedrite and anthophyllite are specified in Figure 86B1. Both minerals plot very close to the Na-Al-(Fe+Mg) plane because of their low CaO contents. Note that the plagioclase associated with the assemblage chlorite + cummingtonite has changed from albite to oligoclase, enabling the formation of orthoamphibole via a reaction such as chlorite + cummingtonite + albite = orthoamphibole + H_2O. Experimental studies on the stability of ortho-amphibole indicate that aluminous gedrite can be synthesized from chlorite + quartz, but not without small amounts of Na_2O present (see Gilbert *et al.*, Chapter 9, this volume). Natural gedrites invariably contain some sodium; hence, the reaction cited above is preferred for the formation of orthoamphibole in real rocks. The first appearance of gedrite should, in any case, occur in rocks that are very low in CaO, and not with calcic amphibole. Figure 86B2 shows a field for the assemblage gedrite + cummingtonite + chlorite + garnet (note that gedrite plots negatively with respect to Ca in this projection because of the excess of Na/Ca in gedrite). Hornblende-bearing assemblages are those shown in Figure 86B3.

The first appearance of orthoamphibole with calcic amphibole occurs via the reaction

chlorite + cummingtonite + plagioclase $\pm$ garnet → orthoamphibole + hornblende + H_2O

These relations can be viewed in Figure 86C1, where the assemblages gedrite + hornblende + chlorite + plagioclase and gedrite + hornblende + cummingtonite + plagioclase are represented as four-phase volumes. Garnet may also be present in Fe-rich compositions. The assemblage chlorite + hornblende + epidote + plagioclase is still stable, but only in rocks high in Ca and Al. Expansion of Fe and Mg as two components (Figs. 86C2 and C3) reveals that an additional phase can be stable with hornblende + gedrite, resulting in the three three-phase triangles shown around gedrite in Figure 86C3. (The assemblage gedrite + horn-blende + cummingtonite + garnet has been omitted from Fig. 86C2 for clarity.) These assemblages are found in the Post Pond and Ammonoosuc Volcanics near the staurolite isograd. Note that the association chlorite + garnet + epidote (Fig. 86C2) precludes hornblende from coexisting with staurolite at this grade. Gedrite, however, may coexist with staurolite in an assemblage such as chlorite + garnet + gedrite + staurolite in rocks sufficiently low in CaO. It should also be noted that a second orthoamphibole, anthophyllite, may also be present, plotting in Figure 86C3 between cummingtonite and gedrite, but has been omitted for clarity.

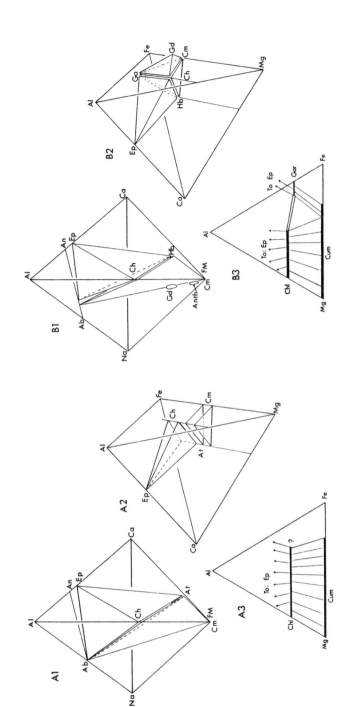

Figure 86 A. Phase diagrams depicting assemblages from the chlorite-biotite zone in the Post Pond Volcanics, New Hampshire and Vermont. A1: projection from quartz and H₂O into the tetrahedron Al-Na-Ca-(Fe+Mg). A2: projection from quartz, plagioclase, and H₂O into the tetrahedron Al-Ca-Fe-Mg. A3: projection from quartz, plagioclase, hornblende, and H₂O onto the plane Al-Fe-Mg. Abbreviations are Ep = epidote, Ab = albite, An = Anor = anorthite, Cm = Cum = cummingtonite, Gd = G = gedrite, Ga = Gar = garnet, Ch = Chl = chlorite, St = Stau = staurolite, Hb = hornblende, At = actinolite, and Anth = anthophyllite.

Figure 86 B. Phase diagrams depicting assemblages from the garnet-oligoclase zone in the Post Pond Volcanics, New Hampshire and Vermont. B1: projection from quartz and H₂O into the tetrahedron Al-Na-Ca-(Fe+Mg). B2: projection from quartz, plagioclase, and H₂O into the tetrahedron Al-Ca-Fe-Mg. B3: projection from quartz, plagioclase, hornblende, and H₂O onto the plane Al-Fe-Mg. For abbreviations see Figure 86 A.

169

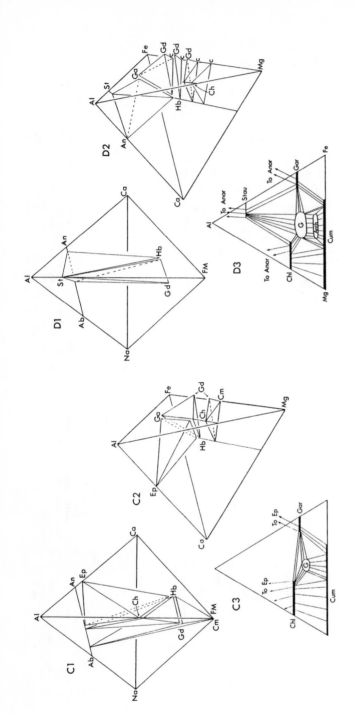

Figure 86 C. Phase diagrams depicting assemblages from the staurolite isograd in the Post Pond Volcanics, New Hampshire and Vermont. C1: projection from quartz and H2O into the tetrahedron Al-Na-Ca-(Fe+Mg). C2: projection from quartz, plagioclase, and H2O into the tetrahedron Al-Ca-Fe-Mg. C3: projection from quartz, plagioclase, hornblende, and H2O onto the plane Al-Fe-Mg. For abbreviations see Figure 86 A.

Figure 86 D. Phase diagrams depicting assemblages from the middle of the staurolite-kyanite zone in the Post Pond Volcanics, New Hampshire and Vermont. D1: projection from quartz and H2O into the tetrahedron Al-Na-Ca-(Fe+Mg). D2: projection from quartz, plagioclase, and H2O into the tetrahedron Al-Ca-Fe-Mg (c = cummingtonite). D3: projection from quartz, plagioclase, hornblende, and H2O onto the plane Al-Fe-Mg. For abbreviations see Figure 86 A.

At conditions equivalent to the middle of the staurolite-kyanite zone, phase relations in the Post Pond Volcanics are as shown in Figure 86D. Epidote has been replaced in aluminous rocks by anorthite (An_{87-92}) and two plagioclase feldspars coexist ($An_{40} + An_{87}$) (Fig. 86D1). Chlorite is absent in all but the most magnesian rocks, and the join chlorite + garnet has been replaced by gedrite + staurolite and hornblende + staurolite in Fe-rich rocks. This gives rise to a large number of four-phase volumes, some of which are shown in Figure 86D2; i.e., hornblende + garnet + staurolite + anorthite; hornblende + garnet + gedrite + cummingtonite (or anthophyllite); hornblende + gedrite + garnet + staurolite (not shown in Fig. 86D2); the four-amphibole assemblage hornblende + cummingtonite + gedrite + anthophyllite; and in Mg-rich rocks, hornblende + gedrite + cummingtonite + chlorite. Notably absent at this metamorphic grade is the association hornblende + cordierite; this assemblage is precluded because of the stable association chlorite + staurolite + anorthite in magnesian rocks.

It should be noted that there is also an abundance of hornblende-absent assemblages that occur in the Post Pond Volcanics at this grade. These assemblages include the phases cordierite, staurolite, gedrite, anthophyllite, chlorite, talc, and wonesite (see Footnote 9), and all plot on the magnesian side of the Al-Fe-Mg face of Figure 86D2 and negatively with respect to Ca. Small variations in the bulk Na/Ca ratio of a rock can therefore have a great effect on the observed mineral assemblage. The result is that a rather bewildering number of relatively low-variance mineral assemblages are possible in these rocks in the lower to middle amphibolite facies.

Medium-grade assemblages. Mineral compositions and phase relations for amphibole assemblages from high in the kyanite-staurolite zone and low in the sillimanite-staurolite-muscovite zone from central Massachusetts (Schumacher, unpublished data) are shown in Figure 87, and those from the lower sillimanite zone from Telemark, Norway (Stout, 1972), are shown in Figure 88. As in the middle of the kyanite-staurolite zone, the orthoamphibole solvus remains open. Two hornblende-cummingtonite-orthoamphibole assemblages appear to contain orthoamphiboles from different limbs of the solvus (Fig. 87). Ratios of $(Fe^{2+} + Mn)/$ $(Fe^{2+} + Mn + Mg)$ for corresponding amphiboles in both of these assemblages are similar; however, the hornblende and the cummingtonite in the assemblage with the gedrite[22] are more aluminous than their counterparts in the assemblage with the anthophyllite. These two three-amphibole assemblages most likely result from slight differences of Al in the bulk composition and suggest that a four-amphibole

----

[22]This orthoamphibole lies in the "gedrite" phase region shown in Figure 87 but contains <1.0 tetrahedral Al, so that it is actually an anthophyllite according to I.M.A. nomenclature (Leake, 1968).

171

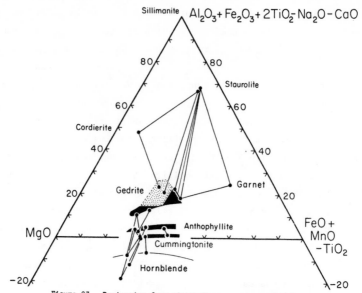

Figure 87. Projection from plagioclase, quartz, and H_2O onto the plane $(Al_2O_3+Fe_2O_3+2TiO_2-Na_2O-CaO)$, $(FeO+MnO-TiO_2)$, MgO for orthoamphibole and cummingtonite assemblages from high in the kyanite-staurolite zone and low in the silli-manite-staurolite-muscovite zone of central Massachusetts.

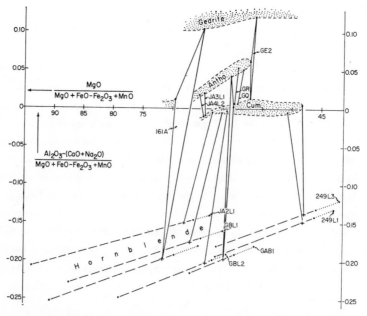

Figure 88. Plagioclase projection of phase relations of amphibolites from Telemark, Norway. Taken from Stout (1972).

172

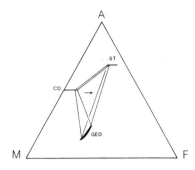

Figure 89. Projection from plagioclase, quartz, and H_2O onto the A-F-M plane, depicting the continuous reaction leading to the development of Na- and Al-rich gedrite. ST = staurolite, CD = cordierite, and GED = gedrite. The arrow represents the direction the reaction is proceeding with increasing temperature.

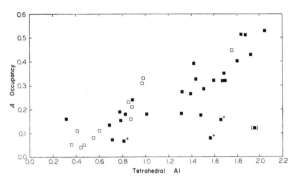

Figure 90. Plot of A-site occupancy versus tetrahedral Al for published orthoamphibole analyses. Taken from Robinson *et al.* (1971b).

assemblage containing hornblende, cummingtonite, and two orthoamphiboles could be present in rocks of appropriate bulk composition at this metamorphic grade. This four-amphibole assemblage is reported by Stout (1971, 1972) in sillimanite-grade rocks from Telemark, Norway.

One significant difference between orthoamphibole amphibolites from the lower sillimanite zone and those from the kyanite-staurolite zone described by Spear (1980) is that the stable association of staurolite and hornblende is absent at higher grade. A reaction such as hornblende + staurolite = orthoamphibole + garnet + plagioclase would prevent tie lines between hornblende and more aluminous phases for Fe-rich bulk compositions.

In rocks with more Al-rich bulk compositions, orthoamphibole assemblages are gedrite-staurolite-cordierite, gedrite-staurolite-garnet, and gedrite-cordierite (Fig. 87). The gedrite in the cordierite assemblage in Figure 87 is highly zoned, and the extent of the zoning is represented by the stippled pattern. Tie lines connect closest gedrite analyses from the zoned grains to staurolite and cordierite compositions. The most aluminous of these gedrite analyses represent the most aluminous and sodic orthoamphiboles yet reported (Schumacher, 1980). Total Fe content of the zoned grains remains nearly constant, but Na and Al vary inversely with Si and Mg. This compositional variation may have resulted from the following continuous reaction: Al-poor gedrite + staurolite + Na-plagioclase → Al-richer gedrite + cordierite + Ca-richer plagioclase, schematically shown in Figure 89.

Substitutions of Na and Al in gedrite. A survey of published analyses of orthoamphiboles by Robinson *et al.* (1971b) showed an essential coupling of A-site occupancy and tetrahedral Al (as well as octahedral R^{3+}), as illustrated in

Figure 90 (see also Figs. 10B, 12B, and 14). These relationships have been explored in detail in several highly zoned gedrite grains in a cordierite-staurolite assemblage (see Figs. 87 and 89) in the lower part of the sillimanite-muscovite-staurolite zone from central Massachusetts.

Figure 91 shows analysis points and contour maps for Na in the A-site and tetrahedral Al for one of these zoned gedrite grains (GED 1). Correspondence of "regional highs and lows" in both of the contour maps reflects systematic variations in the amounts of edenite-tschermakite substitutions. The contouring also shows the irregularity of the zoning. Regions relatively high in Na and Al grade either gently or abruptly into regions of low Na and Al (Figs. 91B,C). The most aluminous and sodic parts of the grain tend to be in the interior of the grain, and the small staurolite inclusions appear to exercise no control over the composition. Another interesting feature of this grain are the two small anthophyllite overgrowths (Fig. 91). The three anthophyllite analyses from these grains are very similar, which suggests both overgrowths formed under similar conditions.

The compositions of the anthophyllites are shown on a plot of A-site occupancy versus tetrahedral Al (Fig. 92). The tie line connects an anthophyllite analysis with the closest gedrite analysis. It should be noted that due to the high variability and very small scale of the zoning, the actual composition of gedrite at the contact with the anthophyllite may be slightly different, and the contour lines at this contact and at the edge of the rest of the grain are highly interpretive.

The extensive zoning in these grains appears to result from retrograding the Na- and Al-rich gedrite and the cordierite, which can be thought of as reversing the direction of the continuous prograde reaction shown in Figure 89. This explanation would also account for small subhedral staurolite inclusions found in the zoned grains (Fig. 91B,C). Anthophyllite overgrowths may have formed when the retrograde composition of gedrite became sufficiently low in Al and Na to encounter the orthoamphibole solvus.

Analyses from several zoned gedrite grains of extreme Al and Na content from central Massachusetts (Schumacher, 1980) and for zoned gedrite of extreme Na content from Labrador (Berg and Wiebe, 1978; Berg, pers. comm., 1981) are shown on the plot of A-site occupancy versus tetrahedral Al in Figure 92. This plot reflects the relative amounts of edenite and tschermaks substitution [Al^{IV}-(A-site) and Al^{IV}-Al^{VI}, respectively], which are the two principal substitution mechanisms causing Na and Al variations in orthoamphiboles. Robinson *et al.* (1971b) have shown that in most natural orthoamphiboles the ratio of A-site occupancy to tetrahedral Al is about 1/4 (Fig. 90), leading to an "ideal gedrite" $Na_{0.5}Fe_2^{2+}Mg_{3.5}Al_{1.5}Si_6Al_2O_{22}(OH)_2$.

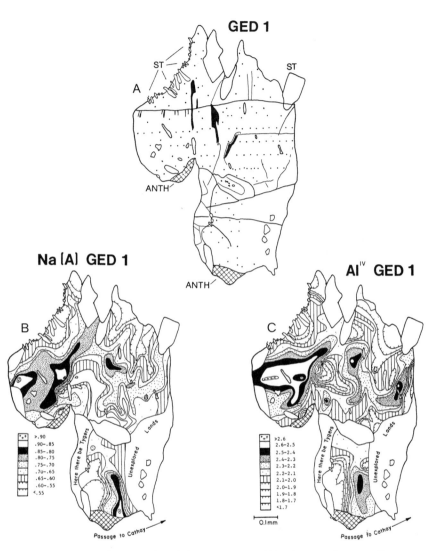

Figure 91. Zoned gedrite grain (GED 1) from low in the sillimanite-muscovite-staurolite zone, central Massachusetts. (A) Location of analysis points. Closed lines represent subhedral staurolite inclusions (some labelled ST). Black lines and patches represent cracks and small areas not suitable for analysis. Cross-hatched areas (labelled ANTH) are anthophyllite overgrowths. Areas which lie outside the main body of analysis points and were not analyzed did not have suitable surfaces. (B) Contour map of Na in the A-site. Contours are in intervals of 0.05 Na in the formula (see legend adjacent to map). (C) Contour map of tetrahedral Al. Contours are in intervals of 0.1 Al in the formula (see legend adjacent to map). All ferrous formulae were used unless this allowed Ca in the A-site, then the 15eNK correction (see "Formulation of electron probe analyses," this chapter) was applied, resulting in minimum ferric estimates for all formulae. Most of the analyses required some correction. (Schumacher, 1980, and unpublished.)

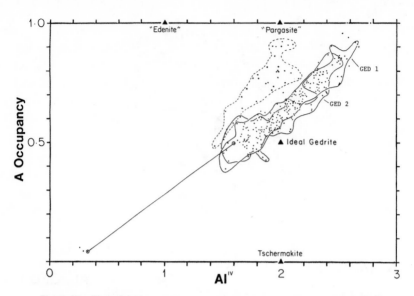

Figure 92. Plot of A-site occupancy versus tetrahedral Al for zoned orthoamphibole grains from central Massachusetts (Schumacher, 1980) and Labrador (Berg and Wiebe, 1978; Berg, pers. comm., 1981). Solid lines enclose areas that show the limit of compositional variation within two mapped grains (GED 1 and GED 2) from central Massachusetts. Dashed line encloses the area that shows the limit of compositional variation in the gedrite from Labrador. Points outside the lines are analyses from grains other than GED 1 and 2 but from the same sample. Tie line connects the analysis of an anthophyllite overgrowth to the closest gedrite analysis.

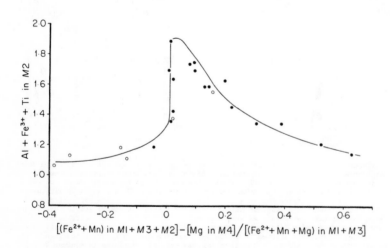

Figure 93. Plot of Al + Fe^{3+} + Ti in M2 versus $(Fe^{2+}+Mn)/(Fe^{2+}+Mn+Mg)$ in M1 plus M3 (see Fig. 25) for orthoamphiboles coexisting with cordierite and/or staurolite. Closed symbols represent microprobe analyses to which either no ferric corrections or minimum ferric corrections have been applied. Open symbols represent wet chemical analyses. Data from Beeson (1978), Robinson and Jaffe (1969b), Spear (1980), Berg and Wiebe (1978), Schumacher (1980), and Schumacher (unpublished data).

The zoned grains in Figure 92 maintain A-site to tetrahedral Al ratios of about 1.0/2.3, reflecting a significant change in the proportions of the two sub stitutions for high Na values (above 0.5 in the A-site). The most sodic gedrite analysis from Labrador approaches the orthoamphibole equivalent of pargasite ("pargasite" in Fig. 92), which has an ideal end-member composition of $NaMg_6Al$ $Si_6Al_2O_{22}(OH)_2$ and is called "sodium gedrite" according to the I.M.A. nomenclature (Leake, 1978). The most aluminous and sodic orthoamphibole analyses from central Massachusetts approach a tetrahedral Al content of 3 and an A-site occupancy of 1 (see Fig. 92), representing completion of both the tschermakite-like and edenite-like substitutions. This suggests an ideal end composition of $NaMg_5Al_2Si_5Al_3O_{22}$ $(OH)_2$, which falls well outside the classification scheme of the I.M.A. nomen-clature (Leake, 1978).

Figure 93 is a plot of octahedral $Al + Fe^{3+} + Ti$ versus $Fe^{2+}/(Fe^{2+} + Mg)$ in M1 plus M3 sites (see Fig. 25) for gedrites coexisting with cordierite and/or stauro-lite. R^{3+} content in M2 peaks as the Fe/Mg ratio in M1 plus M3 approaches zero, which represents the point at which these sites are filled with Mg. One explana-tion for this correlation might be that as the M1 and M3 octahedra fill with Mg, the mean cation size decreases, collapsing the structure somewhat. This may pro-mote a reduction in the mean cation size in M2, which is accomplished by replacing Mg by Al or to a lesser extent Fe^{3+} and Ti. For Mg-rich gedrites with Fe/Mg ratios in M1 and M3 of less than zero, Mg *must* reside in the large M4 site. This accompanies a dramatic reduction of $Al + Fe^{3+} + Ti$ in M2. It may be that placing Mg in the large M4 site requires that significantly more of the tetrahedral sites adjoining M4 be filled with smaller Si atoms. If this is the case, it might explain the decrease of tschermaks component accompanying the entry of Mg into M4 (Fig. 93) and the lower A-site values (edenite component) observed by Spear (1980) for Mg-rich orthoamphiboles. Thus, Fe/Mg ratio of aluminous orthoamphiboles may play a large part in determining the extent to which tschermakite-type substitu-tions can occur.

High-grade assemblages. Orthoamphibole rocks from "Amphibole Hill," south-western New Hampshire (Robinson and Jaffe, 1969b; Schumacher, unpublished data), which occur at higher metamorphic grade in the middle of the sillimanite-musco-vite-staurolite zone than the assemblages from central Massachusetts and Telemark, Norway, have some important distinctions. At this grade, gedrite coexists with aluminosilicate (Fig. 94). Preliminary petrogenetic grids for orthoamphibole rocks presented by Robinson and Jaffe (1969b) and Spear (1978) show kyanite (sill) + gedrite to be favored over staurolite + cordierite at higher pressure. Another distinction is that orthoamphiboles from this region were above the

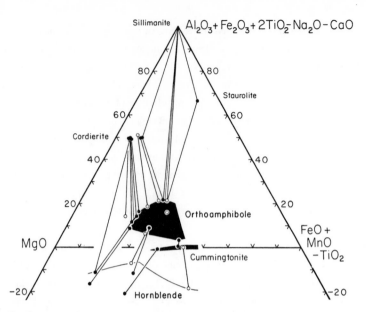

Figure 94. Projection from quartz, plagioclase, and H2O onto the plane (Al2O3+Fe2O3+2TiO2 Na2O-CaO), (FeO+MnO-TiO2), MgO for assemblages from the middle of the sillimanite-muscovite-staurolite zone at "Amphibole Hill," southwestern New Hampshire.

orthoamphibole solvus (Robinson *et al.*, 1971b). Orthoamphiboles of appropriate compositions show various degrees of exsolution, which resulted from encountering the solvus upon cooling.

Although a cummingtonite-hornblende-anthophyllite assemblage has not been found at "Amphibole Hill," its position on Figure 94 is constrained by the assemblages hornblende-cummingtonite and hornblende-anthophyllite.

Figure 95 shows representative mineral assemblages from "Amphibole Hill" in an AFMC tetrahedron. As seen in sample I34I, for Fe-rich and aluminous bulk compositions, staurolite-sillimanite-gedrite is the stable assemblage. Another layer in this sample where the bulk composition was slightly more Mg-rich contains the assemblage cordierite-sillimanite-gedrite. Both of these assemblages occur without plagioclase, but the addition of plagioclase should not affect the Fe-Mg ratios. It would, however, turn these assemblages into four-phase volumes. ·For more Mg-rich rocks, sillimanite disappears and the assemblage becomes cordierite-gedrite-plagioclase, as shown in samples 7AOBX and I34JX (Fig. 95). The most Mg-rich rocks have the uncommon three-phase assemblage of hornblende-cordierite-gedrite (Fig. 95, sample I34GXS-2), and the two-phase assemblage gedrite-cordierite (Fig. 95, sample W95JX). Viewing these two assemblages in the AFMC tetrahedron (Fig. 95) is more satisfactory than using a plagioclase projection (Fig. 94), because neither I34GXS-2 nor W95JX occur with plagioclase, and all the assemblages show consistent Fe-Mg ratios when viewed in the tetrahedron. In both

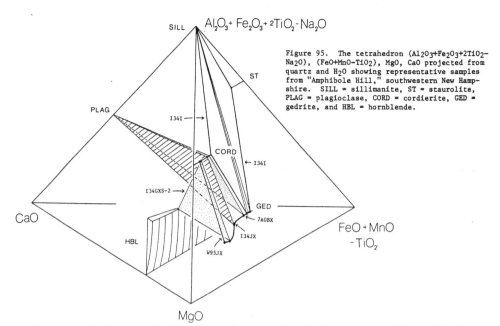

Figure 95. The tetrahedron $(Al_2O_3+Fe_2O_3+2TiO_2-Na_2O)$, $(FeO+MnO-TiO_2)$, MgO, CaO projected from quartz and H_2O showing representative samples from "Amphibole Hill," southwestern New Hampshire. SILL = sillimanite, ST = staurolite, PLAG = plagioclase, CORD = cordierite, GED = gedrite, and HBL = hornblende.

projections it is seen that in order for hornblende to coexist with cordierite (or aluminosilicate), as in sample I34GXS-2, the bulk composition must be Mg-rich.

In these rocks, the Na/Ca ratio also becomes a critical factor in determining the mineral assemblage. The effects of varying the Na/Ca ratios are illustrated in the AFCN tetrahedron shown in Figure 96. The plagioclase in the

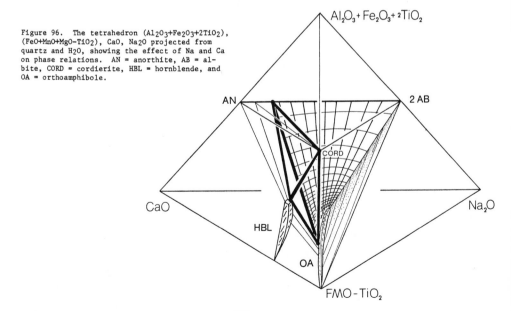

Figure 96. The tetrahedron $(Al_2O_3+Fe_2O_3+2TiO_2)$, $(FeO+MnO+MgO-TiO_2)$, CaO, Na_2O projected from quartz and H_2O, showing the effect of Na and Ca on phase relations. AN = anorthite, AB = albite, CORD = cordierite, HBL = hornblende, and OA = orthoamphibole.

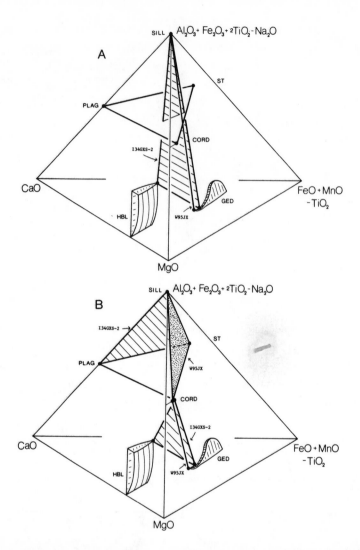

Figure 97. Tetrahedra ($Al_2O_3+Fe_2O_3+2TiO_2-Na_2O$), ($FeO+MnO-TiO_2$), MgO, CaO depicting enclave development at "Amphibole Hill," southwestern New Hampshire. A: the reaction relationships for two pre-enclave assemblages (I34GXS-2 and W95JX). B: assemblages both inside and outside enclaves after the enclave-forming reactions. Abbreviations as in Figure 95. Because quartz is not present in the assemblages, this figure can only represent these relations schematically, and the effect of SiO_2 is not treated.

four-phase volume outlined with heavy tie lines represents the critical plagioclase composition at which the four phases hornblende, cordierite, gedrite, and plagioclase coexist. This assemblage would be very sensitive to changes in the

Na/Ca ratio. Increasing the proportion of Na would move the bulk composition into the three-phase field consisting of cordierite, orthoamphibole, and plagioclase more sodic than the plagioclase of the four-phase assemblage. Increasing the proportion of Ca would move the bulk composition into one of three possible three-phase assemblages: (1) hornblende, cordierite, and plagioclase more calcic than the plagioclase of the four-phase assemblage; (2) hornblende, orthoamphibole, and plagioclase more calcic than the plagioclase of the four-phase assemblage; and (3) hornblende, cordierite, and orthoamphibole, the assemblage found on "Amphibole Hill" (Schumacher, 1981b).

Another interesting feature seen in some orthoamphibole rocks from higher in the sillimanite zone is the development of aluminous enclaves, of which there are two main types. Both kinds of enclaves contain some combination of the aluminous minerals sillimanite, kyanite, corundum, staurolite, sapphirine, and spinel set in a matrix of cordierite or of calcic plagioclase, which is itself surrounded by cordierite (Robinson and Jaffe, 1969a; Schumacher, 1981c). The presence of corundum in some assemblages demonstrates that the amount of SiO_2 also determines the phase assemblage (Robinson and Jaffe, 1969a). Because cordierite has such a high SiO_2 content, corundum can be produced in relatively silicious rocks by reactions such as gedrite + sillimanite $\rightarrow$ cordierite + corundum + H_2O (Schreyer and Siefert, 1969). For the general case covered here, staurolite and sillimanite will be used to represent the aluminous minerals. None of the aluminous minerals or the plagioclase surrounding the aluminous minerals are in contact with the orthoamphibole that makes up the bulk of the rock. Textural evidence suggests that sillimanite found at the cores of enclaves is a relict of an earlier assemblage of sillimanite + orthoamphibole, which is illustrated with sample W95JX in Figure 97A. Enclaves in these rocks appear to have formed by a reaction such as:

sillimanite + orthoamphibole = cordierite + staurolite .

This reaction is schematically represented by crossing tie lines in Figure 97A and would have proceeded until the sillimanite and the orthoamphibole lost communication. The result is two sets of assemblages: (1) the enclave assemblage consisting of relict sillimanite, staurolite, and cordierite, and (2) the assemblage outside the enclave consisting of orthoamphibole and cordierite. Both assemblages have cordierite of the same composition and are shown by sample W95JX in Figure 97B.

The genesis of the plagioclase-bearing enclaves is more complex. In rocks containing this type of enclave, sparse pargasitic hornblende is found outside the enclaves. The pre-enclave assemblage was probably sillimanite-hornblende-orthoamphibole, shown by sample I34GXS-2 in Figure 97A. Enclaves in these rocks could have formed by the following reaction:

sillimanite + hornblende + orthoamphibole =
calcic plagioclase + staurolite + cordierite .

This reaction is schematically represented in Figure 97A by the crossing planes and would have proceeded until communication was lost between sillimanite and hornblende and between sillimanite and orthoamphibole. The result is three sets of assemblages: (1) the enclave assemblage consisting of sillimanite and staurolite enclosed by plagioclase; (2) the assemblage outside the enclave consisting of hornblende, orthoamphibole, and cordierite; and (3) the two-phase assemblage joining assemblages (1) and (2), which consists of cordierite and plagioclase. All three assemblages are shown for sample I34GXS-2 in Figure 97B. Robinson and Jaffe (1969a) have suggested that the enclave-forming (cordierite-forming) reactions occurred during uplift and unloading associated with emplacement of the Keene gneiss dome during late stages of Acadian (Devonian) deformation and regional metamorphism.

METAMORPHOSED IGNEOUS ROCKS AT HIGH TEMPERATURE: THE BREAKDOWN OF AMPHIBOLES

Just as amphiboles may be formed at low temperatures by the breakdown of more hydrous phases (Fig. 7), so they may break down to combinations of less hydrous phases (Fig. 6) either at high temperature or under conditions where the activity of H_2O has been lowered by an increase of another species in the fluid, such as CO_2 (Touret, 1974; Blattner, 1976). The breakdown of hornblende by the generalized reaction

hornblende + quartz = orthopyroxene + augite + plagioclase + H_2O

is commonly recognized as separating two subfacies of the granulite facies. This was explored by Buddington (1963), Engel *et al.* (1964), de Waard (1965), Binns (1965a,b), and many others. The many difficulties with it are discussed at some length by Turner (1968), Winkler (1979), and especially by Dobretsov *et al.* (1972). The last, in particular, emphasize the strong dependence of this reaction on the Fe/Mg ratio of the ferromagnesian silicates and the Na/Ca ratio of the plagioclase. Unfortunately, due to the chemographic complexity of hornblende reactions in such rocks, petrologists have tended to turn their efforts in geothermometry and geobarometry toward simpler mineral assemblages and pairs including opaque oxides, sulfides, feldspars, garnet, biotite, cordierite, Al-silicates, pyroxenes, and quartz-orthopyroxene-olivine, as done in the Adirondacks by Buddington and Lindsley (1964), Bohlen and Essene (1977, 1980), Brown *et al.* (1978), Stoddard (1980), Bohlen *et al.* (1980), and Jaffe *et al.* (1978).

Alternatively, igneous or high-grade metamorphic rocks without hydrous phases may acquire them through aqueous metasomatism, either during falling temperature associated with an earlier peak of igneous or metamorphic activity, or during a separate episode of metamorphism under more hydrous conditions than those of the earlier events. Some examples of the production of amphibolites from pyroxene gabbro or pyroxene granulite include the formation of hornblende-garnet gneiss on the margins of metamorphosed gabbro dikes in South Norway (Brøgger, 1934; Bugge, 1943) and the formation of hornblende gneiss from a pyroxene monzodiorite intrusion in the Belchertown Complex, central Massachusetts (Hall, 1973; Ashwal, 1974; Ashwal *et al.*, 1979), and the Adamant Pluton, British Columbia (Shaw, 1978). In general, the reactions associated with such high-temperature aqueous metasomatism are very similar to high-temperature prograde metamorphic dehydration reactions, except that they run in the reverse sense. The occurrences of such amphibolites formed by hydration support the view that amphibolites and pyroxene granulites can form under identical conditions of pressure and temperature and differ only in activity of H_2O. This view is supported by work in the Adirondacks of Buddington (1963), who describes felsic plutonic bodies subjected to identical pressure and temperature regional metamorphic conditions that have identical bulk chemical compositions, except that some are nearly devoid of H_2O, whereas others are H_2O-bearing. The former have recrystallized to orthopyroxene-augite-garnet granulites, the latter to hornblende-bearing granulites. Buddington considers the differences in H_2O content to have been preserved from the original plutons emplaced into H_2O-poor country rocks. Similar occurrences are described at some length by Dobretsov *et al.* (1972). However, they seem to doubt that such local H_2O activity gradients can be maintained under high-grade metamorphic conditions, but offer no clear alternative. The view of Buddington is reinforced by abundant high-T experimental work (see Gilbert *et al.*, Chapter 9, this volume; Yoder and Tilley, 1962; and so on) showing amphiboles on the liquidus at modest to high H_2O pressures. Whether the amphibole assemblage is prograde or formed by retrograde hydration reactions is not particularly important to learning the nature of the reaction involved.

General chemography

Among the common dehydration breakdown products of amphibole in metamorphosed igneous rocks are plagioclase, quartz, augite, orthopyroxene, garnet,
ilmenite, magnetite, and K-feldspar. Less common breakdown products include
cordierite, sapphirine, spinel, sillimanite, olivine, nepheline, and rutile.
Many of the reactions can be graphically visualized using figures illustrating
the amphibole composition volume, such as Figure 6, Figure 9, and Figure 13, which
contain, in principle, all of the components of the minerals involved. For
example, in addition to the S = Si component, not shown in Figure 13, the A
component contains Al, Fe^{3+}, and Ti^{4+}, the NC component contains Na and Ca, and
the FM component contains Fe^{2+}, Mg, and Mn. Naturally, the lumping of these
components in this way cannot permit an examination of the intimate details of
amphibole breakdown reactions. Nevertheless, a judicious successive splitting
of various parts of these can go far toward giving a graphical image of the
principles involved for those many petrologists without the necessary mathematical background to solve the problems "directly" in abstract n-dimensional
space.

In one version of Figure 13, the N and C components are separated to form
an A-N-C-FM tetrahedron, which can then be simplified by projecting all compositions from the N (albite) apex onto the A-C-FM face. The development and use of
this projection[23] by Goldschmidt (1911) and Eskola (1915) represents one of the
major steps in the understanding of metamorphosed igneous rocks and metamorphism
in general, even though it has been subjected to considerable careless use not
envisioned by the originators. Many of Eskola's ideas were developed during his
study of the Orijärvi area, Finland (1914), one of the classic areas of amphibole
rocks in Europe.

A chief drawback of the A-C-F diagram is that it cannot illustrate the Na
contents of plagioclase or amphiboles, either hornblende or gedrite. Earlier
we demonstrated that any important substitution of Al, Fe^{3+}, or Ti is *always*
accompanied by some Na. A second and better understood drawback is that the
diagram cannot distinguish minerals with different Fe/Mg ratios. This can only
be overcome by splitting FM to form an A-C-F-M tetrahedron. A third drawback
is that the diagram cannot distinguish minerals with different ratios of
Fe^{3+}/Al (or different amounts of $2Ti^{4+}$). This could be overcome by creating an
Al-Fe^{3+}-C-FM tetrahedron. How well metamorphic petrology would be served if we

----

[23]The ACF diagram as originally used was based on the oxides, rather than the
cations as here. The albite projection is achieved by subtracting Na_2O from
Al_2O_3, rather than Na from Al as here.

could all develop the mental capacity to split all the A-C-F components into at least two more and to visualize tie lines in six-, seven-, or eight-dimensional space, without resorting to the use of a computer, as has been done successfully by Greenwood (1975)! With these drawbacks clearly in mind, A-C-F diagrams nevertheless provide useful guides to important assemblages in amphibolites. Each ACF diagram should be thought of as a crude slice through the multicomponent system, usually passing through the amphibole composition volume and giving totally inadequate portrayal of plagioclase composition.

Figure 98 shows a series of such diagrams with increasing metamorphic grade for typical Mg-rich (a) and intermediate to Fe-rich (b) mafic igneous rocks that gives a crude picture of amphibole breakdown reactions. In Figure 98A, which can be considered as typical of the amphibolite facies, hornblendes in Mg-rich rocks (a) occur in five kinds of assemblages: (1) with diopside in calc-silicate rocks; (2) with diopside and plagioclase, with or without epidote, in Ca-rich amphibolites; (3) with plagioclase only in many amphibolites; (4) with plagio- clase and anthophyllite in Al-rich or Ca-poor amphibolites; and (5) with antho- phyllite only in metamorphosed ultramafic rocks. In the same range orthoamphi- boles occur with hornblende alone (5) in ultramafic rocks, with hornblende and plagioclase (4) in low-Ca amphibolites, with plagioclase alone (6) in very low- Ca amphibolites, and with cordierite $\pm$ plagioclase $\pm$ Al-silicate (7) in unusually low-Ca, high-Al rocks (see previous section). For more Fe-rich bulk compositions, the chief differences are that the role of orthoamphibole is largely taken over by cummingtonite, although Fe-rich gedrite may still be present; the role of cordierite is largely taken over by garnet, and staurolite appears near Al- silicate in the highly aluminous region.

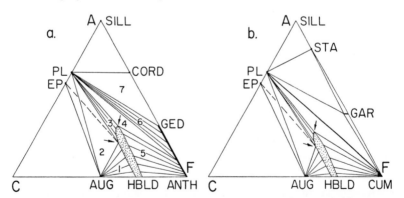

Figure 98 A. ACF diagrams depicting typical phase relations for Mg-rich (a) and intermediate to Fe-rich (b) rocks in the amphibolite facies. SILL = sillimanite, PL = plagioclase, EP = epidote, CORD = cordierite, GED = gedrite, ANTH = antho- phyllite, HBLD = hornblende, AUG = augite (and diopside), STA = staurolite, GAR = garnet, and OPX = orthopyroxene.

185

Figure 98A also illustrates the general nature of some continuous metamorphic reactions that may change amphibole compositions. In assemblage (2) the hornblende may be expected to move to lower Al *and* probably lower Ca, dehydrating to produce more diopside and plagioclase. Assemblage (4) contains the most Al-rich hornblende. Increasing T or dehydration will cause the hornblende to retreat to lower Al content, producing more plagioclase and anthophyllite (and a lower net amount of amphibole). At the same time, the anthophyllite should be expected to decrease in Al content. This continuous reaction is not only a dehydration, but also transfers substantial amounts of Al from octahedral coordination in hornblende to tetrahedral coordination in plagioclase, permitting a substantial increase in entropy (Albee, 1965; see also Hall, 1970). The continuous reaction in assemblage (2) is substantially the same for more Fe-rich compositions, but in assemblage (4), where cummingtonite takes the place of orthoamphibole, the effects described are even more pronounced. This is because cummingtonite, as compared to orthoamphibole, contains virtually no Al, so that all of the Al lost from hornblende *must* go to tetrahedral coordination in plagioclase.

Figure 98B illustrates the same chemical space with several substantial changes that are present at the amphibolite → pyroxene granulite facies transition. The low-Al end of the calcic amphibole field (i.e., actinolite) has broken down to produce augite plus an Fe-Mg silicate. Cameron (1975) has shown that for an intermediate Fe-Mg ratio, cummingtonite is this reaction product and that the reaction takes place at about 600°C in the presence of excess H_2O at P_{fluid} = 2000 bars. The second important change from Figure 98A is that at higher temperatures, cummingtonite and anthophyllite have dehydrated to produce orthopyroxene, with a small field of gedrite still remaining. This new state of affairs, with a new hornblende-augite-orthopyroxene triangle, means that the field of hornblende is now isolated on three sides. The reaction triangle of calcareous amphibolites remains topologically unchanged, and hornblendes associated with plagioclase and augite should continue to decrease in Al content. In the field of low-Ca amphibolites, the place of anthophyllite and cummingtonite is now taken by orthopyroxene. This means that the previously described continuous reactions that reduce the Al-rich limit of the hornblende field and produce plagioclase and Fe-Mg amphibole plus H_2O are replaced by a reaction producing plagioclase and *Fe-Mg pyroxene* plus *much more* H_2O. Thus, the appearance of orthopyroxene at the FM apex of this triangle should lead to much more dramatic reduction in the height of the hornblende field. The new assemblage hornblende-augite-orthopyroxene provides a lower limit on the Al content of hornblende and

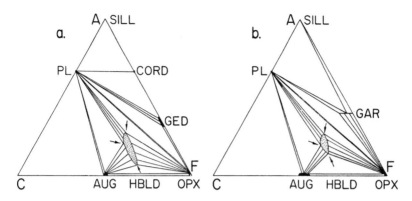

Figure 98 B. ACF diagrams depicting typical phase relations for Mg-rich (a) and intermediate to Fe-rich (b) rocks in the amphibolite facies-pyroxene granulite facies transition. Abbreviations as in Figure 98 A.

a new continuous dehydration reaction by which hornblende loses its actinolite component to augite and orthopyroxene. By this time, it is obvious that hornblende is surrounded by its enemies and it is only a matter of time and temperature until its field shrinks to zero and it is gone!

It may be well to pause here to point out that the aluminous component that is being lost from hornblende in reactions described above is an Al-tschermakite-like component with octahedral Al balanced by tetrahedral Al and also with significant Na in the A-site, as well as some Na in M4. The reactions produce major amounts of plagioclase component, with remaining Fe, Mg, and/or Ca going to pyroxene. The one reaction that increases the aluminous component does so merely by depleting the amount of simple Ca, Mg, Fe amphibole component to produce pyroxenes. However, for dehydration reactions involving the analogous Fe^{3+}-tschermakite-like component and the Ti-tschermakite-like component (plus quartz), the picture is somewhat different for several reasons: (1) the dehydration reactions produce significant amounts of magnetite, hematite, ilmenite, or rutile in addition to one or more pyroxenes and plagioclase (derived from tetrahedral Al); and (2) the entropy effect of changing Al from octahedral coordination in amphibole to tetrahedral coordination in plagioclase is absent. Instead, the comparison is between Fe^{3+} or Ti^{4+} in octahedral positions in amphibole versus the same ions in octahedral positions in oxide minerals (or tetrahedral positions for Fe^{3+} in magnetite). Thus, the entropy effect for changing R^{3+} coordination is far less obvious for Fe^{3+} and Ti^{4+} than for Al^{3+}, and, particularly for Ti^{4+}, may work in the opposite direction. From this perspective it is interesting that the calcic amphibole with the largest amount of octahedral Al is from very low in the amphibolite facies (Table 2, this chapter), whereas the

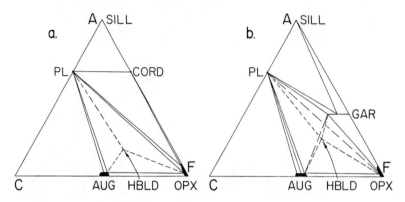

Figure 98 C. ACF diagrams depicting typical phase relations for Mg-rich (a) and intermediate to Fe-rich (b) rocks in the pyroxene granulite facies close to the ultimate breakdown of hornblende. Abbreviations as in Figure 98 A.

most titanian calcic amphiboles are from igneous rocks. A number of studies have recorded a progressive decrease in Al-tschermakite substitution commonly coupled with increasing Fe^{3+}-tschermakite, Ti-tschermakite, pargasite, and K-pargasite substitutions with increasing metamorphic grade (Binns, 1965b; Engel and Engel, 1962).

In Figure 98C we see the hornblende fields greatly reduced by the reactions described above and nearing final destruction. For Mg-rich rocks (a) this will be by the reaction

hornblende + quartz = orthopyroxene + augite + plagioclase + H_2O .

For Fe-rich rocks (b) the exact reaction will depend on the arrangement of tie lines to garnet. In both cases, if there is hornblende left after destruction of quartz, further dehydration will produce olivine from orthopyroxene until all hornblende is used up (see Spear, 1981, for example). All orthoamphibole is gone in Figure 98C; the last orthoamphibole is probably a low-Al gedrite reacting with quartz to produce orthopyroxene, cordierite, and garnet. Dobretsov *et al.* (1972) note that gedrite may persist to higher grade in the absence of quartz in assemblages with sapphirine and/or spinel. The detailed saga of these last amphiboles, including the various compositional tricks they use to stay around longer, is a subject that needs to be explored briefly here and in much more detail in future research.

Breakdown of Fe-Mg amphiboles

As shown in Figure 98A, the Fe-Mg amphiboles occur with hornblende in various low-Ca amphibolites and in a variety of low-Ca, high-Al, and high-Fe-Mg bulk compositions produced in a variety of ways. The story of their breakdown is a continuation of the story of their genesis and evolution, as presented in

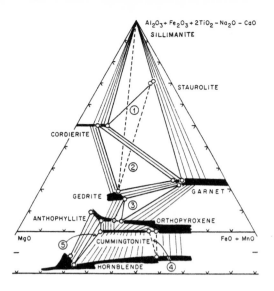

Figure 99. Plagioclase projection in the modified system $Al_2O_3-MgO-FeO+MnO-CaO$ onto the A-F-M plane for assemblages in the sillimanite-orthoclase zone of central Massachusetts. From Robinson and Tracy (1979).

the section "Orthoamphibole and Cummingtonite Amphibolites." For the present purpose, the same plagioclase projection onto the A-F-M triangle provides a useful starting point.

Figure 99 is such a plagioclase projection prepared from a limited number of electron probe analyses reported by Robinson and Tracy (1979). The samples were collected entirely within metamorphic zone V, as defined for pelitic schists in central Massachusetts by Tracy *et al.* (1976). This zone lies just above the terminal breakdown of muscovite (see Tracy, 1978), and pelitic schists are characterized by the assemblage quartz-sillimanite-K feldspar-garnet-biotite-plagioclase-ilmenite-graphite ± pyrrhotite.

The assemblages illustrated in Figure 99 certainly did not all come from exactly the same metamorphic grade. Aside from the deficiencies of the plagioclase projection employed, some of the assemblages do not contain quartz, and one anthophyllite-hornblende assemblage has no plagioclase. Nevertheless, the figure does provide a crude road map of some of the reactions in progress in these high-grade rocks. Assemblage (1) in Figure 99, sillimanite-cordierite-staurolite-garnet-plagioclase-biotite, comes from a rather odd low-K schist. Garnet is probably present as a fourth phase because of minor spessartine and grossular substitution. The appearance of staurolite at such a high grade is at first surprising, because the locality is many miles away from the point where staurolite breaks down in pelitic schists by the generalized reaction muscovite + staurolite + quartz = biotite + garnet + sillimanite + H_2O. However, at this high grade staurolite can still persist in low-K bulk compositions and is

189

"shielded" from occurring with K feldspar by sillimanite-biotite tie lines. In fact, at the metamorphic grade illustrated, biotite effectively shields all of the phases except sillimanite, garnet, and hornblende from occurring with K feldspar. The fact that there are no well documented occurrences of any Fe-Mg amphiboles with K feldspar from anywhere in the world[24] attests to the fact that this shield remains essentially in place until after the breakdown of Fe-Mg amphiboles, i.e., the breakdown of most biotite takes place at higher T than the breakdown of Fe-Mg amphiboles to orthopyroxenes. The shield, however, does withdraw slightly in the next metamorphic zone, where assemblages of cordierite + K feldspar + sillimanite + garnet are characteristic.

Assemblage (2) consists of gedrite, cordierite, and garnet, an assemblage typical of the high-T region on most Fe-Mg amphibole P-T grids (see this paper; also Robinson and Jaffe, 1969b). This rock also contains abundant fine staurolite and kyanite(?) (dashed tie lines), which may be interpreted as a product of retrograde reaction.

Assemblage (3) is dominated by plagioclase, gedrite, garnet, an orthopyroxene (with 0.11-0.14 Al per four cations), and ilmenite, and it apparently lacks quartz. The gedrite, with tetrahedral Al of 1.5-1.8, has a greenish-brown color, much darker than lower-grade gedrites and looking more like hornblende than an orthoamphibole. It has about 0.10 Ti per formula unit, more than twice as much as the anthophyllites and gedrites from the sillimanite-muscovite zone at "Amphibole Hill," southwestern New Hampshire, even comparing wet chemical analyses of the latter that *include* all of the exsolved plates and needles of ilmenite or rutile that characterize these amphiboles (Robinson and Jaffe, 1969b). Within the gedrites are a few colorless patches in *sharply defined contact* with the gedrite host that prove to be anthophyllite with tetrahedral Al of 0.5-0.9 and 0.015-0.04 Ti per formula unit. This occurrence came as a great surprise, because these rocks formed under conditions about 50°C higher than the suite of entirely hypersolvus orthoamphiboles studied from the "Amphibole Hill" area. At present, we speculate that increasing amounts of Ti in the orthoamphiboles, especially gedrite, have a powerful effect in *opening* the orthoamphibole solvus (Fig. 100), even at these high temperatures, and that the anthophyllite patches are relicts from a prograde reaction anthophyllite + garnet = orthopyroxene + gedrite + H_2O. The abundant growth of orthopyroxene around the periphery of

----

[24]Turner (1968) discusses muscovite-anthophyllite assemblages in the Tono Aureole, Japan, as reported by Seki (1957) and Seki and Yamasaki (1957). Seki (pers. comm., 1970) has assured me that all occurrences of orthoamphibole and muscovite in this district are retrograde, disequilibrium associations.

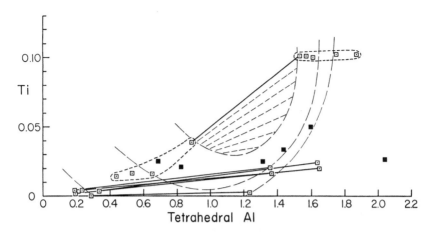

Figure 100. Compositions of single and coexisting orthoamphiboles plotted in terms of Ti per formula unit and tetrahedral Al. Probe pairs (open symbols) with low Ti content are from kyanite-staurolite and low sillimanite zone assemblages of Spear (1981) and Schumacher (unpublished data). Solid symbols are wet chemical analyses of orthoamphiboles from the "Amphibole Hill" area in the middle sillimanite zone, southwestern New Hampshire (Robinson *et al.*, 1971b). The four samples that were analyzed by wet chemical methods (solid squares) with tetrahedral Al below 1.5 crystallized as homogeneous orthoamphibole at 625-650°C and exsolved to submicroscopic or very fine microscopic mixtures of anthophyllite and gedrite on cooling. High Ti pair of anthophyllite and gedrite is from assemblage (3) in Figure 99, in the sillimanite-orthoclase zone (650-675°C). Dashed lines show speculated effect of Ti in opening the orthoamphibole solvus at high temperature.

the large orthoamphibole grains may indicate that this was previously an anthophyllite-gedrite-garnet rock, or it may indicate that after the destruction of anthophyllite, there was progress of a continuous Fe-Mg amphibole dehydration reaction, gedrite → orthopyroxene + garnet + H_2O.

Assemblage (4) is in a quartz-plagioclase-hornblende-cummingtonite (Fe 56) amphibolite with large patches of orthopyroxene (Fe 58) enclosing euhedral quartz. The rock seems to be undergoing the simple reaction cummingtonite = orthopyroxene + quartz + H_2O, although some sort of partial melting may also have been involved. These data fit in perfectly with what is known about this continuous dehydration reaction (Fonarev and Korolkov, 1980). The difference in orthopyroxene composition between assemblage (4) and assemblage (3) may be due to an effect of Al on the stability of orthopyroxene, or may be due to a difference of metamorphic grade. Unlike hornblende and gedrite, the terminal reaction for cummingtonite should normally take place in the presence of quartz.

Assemblage (5), with three coexisting amphiboles, has been described in detail earlier (see section on coexisting amphiboles; also Robinson *et al.*, 1969b). The three-phase assemblage can be considered to be undergoing a continuous Fe-Mg dehydration reaction: anthophyllite + hornblende → cummingtonite + plagioclase + H_2O. This reaction moves toward higher Mg content for two reasons: (1) the net amount of amphibole is reduced producing H_2O; and (2) Al in octahedral co-

191

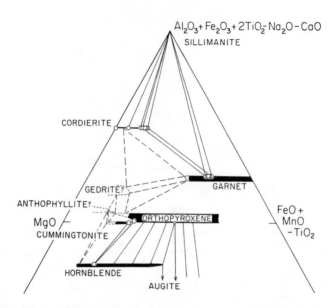

Figure 101. Plagioclase projection onto the A-F-M plane of some phase relations (Robinson and Tracy, 1979) from the sillimanite-orthoclase-garnet-cordierite zone of central Massachusetts (Tracy *et al.*, 1976).

ordination in both hornblende and anthophyllite goes to tetrahedral coordination in plagioclase. Clearly, this reaction is a very "slow train" compared to the orthopyroxene "express" but it has apparently progressed slightly from a cummingtonite composition of Fe 40 at "Amphibole Hill" in the sillimanite-muscovite-staurolite zone to a cummingtonite of Fe 36 in the sillimanite-orthoclase zone. Inconsistencies in this relation for some lower-grade assemblages suggest that the composition of plagioclase may be of equal importance in explaining the progress of this reaction. The anthophyllite-hornblende pair on the extreme left of Figure 99 is from an ultramafic rock (Wolff, 1978) but illustrates the tendency for both anthophyllite and hornblende in coexisting pairs to have higher Al in extremely magnesian rocks.

Figure 101 illustrates the very limited data so far available from metamorphic zone VI in central Massachusetts, characterized by the assemblage sillimanite + K feldspar + garnet + cordierite + biotite in pelitic schists. In this case, the biotite "shield" has retreated, and the sillimanite-cordierite-garnet compositions plotted are in fact in pelitic schists. At this grade no orthoamphibole assemblages have yet been found, and they may not exist, but a geographically narrow belt of cummingtonite-hornblende-orthopyroxene rocks shows

cummingtonite (Fe 31) coexisting with orthopyroxene (Fe 34), a considerable
progress of the cummingtonite-out reaction from Figure 99. Another gneiss
from this zone, but some miles away, shows quartz + orthopyroxene (Fs 50) +
augite + plagioclase + biotite, suggesting that hornblende breakdown has already taken place for this bulk composition and suggesting the retreat of the
hornblende field across the base of the diagram from Fe-rich to Mg-rich compositions.

The ultimate fates of Mg-rich cummingtonite, anthophyllite, and gedrite are
left completely up in the air in Figure 101, and indeed there seems to be no
comprehensive summary in English. Korikovsky (1979) in his diagrams shows many
interesting relationships that would be fascinating to read about in translation.
In his Figure 54 Korikovsky illustrates the reaction cummingtonite + garnet →
hypersthene + gedrite, a necessary transition from the topology illustrated for
"Amphibole Hill" and that of Figure 99. This is followed by the reaction gedrite
+ garnet → hypersthene + cordierite, which takes place while the assemblage
cummingtonite-gedrite-hypersthene exists in rocks with more Mg and less Al.
There is, of course, no hint of the coexistence of anthophyllite and gedrite
in any of this work. Grant (1978) argues on the basis of probe analyses of
specimens from Norway that the terminal reaction for gedrite is gedrite + quartz
= orthopyroxene + cordierite + garnet + albite + H_2O, so that gedrite disappears
in the midst of a triangle. This topology is consistent with the analyses in
Figure 99, in which the gedrite is slightly more Fe-rich than coexisting orthopyroxene. Exactly how the two-phase region orthopyroxene-cordierite is established on the Mg-rich side of the gedrite field is not clear. A possibility
is cummingtonite (or anthophyllite) + gedrite → cordierite + orthopyroxene + H_2O.
The discovery of hornblende + cordierite associations (Schumacher, 1981b) raises
further possibilities, particularly in light of the fact that such assemblages
are common in West Greenland (Robert Dymek, pers. comm., 1981). Rocks with the
same compositions as the abundant orthoamphibole rocks of West Greenland
(Dymek, 1977) have also been found at higher grade, where they are dominated
by orthopyroxene and cordierite. Unfortunately, the critical metamorphic transition zone between orthoamphiboles and orthopyroxenes has not been found
(Robert Dymek, pers. comm., 1981).

In addition, Korikovsky (1979) illustrates the reaction gedrite + garnet
= hypersthene + sillimanite + H_2O, apparently a very high-pressure assemblage;
describes the high-pressure, high-temperature breakdown of gedrite + sillimanite
→ hypersthene + cordierite + quartz (again this would violate the topology proposed by Grant); and discusses gedrite + sapphirine assemblages at some length.

On this basis, it appears that there is a wealth of data in the Russian literature bearing on these problems.

Cummingtonite dehydration reactions. The chemical simplicity of cummingtonites has been pointed out extensively earlier in this chapter, and the apparent systematic nature of their breakdown with increasing metamorphic grade has been illustrated using Figures 99 and 101. Figure 102 shows that with respect to Ca, Al, and Na, the orthopyroxenes coexisting with cummingtonite are even simpler in composition, though both minerals occur in rocks with hornblende, plagioclase, and other "impure" phases (see also Hörmann *et al.*, 1980, Fig. 21). This raises the possibility that equilibria involving cummingtonite, orthopyroxene, olivine, and quartz can be treated to a first approximation in the system SiO_2-MgO-FeO and tied in rather closely with experimental work that has recently been completed in that system (Fonarev and Korolkov, 1980; Fonarev *et al.*, 1979; Gilbert *et al.*, Chapter 9, this volume).

In Figure 103A are plotted all of the quartz-cummingtonite, cummingtonite-olivine, and orthopyroxene-olivine assemblages known from the sillimanite-muscovite zone in central Massachusetts. Some of those near the Fe-rich side are from Devonian iron-rich beds described by Huntington (1975) and contain considerable MnO, which may influence slopes of tie lines. There is also one cummingtonite (grunerite)-orthopyroxene-olivine assemblage to be discussed below. Figure 103B shows assemblages available from the sillimanite-orthoclase and higher zones in central Massachusetts. Figure 103C shows extended tie lines of selected mineral pairs (with relatively low Mn) assembled from the previous two figures. All of the tie lines seem to radiate roughly from a single point, indicating that there is little or no difference in slopes of cummingtonite-orthopyroxene, cummingtonite-olivine, and orthopyroxene-olivine tie lines. Figure 103D is a blow-up showing the one assemblage of cummingtonite-orthopyroxene-olivine. If the plot is made on the basis of Fe only, orthopyroxene lies on the Mg-rich side of the cummingtonite-olivine tie line. If Mn is added to Fe, then orthopyroxene lies on the Fe-rich side. The nature of the continuous Fe-Mg reaction by which cummingtonite plus olivine breaks down to orthopyroxene is dependent on which of these two alternatives is right. Gole and Klein (1981b) present analyses of two such assemblages, plus quartz, with lower Mn; in both, the orthopyroxene lies on the *Fe-rich* side of the cummingtonite-olivine tie line. The two alternative possibilities are illustrated in Figure 104 for increasing T or decreasing aH_2O. In I the orthopyroxene is more magnesian than the coexisting cummingtonite-olivine line, so the dehydration begins at the Mg end and proceeds toward higher Fe content. This reaction eventually collides with the continuous dehydration

194

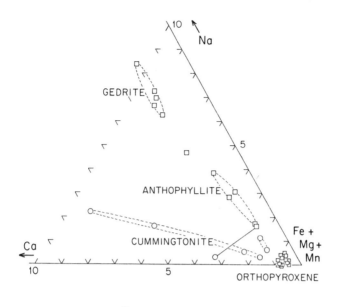

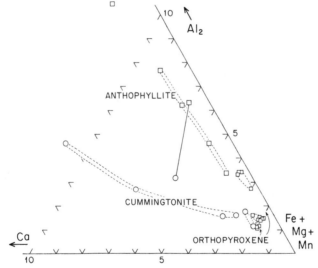

Figure 102. Comparisons of the compositions of orthopyroxenes, cummingtonites, and orthoamphiboles from high grade metamorphic zones in central
Massachusetts in terms of Na-Ca-(Fe+Mg+Mn) (top) and Al$_2$-Ca-(Fe+Mg+Mn) (bottom). Orthopyroxenes have lower Ca, Na and Al$_2$ than coexisting Fe-Mg
amphiboles. Orthopyroxenes coexisting with anthophyllite and gedrite
have higher Al than others. Some cummingtonites show variable Ca, as
well as Na and Al$_2$, as a result of variable amounts of hornblende exsolution lamellae. Anthophyllites and gedrites show high and variable Na
and Al$_2$ (gedrites are off scale for Al$_2$). The cummingtonite-anthophyllite
pair is from assemblage 5 of Figure 99.

195

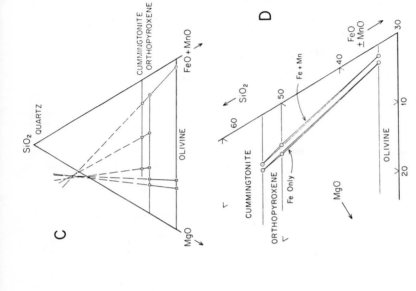

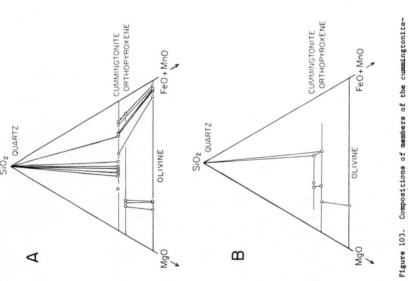

Figure 103. Compositions of members of the cummingtonite-grunerite series, of orthopyroxenes, and of olivines from central Massachusetts plotted in the system SiO_2-MgO-(FeO+MnO). (A) Assemblages from the sillimanite-muscovite zone from Huntington (1975), Wolff (1978), and Robinson and Jaffe (1969b). (B) Assemblages from the sillimanite-orthoclase and sillimanite-orthoclase-garnet-cordierite zone from Wolff (1978) and Robinson and Tracy (1979).

(C) Extended tie lines for two orthopyroxene-olivine, two cummingtonite-orthopyroxene, and one cummingtonite-ortho-pyroxene-olivine assemblage. (D) Expanded view of the cummingtonite-orthopyroxene-olivine assemblage reported by Huntington (1975). The three phases are nearly collinear, and the topology is different depending on whether MnO is or is not included with FeO.

196

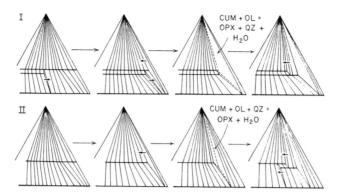

Figure 104. Two alternative sequences for the appearance of orthopyroxene and breakdown of cummingtonite-grunerite in the system SiO_2-MgO-FeO, dependent on the topology of the cummingtonite-orthopyroxene-olivine-quartz equilibrium. Sequence I is consistent with the possibility that the assemblages of Figure 103A could all occur under the same conditions of activity of H_2O. Sequence II is identical to that proposed by Fonarev and Korolkov (1980) and consistent with the analyses of Gole and Klein (1981b).

cummingtonite → fayalite + quartz (Fonarev et $al.$, 1979) to produce the reaction cummingtonite + olivine = orthopyroxene + quartz + H_2O. Above this temperature the continuous reaction cummingtonite → orthopyroxene + quartz proceeds toward more Mg-rich compositions. Alternative I has some support in the assemblages shown in Figure 103A and B, in that Mg-rich ultramafic rocks contain olivine + orthopyroxene, whereas Fe-rich rocks at the same grade contain cummingtonite + olivine.

In alternative II (Fig. 104) cummingtonite begins to break down to quartz + fayalite at the Fe-rich end as in I, but encounters a special equilibrium, where orthopyroxene first appears by the reaction cummingtonite + olivine + quartz → orthopyroxene + H_2O. From this point onward there are two continuous Fe-Mg reactions, proceeding toward more Mg-rich compositions: the $orthopyroxene$-in $reaction$ and, following it, the $cummingtonite$-out $reaction$. This is the exact topologic sequence illustrated by Fonarev and Korolkov (1980), but it is not clear whether this was based on real composition data or obtained through habit and use of a quartz projection to study the equilibria. It appears that their experiments do not include the crucial equilibrium, and their equilibrations and composition determinations may not be sensitive enough to decide the question. However, their sequence is consistent with the analyses of Gole and Klein (1981b). If alternative II is correct, then it is necessary to assume that the Massachusetts ultramafic bodies, which are very small, underwent metamorphic crystallization at a lower aH_2O than the iron-rich beds nearby. This seems unlikely, especially since graphite and some carbonate minerals are still preserved in the iron-rich beds (Huntington, 1975). A third possibility is that irregularities in the three different solid solution series cause there to be collinearities

197

of the three phases at several times, creating a chaotic but interesting series of dehydration reactions.

Regardless of the cummingtonite-orthopyroxene-olivine problem, the experimental results on the reaction cummingtonite $\rightarrow$ orthopyroxene + quartz + H_2O are in agreement with the natural assemblages from central Massachusetts. Cummingtonite consistently has Fe/(Fe+Mg) 0.02 to 0.03 less than the coexisting pyroxene, resulting in an incredibly narrow pseudobinary reaction loop, and the reaction proceeds from Fe-rich to Mg-rich compositions with increasing temperature. At 4900 bar P_{H_2O} and on the QFM buffer, the cummingtonite breakdown temperatures are as follows:

        740°C for cummingtonite Fe 75,

        760°C for cummingtonite Fe 66.5, and

        780°C for cummingtonite Fe 58.5.

Reduction of aH_2O in the natural situation would reduce these temperatures to somewhat below 700°C.

Appearance of pyroxenes in amphibolites and hornblende gneisses

It should be clear from the A-C-F diagrams of Figure 98 that the reactions by which pyroxenes appear in amphibolites depend very heavily on the bulk composition. For example, the reactions by which pyroxenes appear in experiments run in the pyroxene quadrilateral, such as those of Cameron (1975), are very different from those occurring in plagioclase-bearing amphibolites. Even in plagioclase amphibolites, the sequence of appearance of augite and of orthopyroxene depends on the proportions of Ca and Al (and Na). In the experiments on olivine tholeiite on the QFM buffer run at 1 kbar P_{fluid} by Spear (1981), for example, Ca pyroxene appears first at 770°C, followed at 800°C by orthopyroxene and at 825°C by olivine. Amphibole itself does not go out until 910°C. In the cummingtonite amphibolites described above, orthopyroxenes appear but no Ca pyroxenes.

These ideas are graphically explored in Figure 105. The first row of figures is a set of ACF diagrams illustrating the relations of hornblende to plagioclase and pyroxenes. The Na/Ca ratio of plagioclase is ignored, but the bulk FeMg ratio is indicated by the dashed lines in the quadrilaterals below. The second row shows equilibria on the H_2O- and quartz-saturated pyroxene quadrilateral. This is the same as the right-hand half of the base of the ACF triangle expanded to show Fe to the right and Mg to the left. The third row is a projection from plagioclase onto the same base (see Fig. 83). In this the hornblende field is large because there is an extensive array of plagioclase-hornblende tie lines.

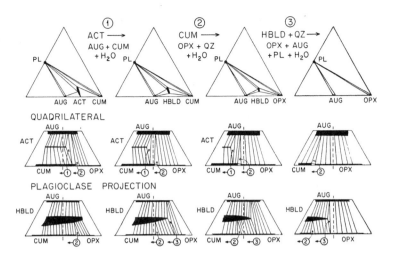

Figure 105. Effect of bulk composition on the appearance of pyroxenes in amphibolites. Top row: A-C-F diagrams for an Fe/(Fe+Mg) ratio of about 0.50 (Fe50) showing sequence of topologies produced by three reactions. T increases to the right. Middle row: Sequence of reactions on the H_2O saturated pyroxene quadrilateral as worked out in experiments by Cameron (1975). Dashed line at Fe50 represents bulk composition of the experiments. Bottom row: projections from plagioclase onto the quadrilateral base, showing the sequence of reactions to be expected in plagioclase-bearing rocks with different Fe/Mg ratios and Ca contents.

At the lowest temperature (Fig. 105), actinolite occurs between augite and cummingtonite at the FM apex and in the quadrilateral. Plagioclase amphibolites have augite + hornblende, hornblende only, or hornblende + cummingtonite. In reaction (1) actinolite breaks down to augite plus cummingtonite in a continuous Fe-Mg reaction. This is seen as a continuously moving triangle in the quadrilateral, passing through the dashed Fe 50 bulk composition line; the triangle completely passes through the Fe 50 line in the temperature range 610-710°C at 2000 bars, according to Cameron (1975). Reaction (1) has no effect on plagioclase amphibolites. Reaction (2) is the continuous Fe-Mg reaction by which cummingtonite breaks down to orthopyroxene. When this slim reaction triangle passes through the dashed bulk composition line of the quadrilateral, cummingtonit goes to orthopyroxene, and no further amphiboles are possible in the quadrilateral This same reaction causes plagioclase-cummingtonite amphibolites to become orthopyroxene amphibolites but has no effect on plagioclase-augite amphibolites. According to Cameron, this reaction triangle passes through the Fe 50 composition line in the temperature range 725°-780°C at 2000 bars P_{H_2O}. Fonarev and Korolkov (1980) suggest that cummingtonite Fe 50 breaks down to orthopyroxene near 780°C at 2940 bars P_{H_2O}.

Reaction (3) is the terminal one for hornblende plus quartz in such bulk compositions. It has no effect in the quadrilateral, but profoundly effects plagioclase amphibolites, first permitting augite and orthopyroxene to occur together with plagioclase, and then doing away with hornblende. So far as we know, this reaction has not yet been investigated for the Fe 50 composition. Unlike reactions (1) and (2), in reaction (3) the Na/Ca ratios of both hornblende and plagioclase are crucial.

The ultimate demise of hornblende

It is important to recognize that there is no such thing as the ultimate hornblende, but only the ultimate hornblende for any given rock composition. Similarly, it is wrong to suggest that hornblende composition changes thus and so with increasing metamorphic grade, because the direction of change is very heavily dependent on the rock composition involved. This point is brought out in Figure 98B, where we have seen the approximate direction of change of hornblende in three different assemblages. In plagioclase-augite amphibolite, hornblende *decreases* in Ca and in Al; in plagioclase-orthopyroxene amphibolite, hornblende *increases* in Ca and *decreases* in Al; and in augite-orthopyroxene amphibolite, hornblende *increases* in Al. Hornblendes in the three assemblages converge on a point which seems to be the ultimate hornblende. However, this is only an illusion brought on by lumping Fe+Mg and Na+Ca to produce the diagram. The Fe+Mg problem is relieved in the plagioclase projection of Figure 105. Here we see a reaction triangle with hornblende on the Mg-rich side and the projected plane plagioclase-augite-orthopyroxene on the Fe-rich side. This arrangement is almost certainly the case in nearly all natural assemblages (see Jaffe *et al.*, 1978; Hörmann *et al.*, 1980). As the reaction proceeds, the hornblende apex of the triangle moves away from the bulk composition toward more Mg-rich compositions, whereas the line or plane of reaction products moves toward the bulk composition and also toward higher Mg-content. The ultimate hornblende *for the rock* is then the last bit of hornblende present as the plane of reaction products overtakes the bulk composition.

The effects of Fe-Mg ratio are further explored in a remarkable diagram (Fig. 106) prepared by Reinhardt and Skippen (1970), based on phase relations in the Westport area, Ontario. This is a plagioclase *and* K feldspar projection onto the A-F-M face (compare with Fig. 101) but lies exactly on the K-rich side of what remains of the "biotite shield." In Fe-rich rocks all hydrous minerals have broken down. In more Mg-rich rocks hornblende is involved in three continuous Fe-Mg reactions:

(1) Hornblende + quartz → orthopyroxene + augite + plagioclase + H_2O, in which hornblende becomes Mg-richer.

(2) Hornblende + biotite + quartz → orthopyroxene + K feldspar + plagioclase + H_2O, in which orthopyroxene becomes Mg-richer.

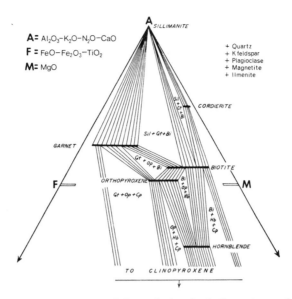

A = Al₂O₃–K₂O–N₂O–CaO
F = FeO–Fe₂O₃–TiO₂
M = MgO

+ Quartz
+ K feldspar
+ Plagioclase
+ Magnetite
+ Ilmenite

Figure 106. Tentative interpretation of phase relations in the Westport area, Ontario, by Reinhardt and Skippen (1970). This is a projection from plagioclase and K-feldspar (as well as quartz, magnetite, and ilmenite) onto the A-F-M plane and is similar to Figure 101, except for reversal of F and M and treatment of K₂O.

(3) Biotite + augite ⇄ hornblende + K feldspar + plagioclase, for which
the reaction direction is uncertain.

Note that the hornblende-cummingtonite-orthopyroxene assemblage of Figure 101 could actually be stable at this grade, but be entirely "shielded" by biotite-hornblende tie lines.

So far, we have tended to ignore the effect of the Na/Ca ratio of coexisting plagioclase on the breakdown of hornblende, as well as the Na/Ca ratio of the hornblende itself. However, this was only a matter of convenience in early stages of explanation and would be fatal to ignore completely, particularly in light of what we now understand about the chemistry of calcic amphiboles. In particular, aluminous calcic amphiboles all have a substantial amount of Na in the A-site and to some extent in the M4-site that must be considered in the ultimate breakdown of hornblende. Since we know that the pure Ca amphibole, actinolite, breaks down at lower temperature, it is obvious that the ultimate hornblende contains substantial Na and must have a plagioclase of intermediate composition, not anorthite, as its ultimate breakdown product.

The conception outlined above is illustrated for Mg-rich amphibolites in Figure 107, itself an expansion of Figure 14. In this situation all the break-down products of amphibole are plagioclase, augite and orthopyroxene in the classic reaction of Buddington (1963). Figure 107a is the A-NC-FM triangle expanded

201

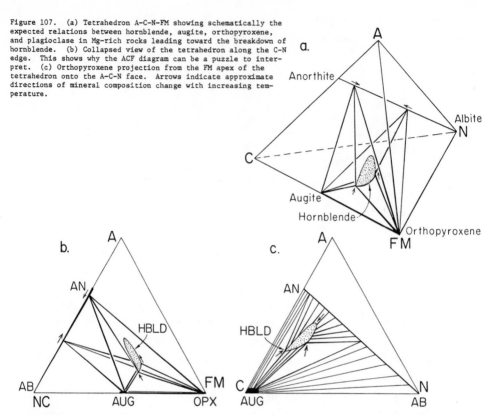

Figure 107. (a) Tetrahedron A-C-N-FM showing schematically the expected relations between hornblende, augite, orthopyroxene, and plagioclase in Mg-rich rocks leading toward the breakdown of hornblende. (b) Collapsed view of the tetrahedron along the C-N edge. This shows why the ACF diagram can be a puzzle to interpret. (c) Orthopyroxene projection from the FM apex of the tetrahedron onto the A-C-N face. Arrows indicate approximate directions of mineral composition change with increasing temperature.

to a tetrahedron by splitting N and C. The view in Figure 107b is directly along the N-C edge with anorthite closest and albite most distant. Figure 107c is a projection from the FM (orthopyroxene) apex onto the A-C-N face, showing assemblages with orthopyroxene. Since the pure Ca amphibole has already gone, anorthite and other calcic plagioclases are in equilibrium with augite and orthopyroxene. This is on the Ca-rich side of the reaction volume hornblende + quartz → plagioclase + augite + orthopyroxene + H_2O, in which hornblende lies on the *Na-rich side* of the plane plagioclase-augite-orthopyroxene. Hornblende disappears from such calcic compositions when the plane of reaction products reaches the bulk composition. In the Na-rich part of the diagram, there is a similar reaction volume, but in this case hornblende lies on the *Ca-rich side* of the plane plagioclase-augite-orthopyroxene, and hornblende disappears from such a rock when the plane of reaction products reaches the bulk composition. It will be seen that the two reaction volumes are approaching each other and will ultimately collide and collapse to form a single plagioclase-augite-orthopyroxene plane with a point of hornblende at the center. This might be considered the "ultimate hornblende," although its attainment in any rock would be very unlikely. One of the important

202

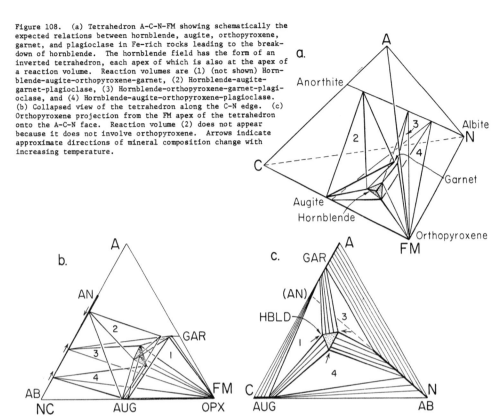

Figure 108. (a) Tetrahedron A-C-N-FM showing schematically the expected relations between hornblende, augite, orthopyroxene, garnet, and plagioclase in Fe-rich rocks leading to the breakdown of hornblende. The hornblende field has the form of an inverted tetrahedron, each apex of which is also at the apex of a reaction volume. Reaction volumes are (1) (not shown) Hornblende-augite-orthopyroxene-garnet, (2) Hornblende-augite-garnet-plagioclase, (3) Hornblende-orthopyroxene-garnet-plagioclase, and (4) Hornblende-augite-orthopyroxene-plagioclase. (b) Collapsed view of the tetrahedron along the C-N edge. (c) Orthopyroxene projection from the FM apex of the tetrahedron onto the A-C-N face. Reaction volume (2) does not appear because it does not involve orthopyroxene. Arrows indicate approximate directions of mineral composition change with increasing temperature.

features of Figure 107 is what it tells about the deceptiveness of the ACF diagram. It does show that prograde metamorphism *will* reduce the Al content of the most aluminous hornblende in equilibrium with orthopyroxene and plagioclase, *but* in the two reaction assemblages involving plagioclase and augite (+ orthopyroxene), prograde metamorphism *increases* the Al content of hornblende.

For more Fe-rich compositions, as shown in Figure 108, garnet is likely to be an additional hornblende breakdown product. In Figure 108, the three views are the same as in Figure 107, although the patterns are more complex due to the presence of garnet. This leaves the Na-rich reaction volume (4) intact, but replaces the Ca-rich reaction volume with *three new ones*: (1) garnet-augite-orthopyroxene-hornblende (tie lines omitted in Fig. 108a but included in 108b and 108c); (2) garnet-augite-plagioclase-hornblende; and (3) garnet-plagioclase-orthopyroxene-hornblende. In (2) the plagioclase becomes more sodic with increasing dehydration, because hornblende is more sodic than the augite-garnet-plagioclase plane. In (3) the plagioclase becomes more calcic, because hornblende is more calcic than the plagioclase-garnet-orthopyroxene plane. In (1) the hornblende is more sodic than the product plane, but the latter is nearly constrained close to the

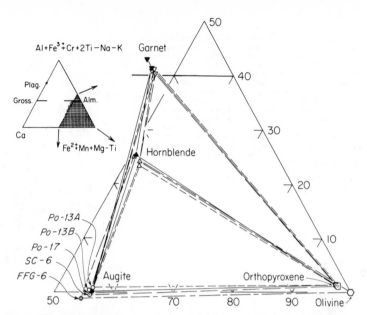

Figure 109. Modified ACF diagram showing compositions of coexisting hornblendes, garnets, augites, orthopyroxenes, and olivine from iron-rich microperthite gneisses from the Mt. Marcy area, Adirondack Mountains. From Jaffe *et al.* (1978). Plotted compositions of hornblendes in these rocks are extremely similar and lie close to the augite-garnet tie lines. The augite has considerable ferrosilite component, whereas the garnet has around 20% grossular+andradite component.

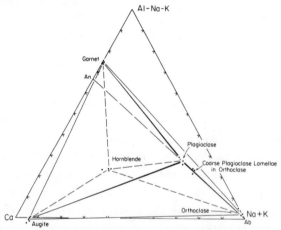

Figure 110. Orthopyroxene projection in the tetrahedron (Al-Na-K), (Na+K), (Ca), (Fe+Mn+Mg) onto the (Al-Na-K), (Na+K), (Ca) face, showing hornblende and its projected breakdown products augite, garnet, plagioclase, and orthoclase (plus orthopyroxene), for Fe-rich Adirondack rocks. From Jaffe *et al.* (1978). Na+K is not presented as 2Na+2K, as in Figures 106 and 107. A three dimensional effect may be obtained by mentally splitting Na and K, with Na in front. Hornblende then appears within a tetrahedral volume bounded by augite, garnet, plagioclase, and orthoclase.

ACFM face of the tetrahedron. The composition volume of hornblende itself is a tiny inverted tetrahedron, each apex of which is also the hornblende apex of one of the four reaction volumes. In this situation, ultimate hornblende comes when

204

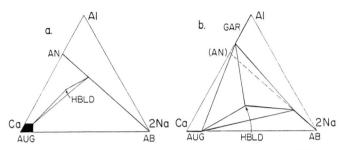

Figure 111. Evaluation of Adirondack hornblendes (a) A104 (Engel and Engel, 1962; Engel *et al.*, 1964) and (b) Po-17 (Jaffe *et al.*, 1978) in terms of plagioclase composition. In this figure Fe^{3+} and $2Ti^{4+}$ have been removed from A, leaving Al-Na-K only; and 2K has been removed from 2Na+2K, so that hornblende may be evaluated in terms of its pure Ab-An components. The figure is already an orthopyroxene projection, so that these additional procedures make it into a magnetite + ilmenite + K-feldspar projection as well.

the four apices of the tiny hornblende volume merge to a point at the same time as the four reaction volumes merge into a single reaction volume in which the ultimate hornblende (+ quartz) breaks down to plagioclase, orthopyroxene, augite, and garnet. In this situation, because the final reaction volume is relatively large, the possibility of observing such ultimate hornblende is also large.

What is such ultimate hornblende like? Obviously, much will depend on details of various element ratios. However, a number of specimens of Adirondack granulite facies rocks seem to contain examples. Analyses from four such rocks that are very rich in iron and in which augite Fe/(Fe+Mg) ratios vary from 0.793 to 0.949 are shown in an ACF diagram in Figure 109 (Jaffe *et al.*, 1978). Figure 110 shows relations similar to those of Figure 108c. In this projection each of the four merged reaction volumes of Figure 108 can be identified with hornblende at the apex of all. In these Fe-rich rocks at least, where potassium is enriched in the feldspar and the hornblende, the hornblende lies a long way from the Na-K-free plane.

In Figure 111 more precise relations between hornblende and plagioclase are explored in an orthopyroxene projection, using an example from an Mg- and Ca-rich mafic rock studied by Engel and Engel (1962, sample A104) and an extremely Fe-rich and fairly Na-rich felsic rock from Jaffe *et al.* (1978, sample Po-17). For this purpose, the magnetite and ilmenite components of hornblende, augite, and garnet are removed by subtracting out Fe^{3+} and $2Ti^{4+}$ from the A-component, and the orthoclase component of hornblende is removed by subtracting out 2K from the N component. Even in the mafic rock in Figure 111a, the K in the hornblende is 0.322 per formula unit, so that removal of K moves the effective "anorthite" in the hornblende to a value of about "An_{66}" compared to An_{61} in the rock. The position of the "twin" assemblage with more anorthitic plagioclase is, of course, unknown. By contrast, the hornblende of Figure 111b is central to an enormous portion of the chemographic space. Although the "terminal" hornblende has an actual composition of "An_{38}," because of the participation of garnet, the actual hornblende in the assemblage is only An_{20}.

There is a major question for such rocks: Why is the ultimate hornblende preserved at all? Answers lie in two directions. First, there is a good possibility that in these very dry rocks H_2O has ceased to behave as a perfectly mobile component (Korzhinskii, 1959) and has become inert, thus accounting for an additional phase, namely hornblende. Second, there is a likelihood that these hornblendes are enriched in chlorine (Buddington and Leonard, 1953), not soluble in any other phase present in the rock and hence tending to stabilize the very small amounts of remaining hornblende.

Despite the differences in Fe/Mg ratios, the hornblendes shown in Figures 108, 109, and 111 are hastingsites with 1.7-1.8 tetrahedral Al, 0.15-0.40 octahedral Al, 0.25-0.30 Ti^{4+}, and 0.35-0.45 Fe^{3+}. They have about 0.15-0.20 Na in M4 and an A-occupancy of 0.55-0.87, of which 0.32 to 0.38 is K. To find out what their anhydrous products would be (ignoring garnet), they can be recast on a cation percentage basis as follows for the Engel and Engel (1962) sample A104 and Jaffe *et al.* (1978) sample Po-17, respectively: orthoclase 8.3%, 9.2%; albite 9.5%, 17.2%; anorthite 19.0%, 10.6%; normative plagioclase An_{66}, An_{38}; magnetite 3.4%, 3.1%; ilmenite 2.6%, 2.8%; diopside-hedenbergite 22.8%, 25.6%; enstatite-ferrosilite 24.1%, 21.9%; $Fe^{2+}/(Fe^{2+} + Mg)$ 0.45, 0.94; and H_2O 10.3%, 9.6%. Quartz required to produce these minerals would be 1.861 and 2.913 cations per formula unit of hornblende. Only trace amounts of quartz are present in the first rock, so that for the reaction to progress olivine would have to be produced instead of orthopyroxene. Quartz is abundant in the second rock.

Other reactions are those that control the Fe^{3+} and Ti^{4+} of ultimate hornblende. In the Adirondack samples, coexisting magnetite and ilmenite are the saturating Fe^{3+} and Ti^{4+} phases. The effects of these components, like the effect of Al, can be fruitfully explored in modified A-C-F diagrams substituting successively Fe^{3+} and $Fe^{2+}_{0.5}Ti^{4+}_{0.5}$ for Al.

AMPHIBOLES IN METAMORPHOSED CALCAREOUS SEDIMENTARY ROCKS

Every metamorphic petrologist is relatively familiar with the role of tremolite, as made famous in Bowen's (1940) poem, in the metamorphism of siliceous dolomitic carbonate rocks in the system $CaO-MgO-SiO_2-H_2O-CO_2$. This subject is well covered in textbooks and a number of review papers (Kerrick, 1974; Skippen, 1974; Slaughter *et al.*, 1975, Greenwood, 1976; Rice, 1977) and will also, reportedly, be covered in the MSA Short Course in Fall 1982. Experimental work, theoretical studies, and work on natural occurrences have received wide attention and are undergoing constant refinement. Several recent studies have attempted to take into account the solid solution of Fe into tremolite (Thompson, 1975; Valley and Essene, 1980) and also the important substitutions of F and Cl for (OH) (Petersen *et al.*, 1981; Moore and Kerrick, 1976; Kearns *et al.*, 1980; Troll and Gilbert, 1972), which can have a significant effect on the amphibole stability in terms of P, T, and fluid composition.

Far less attention has been paid to amphiboles in impure calcareous sedimentary rocks, the very common calc-silicate rocks associated with metamorphosed shales in so many metamorphic belts. Some of these amphiboles commonly have the same or similar Na, Al, possibly Fe^{3+} and Ti as amphiboles in metamorphosed mafic igneous rocks, although mineral assemblages can be quite different. Indeed, there are occurrences where it is extremely difficult to decide whether the protolith was a contaminated volcanic tuff or an extremely impure calcareous sedimentary rock (Evans and Leake, 1960). For such sedimentary protoliths, the approach to phase equilibria outlined for amphibolites (see sections on metamorphosed basaltic rocks, this paper) should prove equally useful.

Carmichael (1970) used the prograde appearance of hornblende in impure calcareous rocks to denote an isograd largely controlled by H_2O-CO_2 content of metamorphic fluid, which "cuts across" metamorphic isograds in pelitic schists of the same Whetstone Lake area, Ontario. Winchester (1972, 1974) has explored reactions in which hornblende appears with increasing grade in calc-silicate gneisses of the Moine series, Scotland. It would appear that additional detailed mineralogical and petrological studies of the amphiboles, garnets, pyroxenes, epidotes, plagioclases, and other minerals in these abundant but generally neglected rocks could provide additional useful information on metamorphic conditions. Thompson (1975) has provided an important first step at tackling the complex equilibria in such rocks, using specimens of calc-mica schist from Gassetts, Vermont.

It is very common for metasomatic reaction rims to form between calcareous layers or concretions and their pelitic host rocks. "Hornblende" is a very common constituent of such rims, usually adjacent to a biotite-rich selvage against the country rock and surrounding the more Ca-rich interior of the layer or boudin that is commonly dominated by diopside, calcic plagioclase, grossular, calcite, or zoisite (Vidale, 1969). Ca amphibole, usually an actinolite of intermediate Fe-Mg ratio, is also a common constituent of Fe-rich skarns associated with igneous contacts, where it may be associated with magnetite, hematite, andradite, hedenbergite, and calcite (Burt, 1971; Taylor and Liou, 1978), either as a prograde or retrograde phase.

Quite possibly, despite all that has gone before, your favorite metamorphic amphibole occurrence has been neglected.   Two obvious omissions come to mind immediately.

The type B eclogites (see the section covering eclogite relations of metamorphosed basaltic rocks, this chapter), including those originally studied by Eskola in western Norway, commonly contain hornblende, in some examples as a retrograde hydration product.   It is disconcerting to note that such "amphibolized" eclogite looks superficially like any other garnet amphibolite.   This can lead one to consider eclogite as possibly the "dry" version of the amphibolite facies, a view supported by the work of Morgan (1970) in Venezuela.   In summer 1981, W. L. Griffin of Oslo University led a comprehensive field trip to the highly varied eclogites of the "basal gneiss terrain" of western Norway in connection with the IGCP Caledonide Project and prepared an up-to-date summary. The following references to papers presented at the IGCP Meeting in Uppsala, Sweden were added in proof:

Griffin, W. L., Austreim, H., Brastad, K., Bryhni, I., Krill, A., Krogh, E., Mork, M. B. E., Qvale, H. and Torudbakken, B. (1981) High pressure metamorphism in the Scandinavian Caledonides (abstr.). Terra Cognita, 1, 48.

Griffin, W. L. and Qvale, H. (1981) Superferric eclogites and the crustal origin of garnet peridotites, Almklovdalen, Norway (abstr.). Terra Cognita, 1, 48.

Carswell, D. A. and Harvey, M. A. (1981) The intrusive history and tectono-metamorphic evolution of the basal gneiss complex in the Molde Fjord region, west Norway (abstr.). Terra Cognita, 1, 39.

In our coverage of amphiboles in greenschists and blueschists, we neglected to comment on amphiboles in low-greenschist to sub-greenschist rocks, specifically in the pumpellyite-actinolite facies rocks (Hashimoto, 1966; Seki, 1965; Coombs *et al.*, 1970).   However, the amphiboles appear to be monotonous actinolites with little or no Na_2O and less than 1 wt % Al_2O_3 (Robinson and Tracy, unpublished data from Chatham Island, New Zealand Plateau), coexisting with albite, chlorite, pumpellyite, sphene, and locally relict augite.

SUGGESTIONS FOR FUTURE RESEARCH

It seems to these authors that, if the hopes for amphiboles expressed by Eskola (1939, p. 357) are to be realized, there is much good work yet to be done in a variety of categories, as follows:

(1)   More sophisticated and precise analytical tools need to be developed that will make possible more correct designation of amphibole

compositional formulae. Of particular importance are better ways to determine the oxidation state of Fe; the exact proportions of OH, F, and Cl; exact site occupancies; and microstructures significant to genetic history.

(2) Better use needs to be made of the petrographic microscope and the electron microprobes that are currently available, including

    (a) More complete analyses that will permit more accurate formulation, especially of MnO, TiO_2, and K_2O, which have commonly been omitted in the past;

    (b) Analyses of all phases present in each rock to give an accurate picture of all possible significant equilibria (better a few specimens very well characterized than many poorly described).

    (c) More attention to details of mineral zoning, which have great potential for telling something about the sequence of metamorphic events.

(3) Better and more extensive use needs to be made of currently understood two- and three-dimensional graphical techniques that can be readily understood by most petrologists and are very effective in illustrating general principles. This should be coupled with more sophisticated mathematical approaches involving net transfer and exchange reactions that potentially can be tied in with thermodynamic models.

In the end, the very complexity of the amphibole group, which in the past has scared off petrologists in large numbers, is what permits amphiboles to interact chemically with such a wide variety of other phases, and hence potentially to tell a story of metamorphism unequalled by other minerals.

ACKNOWLEDGMENTS

The work of Robinson and Schumacher was supported by NSF Grant EAR-79-11207. Computations of amphibole formulae were done in the University of Massachusetts X-ray Fluorescence Analytical Facility with the assistance of Joel Sparks. Figures 1-7, 9, 13, 15, 22, 23, 25, 27, 28, 34, and 37 were drafted by Marie Litterer, and she also lettered Figures 8, 10, 12, 14, 16-19, 99, 104 and 105. Kurt T. Hollocher drafted Figure 38 and lettered Figures 36, 93, 107, 108, and 111. Charles Shearer and Kurt T. Hollocher were of great assistance, often at critical moments, in plotting data and mounting figures, and were responsible for collecting and organizing references. The project would have been impossible without the prompt and expert typing of Dorothy Morrison and Katherine Boliski. Photographic reduction of many figures was expertly carried out, often on very short notice, by John Collis at Hamilton I. Newell, Co. Finally, Howard Jaffe should be acknowledged for his long-term guidance over the years on evaluation of analyses, preparation of structural formulae of amphiboles, and critical observations of optical properties and exsolution features.

The work of Frank Spear was supported by NSF Grant EAR-79-11166.

Some of the work of Jo Laird received financial support from ETH Zurich, where ideas presented here concerning independent heterogeneous reactions in mafic schist were first generated and reflect countless hours of work by and discussions with James B. Thompson, Jr., and Alan B. Thompson. Wally Bothner and Anna Burack helped greatly in late stages by drafting, proofreading, and assembling figures.

The work of Cornelis Klein was supported by NSF Grant EAR-80-20377.

The work of Bernard Evans was supported by NSF Grant EAR-78-03350. The following workers provided him with unpublished analyses of ultramafic amphiboles: Peter Misch (N. Cascades, Washington), L. G. Medaris (Seiad, California; Finero, Italy; Almklovdalen, Norway), B. R. Frost (Wind Rivers, Wyoming), N. Desmarais (Ruby Range, Montana), and G. Y. Bussod (Kilbourne Hole, N. M.). D. J. Borns and Peter Misch reviewed this part of the manuscript.

The computations and computer plotting of Barry Doolan were carried out at the University of Vermont Computer Center.

To each of these persons and institutions we separately and collectively express our grateful acknowledgment.

> "Depend on it sir. When a man knows he's to be hanged in a
> fortnight, it concentrates his mind wonderfully."
>
> *Samuel Johnson*

Manuscript completed August 1981.

Abraham, K. and Schreyer, W. (1973) Petrology of a ferruginous hornfels from Rieckensgluck, Harz Mountains, Germany. Contrib. Mineral. Petrol. 40, 275-292.

Albee, A. L. (1965) A petrogenetic grid for the Fe-Mg silicates of pelitic schists. Amer. J. Sci. 263, 512-536.

Allen, J. M. and Goldie, R. (1978) Coexisting amphiboles from the Noranda area, Quebec: extension of the actinolite-hornblende miscibility gap to iron-rich bulk compositions. Amer. Mineral., 63, 205-209.

Aoki, K. (1970) Petrology of kaersutite-bearing ultramafic and mafic inclusions in Iki Islands, Japan. Contrib. Mineral. Petrol. 25, 270-283.

_____ (1971) Petrology of mafic inclusions from Itinome-gata, Japan. Contrib. Mineral. Petrol. 30, 314-331.

_____ (1975) Origin of phlogopite and potassic richterite bearing peridotite xenoliths from South Africa. Contrib. Mineral. Petrol. 53, 145-156.

Arai, S. (1975) Contact metamorphosed dunite-harzburgite complex in the Chugoku District, Western Japan. Contrib. Mineral. Petrol. 52, 1-16.

Ashwal, L. D. (1974) *Metamorphic hydration of augite-orthopyroxene monzodiorite to hornblende granodiorite gneiss, Belchertown batholith, central Massachusetts.* Contrib. No. 18, Dept. of Geology, University of Massachusetts, Amherst, 124 p.

_____, Leo, G. W., Robinson, P., Zartman, R. E. and Hall, D. J. (1979) The Belchertown Quartz Monzodiorite Pluton, west-central Massachusetts: A syntectonic Acadian intrusion. Amer. J. Sci. 279, 936-969.

Bailey, E. H., Irwin, W. P. and Jones, D. L. (1964) Franciscan and related rocks and their significance in the geology of western California. Calif. Div. Mines Geol. Bull. 183, 89-112.

Bancroft, G. M. and Burns, R. G. (1969) Mössbauer and absorption spectral study of alkali amphiboles. Mineral. Soc. Amer. Spec. Paper 2, 137-148.

Banno, S. (1964) Petrologic studies on Sanbagawa crystalline schists in the Bessi-Ino district, central Shikoku, Japan. Tokyo Univ. Fac. Sci. J. Sec. II, 15, 203-319.

Becker, R. H. and Clayton, R. N. (1976) Oxygen isotope study of a Precambrian banded iron-formation, Hamersley Range, Western Australia. Geochim. Cosmochim. Acta 40, 1153-1165.

Beeson, R. (1978) The geochemistry of orthamphiboles and coexisting cordierites and phlogopites from south Norway. Contrib. Mineral. Petrol. 66, 5-14.

Berg, J. H. and Wiebe, R. A. (1978) A new orthorhombic amphibole end member in a granulite xenolith from Labrador (abstract). EOS 59, 394.

Best, M. G. (1970) Kaersutite-peridotite inclusions and kindred megacrysts in basanitic lavas, Grand Canyon, Arizona. Contrib. Mineral. Petrol. 27, 25-44.

_____ (1974) Mantle-derived amphibole within inclusions in alkalic-basaltic lavas. J. Geophys. Res. 79, 2107-2113.

_____ (1975) Migration of hydrous fluids in the upper mantle and potassium variation in calc-alkalic rocks. Geology 3, 429-432.

Best, N. F. (1978) A preliminary study of the tremolite-edenite solid solution series In. *Progress in Experimental Petrology,* Natural Environmental Res. Council Pub. Ser. D., No. 11, 162-163.

Beukes, N. J. (1973) Precambrian iron formations of Southern Africa. Econ. Geol. 68, 960-1003.

Bickle, M. J. and Powell, R. (1977) Calcite-dolomite geothermometry for iron-bearing carbonates. The Glockner area of the Tauren Window, Austria. Contrib. Mineral. Petrol. 59, 281-292.

Billings, M. P. and White, W. S. (1950) Metamorphosed mafic dikes of the Woodsville quadrangle, Vermont and New Hampshire. Amer. Mineral. 35, 629-643.

Binns, R. A. (1965a) Hornblendes from some basic hornfelses in the New England region, South Wales. Mineral. Mag. 34, 52-65.

_____ (1965b) The mineralogy of metamorphosed basic rocks from the Willyama Complex, Broken Hill district, New South Wales, Pt. I. Hornblendes. Mineral. Mag. 35, 305-326.

_____ (1967) Barroisite-bearing eclogite from Naustdal Sogn og Fjordane, Norway. J. Petrol. 8, 349-371.

Black, P. M. (1970) Coexisting glaucophane and riebeckite-arfvedsonite from New Caledonia. Amer. Mineral. 55, 1061-1064.

_____ (1973) Mineralogy of New Caledonian Metamorphic rocks II. Amphiboles from the Ouégoa District. Contrib. Mineral. Petrol. 39, 55-64.

_____ (1974) Oxygen isotope study of metamorphic rocks from the Ouégoa district, New Caledonia. Contrib. Mineral. Petrol. 47, 197-206.

_____ (1977) Regional high-pressure metamorphism in New Caledonia: Phase equilibria in the Ouégoa district. Tectonophysics, 43, 89-107.

Blackburn, W. H. and Navarro, E. (1977) Garnet zoning and polymetamorphism in the eclogite rocks of Isla de Margarita, Venezuela. Canadian Mineral. 15, 257-266.

Blattner, Peter (1976) Replacement of hornblende by garnet in granulite facies assemblages near Milford Sound, New Zealand. Contrib. Mineral. Petrol. 55, 181-190.

Bocquet, Jacqueline (1974) Blue amphiboles of the Western Alps, chemistry and physical characters. Schweiz. Mineral. Petrol. Mitt. 54, 425-448.

Boettcher, A. L. and Wyllie, P. J. (1967) Revision of the calcite-aragonite transition, with the location of a triple point between calcite I, calcite II, and aragonite. Nature 213, 792-793.

_____ and _____ (1968) The calcite-aragonite transition measured in the system $CaO-CO_2-H_2O$. J. Geol. 76, 314-330.

Bøggild, O. B. (1905) Mineralogia Groenlandica. Medd. Grønland 32, 400.

_____ (1924) On the labradorization of the feldspars. K. Danske Videnskab. Selskab, Mat.-Fys. Medd. 6, 1-79.

Bohlen, S. R. and Essene, E. J. (1977) Feldspar and oxide thermometry of granulites in the Adirondack Highlands. Conbrib. Mineral. Petrol. 62, 153-169.

_____ and _____ (1980) Evaluation of coexisting garnet-biotite, garnet-clinopyroxene, and other Mg-Fe exchange thermometers in Adirondack granulites: summary. Geol. Soc. Amer. Bull. 91, 107-109.

_____, _____ and Hoffman, K. S. (1980) Update on feldspar and oxide thermometry in the Adirondack Mountains, New York. Geol. Soc. Amer. Bull. 91, 110-113.

Bonnichsen, B. (1969) Metamorphic pyroxenes and amphiboles in the Biwabik Iron Formation, Dunka River area, Minnesota. Mineral. Soc. Amer. Spec. Paper 2, 217-241.

Borg, I. (1967) Optical properties and cell parameters in the glaucophane-riebeckite series. Contr. Mineral. Petrol. 15, 67-92.

Boriani, A. (1965) L'anfibolite a orenblenda e cummingtonite di Ornavasso (Val d'Ossola). Soc. Mineral. Italiana Rend. 21, 25-34.

Bowen, N. L. (1940) Progressive metamorphism of siliceous limestone and dolomite. J. Geol. 48, 225-274.

Boyd, F. R. (1971) Pargasite-spinel peridotite xenolith from the Wesselton Mine. Carnegie Inst. Wash. Yearbook 70, 138-142.

Brady, J. B. (1974) Coexisting actinolite and hornblende from west-central New Hampshire. Amer. Mineral. 59, 529-535.

Brøgger, W. C. (1934) On several archaean rocks from the south coast of Norway. Vid.-Akad Skr. 1933, no. 8.

Brothers, R. N. (1970) Lawsonite-albite schists from northernmost New Caledonia. Contrib. Mineral. Petrol. 25, 185-202.

Brown, E. H. (1967) The greenschist facies in part of eastern Otago, New Zealand. Contrib. Mineral. Petrol. 14, 259-292.

_____ (1971) Phase relations of biotite and stilpnomelane in the greenschist facies. Contrib. Mineral. Petrol. 31, 275-299.

_____ (1974) Comparison of the mineralogy and phase relations of blueschists from the north Cascades, Washington, and greenschists from Otago, New Zealand. Geol. Soc. Amer. Bull. 85, 333-344.

_____ (1975) A petrogenetic grid for reactions producing biotite and other Al-Fe-Mg silicates in the greenschist facies. J. Petrol. 16, 258-271.

_____ (1977) The crossite content of Ca-amphibole as a guide to pressure of metamorphism. J. Petrol. 18, 53-72.

_____ and Bradshaw, J. Y. (1979) Phase relations of pyroxene and amphibole in greenstone, blueschist and eclogite of the Franciscan Complex, California. Contrib. Mineral. Petrol. 71, 67-83.

Brown, P. E., Essene, E. J. and Kelly, W. C. (1978) Sphalerite geobarometry in the Balmat-Edwards district, New York. Amer. Mineral. 63, 250-257.

Brown, W. H., Fyfe, W.S. and Turner, F.J.(1962) Aragonite in California glaucophane schists, and the kinetics of the aragonite-calcite transition. J. Petrol. 3, 566-582.

Buddington, A. F. (1963) Isograds and the role of H_2O in metamorphic facies of orthogneisses of the northwest Adirondack area, New York. Geol. Soc. Amer. Bull. 74, 1155-1182.

_____ and Leonard, B. F. (1953) Chemical petrology and mineralogy of hornblendes in northwest Adirondack granitic rocks. Amer. Mineral. 38, 891-902.

_____ and Lindsley, D. H. (1964) Iron-titanium oxide minerals and synthetic equivalents. J. Petrol. 5, 310-357.

Bugge, J. A. W. (1943) Geological and petrographical investigations in the Kongsberg-Bamble formation. Norsk. Geol. Unders. 160.

Burt, D. M. (1971) The facies of some Ca-Fe Si skarns in Japan. Carnegie Inst. Wash. Yearbook 70, 178-184.

Buseck, P. R., Nord, G. L., and Veblen, D. R. (1980) Subsolidus phenomena in pyroxenes (117-211). In, Prewitt, C. T., Editor, Pyroxenes, Mineral. Soc. Amer. Reviews in Mineralogy 7, 117-211.

Bussod, G.Y. (1981) Thermal and kinematic history of mantle xenoliths from Kilbourne Hole, New Mexico. M.S. thesis, University of Washington, Seattle, Washington.

Butler, P. Jr. (1969) Mineral compositions and equilibria in the metamorphosed iron-formation of the Gagnon region, Quebec, Canada. J. Petrol. 10, 56-101.

Cady, W.M. (1969) Regional tectonic synthesis of northwestern New England adjacent Quebec. Geol. Soc. Amer. Mem. 120.

Callegari, E. (1966) Osservazioni su alcune cummingtonite del massiccio dell'Adamello. Mem. Acad. Patavina Sci., Lett., Arti, Padua, 78, 273-310.

Cameron, K.L. (1975) An experimental study of actinolite-cummingtonite phase relations with notes on the synthesis of Fe-rich anthophyllite. Amer. Mineral. 60, 375-390.

Cameron, M., Sueno, S., Prewitt, C.T. and Papike, J.J. (1973) High-temperature crystal chemistry of K-fluor-richterite (abstr.). EOS 54, 497-498.

Carmichael, D.M. (1970) Intersecting isograds in the Whetstone Lake area, Ontario. J. Petrol. 11, 147-181.

_____, Moore, J.M., Jr., and Skippen, G.B. (1978) Isograds around the Hastings metamorphic "low." In Currie, A.L. and Mackasey, W.O., Editors, *Toronto 1978 Field Trips Guidebook*, Annual meeting of GSA, GAC, MAC, p. 325-346.

Carpenter, M.A. (1978) Kinetic control of ordering and exsolution in omphacite. Contrib. Mineral. Petrol. 67, 17-24.

_____ (1979) Omphacites from Greece, Turkey, and Guatemala: composition limits of cation ordering. Amer. Mineral. 64, 102-108.

_____ (1980) Sodic pyroxenes from Nybo, Norway: Solid solution and cation ordering at high temperatures (abst.) EOS 61, 403.

Cawthorn, R.G. (1975) The amphibole peridotite-metagabbro complex, Finero, Northern Italy. J. Geol. 83, 437-454.

Chinner, G.A. and Fox, J.S. (1974) The origin of cordierite-anthophyllite rocks in the Land's End aureole. Geol. Mag. 111, 397-408.

Choudhuri, A. (1974) Distribution of Fe and Mg in actinolite, hornblende and biotite in some Precambrian metagreywackes from Guyana, South America. Contrib. Mineral. Petrol. 44, 45-55.

Clark, M.D. (1978) Amphibolite rocks from the Precambrian of Grand Canyon: Mineral chemistry and phase petrology. Mineral. Mag. 42, 199-207.

Clark, S.P., Jr. (1957) A note on calcite-aragonite equilibrium. Amer. Mineral. 42, 564-566.

Coleman, R.G. (1967) Glaucophane schists from California and New Caledonia. Tectonophysics 4, 479-498.

_____ (1972) Blueschist metamorphism and plate tectonics. 24th Internat. Geol. Congr. Rept. Sec. 2, 19-26.

_____ and Lee, D.E. (1963) Galucophane-bearing metamorphic rock types of the Cazadero area, California. J. Petrol. 4, 260-301.

_____, _____, Beatty, L.B., Brannock, W.W. (1965) Eclogites and eclogites: Their differences and similarities. Geol. Soc. Amer. Bull. 76, 483-508.

_____ and Papike, J.J. (1968) Alkali amphiboles from the blueschists of Cazadero, California. J. Petrol. 9, 105-122.

Compagnoni, R. (1977) The Sesia-Lanzo Zone: High pressure-low temperature metamorphism in the Austroalpine contenental margin. Soc. Italiana Mineral. Petrol. Rendiconti 33, 335-374.

Compton, R.R. (1958) Significance of amphibole paragenesis in the Bidwell Bar region, California. Amer. Mineral. 43, 890-907.

Coombs, D.S., Horodyski, R.J., and Naylor, R.S. (1970) Occurrence of prehnite-pumpellyite facies metamorphism in northern Maine. Amer. J. Sci. 268, 142-156.

Cooper, A.F. (1972) Progressive metamorphism of metabasite rocks from the Haast Schist group of southern New Zealand. J. Petrol. 13, 457-492.

_____ and Lovering, J.F. (1970) Greenschist amphiboles from Haast River, New Zealand. Contr. Mineral. Petrol. 27, 11-24.

Crawford, W.A. and Fyfe, W.S. (1964) Calcite-aragonite equilibrium at 100°C. Science, 144, 1569-1570.

_____ and _____ (1965) Lawsonite equilibria. Amer. J. Sci. 263, 262-270.

Crowley, P.D. and Spear, F.S. (1981) The orthoamphibole solvus: P, T, X (Fe-Mg) relations. (abstr.) Geol. Soc. Amer. Abstr. with Prog., in press.

Dahl, P.S. (1979) Comparative geothermometry based on major-element and oxygen isotope distributions in Precambrian metamorphic rocks from southwestern Montana. Amer. Mineral. 64, 1280-1293.

Das Gupta, S. P. (1972) Coexisting hornblende-cummingtonite from the Kheti copper belt, Rajasthan, India. Mineral. Mag. 38, 890-893.

Deer, W. A., Howie, R. A., and Zussman, J. (1963) *Rock-forming Minerals, Vol. 2, Chain Silicates.* Longmans, Green & Co., Ltd., London, 379 p.

Desmarais, N. (1981) Precambrian metamorphic rocks in the Ruby Range, Montana. Precambrian Research (in press).

Desmons, J. (1977) Mineralogical and petrological investigations of Alpine metamorphism in the internal French Western Alps. Amer. J. Sci. 277, 1045-1066.

_____ and Ghent, E. D. (1977) Chemistry, zonation and distribution coefficients of elements in eclogitic minerals from the eastern Sesia unit, Italian Western Alps. Schweiz. Mineral. Petrog. Mitt. 57, 397-411.

_____ and O'Neil, J. R. (1978) Oxygen and hydrogen isotope compositions of eclogites and associated rocks from the eastern Sesia Zone (Western Alps, Italy). Contrib. Mineral. Petrol. 67, 79-85.

Deutsch, A. (1979) Serpentinite und Rodingite der Cima Sgui (NW Aduladeck, Ticino). Schweiz. Mineral. Petrogr. Mitt. 59, 319-348.

Dimanche, F. (1970) Les amphiboles et leurs associations dans les skarns a magnetite du Ginevro (ile d'Elba, Italio). Bull. Franc. Min. Crist. 93, 69-100.

Dimroth, E. and Chauvel, J. J. (1973) Petrography of the Sokoman Iron Formation in part of the central Labrador Trough, Quebec, Canada. Geol. Soc. Amer. Bull. 84, 111-134.

Dobretsov, N. L., Kostyuk, Ye. A., Lavrent'yev, Yu. G., Ponomareva, L. G., Pospelova, L. N., and Sobolev, V. S. (1971) Immiscibility in the sodium-calcium amphibole series and its classification. Doklady Akad. Nauk. SSSR 199, 100-103.

_____, Klestov, V. V., Reverdatto, V. V., Sobolev, N. V. and Sobolev, V. S. (1972) *The Facies of Metamorphism.* Sobolev, V. S., Ed. (Translated by D. A. Brown). Australian National Univ., Canberra, A.C.T.

_____, _____, and Sobolev, V. S. (1973) *The Facies of Regional Metamorphism at Moderate Pressures.* Sobolev, V. S., Ed. (Translated by D. A. Brown), Australian National Univ., Canberra, A.C.T.

_____, Sobolev, V. S., Sobolev, N. V., and Khlestov, V. V. (1975) *The Facies of Regional Metamorphism at High Pressures.* Sobolev, V. S., Ed. (Translated by D. A. Brown). Australian National Univ., Canberra, A.C.T.

Doolan, B. L., Drake, J. C., and Crocker, David. (1973) Actinolite and subcalcic hornblende from a greenstone of the Hazen's Notch Formation, Lincoln Mountain Quadrangle, Warren, Vermont (abstr.). Geol. Soc. Amer. Abstr. with Prog. 5, 157.

_____, Zen, E-an, and Bence, A. E. (1978) Highly aluminous hornblendes: compositions and occurrences from southwestern Massachusetts. Amer. Mineral. 63, 1088-1099.

du Toit, A. L. (1945) The origin of the amphibole asbestos deposits of South Africa. Geol. Soc. South Africa 48, 161-206.

Dymek, R. F. (1977) *Mineralogic and Petrologic Studies of Archaean Metamorphic Rocks from West Greenland, Lunar Samples, and the Meteorite Kopoeta.* Ph.D. thesis, California Inst. of Technology, Pasadena, 382 p.

Dymond, J., Corliss, J. B. and Stillinger, R. (1976) Chemical composition and metal accumulation rates of metalliferous sediments from Sites 319, 320B, and 321. In *Initial Reports, Deep Sea Drilling Project* 34, 575-589. U.S. Gov't Printing Office.

Ehrenberg, S. N. (1975) Feather River ultramafic body, Northern Sierra Nevada, California. Geol. Soc. Amer. Bull. 86, 1235-1243.

Ellis, D. J. and Green, D. H. (1979) An experimental study of the effect of Ca upon garnet-clinopyroxene Fe-Mg exchange equilibria. Contrib. Mineral. Petrol. 71, 13-22.

Engel, A. E. J. and Engel, C. G. (1962) Hornblendes formed during progressive metamorphism of amphibolites, northwest Adirondack Mountains, New York. Geol. Soc. Amer. Bull. 73, 1499-1514.

_____, _____ and Havens, R. G. (1964) Mineralogy of amphibolite interlayers in the gneiss complex, northwest Adirondack Mountains, New York. J. Geol. 72, 131-156.

England, P. C. and Richardson, S. W. (1977) The influence of erosion upon the mineral facies of rocks from different metamorphic environments. J. Geol. Soc. London 134, 201-213.

Ernst, W. G. (1963a) Petrogenesis of glaucophane schists. J. Petrol. 4, 1-30.

_____ (1963b) Polymorphism in alkali amphiboles. Amer. Mineral. 48, 241-260.

_____ (1964) Petrochemical study of coexisting minerals from low-grade schists, Eastern Shikoku, Japan. Geochim. Cosmochim. Acta 28, 1631-1668.

_____ (1966) Amphibole phase relations, pp. E-1 to E-41. In Smith, J. V. Ed., *Short Course Lecture Notes: Chain Silicates.* Amer. Geol. Inst.

_____ (1968) *Amphiboles: Crystal Chemistry, Phase Relations and Occurrence.* Springer-Verlag, New York, 125 p.

_____ (1971) Do mineral parageneses reflect unusually high-pressure conditions of Franciscan metamorphism? Amer. J. Sci. 270, 81-108.

_____ (1972a) Ca-amphibole paragenesis in the Shirataki District, central Shikoku, Japan. Geol. Soc. Amer. Mem. 135, 73-94.

_____ (1972b) Occurrence and mineralogical evolution of blueschist belts with time. Amer. J. Sci. 272, 657-668.

_____ (1973) Interpretative synthesis of metamorphism in the Alps. Geol. Soc. Amer. Bull. 84, 2053-2078.

_____, (Ed.) (1975a) *Metamorphism and Plate Tectonic Regimes.* Dowden, Hutchinson, and Ross, Stroudsburg, Pennsylvania.

_____, (Ed.) (1975b) *Subduction Zone Metamorphism.* Dowden, Hutchinson and Ross, Stroudsburg, Pennsylvania.

_____ (1976) *Petrologic Phase Equilibria.* W. H. Freeman and Co., San Francisco, 333 p.

_____ (1977) Tectonics and prograde versus retrograde P-T trajectories of high-pressure metamorphic belts. Soc. Italiana Mineral. Petrol. Rendiconti 33, 191-220.

_____ (1978) Petrochemical study of some lherzolitic rocks from the Western Alps. J. Petrol. 19, 341-392.

_____ (1979) Coexisting sodic and calcic amphiboles from high-pressure metamorphic belts and the stability of barroisitic amphibole. Mineral. Mag. 43, 269-278.

_____ (1981) Petrogenesis of eclogites and peridotites from the Western and Ligurian Alps. Amer. Mineral. 66, 443-472.

_____ and Dal Piaz, V. G. (1978) Mineral paragenesis of eclogitic rocks and related mafic schists of the Piemonte ophiolite nappe, Breuil-St. Jacques area, Italian Western Alps. Amer. Mineral. 63, 621-640.

_____, Seki, Y., Onuki, H. and Gilbert, M. C. (1970) Comparative study of low-grade metamorphism in the California Coast Ranges and the outer Metamorphic Belt of Japan. Geol. Soc. Amer. Mem. 124, 276 p.

Eskola, P. (1914) On the petrology of the Orijärvi region in southwestern Finland. Bull. Comm. Geol. Finlande, No. 40, 274p.

_____ (1915) Om sambandet mellan kemisk och mineralogisk sammansättning hos orjarvitraktens metamorfa Bergarter. Bull. Comm. Geol. Finlande, No. 44, 145p.

_____ (1920) The mineral facies of rocks. Norsk. Geol. Tidsskr. 6, 143-194.

_____ (1939) *Die enstehung der Gesteine.* Springer-Verlag, Berlin.

_____ (1950) Paragenesis of cummingtonite and hornblende from Muuruvesi, Finland. Amer. Mineral. 35, 728-734.

Eugster, H. P., Albee, A. L., Bence, A. E., Thompson, J. B., Jr., and Waldbaum, D. R. (1972) The two-phase region and excess mixing properties of paragonite-muscovite crystalline solutions. J. Petrol. 13, 147-179.

Evans, B. W. and Leake, B. E. (1960) The composition and origin of the striped amphibolites of Connemara, Ireland. J. Petrol. 1, 337-363.

_____ (1977) Metamorphism of alpine peridotite and serpentinite. Ann. Rev. Earth Planet. Sci. 5, 397-447.

_____ and Frost, B. R. (1975) Chrome-spinel in progressive metamorphism-a preliminary analysis. Geochim. Cosmochim. Acta. 39, 959-972.

_____ and Guidotti, C. V. (1966) The sillimanite-potash feldspar isograd in western Maine, U.S.A. Contrib. Mineral. Petrol. 12, 25-62.

_____ and Trommsdorff, V. (1974) Stability of enstatite + talc, and CO_2-metasomatism of metaperidotite, Val d'Efra, Lepontine Alps. Amer. J. Sci. 274, 274-296.

_____ and _____. (1978) Petrogenesis of garnet lherzolite, Cima di Gagnone, Lepontine Alps. Earth Planet. Sci. Letters 40, 333-348.

Ewart, A., Hildreth, W., and Carmichael, I.S.E. (1975) Quaternary acid magma in New Zealand. Contrib. Mineral. Petrol. 51, 1-27.

Fabries, J. and Perseil, E. A. (1971) Nouvelles observations sur les amphiboles orthorhombiques. Bull. Soc. franc. Mineral. Crist. 94, 385-395.

Fajklewicz, A. (1968) Hornblende from amphibole rocks of Kletao (Lower Silesia). Polska Akad. Nauk., Prace Min. 14, 31-44.

Faye, G. H. and Hogarth, D. D. (1969) On the origin of "reverse pleochroism" of a phlogopite. Canadian Mineral. 10, 25-34.

Feininger, T. (1980) Eclogite and related high-pressure regional metamorphic rocks from the Andes of Ecuador. J. Petrol. 21, 107-140.

Fleet, M. E. and Barnett, R. L. (1978) Al^{IV}/Al^{VI} partitioning in calciferous amphiboles from the Frood Mine, Sudbury, Ontario. Canadian Mineral. 16, 527-532.

Floran, R. J. (1975) *Mineralogy and Petrology of the Sedimentary and Contact Metamorphosed Gunflint Iron Formation, Ontario-Minnesota.* Ph.D. Dissertation, State University of New York, Stony Brook, N.Y.

_____ and Papike, J. J. (1978) Mineralogy and petrology of the Gunflint Iron Formation, Minnesota-Ontario: correlation of compositional and assemblage variations at low to moderate grade. J. Petrol. 19, 215-288.

Floyd, P. A. (1965) Metasomatic hornfelses of the Land's End aureole of Tater-du, Cornwall. J. Petrol. 6, 223-245.

Fonarev, V. I. and Korolkov, G. Ja. (1980) The assemblage orthopyroxene + cummingtonite + quartz. The low-temperature stability limit. Contrib. Mineral. Petrol. 73, 413-420.

_____, _____ and Dokina, T. N. (1979) Laboratory data on the stability field of the cummingtonite + olivine + quartz association (translation). Geochem. International 16, no. 4, 21-32.

Francis, D. M. (1976) The origin of amphibole in lherzolite xenoliths from Nunivak Island, Alaska. J. Petrol. 17, 357-378.

_____ (1977) Amphibole pyroxenite xenoliths: Cumulate or replacement phenomena from the upper mantle, Nunivak Island, Alaska. Contrib. Mineral. Petrol. 58, 51-62.

Franz, G. and Althaus, E. (1977) The stability relations of the paragenesis paragonite-zoisite-quartz. N. Jb. Mineral. 130, 159-167.

French, B. M. (1968) *Progressive contact metamorphism of the Biwabik Iron Formation, Mesabi Range, Minnesota.* Minnesota Geol. Surv. Bull. 45.

Frey, F. A. and Green, D. H. (1974) The mineralogy and origin of lherzolite inclusions in Victorian basanites. Geochim. Cosmochim. Acta 38, 1023-1059.

Frey, M., Hunziker, J. C., Frank, W., Bocquet (Desmons), J., Dal Piaz, G. V., Jäger, E., and Niggli, E. (1974) Alpine metamorphism of the Alps, a review. Schweiz. Mineral. Petrog. Mitt. 54, 247-290.

Frey, Martin. (1969) Die Metamorphose des Keupers vom Tafeljura bis zum Lukmanier-Geibiet. Beitr. Geol. Karte Schweiz. (N.F.) 137, Lieferung.

Froese, E. (1969) Metamorphic rocks from the Coronation Mine and surrounding area. In *Symposium on the Geology of Coronation Mine, Saskatchewan,* A. R. Byers, ed., Geol. Surv. Canada 68-5, 55-78.

Frost, B. R. (1975) Contact metamorphism of serpentinite, chloritic blackwall and rodingite at Paddy-Go-Easy Pass, Central Cascades, Washington. J. Petrol. 16, 272-313.

_____ (1976) Limits to the assemblage forsterite + anorthite as inferred from peridotite hornfelses, Icicle Creek, Washington. Amer Mineral. 61, 732-750.

Fry, N. and Fyfe, W. S. (1971) On the significance of the eclogite facies in alpine metamorphism. Verh. Geol. Bundesanstalt, Vienna 2, 257-265.

Fyfe, W. S., Turner, F. J. and Verhoogen, J. (1958) Metamorphic reactions and metamorphic facies. Geol. Soc. Amer. Mem. 73, 259 p.

Gable, D. J. and Sims, P. K. (1970) *Geology and Regional Metamorphism of some High-Grade Cordierite Gneisses, Front Range, Colorado.* Geol. Soc. Amer. Spec. Paper 128, 84 p.

Gair, J. E. (1975) *Bedrock Geology and Ore Deposits of the Palmer Quadrangle, Marquette County, Michigan.* U. S. Geol. Surv. Prof. Paper 769.

Ganguly, J. (1973) Activity-composition relation of jadeite in omphacite pyroxene: Theoretical deductions. Earth Planet. Sci. Letters 19, 145-153.

_____ (1979) Garnet and clinopyroxene solid solutions, and geothermometry based on Fe-Mg distribution coefficient. Geochim. Cosmochim. Acta 43, 1021-1029.

Garrison, J. R. (1981) Coal Creek Serpentinite, Llano Uplift, Texas: A fragment of an incomplete Precambrian ophiolite. Geology 9, 225-230.

Ghent, E. D. and Coleman, R. G. (1973) Eclogites from southwestern Oregon. Geol. Soc. Amer. Bull. 84, 2471-2488.

Gillmeister, N. (1971) *The Petrology, Stratigraphy and Structure of the Precambrian Metamorphic Rocks of the central Tobacco Root Mountains with special emphasis on Electron Microprobe Analysis of High Grade Mineral Assemblages.* Ph.D. Dissertation, Harvard University, Cambridge, Mass.

Gittos, M. F., Lorimer, G. W., and Champness, P. E. (1976) The phase distributions in some exsolved amphiboles. In *Electron Microscopy in Mineralogy,* Wenk, H. R., Ed., Springer-Verlag, Berlin, p. 238-247.

Goffe, B. (1977) Succession de subfacies métamorphiques en Vanoise méridionale (Savoie). Contrib. Mineral. Petrol. 62, 23-41.

Goldman, D. S. (1979) A reevaluation of the Mössbauer spectroscopy of calcic amphiboles. Amer. Mineral. 64, 109-118.

_____ and Rossman, G. R. (1977) The identification of Fe^{2+} in the M(4) site of calcic amphiboles. Amer. Mineral. 62, 205-216.

Goldschmidt, V. M. (1911) Die Kontaktmetamorphose im Kristianiagebiet. Vid. Selsk. Skr. 1911.

Gole, M. J. (1979) *Metamorphosed Banded Iron-Formations in the Archean Yilgarn Block, Western Australia*. Ph.D. Dissertation, University of Western Australia, Nedlands, W.A.

_____ (1980) Formation of grunerite in banded iron-formation (BIF), Yilgarn Block, Western Australia (abstr.). Geol. Soc. Amer. Abstr. with Prog. 12, 227.

_____ and Klein, C. (1981a) Banded iron - formations through much of Precambrian time. J. Geol. 89, 169-183.

_____ and _____ (1981b) High grade metamorphic Archean banded iron-formations, Western Australia: assemblages with coexisting pyroxenes±fayalite. Amer. Mineral. 66, 87-99.

Goroshnikov, V. I. and Yur'yev, L. D. (1965) Cordierite-polyamphibole and anythophyllite-cordierite rocks of the north Krivoy Rog district. Doklady Akad. Nauk SSSR 163, 140-143.

Gosso, G. (1977) Metamorphic evolution and fold history in the eclogitic micaschists of the upper Gressoney Valley (Sesia-Lanzo Zone, Western Alps). Soc. Italiana Mineral.Petrol. Rendiconti 33, 389-407.

Graham, C. M. (1974) Metabasite amphiboles of the Scottish Dalradian. Contrib. Mineral. Petrol. 47, 165-185.

Grant, J. A. (1968) Partial melting of common rocks as a possible source of cordierite-anthophyllite assemblages. Amer. J. Sci. 266, 908-931.

_____ (1973) Phase equilibria in high-grade metamorphism and partial melting of pelitic rocks. Amer. J. Sci. 273, 289-317.

_____ (1978) Orthoamphibole and orthopyroxene relations in high-grade metamorphism of pelitic rocks (abstr.). Geol. Soc. Amer. Abstr. with Prog. 10, 411.

Grapes, R. H. (1975) Actinolite-hornblende pairs in metamorphosed gabbros, Hidaka Mountains, Hokkaido. Contrib. Mineral. Petrol. 49, 125-140.

_____ and Graham, C. M. (1978) The actinolite-hornblende series in metabasites and the so-called miscibility gap: a review. Lithos 11, 85-97.

Gray, J. R. and Yardley, B. W. D. (1979) A Caledonian blueschist from the Irish Dalradian. Nature 278, 736-737.

Green, D. H. (1964) The petrogenesis of the high temperature peridotite intrusion in the Lizard area, Cornwall. J. Petrol. 5, 134-188.

Greenwood, H. J. (1975) Thermodynamically valid projections of extensive phase relationships. Amer. Mineral. 60, 1-8.

_____ (1976) Metamorphism at moderate temperatures and pressures. In *The Evolution of the Crystalline Rocks*, Bailey, D. K. and Macdonald, R., eds., Academic Press, New York, p. 187-259.

_____ (1979) Thermodynamic properties of edenite. In Current Research, Part B, Geol. Surv. Canada Paper 79-1B, 365-370.

Griffin, W. L. (1973) Lherzolite nodules from the Fen Alkaline Complex, Norway. Contrib. Mineral. Petrol. 38, 135-146.

Haase, C. S. (1979) *Metamorphic Petrology of the Negaunee Iron Formation, Marquette District, Northern Michigan*. Ph.D. Dissertation, Indiana University, Bloomington, IN.

_____ (1981) Metamorphic petrology of the Negaunee Iron Formation, Marquette District, Northern Michigan: Mineralogy, metamorphic reactions and phase equilibria. Econ. Geol. (in press).

Hafner, S. S. and Huckenholz, H. G. (1971) Mössbauer spectrum of synthetic ferridiopside. Nature 233, 9-11.

Hall, D. J. (1970) *Compositional Variations in Biotites and Garnets from Kyanite and Sillimanite Zone Mica Schists, Orange Area, Massachusetts and New Hampshire*. Contrib. 4, Dept. Geology, University of Massachusetts, Amherst, Mass., 110 p.

_____ (1973) *Geology and Geophysics of the Belchertown batholith, west-central Massachusetts*. Ph.D. Dissertation, University of Massachusetts, Amherst, Mass., 110 p.

Harte, B. and Graham, C. M. (1975) The graphical analysis of greenschist to amphibolite facies mineral assemblages in metabasites. J. Petrol. 16, 347-370.

Hashimoto, M. (1966) On the prehnite-pumpellyite metagreywacke facies. Geol. Soc. Japan. J. 72, 253-265.

_____ (1973) Riebeckite-aegirine-quartz schist of Ishigakishima. Mem. Nat. Sci. Mus. Tokyo 7, 19-24.

Haslam, H. W. and Walker, B. G. (1971) A metamorphosed pyroxenite at Nero Hill, central Tanzania. Mineral. Mag. 38, 58-63.

Hawthorne, F. C. (1976) The crystal chemistry of the amphiboles: V. The structure and chemistry of arfvedsonite. Canadian Mineral. 14, 346-356.

_____, Griep, J. L. and Curtis, L. (1980) A three amphibole assemblage from the Talon Lake sill, Peterborough County, Ontario. Canadian Mineral. 18, 275-284.

Hietanen, A. (1959) Kyanite-garnet-gedritite near Orofino, Idaho. Amer. Mineral. 44, 539-564.

_____ (1974) Amphibole pairs, epidote minerals, chlorite and plagioclase in metamorphic rocks, northern Sierra Nevada, California. Amer. Mineral. 59, 22-40.

Himmelberg, G. R. and Papike, J. J. (1969) Coexisting amphiboles from blueschist facies metamorphic rocks. J. Petrol. 10, 102-114.

Hlabse, T. and Kleppa, O. J. (1968) The thermochemistry of jadeite. Amer. Mineral. 53, 1281-1292.

Hoffer, Edgar and Grant, J. A. (1980) Experimental investigation of the formation of cordierite-orthopyroxene parageneses in pelitic rocks. Contrib. Mineral. Petrol. 73, 15-22.

Holland, T. J. B. (1979a) Experimental determination of the reaction paragonite=jadeite+kyanite +H_2O, and internally consistent thermodynamic data for part of the system $Na_2O-Al_2O_3-SiO_2-H_2O$, with applications to eclogites and blueschists. Contrib. Mineral. Petrol. 68, 293-301.

_____ (1979b) High water activities in the generation of high pressure kyanite eclogites of the Tauern Window, Austria. J. Geol. 87, 1-27.

_____ (1980) The reaction albite=jadeite+quartz determined experimentally in the range 600-1200°C. Amer. Mineral. 65, 129-134.

_____ and Richardson, S. W. (1979) Amphibole zonation in metabasites as a guide to the evolution of metamorphic conditions. Contrib. Mineral. Petrol. 70, 143-148.

Holm, R. F. (1971) Some garnets, pyroxenes and amphiboles from nepheline gneisses in Ghana. Amer. Mineral. 56, 2111-2132.

Hörmann, P. K., Raith, M., Raase, P., Ackermand, D. and Seifert, F. (1980) *The Granulite Complex of Finnish Lapland: Petrology and Metamorphic Conditions in the Ivalojoki-Inarijärvi Area.* Geol. Surv. Finland Bull. 308, 95 p.

Huebner, J. S. (1980) Pyroxene phase equilibria at low pressure. In *Pyroxenes,* Prewitt, C. T., ed., Mineral. Soc. Amer. Rev. Mineral. 7, 213-288.

Humphris, S.E. and Thompson, G. (1978) Hydrothermal alteration of oceanic basalts by seawater. Geochim. Cosmochim. Acta 42, 107-125.

Hunt, J. A. and Kerrick, D. M. (1977) The stability of sphene; experimental redetermination and geologic implications. Geochim. Cosmochim. Acta 37, 2533-2546.

Hunter, W. C. and Smith, D. (1981) Garnet peridotite from Colorado Plateau ultramafic diatremes, hydrates, carbonates, and comparative geothermometry. Contrib. Mineral. Petrol. 76, 312-320.

Huntington, J. C. (1975) *Mineralogy and Petrology of Metamorphosed Iron-Rich Beds in the Lower Devonian Littleton Formation, Orange Area, Massachusetts.* Contrib. 19 (M.S. Thesis), Dept. Geol. & Geogr., Univ. Massachusetts, Amherst, MA, 106p.

Hutchison, J. L., Irusteta, M. C. and Whittaker, E. J. W. (1975) High resolution electron microscopy and diffraction studies of fibrous amphiboles. Acta Crystallogr. A31, 794-801.

Immega, I. and Klein, C. (1976) Mineralogy and petrology of some metamorphic Precambrian iron-formations in southwestern Montana. Amer. Mineral. 61, 1117-1144.

Iwasaki, M. (1963) Metamorphic rocks of the Kotu-Bizan area, eastern Shikoku. Tokyo Univ. Fac. Sci. J. Sec. II, 15, 1-90.

Jaffe, H. W., Groeneveld Meyer, W. O. J. and Selchow, D. H. (1961) Manganoan cummingtonite from Nsuta, Ghana. Amer. Mineral. 46, 642-653.

_____, Robinson, P. and Klein, C. (1968) Exsolution lamellae and optic orientation of clinoamphiboles. Science 160, 776-778.

_____, _____, and Tracy, R. J. (1978) Orthoferrosilite and other iron-rich pyroxenes in microperthite gneiss of the Mount Marcy area, Adirondack Mountains. Amer. Mineral. 63, 1116-1136.

James, H. L. (1955) Zones of regional metamorphism in the Precambrian of Northern Michigan. Geol. Soc. Amer. Bull. 66, 1455-1488.

_____ and Clayton, R. N. (1962) Oxygen isotope fractionation in metamorphosed iron-formations of the Lake Superior region and in other iron-rich rocks. In *Petrologic Studies: A Volume to Honor A. F. Buddington,* Engel, A. E. J., Jones, H. C. and Leonard, H. F., eds., Geol. Soc. Amer., 217-239.

James, R. A., Grieve, R. A. F., and Pauk, L. (1978) The petrology of cordierite-anthophyllite gneisses and associated mafic and pelitic gneisses at Manitouwadge, Ontario. Amer. J. Sci. 278, 41-63.

Jamieson, J. C. (1953) Phase equilibria in the system calcite-aragonite. J. Chem. Physics 21, 1385-1390.

Jamieson, R. A. (1977) The first metamorphic sodic amphibole identified from the Newfoundland Appalachians - its occurrence, composition and possible tectonic implications. Nature 265, 428-430.

Johannes, W., Bell, P. M., Boettcher, A. L., Chipman, D. W., Hays, J. F., Mao, H. K., Newton, R. C. and Seifert, F. (1971) An interlaboratory comparison of piston-cylinder pressure calibration using the albite breakdown reaction. Contrib. Mineral. Petrol. 32, 24-38.

_____ and Puhan, D. (1971) The calcite-aragonite transition, reinvestigated. Contrib. Mineral. Petrol. 31, 28-38.

Kamineni, D. C. (1975) Chemical mineralogy of some cordierite-bearing rocks near Yellowknife, Northwest Territories, Canada. Contrib. Mineral. Petrol. 53, 293-310.

Kearns, L. E., Kite, L. E., Leavens, P. B. and Nelen, J. A. (1980) Fluorine distribution in the hydrous silicate minerals of the Franklin Marble, Orange County, New York. Amer. Mineral. 65, 557-562.

Kerrick, D. M. (1968) Experiments on the upper stability limit of pyrophyllite at 1.8 kilobars and 3.9 kilobars water pressure. Amer. J. Sci. 266, 204-214.

_____ (1974) Review of metamorphic mixed-volatile (H_2O-CO_2) equilibria. Amer. Mineral. 59, 729-762.

Kisch, H. J. (1969) Magnesiocummingtonite -- $P2_1/m$: A Ca- and Mn-poor clinoamphibole from New South Wales. Contrib. Mineral. Petrol. 21, 319-331.

_____ and Warnaars, F. W. (1969) Distribution of Mg and Fe in cummingtonite-hornblende and cummingtonite-actinolite pairs from metamorphic assemblages. Contrib. Mineral. Petrol. 24, 245-267.

Klein, C. (1964) Cummingtonite-grunerite series: a chemical, optical and X-ray study. Amer. Mineral. 49, 963-982.

_____ (1966) Mineralogy and petrology of the metamorphosed Wabush Iron Formation, southwestern Labrador. J. Petrol. 7, 240-305.

_____ (1968) Coexisting amphiboles. J. Petrol. 9, 281-330.

_____ (1969) Two-amphibole assemblages in the system actinolite-hornblende-glaucophane. Amer. Mineral. 54, 212-237.

_____ (1973) Changes in mineral assemblages with metamorphism of some banded Precambrian iron-formations. Econ. Geol. 68, 1075-1088.

_____ (1974) Greenalite, stilpnomelane, minnesotaite, crocidolite and carbonates in a very low grade metamorphic Precambrian iron-formation. Canadian Mineral. 12, 475-498.

_____ (1978) Regional metamorphism of Proterozoic iron-formation, Labrador Trough, Canada. Amer. Mineral. 63, 898-912.

_____ and Gole, M. J. (1981) Mineralogy and petrology of parts of the Marra Mamba Iron Formation, Hamersley Basin, Western Australia. Amer. Mineral. 66, 507-526.

_____ and Ito, J. (1968) Zincian and manganoan amphiboles from Franklin, New Jersey. Amer. Mineral. 53, 1264-1275.

_____ and Waldbaum, D. R. (1967) X-ray crystallographic properties of the cummingtonite-grunerite series. J. Geol. 75, 379-392.

Korikovsky, S. P. (1979) *Faat'si Metamorphizma Metapelitov*. Academy of Science, USSR, Moscow, 263 p.

Kornprobst, J., Kienast, J. R. and Vilminot, J. C. (1979) The high-pressure assemblages at Milos, Greece. Contrib. Mineral. Petrol. 69, 49-63.

Korzhinskii, D. S. (1959) *Physicochemical Basis of the Analysis of the Paragenesis of Minerals*. Consultants Bureau, New York, 142 p.

Kostyuk, E. A. and Sobolev, V. S. (1969) Paragenetic types of calciferous amphiboles and metamorphic rocks. Lithos 2, 67-81.

Kranck, S. H. (1961) A study of phase equilibria in a metamorphic iron-formation. J. Petrol. 2, 137-184.

Kretz, R. and Jen, L. S. (1978) Effect of temperature on the distribution of Mg and Fe^{2+} between calcic pyroxene and hornblende. Canadian Mineral. 16, 533-537.

Krogh, E. J. and Räheim, A. (1978) Temperature and pressure dependence of Fe-Mg partitioning between garnet and phengite, with particular reference to eclogites. Contrib. Mineral. Petrol. 66, 75-80.

Kulke, H. G. (1976) *Die salinare Trias des Atlas-System (Nordwest-Afrika). Fazies-verteilung, Tektonik, Morphologie, Petrographie, Mineralogie und Geochemie*. Habilitationsschrift, Ruhr-University, Bochum, West Germany.

Kuniyoshi, S. and Liou, J. G. (1976) Contact metamorphism of the Karmutsen Volcanics, Vancouver Island, British Columbia. J. Petrol. 17, 73-99.

Kushiro, I. (1969) Clinopyroxene solid solutions formed by reactions between diopside and plagioclase at high pressures. Mineral. Soc. Amer. Spec. Paper 2, 179-191.

Laird, J. (1977) *Phase Equilibria in Mafic Schist and the Polymetamorphic History of Vermont.* Ph.D. Dissertation, California Institution of Technology, Pasadena, CA.

_____ (1980) Phase equilibria in mafic schist from Vermont. J. Petrol. 21, 1-37.

_____ and Albee, A. L. (1981a) High-pressure metamorphism in mafic schist from northern Vermont. Amer. J. Sci. 281, 97-126.

_____ and _____ (1981b) Pressure, temperature, and time indicators in mafic schist: Their application to reconstructing the polymetamorphic history of Vermont. Amer. J. Sci. 281, 127-175.

_____, Thompson, A. B., and Thompson, J. B. Jr. (1978) Amphibole reactions in mafic schist (abstr.). EOS, Amer. Geophys. Union Trans. 59, 408.

_____, and _____ (1979) P, T calibration of amphibole reactions in mafic schist (abstr.). EOS, Amer. Geophys. Union Trans. 60, 424.

Lal, R. K. (1969) Paragenetic relations of aluminosilicates and gedrites from Fishtail Lake, Ontario, Canada. Lithos 2, 187-196.

_____ and Moorhouse, W. W. (1968) Cordierite-gedrite rocks and associated gneisses of Fishtail Lake, Harcourt Township, Ontario. Canadian J. Earth Sci. 6, 145-165.

Leake, B. E. (1965) The relationship between tetrahedral aluminum and the maximum possible octahedral aluminum in natural calciferous and sub-calciferous amphiboles. Amer. Mineral. 50, 843-851.

_____ (1968) A catalog of analyzed calciferous and sub-calciferous amphiboles together with their nomenclature and associated minerals. Geol. Soc. Amer. Spec. Paper 68, 210 p.

_____ (1971) On aluminous and edenitic hornblendes. Mineral. Mag. 38, 389-407.

_____ (1978) Nomenclature of amphiboles. Amer. Mineral. 63, 1023-1053.

Leavy, B. D. and Hermes, O. D. (1979) Mantle xenoliths from southeastern New England. In *The Mantle Sample: Inclusions in Kimberlites and Other Volcanics,* Boyd, F. R. and Meyer, H. O. A., eds., Amer. Geophys. Union: Proc. Second Internat. Kimberlite Conf., 374-381.

Liou, J. G. (1970) P-T stabilities of laumontite, wairakite, lawsonite, and related minerals in the system $CaAl_2Si_2O_8-SiO_2-H_2O$. J. Petrol. 12, 379-411.

_____, Ho. C. O. and Yen, T. P. (1975) Petrology of some glaucophane schists and related rocks from Taiwan. J. Petrol. 16, 80-109.

_____, Kuniyoshi, S. and Ito, K. (1974) Experimental studies of the phase relations between greenschist and amphibolite in a basaltic system. Amer. J. Sci. 274, 613-632.

Lombardo, B., Compagnoni, R., Fiora, L., and Facchinelli, A. (1977) Composition of some sodic pyroxenes from the eclogitic micaschists of lower Val d'Aosta (Sesia-Lanzo zone, Western Alps). Soc. Italiana Mineral. Petrol., Rendiconti, 33, 375-387.

Lovering, J. F. and White, A. J. R. (1969) Granulitic and eclogitic inclusions from basic pipes at Delegate, Australia. Contrib. Mineral. Petrol. 21, 9-52.

Makanjuola, A. A. and Howie, R. A. (1972) The mineralogy of the glaucophane schists and associated rocks from Ile de Groix, Brittany, France. Contrib. Mineral. Petrol. 35, 83-118.

Manghnani, M. (1970) Analcime-jadeite phase boundary. Phys. Earth Planet. Interiors 3, 456-461.

Maresch, W. V. (1977) Experimental studies of glaucophane: An analysis of present knowledge. Tectonophysics 43, 109-125.

_____ and Abraham, K. (1977) Chemographic analysis of reaction textures in an eclogite from the island of Margarita (Venezuela). N. Jahrb. Mineral. Abh. 130, 103-113.

Maxwell, J. A. (1968) *Rock and Mineral Analysis.* (Vol. 27 of *Chemical Analysis*). Interscience Publishers, N. Y., 584 p.

Medaris, L. G. (1980) Petrogenesis of the Lien peridotite and associated eclogites, Almklovdalen, Western Norway. Lithos 13, 339-353.

Milton, C. and Eugster, H. P. (1959) Mineral assemblages of the Green River Formation. In *Researches in Geochemistry,* Abelson, P. H., ed., John Wiley and Sons, New York, 118-151.

_____, Ingram, B. and Breger, I. (1974) Authigenic magnesioarfvedsonite from the Green River Formation, Duchesne County, Utah. Amer. Mineral. 59, 830-836.

Misch, P. and Rice, J. M. (1975) Miscibility of tremolite and hornblende in progressive Skagit Metamorphic Suite, North Cascades, Washington. J. Petrol. 16, 1-21.

Miyashiro, A. (1957) The chemistry, optics and genesis of the alkali amphiboles. J. Fac. Sci. Univ. Tokyo Sec II, 11, 57-83.

_____ (1958) Regional metamorphism of the Gosaisyo-Takanuki district in the central Abukuma Plateau. J. Fac. Sci. Univ. Tokyo Sec. II, 11, 219-272.

_____ (1961) Evolution of metamorphic belts. J. Petrol. 2, 277-311.

_____ (1968) Metamorphism of mafic rocks. In *Basalts, Vol. 2,* Hess, H. H. and Poldervaart, A., eds., John Wiley and Sons, New York, 799-834.

_____ (1973) *Metamorphism and Metamorphic Belts.* John Wiley and Sons, New York, 492 p.

_____ and Banno, S. (1958) Nature of glaucophanitic metamorphism. Amer. J. Sci. 256, 97-110.

Moody, J. B., Meyer, D. and Jenkins, J. E. (1980, manuscript and pers. comm.) Quantitative characterization of the greenschist/amphibolite boundary in mafic systems. Submitted to Amer. J. Sci.

Moore, D. E. and Liou, J. G. (1979) Mineral chemistry of some Franciscan blueschist facies metasedimentary rocks from the Diablo Range, California. Geol. Soc. Amer. Bull. 90, 1737-1781.

Moore, J. N. and Kerrick, D. M. (1976) Equilibria in siliceous dolomites of the Alta aureole, Utah. Amer. J. Sci. 276, 502-524.

Morey, G. B., Papike, J. J., Smith, R. W. and Weiblen, P. W. (1972) Observations on the contact metamorphism of the Biwabik Iron Formation, East Mesabi District, Minnesota. Geol. Soc. Amer. Memoir 135, 225-264.

Morgan, B. A. (1970) Petrology and mineralogy of eclogite and garnet amphibolite from Puerto Cabello, Venezuela. J. Petrol. 11, 101-145.

Mottl, M. J. (1976) *Chemical Exchange between Seawater and Basalt during Hydrothermal Alteration of the Oceanic Crust.* Ph.D. Dissertation, Harvard University, Cambridge, Massachusetts.

Mueller, R. F. (1960) Compositional characteristics and equilibrium relations in mineral assemblages of a metamorphosed iron-formation. Amer. J. Sci. 258, 449-497.

_____ (1961) Analysis of relations among Fe, Mg, and Mn in certain metamorphic minerals. Geochim. Cosmochim. Acta 25, 267-296.

Muir Wood, R. (1980) Compositional zoning in sodic amphiboles from the blueschist facies. Mineral. Mag. 43, 741-752.

Munhá, J. (1979) Blue amphiboles, metamorphic regime and plate tectonic modelling in the Iberian Pyrite Belt. Contrib. Mineral. Petrol. 69, 279-289.

Nemec, D. (1968) Die Stellung des Amphibole der Mineralparagenese westmahrischer Skarngesteine. Tschermaks Mineral. Petrol. Mitt. 12, 321-349.

_____ (1970) Chemische Zusammensetzung der Ca-amphibole aus den regionalmetamorphen skarnen Westmehrens. N. Jahrb. Mineral. Abh. 113, 50-67.

Newton, R. C. and Fyfe, W. S. (1976) High pressure metamorphism. In *The Evolution of the Crystalline Rocks*, Bailey, D. K. and MacDonald, R., eds., Academic Press, London, 101-186.

_____ and Kennedy, G. C. (1963) Some equilibrium reactions in the join $CaAl_2Si_2O_8$-H_2O. J. Geophys. Res. 68, 2967-2984.

_____ and Smith, J. V. (1967) Investigations concerning the breakdown of albite at depth in the earth. J. Geol. 75, 268-286.

Nitsch, K.-H. (1971) Die Niedrig-temperaturgrenze des Anorthit-stabilitätsfeldes. Fortschr. Mineral. 49, 34-36.

_____ (1972) Das P-T-X_{CO_2}- Stabilitätsfeld von Lawsonit. Contrib. Mineral. Petrol. 34, 116-134.

Oba, T. (1980) Phase relations in the tremolite-pargasite join. Contrib. Mineral. Petrol. 71, 247-256.

Obata, M. (1980) The Ronda peridotite: Garnet-, spinel-, and plagioclase-lherzolite facies and the P-T trajectories of a high-temperature mantle intrusion. J. Petrol. 21, 533-572.

Okay, A. I. (1980a) Mineralogy, petrology, and phase relations of glaucophane-lawsonite zone blueschists from the Tavsanli region, northwest Turkey. Contrib. Mineral. Petrol. 72, 243-255.

_____ (1980b) Sodic amphiboles as oxygen fugacity indicators in metamorphism. J. Geol. 88, 225-232.

Okrusch, M., Seidel, E. and Davis, E. N. (1978) The assemblage jadeite-quartz in the glaucophane rocks of Sifnos (Cyclades Archipelago, Greece). Neues Jahrb. Mineral. Abh. 132, 284-308.

Oterdoom, W. H. (1978) Tremolite- and diopside-bearing serpentine assemblages in the CaO-MgO-SiO_2-H_2O multisystem. Schweiz. Mineral. Petrog. Mitt. 58, 127-138.

Papike, J. J., Cameron, K. L. and Baldwin, K. (1974) Amphiboles and pyroxenes: Characterization of other than quadrilateral components and estimates of ferric iron from microprobe data (abstr.). Geol. Soc. Amer. Abstr. with Prog. 6, 1053.

_____, _____ and Shaw, K. W. (1973) Chemistry of coexisting actinolite-cummingtonite and hornblende-cummingtonite from metamorphosed iron-formations (abstr.). Geol. Soc. Amer. Abstr. with Prog. 5, 763-764.

_____ and Clark, J. R. (1968) The crystal structure and cation distribution of glaucophane. Amer. Mineral. 53, 1156-1173.

_____ and Ross, M. (1970) Gedrites: Crystal structures and intracrystalline cation distributions. Amer. Mineral. 55, 1945-1972.

_____, _____ and Clark, J. R. (1969) Crystal-chemical characterization of clinoamphiboles based on five new structure refinements. Mineral. Soc. Amer. Spec. Paper 2, 117-136.

Peacock, M. A. (1928) The nature and origin of the amphibole-asbestos of South Africa. Amer. Mineral. 13, 241-285.

Percival, J. A. and Helmstaedt, H. (1979) A P-T petrogenetic grid based on low-potash pelites from Hackett River, Northwest Territories. Geol. Soc. Amer. Abstr. with Prog. 11, 493.

Perkins, D., III and Newton, R.C. (in press) The composition of coexisting pyroxenes and garnet in the system $CaO-MgO-Al_2O_3-SiO_2$ at 900°-1100°C at high pressures. Contrib. Mineral. Petrol.

Petersen, E. U., Valley, J. W. and Essene, E. J. (1981) Fluorphlogopite and fluortremolite in Adirondack marbles: Phase equilibria and C-O-H-F-S fluid compositions (abstr.). EOS 62, 422.

Pfeifer, H. R. (1979) *Fluid-Gesteins-Interaktion in Metamorphen Ultramafititen der Zentralalpen.* Dissertation Nr. 6379, E.T.H., Zürich.

Phillips, F. C. (1930) Some mineralogical and chemical changes induced by progressive metamorphism in the Green Bed group of the Scottish Dalradian. Mineral. Mag. 22, 239-256.

Pinsent, R. H. and Hirst, D. M. (1977) The metamorphism of the Blue River Ultramafic Body, Cassiar, British Columbia, Canada. J. Petrol. 18, 567-594.

Pirani, R. (1952) I minerali del gruppo dell'Ortler-IV. Antofillite e actinolite di Val di Presimo. Solubità di questa actinolite. Atli (Rend.) Accad. Naz. Lincei, Cl. Sci. fis. Mat. Nat. Ser. 8, v. 13, sem. 2, 83-88.

Powell, R. (1975) Thermodynamics of coexisting cummingtonite-hornblende pairs. Contrib. Mineral. Petrol. 51, 29-37.

Prewitt, C. T., Papike, J. J. and Ross, M. (1970) Cummingtonite: a reversible nonquenchable transition from $P2_1/m$ to $C2/m$ symmetry. Earth Planet. Sci. Lett. 8, 448-450.

Raase, P. (1974) Al and Ti contents of hornblende, indicators of pressure and temperature of regional metamorphism. Contrib. Mineral. Petrol. 45, 231-236.

Rabbitt, J. C. (1948) A new study of the anthophyllite series. Amer. Mineral. 33, 263-323.

Räheim, A. and Green, D. H. (1974) Experimental determination of the temperature and pressure dependence of the Fe-Mg partition coefficient for coexisting garnet and clinopyroxene. Contrib. Mineral. Petrol. 48, 179-203.

Raith, M. (1976) The Al-Fe(III) epidote miscibility gap in a metamorphic profile through the Penninic series of the Tauren Window, Austria. Contrib. Mineral. Petrol. 57, 99-117.

Reamsbottom, S. B. (1974) *Geology and Metamorphism of the Mount Breakerridge Area, Harrison Lake, B.C.* Ph.D. Dissertation, University of British Columbia, Vancouver, B. C.

Reinhardt, E. W. and Skippen, G. B. (1970) Petrochemical study of Grenville granulites. Geol. Surv. Canada Rept. Activities Paper 70-1, 48-54.

Reinsch, D. (1977) High pressure rocks from Val Chiusella (Sesia-Lanzo Zone, Italian Alps). N. Jahrb. Mineral. Abh. 130, 89-102.

_____ (1979) Glaucophanites and eclogites from Val Chiusella, Sesia-Lanzo Zone (Italian Alps). Contrib. Mineral. Petrol. 70, 257-266.

Ribbe, P. H. (1975) Exolution textures and interference colors in feldspars. In *Feldspar Mineralogy*, Ribbe, P. H., ed., Mineral. Soc. Amer. Short Course Notes, Vol. 2, R73-R96.

Rice, J. M. (1977) Progressive metamorphism of impure dolomitic limestone in the Marysville aureole, Montana. Amer. J. Sci. 277, 1-24.

_____, Evans, B. W. and Trommsdorff, V. (1974) Widespread occurrence of magnesiocummingtonite in ultramafic schists, Cima di Gagnone, Ticino, Switzerland. Contrib. Mineral. Petrol. 43, 245-251.

Robbins, D. W. and Strens, R. G. J. (1972) Charge-transfer in ferromagnesian silicates: the polarized electronic spectra of trioctahedral micas. Mineral. Mag. 38, 551-563.

Robinson, P. (1963) *Gneiss Domes of the Orange Area, West Central Massachusetts and New Hampshire.* Ph.D. Dissertation, Harvard, University, 253 p.

_____ (1980) The composition space of terrestrial pyroxenes-internal and external limits. In *Pyroxenes*, Prewitt, C. T., ed., Mineral. Soc. Amer. Reviews in Mineralogy 7, 419-494.

_____ and Jaffe, H. W. (1969a) Aluminous enclaves in gedrite-cordierite gneiss from southwestern New Hampshire. Amer. J. Sci. 267, 389-421.

_____ and _____ (1969b) Chemographic exploration of amphibole assemblages from central Massachusetts and southwestern New Hampshire. Mineral. Soc. Amer. Spec. Paper 2, 251-274.

_____, _____, Klein, C. and Ross, M. (1969) Equilibrium coexistence of three amphiboles. Contrib. Mineral. Petrol. 22, 248-258.

_____, _____, Ross, M., and Klein, C. (1971a) Orientations of exsolution lamellae in clinopyroxenes and clinoamphiboles: Consideration of optimal phase boundaries. Amer. Mineral. 56, 909-939.

_____, Ross, M. and Jaffe, H.W. (1970) The composition field of anthophyllite and the anthophyllite miscibility gap (abstr.). Amer. Mineral. 55, 307-309.

_____, _____ and _____ (1971b) Composition of the anthophyllite-gedrite series, comparisons of gedrite-hornblende, and the anthophyllite-gedrite solvus. Amer. Mineral. 56, 1005-1041.

_____, _____, Nord, G. L., Jr., Smyth, J. R. and Jaffe, H. W. (1977) Exsolution lamellae in augite and pigeonite: Fossil indicators of lattice parameters at high temperature and pressure. Amer. Mineral. 62, 857-873.

_____ and Tracy, R. J. (1979) Gedrite-cordierite, gedrite-orthopyroxene, and cummingtonite-orthopyroxene assemblages from ferromagnesian gneisses, sillimanite-K-feldspar zone, central Massachusetts (abstr.). Geol. Soc. Amer. Abstr. with Prog. 11, 504.

de Roever, E. W. F., Beunk, F. F. and Kieft, C. (1976) Blue amphibole-albite-chlorite assemblages from Fuscaldo (S. Italy) and the role of glaucophane in metamorphism. Contrib. Mineral. Petrol. 58, 221-234.

de Roever, W. P. (1955) Some remarks concerning the origin of glaucophane in the North Berkeley Hill, California. Amer. J. Sci. 253, 240-246.

_____ (1956) Some differences between post-Paleozoic and older regional metamorphism. Geol. en Mijnb., new ser. 18, 123-127.

Rona, P. A., Bostoom, K. and Epstein, S. (1980) Hydrothermal quartz vug from the Mid-Atlantic Ridge. Geology 8, 569-572.

Ross, C. S. (1941) Occurrence and origin of the titanium deposits of Nelson and Amherst Counties, Virginia. U.S. Geol. Surv. Prof. Paper 198, 58 p.

Ross, M., Papike, J. J. and Shaw, K. W. (1969) Exsolution textures in amphiboles as indicators of subsolidus thermal histories. Mineral. Soc. Amer. Spec. Paper 2, 275-299.

_____, _____ and Weiblen, P. W. (1968) Exsolution in clinoamphiboles. Science 159, 1099-1104.

Sampson, G. A. and Fawcett, J. J. (1977) Coexisting amphiboles from the Hastings region of southeastern Ontario. Canadian Mineral. 15, 283-296.

Savage, D. and Sills, J. D. (1980) High pressure metamorphism in the Scourian of NW Scotland: evidence from garnet granulites. Contrib. Mineral. Petrol. 74, 153-164.

Savolahti, A. (1966) On rocks containing garnet, hypersthene, cordierite and gedrite in the Kiuruvesi region, Finland. Comptes Rendus de la Société géologique de Finlande 38, 343-386.

Schliestedt, M. (1980) *Phasengleichgewichte in Hochdruckgesteinen von Sifnos, Griechenland.* Ph.D. Dissertation, Technische Universität Braunschweig, F. R. Germany.

Schneiderman, J. S. (1981) Orthoamphiboles in cordierite-anthophyllite-bearing rocks from Orijärvi, Finland. Senior Thesis, Yale University, 50 p.

Schreyer, W. (1977) Whiteschists: Their compositions and pressure temperature regimes based on experimental, field, and petrographic evidence. Tectonophysics 43, 127-144.

_____ and Abraham, K. (1976) Three-stage metamorphic history of a whiteschist from Sar e Sang, Afghanistan, as part of a former evaporite deposit. Contrib. Mineral. Petrol. 59, 111-130.

_____ and Seifert, F. (1969) Compatibility relations of the aluminum silicates in the systems $MgO-Al_2O_3-SiO_2-H_2O$ and $K_2O-MgO-Al_2O_3-SiO_2-H_2O$ at high pressures. Amer. J. Sci. 267, 371-388.

Schuiling, R. D. and Vink, B. W. (1967) Stability relations of some titanium minerals (sphene, perovskite, rutile, anatase). Geochim. Cosmochim. Acta 31, 2399-2411.

Schumacher, J. C. (1980) Gedrite of extreme Al and Na content in the metamorphosed Ammonoosuc Volcanics, sillimanite-staurolite zone, central Massachusetts (abstr.). Geol. Soc. Amer. Abstr. with Progr. 12, 518.

_____ (1981a) Preliminary geochemistry of the metamorphosed Ammonoosuc Volcanics north-central Massachusetts (abstr.). Geol. Soc. Amer. Abstr. with Progr. 13, 175.

_____ (1981b) Coexisting hornblende-cordierite-gedrite in gedrite-cordierite gneiss, southwestern New Hampshire (abstr.). EOS 62, 422.

_____ (1981c) Compositions of sapphirine, staurolite, zincian spinel, and calcic plagioclase from aluminous enclaves in gedrite-cordierite gneiss, southwestern New Hampshire (abstr.). Geol. Soc. Amer. Abstr. with Progr. 13, in press.

Seidel, E. and Okrusch, M. (1976) Regional distribution of critical metamorphic minerals in the southern Aegean. Bull. Soc. Geol. France 1976, no. 2, 347-350.

Seifert, F. (1978) Equilibrium Mg-Fe^{2+} cation distribution in anthophyllite. Amer. J. Sci. 278, 1323-1333.

Seitsaari, J. (1952) On association of cummingtonite and hornblende. Acad. Sci. Fennicae Annales, Ser. A., III Geol-Geog. 30, 1-20.

Seki, Y. (1957) Petrological study of hornfelses in the central part of the median zone of the Kitakami Mountainland, Iwate Prefecture. Sci. Repts. Saitama Univ. Ser. B, 2, 307-373.

_____ (1965) Prehnite in low grade metamorphism. Sci. Repts. Saitama Univ. Ser. B, 5, 29-43.

_____ (1972) Lower-grade stability limit of epidote in the light of natural occurrences. J. Geol. Soc. Japan 78, 405-413.

_____ and Yamasaki, M. (1957) Aluminian ferroanthophyllite from the Kitakami mountainland, northeastern Japan. Amer. Mineral. 42, 506-520.

Serdynchenko, D. P. (1968) On the amphiboles of the hastingsite-pargasite series. Mineral. Soc. I.M.A. Vol. (I.M.A. Papers and Proc. 5th Gen. Meeting, Cambridge, 1966), 285-290.

Shaw, D. (1978) Structural setting of the Adamant pluton, northern Selkirk mountains, British Columbia. Geol. Surv. Canada Prof. Paper 78-1A, 83-85.

Shearer, C. K, Schumacher, J. C. and Robinson, P. (1981) Zoned hastingsite → ferri-katophorite-taramite phenocrysts, an amphibole + orthoclase = aegerine-augite + biotite reaction, and a new sodic amphibole in nepheline-sodalite syenite, Red Hill, New Hampshire. Geol. Soc. Amer. Abstr. with Progr. 13, in press.

Shido, F. (1958) Plutonic and metamorphic rocks of the Nakoso and Iritono districts in the central Abukuma Plateau. Tokyo Univ. Fac. Sci. J. Sec II, 11, 131-217.

_____ and Miyashiro, A. (1959) Hornblendes of the basic metamorphic rocks. Tokyo Univ. Fac. Sci. J. Sec. II, 12, 85-102.

Shimazaki, H., Bunno, M. and Ozawa, T. (in press) Sadanagaite, a new silica-poor member of calcic amphibole from Japan. Amer. Mineral.

Simmons, E. C., Lindsley, D. H. and Papike, J. J. (1974) Phase relations and crystallization sequence in a contact metamorphosed rock from the Gunflint Iron Formation, Minnesota. J. Petrol. 15, 539-565.

Sivaprakash, C. (1981) Chemographic analysis of metabasite assemblages from central Scottish Highlands. Lithos 14, 29-33.

Skippen, G. (1974) An experimental model for low pressure metamorphism of siliceous dolomitic marble. Amer. J. Sci. 274, 487-509.

Slaughter, J., Kerrick, D. M. and Wall, V. J. (1975) Experimental and thermodynamic study of equilibria in the system $CaO-MgO-SiO_2-H_2O-CO_2$. Amer. J. Sci. 275, 143-162.

Smith, D. (1979) Hydrous minerals and carbonates in peridotite inclusions from the Green Knobs and Buell Park Kimberlite diatremes on the Colorado Plateau. In _The Mantle Sample: Inclusions in Kimberlites and Other Volcanics_, Boyd, F. R. and Meyer, H. O. A., eds., Amer. Geophys. Union, Proc. 2nd Intern. Kimberlite Conf., 345-356.

Smith, J. V. (1959) Graphical representation of amphibole compositions. Amer. Mineral. 44, 437-440.

Smith, R. E., Pedrix, J. L. and Parks, T. C. (1981) Burial metamorphism in the Hamersley Basin, Western Australia. J. Petrol., in press.

Soen, O. I. (1968) Magnesium-metasomatism in basic hornfelses near Farminhao, Viseu District (northern Portugal). Chem. Geol. 3, 249-279.

Spear, F. S. (1977) Phase equilibria of amphibolites from the Post Pond Volcanics, Vermont. Carnegie Inst. Wash. Yearbook 76, 613-619.

_____ (1978) Petrogenetic grid for amphibolites from the Post Pond Volcanics, Vermont. Carnegie Inst. Wash. Yearbook 77, 805-808.

_____ (1980) The gedrite-anthophyllite solvus and the composition limits of orthoamphibole from the Post Pond Volcanics, Vermont. Amer. Mineral. 65, 1103-1118.

_____ (1981) An experimental study of hornblende stability and compositional variability in amphibolite. Amer. J. Sci. 281, 697-734.

_____, Hazen, R. M. and Rumble, D., III (1981) Wonesite: a new rock-forming silicate from the Post Pond Volcanics, Vermont. Amer. Mineral. 66, 100-105.

Springer, R. K. (1974) Contact metamorphosed ultramafic rocks in the Western Sierra Nevada Foothills, California. J. Petrol. 15, 160-195.

Starkov, G. N. (1972) Anthophyllites from a cortlandite-norite complex of the Kamchatka central range. Zap. Vses. Mineral. Obhch. 101, 349-352.

Steele, I. M., Bishop, F. C., Smith, J. V. and Windley, B. F. (1977) The Fiskenaesset complex, West Greenland, Part III. Grønlands Geol. Undersøgelse Bull. 134, 1-38.

Steffe, D. D. (1979) _The Chemistry of Calcic and Subcalcic Amphiboles from Selected Igneous and Metamorphic Environments_. M. S. Thesis, University of Vermont, Burlington, VT, 164 p.

Stephenson, N. C. N. and Hensel, H. D. (1979) Intergrown calcic and Fe-Mg amphiboles from the Wongwibinda metamorphic complex, N.S.W., Australia. Canadian Mineral. 17, 11-23.

Stoddard, E. F. (1980) Metamorphic conditions at the northern end of the northwest Adirondack Lowlands. Geol. Soc. Amer. Bull. 91 (Part I), 100-102; 91 (Part II), 489-616.

_____ and Miller, C. (1979) Phase petrology of cordierite-anthophyllite rocks, Old Woman-Piute Range, Southeastern California (abstr.). Geol. Soc. Amer. Abstr. with Progr. 11, 130.

Storre, B. and Nitsch, K.-H. (1972) Die Reaktion 2 Zoisit + 1 CO_2 $\rightleftarrows$ 3 Anorthit + 1 Calcit + 1 H_2O. Contrib. Mineral. Petrol. 35, 1-10.

Stout, J. H. (1969) An electron microprobe study of coexisting orthorhombic amphiboles (abstr.). EOS 50, 359.

_____ (1970) Three-amphibole assemblages and their bearing on the anthophyllite-gedrite miscibility gap (abstr.). Amer. Mineral. 55, 312-313.

_____ (1971) Four coexisting amphiboles from Telemark, Norway. Amer. Mineral. 56, 212-224.

_____ (1972) Phase petrology and mineral chemistry of coexisting amphiboles from Telemark, Norway. J. Petrol. 13, 99-146.

Sueno, S., Papike, J. J., Prewitt, C. T. and Brown, G. E. (1972) Crystal structure of high cummingtonite. J. Geophys. Res. 77, 5767-5777.

Sugi, K. (1931) On the metamorphic facies of the Misaka Series in the vicinity of Nakagawa Province, Sagami. Japan. J. Geol.-Geography 9, 87-142.

Sundius, N. (1933) Uber die Mischungslücken zwischen Anthophyllit-gedrit, Cummingtonit-grunerit und tremolit-aktinolith. Tschermak Mineral. Petrog. Mitt. 43, 422-440.

_____ (1946) The classification of the hornblendes and the solid solution relations in the amphibole group. Ärsbok Sver. Geol. Undersök 40(C).

Tagiri, M. (1977) Fe-Mg partition and miscibility gap between coexisting calcic amphiboles from the Southern Abukuma Plateau, Japan. Contrib. Mineral. Petrol. 62, 271-281.

Taylor, B. E. and Liou, J. G. (1978) The low temperature stability of andradite in C-O-H fluids. Amer. Mineral. 63, 378-393.

Taylor, H. P., Jr. and Coleman, R. G. (1968) O^{18}/O^{16} ratios of coexisting minerals in glaucophane-bearing metamorphic rocks. Geol. Soc. Amer. Bull. 79, 1727-1756.

Tella, S. and Eade, K. E. (1978) Coexisting cordierite-gedrite-cummingtonite from Edehon Lake map area, Churchill structural province, District of Keewatin. Geol. Surv. Canada, Paper 78-1C, 7-12.

Thompson, A. B. (1970) Laumontite equilibria and the zeolite facies. Amer. J. Sci. 269, 267-275.

_____ (1971) Analcite-albite equilibria at low temperatures. Amer. J. Sci. 271, 79-92.

Thompson, A. B. (1975) Mineral reactions in calc-mica schist from Gassetts, Vermont, U.S.A. Contrib. Mineral. Petrol. 53, 105-127.

Thompson, J. B. Jr. (1959) *Lecture Notes from Mineralogy 152.* Harvard University, Cambridge, MA.

_____ (1970) Geometrical possibilities for amphibole structures: model biopyriboles (abstr.). Amer. Mineral. 55, 292-293.

_____ (1978) Biopyriboles and polysomatic series. Amer. Mineral. 63, 239-249.

_____, Laird, J. and Thompson, A. B. (in press) Reactions in amphibolite, greenschist and blueschist. J. Petrol.

_____ and Thompson, A. B. (1976) A model system for mineral facies in pelitic schists. Contrib. Mineral. Petrol. 58, 243-277.

Tiba, T., Hashimoto, M. and Kato, A. (1970) An anthophyllite-hornblende pair from Japan. Lithos , 335-340.

Tilley, C. E. (1935) Metasomatism associated with greenstone-hornfelses of Kenidjack and Botallack, Cornwall. Mineral. Mag. 24, 181-202.

_____ (1937) Anthophyllite-cordierite granulites of the Lizard. Geol. Mag. 74, 300-309.

_____ (1939) The kyanite-gedrite paragenesis. Geol. Mag. 76, 326-330.

_____ and Flett, J. S. (1929) Hornfelses from Kenidjack. Geol. Surv. Great Britain. Summ. Prog. Part II, 24-41.

Touret, J. (1974) Faciès granulite et fluides carboniques. Centenaire de la Soc. Geol. de Belgique. Gèologie des Domaines Cristallins, Liege, 267-287.

Tracy, R. J. (1978) High grade metamorphic reactions in pelitic schist, west-central Massachusetts. Amer. J. Sci. 278, 150-178.

_____, Robinson, P. and Thompson, A. B. (1976) Garnet composition and zoning in the determination of temperature and pressure of metamorphism, central Massachusetts. Amer. Mineral. 61, 762-775.

Trendall, A. F. and Blockley, J. G. (1970) The Iron Formations of the Precambrian Hamersley Group, Western Australia. Geol. Surv. of Western Australia Bull. 119.

Triboulet, C. (1974) Les glaucophanites et roches associées de l'île de Groix (Morbihan, France): étude minéralogique et pétrogénétique. Contrib. Mineral. Petrol. 45, 65-90.

_____ (1978) Co-existing blue and blue-green amphiboles from Ile de Groix (Morbihan, France). J. Petrol. 19, 653-668.

Troll, G. and Gilbert, M. C. (1972) Fluorine-hydroxyl substitution in tremolite. Amer. Mineral. 57, 1386-1403.

Trommsdorff, V. and Evans, B. W. (1972) Progressive metamorphism of antigorite schist in the Bergell tonalite aureole (Italy). Amer. J. Sci. 262, 423-437.

_____ and _____ (1974) Alpine metamorphism of peridotitic rocks. Schweiz. Mineral. Petrog. Mitt. 54, 333-352.

Trzcienski, W. E. Jr. (1971) *Staurolite and Garnet Parageneses and Related Metamorphic Reactions in Metapelites from the Whetstone Lake Area, Southeastern Ontario*. Ph.D. Dissertation, McGill University, Montreal, 150 p.

_____ (1976) Crossitic amphibole and its possible tectonic significance in the Richmond area, southeastern Quebec. Canadian J. Earth Sci. 13, 711-714.

_____ (1979) Glaucophane: Product of a continuous reaction at Armstrong Brook, New Brunswick, Canada (abstr.). Geol. Soc. Amer. Abstr. with Progr. 11, 530.

Tuominen, H. V. and Mikkola, T. (1950) Metamorphic Mg-Fe enrichment in the Orijärvi region as related to folding. Bull. Comm. Geol. Finlande 150, 67-92.

Turner, F. J. (1968) *Metamorphic Petrology*. McGraw-Hill, New York, 533p.

Vallance, T. G. (1967) Mafic rock alteration and isochemical development of some cordierite-anthophyllite rocks. J. Petrol. 8, 84-96.

Valley, J. W. and Essene, E. J. (1980) Calc-silicate reactions in Adirondack marbles: The role of fluids and solid solutions. 91-I, 114-117; 91-II, 720-815.

Vance, J. A. and Dungan, M. A. (1977) Formation of peridotites by deserpentinization in the Darrington and Sultan Areas, Cascade Mountains, Washington. Geol. Soc. Amer. Bull. 88, 1497-1508.

van de Kamp, P. C. (1970) The Green Beds of the Scottish Dalradian series: Geochemistry, origin, and metamorphism of mafic sediments. J. Geol. 78, 281-303.

Vaniman, D. T., Papike, J. J. and Labotka, T. (1980) Contact metamorphic effects of the Stillwater Complex, Montana: the concordant iron-formation. Amer. Mineral. 65, 1087-1103.

Varne, R. (1970) Hornblende lherzolite and the upper mantle. Contrib. Mineral. Petrol. 27, 45-51.

Vermaas, F. H. S. (1952) The amphibole asbestos of South Africa. Geol. Soc. South Africa, Trans and Proc. 55, 199-232.

Vernon, R. H. (1962) Coexisting cummingtonite and hornblende in amphibolite from Duchess, Queensland, Australia. Amer. Mineral. 47, 360-370.

Vidale, R. J. (1969) Metasomatism in a chemical gradient and the formation of calc-silicate bands. Amer. J. Sci. 267, 857-874.

Vinx, R. and Jung, D. (1977) Pargasitic-kaersutitic amphibole from a basanitic diatreme at the Rosenberg, North of Kassel (North Germany). Contrib. Mineral. Petrol. 65, 135-142.

Vogel, D. E. and Garlick, G. D. (1970) Oxygen-isotope ratios in metamorphic eclogites. Contrib. Mineral. Petrol. 28, 183-191.

Waard, D. de. (1965) A proposed subdivision of the granulite facies. Amer. J. Sci. 163, 455-461.

Watters, W. A. (1959) An association of hornblende and cummingtonite from Ringaringa, Stewart Island, New Zealand. New Zealand J. Geol. Geophys. 2, 248-256.

Wegmann, C. E. and Kranck, E. H. (1931) *Beiträge zur Kenntnis der Svecofenniden in Finnland*. Bull. Comm. Geol. Finlande, 163 p.

Wenk, E. (1970) Zur Regionalmetamorphose und Ultrametamorphose im Lepontin. Fortschr. Mineral. 47, 34-51.

_____ and Keller, F. (1969) Isograde in Amphibolitserien der Zentralalpen. Schweiz. Mineral. Petrog. Mitt. 49, 157-198.

_____, Schwander, H. and Stern, W. (1974) On calcic amphiboles and amphibolites from the Lepontine Alps. Schweiz. Mineral. Petrog. Mitt. 54, 97-149.

Wilshire, H. G. and Trask, N. L. (1971) Structural and textural relationships of amphibole and phlogopite in peridotite inclusions, Dish Hill, California. Amer. Mineral. 56, 240-255.

Winchester, J. A. (1972) The petrology of the Moinian calc-silicate gneisses from Fannich Forest, and their significance as indicators of metamorphic grade. J. Petrol. 13, 405-424.

_____ (1974) The three dimensional pattern of polyphase metamorphism in the Moinian assemblage of northern Ross-shire, Scotland. J. Geol. 82, 637-649.

Winkler, H. G. F. (1979) *Petrogenesis of Metamorphic Rocks*, 5th ed. Springer-Verlag, N.Y., 348p.

Wiseman, J. D. H. (1934) the central and southwest highland epidiorites: a study in progressive metamorphism. Quarterly J. Geol. Soc. London 90, 354-417.

Wolff, R. A. (1978) *Ultramafic Lenses in the Middle Ordovician Partridge Formation, Bronson Hill Anticlinorium, Central Massachusetts.* Contrib. 34 (M.S. Thesis), Dept. Geol. & Geogr. Univ. Massachusetts, Amherst, MA, 162p.

Yakovleva, A. K. and Kolesnikova, V. V. (1967) Characteristics of the high-magnesium cummingtonite from ultrabasic rocks. Zap. Vses. Mineral. Obshch. 96, 662-670.

Yoder, H. S. and Tilley, C. E. (1962) Origin of basalt magmas: An experimental study of natural and synthetic rock systems. J. Petrol. 3, 342-532.

Yund, R. A. (1975) Microstructure, kinetics, and mechanisms of alkali feldspar exsolution. In *Feldspar Mineralogy*, Ribbe, P. H., ed., Mineral Soc. Amer. Short Course Notes, Vol. 2, Y29-Y57.

Zajac, I. S. (1974) *The Stratigraphy and Mineralogy of the Sokoman Formation in the Knob Lake Area, Quebec and Newfoundland.* Geol. Surv. Canada Bull. 220.

Zotov, I. A. and Sidorenko, G. A. (1967) Magnesian gedrite from the southwestern Pamirs. Dokl. Akad. Nauk. SSSR 180, 138-141.

Chapter 2

EXPERIMENTAL STUDIES OF AMPHIBOLE STABILITY

M. Charles Gilbert, Rosalind T. Helz, Robert K. Popp & Frank S. Spear[*]

INTRODUCTION *(MCG)*

This chapter provides the transition between the discussion of metamorphic amphiboles in the preceding chapter and igneous amphiboles in the next by reviewing experimentally-determined amphibole stability relations. It focuses first on simple dehydration reactions in the subsolidus and then proceeds into incongruent melting reactions. End-member compositions (where these compositions are the bulk chemistry of the experiment) are discussed prior to considering amphibole stabilities in more complicated systems involving whole-rock compositions, and the OH-amphiboles are discussed before F-bearing ones. The extensive literature on lower-temperature experiments involving 2-volatile reactions has not been reviewed. The order of approach is by chemical class, as defined by the dominant occupancy of the M_4 crystallographic site: iron-magnesium, calcic, sodic-calcic, and alkali.

An interesting observation is that, with few exceptions, all of the following discussion focuses on the *upper* thermal stability of amphiboles, because surprisingly little experimental effort has been expended on the determination of the *lower* thermal stabilities and reactions and the conditions limiting lower thermal stabilities. Yet amphiboles weather and react away in many near-surface, and hydrothermal and low-grade metamorphic environments, so that these "neglected" lower limits are in fact relevant geologic problems.

Modern experimental work on amphibole stability and phase relations dates from the 1950's and the pioneering work of F.R. Boyd at the Geophysical Laboratory. His effort resulted in determination of the dehydration reaction of tremolite, $oCa_2Mg_5Si_8O_{22}(OH)_2$, to diopside + enstatite + quartz + vapor, and the breakdown of pargasite, $NaCa_2Mg_4AlSi_6Al_2O_{22}(OH)_2$, to forsterite + diopside + spinel, and + liquid + vapor above 800 bars, or + nepheline + plagioclase + vapor below 800 bars (Boyd, 1959). Because much of this work was accomplished using cold-seal pressure vessels and the Tuttle press, which are inherently simple apparatuses to operate, it spurred additional studies on other relevant end members. Data on stability relations of magnesio-riebeckite, glaucophane,

- - - - - - - - - -

[*] Initials of the authors of each section are given in italics in the section headings.

riebeckite-arfvedsonite immediately followed (Ernst, 1960; 1961; 1962). Ernst's study of magnesio-riebeckite (1960) was not only the first complete presentation of phase relations of an iron-bearing amphibole over f_{O_2}-T-P space, but one of the first for any ferromagnesian silicate. For a review of the experimental methods of achieving f_{O_2} control, particularly the solid buffer techniques (Eugster, 1957; Eugster and Wones, 1962), see Huebner (1971).

Because amphiboles have a complex chemistry as well as contain volatile elements in the O_3 crystallographic site, it is obvious that stability relations will be determined by more than total pressure and temperature. Fugacities of H_2O and F, and Cl, S, and CO_2 are important, the latter three partly because they affect the first two. The history of amphibole experimentation is tied to our ability to handle these variables. Water pressure, because of its profound effect on reactions and in reactions, was controlled first. Because most of the rock-forming amphiboles contain Fe, an element of variable oxidation state, oxidation state or oxygen fugacity had to be regulated, and the Eugster solid buffer technique was widely used. Finally, the relations between amphibole and host rock indicated that bulk composition is important. This is observed in the experimental work in two ways: (1) the profoundly lowered thermal stabilities that Fe^{2+}-rich phases exhibit compared to Mg-rich ones, that OH-phases have compared to F-phases, and that Al-phases have compared to Fe^{3+}-phases; and (2) the lowered stabilities of amphiboles of similar composition as the activity of silica is varied upward from ultramafic bulk compositions to andesitic ones.

End-member studies in the pressure range below 5 kbar continued to be one of the primary foci throughout the 1960's, although some specific metamorphic reactions involving amphiboles in more complex bulk compositions were also investigated (e.g., Akella and Winkler, 1966). The publication of Yoder and Tilley (1962) documented the major role hornblende assumed in water-saturated basaltic compositions. This study was the first to be centered on rock compositions involving amphibole, and it indicated that thermal stabilities continue to increase up to 10 kbar.

Ernst's (1963) work on polymorphism in alkali amphiboles initiated "high" pressure (>10 kbar) studies on amphiboles. He utilized both piston-cylinder (Boyd and England, 1960) and simple squeezer apparatuses (Griggs and Kennedy, 1956) to make runs to 40 kbar. It was not until the late 1960's and into the 1970's, however, that piston-cylinder equipment was used extensively to seek pressure limitations on amphibole stability. The first of these studies was the work of Lambert and Wyllie (1968) with rock compositions and of Gilbert

(1969) on end-member compositions.

Amphiboles are a particularly challenging mineralogical group to handle
experimentally. It turns out that the chemically simplest end members such as
anthophyllite and grunerite with only three oxide constituents each are the
most difficult to synthesize and react -- whereas the chemically much more
complex hornblendes with 5 to 10 oxide constituents are relatively easy to
synthesize and react, but are difficult to characterize because of complex
chemistry. In general it has been proven true that Mg- and (Mg + Al)-end members are more difficult to react, at the same temperature, than the Fe- and
$(Fe^{2+} + Fe^{3+})$-end members. As with most other silicate phases, reactions also
proceed more rapidly at higher temperatures, at higher pressures, and with
liquid and vapor phases, where appropriate for the reaction relations. Finally, it should be noted that amphibole reactions are perhaps up to an order of
magnitude more sluggish than mica reactions, experimentally, requiring experimental run lengths of two to ten times those of comparable micas.

END-MEMBER RELATIONS (MCG, RKP)

Iron-magnesium amphiboles

a. $Mg_7Si_8O_{22}(OH)_2$

The stability relations of the pure orthorhombic Mg-end member (anthophyllite) in the system $MgO-SiO_2-H_2O$ have been the subject of considerable
debate and interest (Greenwood, 1963, 1971; Chernosky, 1976; Hemley et al.,
1977a,b; Chernosky and Autio, 1979; Day and Halbach, 1979; among others). One
major difficulty in elucidating the phase relations has been the extreme
sluggishness of reactions involving anthophyllite. The discovery of multiple-
chain silicate minerals in both natural and synthetic amphiboles (Veblen and
Burnham, 1975; Chernosky and Autio, 1979; see Volume 9A of this series) may
further complicate the experimentally determined phase relations and their
application to natural assemblages.

Greenwood (1963) first demonstrated that anthophyllite could be reacted. Fyfe (1962) also reported experiments defining the breakdown reaction.
Based on experiments in the system $MgO-Si_2O-H_2O$ at pressures up to 4 kbar, and
on thermodynamic data extracted from the experiments, Greenwood proposed the
phase relations shown in Figure 1, in which the upper pressure stability of
anthophyllite is limited by the reaction A = T + E (see Table 1 for abbreviations used in Figs. 1-5). Greenwood (1971) subsequently revised the calculated slope of the A = T + E equilibrium (Fig. 2) and proposed that the upper

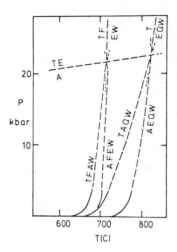

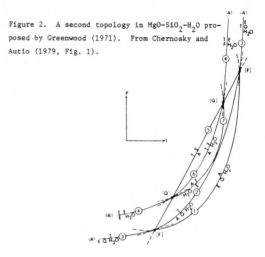

Figure 2. A second topology in $MgO-SiO_2-H_2O$ proposed by Greenwood (1971). From Chernosky and Autio (1979, Fig. 1).

Figure 1. Topology of equilibria in the system $MgO-SiO_2-H_2O$ proposed by Greenwood (1963). From Day and Halbach (1979, Fig. 1).

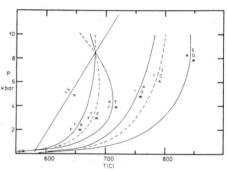

Figure 4. Phase relations in the system $MgO-SiO_2-H_2O$ calculated from experiments and calorimetry using "mid-point" criterion. From Day and Halbach (1979, Fig. 13).

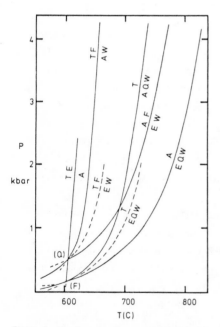

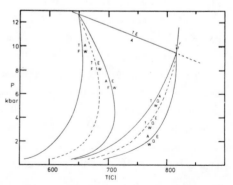

Figure 3. Topology in the system $MgO-SiO_2-H_2O$ proposed by Hemley et al. (1977b). From Day and Halbach (1979, Fig. 2).

Figure 5. Phase relations calculated from thermodynamic data using minimum deviation criterion. From Day and Halbach (1979, Fig. 14).

Table 1.   Abbreviations for phases in Figures 1-5

A - anthophyllite	T - talc
E - enstatite	Q - quartz
F - forsterite	W - water vapor

pressure stability of anthophyllite extends to higher pressures at temperatures over 600°C.

Based on a novel approach in which the concentration of aqueous silica in equilibrium with both synthetic and natural Mg silicate mineral phases was precisely determined, Hemley et al. (1977a,b) proposed P-T relations shown in Figure 3, in which the (Q) and (F) invariant points are located at pressures below 1 kbar.

Chernosky and Autio (1979) redetermined the AEQW and TAQW equilibria (see Figs. 3 and 6) for synthetic phases, using the standard appearance-disappearance-of-phase technique. Combining these results with those of Chernosky (1976) on the TEOW equilibrium, they concluded that the three univariant equilibria could, in fact, intersect at a pressure below 200 bars, thereby lending support to the location of the (F) invariant point preferred by Hemley et al. The apparently concordant results of the two widely differing techniques are encouraging.

Day and Halbach (1979) used linear programming methods to derive the possible set of P-T phase diagrams consistent with the experimental results of Chernosky (1976), Chernosky and Autio (1979), and Skippen (1971). Their approach concluded that a considerable range of topologies is permitted by the reversal brackets of the experiments, but that the "best fit" diagram (Fig. 4) has the topology suggested by Greenwood (1971). A similar analysis of topologies permitted by thermodynamic parameters of minerals measured calorimetrically concluded that no feasible solutions are possible using thermodynamic data within 2 e.s.d.'s of the reported values. Although it is not possible to determine the identity of the mineral or minerals responsible for the discrepancies in experimental data, Day and Halbach suggest that talc is the most likely possibility, because feasible solutions are possible when the properties of talc are removed from the data set. A topology similar to that proposed by Greenwood (1963) results from a data set in which all calorimetric data with the exception of those for talc are consistent with the experimental data (Fig. 5). It was concluded that the discrepancy between the topologies can most easily be resolved if there are significant differences between the properties of the talc used in the experiments and that used in the calorimetric

233

studies. It was also concluded that the presence of multiple-chain silicates (Veblen and Burnham, 1975; Volume 9A of this series) could have affected the experiments.

The phase relations of anthophyllite thus are not fully resolved, at least in light of the Day-Halbach analysis. As suggested by several authors, the discrepancies most likely can be resolved by experimental location of the A = T + E univariant curve using chemically and structurally well-characterized talc, enstatite, and anthophyllite.

b. $Fe_7Si_8O_{22}(OH)_2$

The problems of synthesis and reaction rates are perhaps even more restrictive for the pure monoclinic Fe-end member (grunerite). Synthesis of grunerite from severely ground hematite and quartz was first reported by Forbes (1971). Maximum yields of 5-10 volume percent were achieved.

More recently, Forbes (1977) presented the experimentally determined upper stability relations of grunerite as a function P, T and f_{O_2} to 3 kbar and 700°C. Starting material for most runs was well-ground hematite plus quartz, seeded with approximately 1.5 wt percent natural grunerite. Equilibrium was thought established by optical detection of the increase or decrease in the amount of amphibole in run products over the 1.5 percent initial amount. Maximum increase to approximately 10 percent amphibole was reported, whereas complete disappearance was reported in a number of runs. In addition, in several runs, grunerite was nucleated from the assemblage fayalite + quartz and from the assemblage quartz + fayalite + magnetite. Figure 6 depicts the dehydration of grunerite in P-T space at f_{O_2} defined by the fayalite-magnetite-quartz buffer assemblage. It is clear from this figure (and comparison with later Figs. 22 and 32) that if Forbes' grunerite curve is correct, then substitution of Fe for Mg in $(Fe, Mg)_7Si_8O_{22}(OH)_2$ has less thermal effect than the same substitution in other investigated amphibole pairs. Figure 7 represents the f_{O_2} - T relations for grunerite at a pressure of 1 kbar. These results are further discussed in relation to the upper stability relations of intermediate solid solutions (see next section).

c. Intermediate compositions

The phase relations of natural intermediate amphiboles on the join $Mg_7Si_8O_{22}(OH)_2$ - $Fe_7Si_8O_{22}(OH)_2$ are complicated by the structural differences between the anthophyllite (Pnma) and cummingtonite (C2/m) structure types (see papers by Hawthorne and Ghose in Volume 9A of this series). No experimental investigations on that transition have been reported. Popp et al.

234

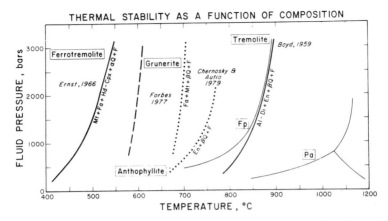

THERMAL STABILITY AS A FUNCTION OF COMPOSITION

Figure 6. Upper thermal stability of several Mg-Fe amphibole pairs illustrating effects of substitutions Mg-Fe, Mg+Fe-Ca, and combined Na+Al-Si and Al+Al-Mg or Fe+Si. Thermal stability of the Fe-end members is shown at or near their maxima. Pargasite (Pa) and ferropargasite (Fp) shown at WM buffer conditions, are in light lines and shown in more detail in a later figure. Tremolite and ferrotremolite (FMQ) are in heavy lines. Anthophyllite and grunerite (FMQ) are in heavy dots. The dashed line is an alternative position for grunerite based on the data of Fonorev, Popp, and others as discussed in the text and shown in Figures 11, 12, and 13.

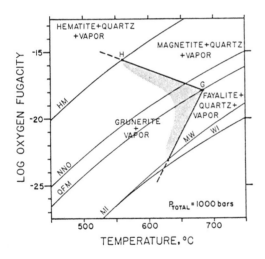

Figure 7. f_{O_2}-T stability limits for grunerite at 1000 bars fluid pressure. From Forbes (1977, Fig. 5).

(1976) reported synthesis of an apparently continuous series of optically orthorhombic amphiboles ranging from 14 to 86 mole percent Fe-end member (Fig. 8). Subsequent electron diffraction studies (Veblen, pers. comm.) revealed that the amphiboles are structurally complex: the Mg-rich compositions contain significant multiple-chain material. The amount of multiple-chain material decreases with increasing Fe content, but this is accompanied by an increase in stacking disorder of chains parallel to the a axis. The observed properties may thus represent those of a "bulk" or "average" amphibole with

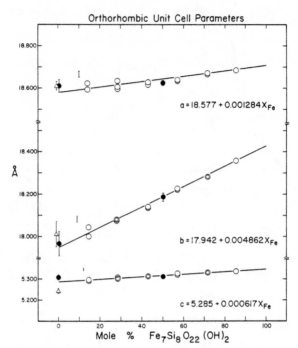

Figure 8. Unit-cell parameters of synthetic orthorhombic amphiboles. Open circles from Popp et al. (1976), triangles from Greenwood (1963), solid circles from Cameron (1975). After Popp et al. (1976).

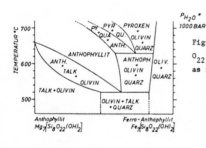

Figure 9. Phase relations in the system $Mg_7Si_8O_{22}(OH)_2$-$Fe_7Si_8O_{22}(OH)_2$, based on synthesis runs as interpreted by Hinrichsen (1967, Fig. 4).

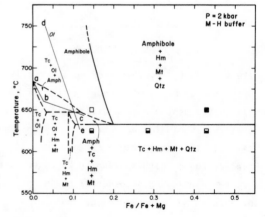

Figure 10. Condensed T-X section of phase relations on the Mg_7-$Fe_7Si_8O_{22}(OH)_2$ join. Symbols: solid and open, growth of high-temperature assemblages at the expense of talc; half-shaded, growth of talc. From Popp et al., (1977a).

variations in the stacking of layers parallel to a.

Low-temperature stability limits.　The possible constraints on the low-temperature stability limits of the Mg-end member (anthophyllite) are shown in Figures 1-5. With the exception of early attempts to synthesize grunerite by the thermal breakdown of minnesotaite (Flashen and Osborn, 1957), experimental investigations on the low-temperature stability of the Fe-end member are lacking. The problem of slow reaction rates encountered in higher temperature studies is greatly compounded at lower temperatures. Several studies on the low-temperature relations of synthetic orthorhombic amphiboles have been reported. Hinrichsen (1967) presented a T-X section at 1000 bars for the entire Mg_7-Fe_7 join, depicting both the high- and low-temperature relations. His diagram (Fig. 9) is apparently based mainly on synthesis runs made on oxylate-oxide-carbonate starting materials at f_{O_2} defined by external IM and WM buffers. Inasmuch as the high-temperature relations depicted appear to contradict more recent results of studies made using natural starting materials, the low-temperature relations should probably also be considered as synthesis rather than equilibrium relations.

　　Popp et al. (1977a) investigated the low-temperature stability of synthetic orthorhombic amphiboles at 2 kbar and f_{O_2} defined by the MH buffer (Fig. 10). The curve representing the maximum Fe content of amphibole, as well as the isotherm limiting the lower stability of amphibole, were located by reversed experiments. The phase relations depicted in the Mg-rich portion of the diagram are hypothetical but are consistent with a number of other experimental studies of amphibole, talc, and olivine stability. The Fe content of natural anthophyllite in amphibole + hematite + magnetite + quartz in natural assemblages is in good agreement with those predicted from Figure 10. In addition, the temperature of formation of amphibole-talc assemblages predicted from the diagram is in reasonably good agreement with temperature estimates made using other mineral assemblages (see Popp et al., 1977a).

High-temperature stability limits.　The upper thermal stability of intermediate amphiboles has been the subject of considerably more investigation as compared to the low-temperature stability limits.

　　The high-temperature relations of synthetic orthorhombic amphiboles at 2 kbar and f_{O_2} defined by FMQ based on the experiments of Greenwood (1963), Cameron (1975), and Popp et al. (1977a) are shown in Figure 11. Despite the fact that the diagram is consistent with all the experiments, the compositions of coexisting amphibole and orthorhombic pyroxene predicted by the diagram are

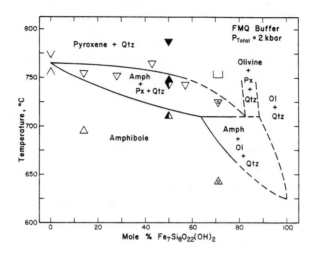

Figure 11. Condensed T-X section on the Mg_7-Fe_7 join. Symbols: arrows, Greenwood (1963); solid and half-shaded triangles, Cameron (1975); open triangles, amph = amph+opx+qtz; triangles with circles, amph = amph+ol+qtz; square bracket, amph+ol+qtz → amph+opx+qtz (Popp et al., 1977a).

far too widely separated (e.g., 40 mole percent for many temperatures) when compared to natural assemblages. Even though naturally occurring amphibole-orthopyroxene assemblages are often complicated by exsolution features in both minerals and generally contain at least minor amounts of calcium, Fe contents of Fe-Mg amphibole are generally less than 10 mole percent lower than those of coexisting orthopyroxene (e.g., Himmelberg and Phinney, 1967; Butler, 1969; Bonnichsen, 1969; Vaniman et al., 1980). It must, therefore, be concluded that either the synthetic amphiboles have stability relations that are far different from natural minerals, or that inconsistencies exist in the data.

Experimental studies of Fe-bearing natural anthophyllites have not been reported.

Fonarev and his co-workers (Fonarev et al., 1976; 1977a,b,c; 1979; 1980) have completed extensive experiments on the phase relations of cummingtonite - grunerite in the Fe-rich portion of the join at f_{O_2} defined by the FMQ buffer. Charges consisting of natural amphibole ± synthetic orthopyroxene, olivine, and quartz were investigated by appearance-disappearance-of-phase techniques, as well as by monitoring changes in mineral compositions in run products. In addition to the reported equilibrium relations, reaction mechanisms and kinetics were studied by monitoring phase abundances with time. The mechanism of the reactions by which the charges achieve their final compositions requires some discussion. The starting materials were in the necessary proportions to

238

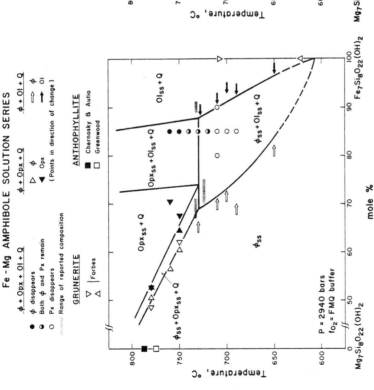

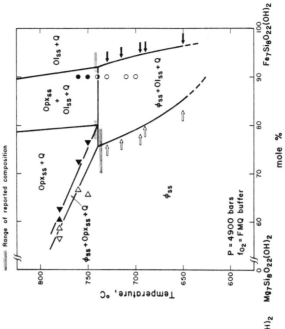

Figure 12. Experimental data from Fonarev and coworkers (1976; 1977a,b,c; 1980) relevant to the Fe-rich portion of the system $Mg_7-Fe_7Si_8O_{22}(OH)_2$. Discussion of procedures and reaction paths in text. Data for end members from Chernosky and Autio (1979), Forbes (1977), and Greenwood (1963).

Figure 13. Experimental data from Fonarev and coworkers (1976; 1977a,b,c; 1980) relevant to the system $Mg_7-Fe_7Si_8O_{22}(OH)_2$. Comparison with Figure 12 shows expansion of the amphibole field at increased total pressure.

fall "on composition" for a single-phase amphibole. At the termination of runs, compositions of the solid solutions were analyzed with X-ray determinative curves. (The precision limits reported are better than the following: amphibole $\pm$ 1.5 mole percent; opx $\pm$ 3 percent, olivine $\pm$ 0.5 percent). The mechanism by which an initial Mg-rich amphibole and Fe-rich olivine, for example, reach their final compositions is as follows (see Figs. 12 and 13). An Fe-rich amphibole close to, but slightly more Mg-rich than the final composition, nucleates early in the run (~1 day). With time, the proportion of this composition increases at the expense of the initial amphibole (which persists with little change in composition) until that initial amphibole is completely used up. Complete reaction was observed in some runs, but in many cases, initial amphibole remained at the termination of the runs. The final Fe-rich amphibole is slightly (generally of the order of 2-3 mole percent) more Mg-rich than in runs that proceeded to completion. Thus in many runs, two amphiboles of different compositions, and in some cases a third amphibole of intermediate composition, are present in the run products. Taken as a whole, however, the runs that proceeded to completion give results that are consistent with those containing metastable starting amphibole. Similar behavior is also observed for pyroxene, i.e., presence of two pyroxenes of different compositions in short-term runs. Olivine of only one composition was observed in run products, however.

The results of runs are summarized in Figures 12 (2940 bars) and 13 (4900 bars). Arrows and triangles on the diagrams represent the most drastic changes observed in mineral compositions and point in the direction of change. Circles represent results of appearance-of-phase type runs.

Comparison of these figures with Figure 11 for synthetic amphiboles gives reasonably good agreement for the predicted temperature of the 2 kbar amphibole-orthopyroxene-olivine-quartz-vapor invariant temperature. The width of the amphibole-pyroxene-quartz-vapor field in Figures 12 and 13 is much more consistent with natural assemblages, however.

The reversal brackets for pure grunerite breakdown at 3 kbar for the FMQ buffer as determined by Forbes (1977) are also shown in Figure 12. The lower-pressure reversal brackets for the FMQ buffer shown in Figure 6 constrain the curve to pass through or at only slightly lower temperatures than the high-temperature reversal in Figure 12, unless the slope of the grunerite dehydration curve has become negative (unlikely at 2-3 kbar). The results of Fonarev and co-workers and those of Forbes thus contain serious inconsistencies relating to the maximum temperature stability of pure grunerite end-member at 3 kbar:

the data of Forbes indicated a temperature stability of 700°C, whereas those of Fonarev require temperatures at least as low as 650°C, but temperatures can reasonably be extrapolated to the range 600°C. Consequently, Figure 6 also shows a proposed curve (dashed line) for grunerite stability consistent with Fonarev's data of Figures 12 and 13.

The discrepancy between the two sets of data cannot be easily resolved. It should be noted that neither Forbes' data nor those of Fonarev relating to the amphibole-olivine-quartz-vapor field have been unquestionably reversed. Forbes reports only one run at FMQ (675°C, 1 kbar) in which amphibole nucleated and grew from the high-temperature assemblage fayalite-magnetite-quartz-vapor. In the remainder of the runs, seeded grunerite (see discussion above) either grew at the expense of, or was consumed by the starting assemblage of hematite plus quartz. Inasmuch as the hematite-quartz starting material is considerably out of equilibrium at f_{O_2} defined by the FMQ buffer, the possibility of initial metastable formation of grunerite is a possibility.

Equilibrium in runs defining the amphibole-olivine-quartz-vapor field is difficult to evaluate in the studies of Fonarev et al. The isotherm defining the upper limit of the field is well reversed according to the reported data. The limbs of the field, however, were located by monitoring the changes in amphibole and olivine compositions after runs. It should be noted that the compositions of these minerals plotted in Figure 13 have each been approached from only one direction: amphibole from the Mg-rich direction; olivine from the Fe-rich direction. The possibility still remains that, given sufficient time, the amphibole, olivine, and quartz might further react to produce a single-phase amphibole. Equilibrium could be demonstrated by even a single run starting with amphibole of a composition that falls within the field, in which the starting amphibole decomposes to Mg-rich amphibole, olivine, and quartz.

Comparison of Figures 12 and 13 with naturally occurring amphibole, orthopyroxene, olivine $\pm$ quartz $\pm$ magnetite assemblages results in varying degrees of agreement. It should be emphasized at the start that the presence of at least small amounts of calcium in all the natural assemblages, exsolution features within pyroxene and amphibole, the interpretation of attainment of equilibrium in natural assemblages, as well as differences in P, T, P_{H_2O}, and f_{O_2} can all affect comparisons between natural assemblages and the experiments.

Bonnichsen (1969) reported seven samples with coexisting quartz, orthopyroxene, olivine, cummingtonite $\pm$ magnetite from the metamorphosed Biwabik iron formation adjacent to its contact with the igneous Duluth complex. Cummingtonite is reported to be retrograde, forming from both olivine and

orthopyroxene. Average compositions of minerals (expressed in mole percent Fe-
end member) of the seven samples are: olivine = 0.89(.03); orthopyroxene =
0.73(.05); cummingtonite = 0.69(.05). Estimates of the conditions of metamorphism range from 1.5-3 kbar, and 675-750°C as a lower limit for the peak conditions (Bonnichsen, 1975). Comparison with the 2.9 kbar diagram (Fig. 12) gives
excellent agreement between the natural mineral compositions and those predicted
for the amphibole-orthopyroxene-olivine-quartz assemblage. The temperature minimum for the peak of metamorphism (730°C) required for retrograde amphibole
formation falls within the temperature range reported above.

Simmons et al. (1974) and Vaniman et al. (1980) have investigated iron
formations metamorphosed by the Duluth and Stillwater complexes, respectively.
Temperature-pressure conditions of both areas are similar (P $\cong$ 2 kbar, T $\cong$
800°C based mainly on exsolution features in pyroxenes). Estimates of f_{O_2}
range from slightly less than FMQ for the Duluth rocks, to intermediate
between FMQ and NNO for the Stillwater rocks. Both studies report primary and
retrograde Fe-Mg amphiboles. Simmons et al. report primary cummingtonite of
Fe/(Fe+Mg) = 0.69, whereas Vaniman et al. report primary cummingtonite of Fe/
(Fe+Mg) = 0.65-0.73 and grunerite of 0.82-0.89. The estimated temperatures of
these natural assemblages are clearly much above the maximum thermal stability
of the amphibole. The differences between the data are difficult to reconcile.
One possibility is that the presence of Ca in natural cummingtonite-grunerite
increases the thermal stability of the amphiboles reported above. The results
of Forbes (1977) indicate that pure grunerite has a maximum thermal stability
at f_{O_2} defined by FMQ and thus variation in f_{O_2} is not likely to increase the
maximum temperature stability. Simmons et al. infer the probable presence of
quartz at the peak of metamorphism, and Vaniman et al. report quartz in some
amphibole assemblages. For that reason a possible increase in thermal stability for amphibole in quartz-free assemblages cannot be invoked to resolve the
differences.

f_{O_2} - f_{S_2} *stability.* Several experimental studies have been carried out on
both synthetic and natural Fe-Mg amphiboles in order to determine the effect of
f_{O_2} on the limits of substitution of Fe for Mg in amphibole, as governed by an
oxidation reaction of the type

$$Fe_7Si_8O_{22}(OH)_2 \text{ (in amphibole)} + O_2 = \text{iron oxide} + \text{quartz} + H_2O$$

(Fonarev et al., 1976; 1977a,b,c,; 1980; Popp et al., 1977a). The results of
these studies at f_{O_2} defined by the FMQ buffer (Figs. 11, 12, and 13) indicate
that the Fe-rich limit for solid solution extends completely to the Fe-end

242

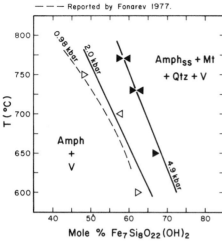

Figure 14. Amphibole solution limits at f_{O_2} defined by the NNO buffer as a function of total fluid pressure.

member, at least at lower temperatures. At higher temperatures, the limit of solid solution is marked by the appearance of either pyroxene or olivine rather than iron oxide.

The range of amphibole solid solution is limited by the appearance of magnetite at the higher f_{O_2} defined by the NNO buffer. Figure 14 depicts the experimental results obtained by Popp et al. (1977a) and Fonarev et al. (1976, 1977c). Plotted are results of runs which define the Fe-rich limit of amphibole solid solution as a function of temperature at 0.98, 2.0, and 4.9 kbar. All studies relied on the determination of amphibole compositions by X-ray diffraction techniques, and the reported equilibrium compositions have been approached from both Mg-rich and Fe-rich directions. The 2.0 and 4.9 kbar data plotted in Figure 14 represent the experimental reversals, whereas the 0.98 kbar data represent only the location of the curve as reported by Fonarev et al. (1976). The results of the studies are in reasonable agreement, given the estimated errors in measurement of amphibole compositions (± 4 mole percent for the 2 kbar data, ± 1.5 to 2 percent for the 0.98 and 4.9 kbar data), and the fact that the 2 kbar data relate to the synthetic orthoamphiboles investigated by Popp et al., whereas the others relate to natural cummingtonite.

At the f_{O_2} defined by the MH buffer, the range of iron substitution is limited to Mg-rich compositions. The only experiments reported in such systems are those of Popp et al. (1977a) depicted in Figure 10. Sulfidation reactions of the type

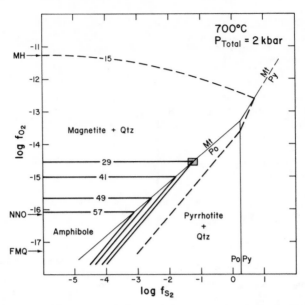

Figure 15. Stability of Mg_7-$Fe_7Si_8O_{22}(OH)_2$ amphiboles on a condensed f_{O_2}-f_{S_2} diagram. Compositions in mole percent Fe-end member. Dashed line calculated from amphiboles determined in S-free experiments. Box indicates uncertainty in location of intersection. From Popp et al. (1977b).

$$Fe_7Si_8O_{22}(OH)_2 \text{ (in amphibole)} + S_2 = \text{iron sulfide} + \text{quartz} + H_2 + O_2$$

can also limit the Fe content of amphiboles in a manner similar to oxidation reactions discussed above. The only experimental data available for S-bearing systems are those of Popp et al. (1977b), who determined the compositions of synthetic Fe-Mg amphiboles in equilibrium with the assemblage pyrrhotite solid solution, magnetite, quartz, and vapor. The results of experiments at 700°C and 2 kbar are presented in terms of a log f_{O_2} versus log f_{S_2} diagram in Figure 15. The heavy lines in the figure indicate the stability fields of amphiboles of different compositions, where the numbers on the curves refer to the mole percent Fe-end member in the amphibole solid solution. The upper f_{O_2}-stability curves represent oxidation of Fe-end member component (see first equation above), whereas the upper f_{S_2}-stability curves represent sulfidation (see second equation above). The intersection of the two curves represents the assemblage amphibole, pyrrhotite, magnetite, quartz, vapor. Even though the results of the study are useful in delimiting the effect of f_{S_2} on amphibole stability, the applications to natural assemblages are limited by the paucity of data on natural assemblages.

244

Calcic amphiboles

These amphiboles are volumetrically the most important group, encompassing the compositional range from tremolite-actinolite through to hornblende. The first systematic experiments on amphibole stability were done on this group (Boyd, 1959). Tremolite dehydrated without melting, and pargasite melted incongruently beyond 800 bars; these became simple models for amphibole behavior in metamorphic and igneous rocks, respectively. More experimental work, in terms of number of studies, has been done with calcic amphiboles than with any other class of amphiboles.

a. The join $Ca_2Mg_5Si_8O_{22}(OH)_2$ - $Ca_2Fe_5Si_8O_{22}(OH)_2$

Compared to the Fe-Mg amphiboles, amphiboles on this join have been the subject of relatively few experimental studies. Even though there are some problems of synthesis of these amphiboles (discussed below), they are, as a whole, easier to synthesize than Fe-Mg varieties. In addition, all compositions on the join crystallize with the same structure type (C2/m), and thus structural complications such as those relating to anthophyllite-cummingtonite are not encountered.

Mg-end member (tremolite).   Tremolite, as well as its fluorine analog, fluor-tremolite, $Ca_2Mg_5Si_8O_{22}F_2$, have been synthesized (Boyd, 1959; Comeforo and Kohn, 1954). The fluorine work is discussed in a later section. The low-pressure stability of OH-tremolite was determined by Boyd (1959) and is shown in Figure 6. Tremolite decomposes to enstatite + diopside + quartz + vapor. Boyd noted the relative difficulty of producing 100 percent yields of synthetic tremolite. More recently, the question of synthetic tremolite being "on composition" has been raised. Wones and Dodge (1977) were also unable to produce 100 percent yields from either gels or synthetic anhydrous mineral assemblages in the presence of excess water vapor. Minor amounts (1-2 percent) of quartz and diopside persisted in runs. Based on similar observations, N. Chatterjee (pers. comm. to D.R. Wones) concluded that tremolite synthesized at 750°C contains 1-5 mole percent $Mg_7Si_8O_{22}(OH)_2$ in solid solution. It was, therefore, argued that stoichiometric tremolite may not be stable above 700°C. In contrast, Troll and Gilbert (1972) concluded that solid solution of $Mg_7Si_8O_{22}(OH)_2$ in synthetic tremolite is not significant, based on comparison of unit cell parameters of OH-tremolite synthesized at 650°C, 1 kbar and at 775°C, 4 kbar with those of several well analyzed natural tremolites. At 800°C, 1 kbar, Oba (1980) also produced tremolite with cell parameters comparable to those of Troll and Gilbert (1972) and Colville et al. (1966).

The high-pressure stability of tremolite was determined by Gilbert and Troll (1974; unpub.) in reversed experiments, and it is displayed in Figure 25 (below). The dehydration reaction was carried upward in pressure to the α quartz-β quartz transition, after which the slope of the curve is demonstrably negative. This point represents the maximum thermal stability of tremolite at about 915°C, 15.5 kbar. The tremolite field is terminated by the reaction

$$Ca_2Mg_5Si_8O_{22}(OH)_2 = 2CaMgSi_2O_6 \text{ (diopside)} + Mg_3Si_4O_{10}(OH)_2 \text{ (talc)}$$

This marks its maximum pressure stability at about 835°C and 26 kbar.

Fe-end member (ferro-tremolite or ferro-actinolite)[1]. The stability of synthetic ferro-tremolite (-actinolite) at f_{O_2} defined by the standard solid buffer assemblages was determined by Ernst (1966). Figure 16 depicts the f_{O_2}-T stability relations at 3 kbar fluid pressure. P-T relations are compared with tremolite in Figure 6. At values of f_{O_2} intermediate between the FMQ and IFQ buffers, the stable high-temperature assemblage is fayalite-hedenbergitic pyroxene-quartz-vapor. Based on natural assemblages reported by Hytönen (1968) and experiments carried out on the join $Ca_2Mg_{2.5}Fe_{2.5}Si_8O_{22}(OH)_2$ - $Mg_{3.5}Fe_{3.5}Si_8O_{22}(OH)_2$, Cameron (1975) suggested that the assemblage cummingtonite-clinopyroxene-quartz-vapor may be the stable high-temperature breakdown assemblage, rather than the assemblage determined by Ernst. In light of the extreme difficulty reported for the nucleation and growth of grunerite in hydrothermal experiments, it is quite possible that the equilibrium investigated by Ernst is metastable relative to grunerite-clinopyroxene-quartz-vapor. This could be true even if the grunerite stability curve of Forbes is 100°C too high, as discussed earlier. The suggested grunerite curve (dashed) in Figure 6 is still about 75°C above that for ferro-tremolite.

Intermediate compositions. The most recent experimental work on intermediate compositions is that of Cameron (1975), who investigated the pseudo-binary join $Ca_2Mg_{2.5}Fe_{2.5}Si_8O_{22}(OH)_2$ - $Mg_{3.5}Fe_{3.5}Si_8O_{22}(OH)_2$, which bridges the miscibility gap between the calcic and iron-magnesium groups. The join is not truly binary because the coexisting Ca-rich (actinolite) and Ca-poor (cummingtonite) amphiboles are Mg-rich and Fe-rich, respectively, as compared to the join itself (Fig. 17). Cameron's study was carried out on synthetic phases crystallized from gels and oxide mixes. Oxygen fugacity was defined by the FMQ buffer. The

- - - - - - - - - -

[1]The International Mineralogical Association prefers the term ferro-actinolite over ferro-tremolite, but inasmuch as many figures had been drafted before this convention was established, we will use both designations.

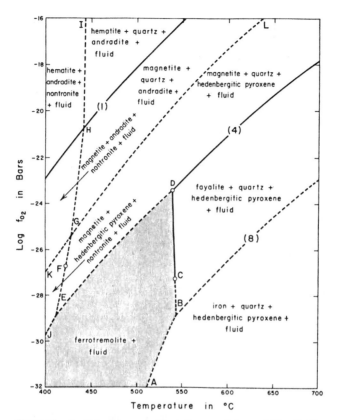

Figure 16. f_{O_2}-T for ferro-tremolite bulk composition at 3 kbar fluid pressure. Numbered boundaries are the buffer curves HM(1), FMQ(4), and IQF(8). Dashed boundaries have not been experimentally determined. From Ernst (1966).

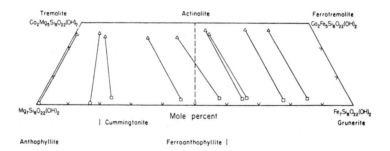

Figure 17. A quadrilateral relating calcic to iron-magnesium amphiboles. Compositions of co-existing natural amphiboles that contain less than 2.5 wt % Al_2O_3 and 1.8 wt % MnO outline the miscibility gap. The dashed line indicates the join studied experimentally by Cameron (1975) and shown in Figure 18. Compositional limits of the natural monoclinic series cummingtonite-grunerite and the natural orthorhombic series anthophyllite-ferro-anthophyllite shown by vertical bars. From Cameron (1975, Fig. 1).

247

stability relations in the system at 2000 bars fluid pressure (Fig. 18) are based on appearance–disappearance–of-phase type experiments, but the limbs of the amphibole solvus were located on the basis of compositions of coexisting Ca-poor and Ca-rich amphiboles as determined by X-ray diffraction techniques. Because of the sluggishness of reactions in the system, none of the field boundaries have been bracketed by complete reversals. It should also be noted that because the tie lines between coexisting amphiboles are not parallel to the join investigated (Fig. 17), the compositions of coexisting actinolites and cummingtonites both become Mg-enriched as the bulk composition of the system becomes more Ca-poor. A systematic, isobaric, isothermal section of the system is shown in Figure 19.

As discussed above in relation to the Fe-end member, Cameron (1975) has suggested that the high-temperature breakdown assemblage observed in his experiments on intermediate Mg-Fe compositions (Ca-poor monoclinic amphibole + clinopyroxene + quartz + vapor) might also extend to the Fe-rich compositions in the system. As a result, Cameron (1971) postulated two possible phase diagrams for the tremolite-ferro-tremolite (= ferro-actinolite) join at fluid pressure = 2000 bars and f_{O_2} in the field of stability of fayalite (Figs. 20 and 21). Temperatures of reactions were estimated from experimental studies where possible (i.e., Boyd, 1959; Ernst, 1966; Cameron, 1971). The diagrams differ only in respect to the high-temperature breakdown assemblage of the Fe-rich compositions.

Ernst (1968) has reviewed the earlier work of Hellner and Schürmann (1966) on the join tremolite-ferro-tremolite and suggested several modifications of the phase relations they presented.

b. Pargasite-hastingsite quadrilateral

The set pargasite-ferro-pargasite-magnesio-hastingsite-hastingsite can be depicted as a quadrilateral following Colville et al. (1966) and Gilbert (1966). These end members and their solid solutions are some of the most complex chemically of all amphiboles and represent many of the relations to be found in the hornblendes. The experimentally determined upper thermal stability limits are plotted in Figure 22. This complexity is indicated not only by the formulas but also by the number of reaction products, which varies from 5 to 7.

Some generalities emerge from inspection of these results. For the pressure range experimentally investigated:

1. All hornblende breakdown produces clinopyroxene.

2. All hornblende reactions involve spinels -- either two or one.

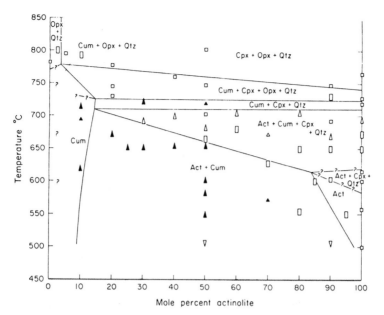

Figure 18. Phase diagram for the pseudobinary join $Mg_{3.5}Fe_{3.5}Si_8O_{22}(OH)_2$-$Ca_2Mg_{2.5}Fe_{2.5}Si_8O_{22}(OH)_2$ + excess H_2O at fluid pressure of 2000 bars and at oxygen fagacities defined by the FMQ buffer. All assemblages coexist with vapor. Symbols: solid triangles, final assemblage produced from a starting assemblage stable in an adjacent field -- the triangle apex points to the boundary separating the fields; open triangles pointing up, Act + Cum + Cpx + Qtz produced by loss of Opx from that assemblage containing Opx; open triangles pointing down, Act + Cum produced from a talc-containing assemblage; open triangles, all other synthesis runs. Approximate temperature uncertainty shown by height of symbol. From Cameron (1975, Fig. 4).

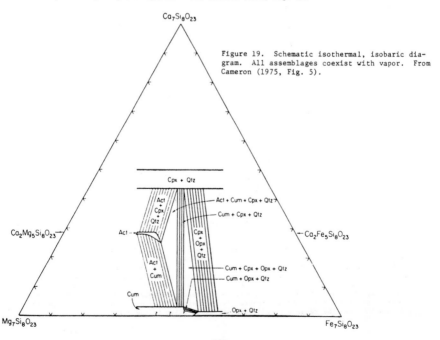

Figure 19. Schematic isothermal, isobaric diagram. All assemblages coexist with vapor. From Cameron (1975, Fig. 5).

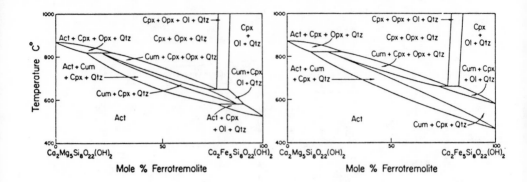

Figure 20. Phase relations on the tremolite-ferrotremolite join as presently understood, within an oxygen fugacity range where fayalite is stable. From Cameron (1971).

Figure 21. Another possible topology for the join tremolite-ferrotremolite if Ernst's (1966) end member breakdown reaction were metastable and the relations as shown in Figure 18 were to exist at the Fe-end member. From Cameron (1971).

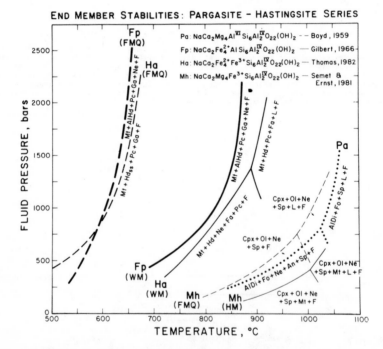

Figure 22. Experimentally-determined breakdown reactions for pargasite, ferro-pargasite, magnesio-hastingsite and hastingsite. Buffer symbols: FMQ, fayalite + magnetite + quartz; WM wüstite + magnetite; HM, hematite + magnetite. Some of the phase symbols are: *clinopyroxene*: Hd_{ss}, AlHd, AlDi, Cpx, all indicating solid solutions, some with significant aluminum; *spinel*: Mt_{ss}, Sp; *olivine*, Fo, Fa, Ol; *plagioclase*, An, Pc; *nepheline*, Ne; *garnet*, Ga; *melt* (silicate liquid), L; and *fluid* (vapor), F. Amphibole end members stable on the low termperature side of the respective curves. As non-Fe-bearing, pargasite shows no stability variation with oxygen fugacity over the range of conditions likely to exist in the Earth's crust.

3. All hornblende reactions require plagioclase and/or nepheline.
4. Olivine is typically involved, particularly for the more Mg-rich compositions.
5. Fe-rich hornblendes commonly react to produce garnet.
6. Incongruent melting of these amphiboles is typically displayed above 850°C, such reactions having their onset between 500 and 1500 bars.

The important effect of oxygen fugacity variation is illustrated in the response of amphibole thermal stability and in changes in reaction assemblages (Figs. 23 and 24). Only pargasite's thermal stability is unaffected by such changes except at very low oxygen fugacities where other constituents build up in the fluid, changing H_2O fugacity. Figure 22 is compiled to show the end-member stability at a buffer condition at or near the amphibole maximum, and also at FMQ, as an appropriate reference state for many crustal environments. Those amphiboles, such as ferro-pargasite and hastingsite, which are dominated by Fe^{2+} typically have maximum stabilities at the IW and WM buffers. Those with more Fe^{3+} have enhanced stabilities at the HM buffer. Furthermore, hastingsite ($Fe_4^{2+}Fe^{3+}$) and ferro-pargasite ($Fe_4^{2+}Al$) undergo more drastic changes with increasing oxygen fugacity than magnesio-hastingsite (Mg_4Fe^{3+}) does with decreasing oxygen fugacity. Magnesio-hastingsite is still stable above 700°C at 400 bars at the IQF buffer.

A number of relevant points on the control which specific ionic substitutions exert on stability can be made with the aid of Figure 22. Presumably the A-site, M_4, and the T_1 and T_2 sites have constant occupancies, so that the only chemical changes are occurring in M_1, M_2, M_3. The amphibole with maximum thermal stability is magnesio-hastingsite. Ferric iron substitution for Al normally *raises* the upper thermal stability as seen by comparing the pairs pargasite-magnesio-hastingsite (∿50°C) and ferro-pargasite-hastingsite (∿25–50°C). On the other hand, substitution of Fe^{2+} for Mg *lowers* the upper stability by ∿200–400°C, depending on oxygen fugacity. The larger temperature decrease at higher oxygen fugacities reflects the more oxidized state of those breakdown assemblages.

All experimental work reported for this quadrilateral is in generally good agreement. A recent set of reversed temperature brackets for pargasite stability (Westrich and Holloway, 1981) between 245 and 658 bars lowers the curve about 15 to 20°C compared to Boyd's (1959) determination. Thomas (1982) points out that a discrepancy does exist between hastingsite and ferro-pargasite data sets at 500 bars pressure on the FMQ buffer, as the curves are transposed in temperature position. Reaction rates at 500 bars in this temperature range for these amphiboles are very sluggish. Run durations of about 1 month are necessary

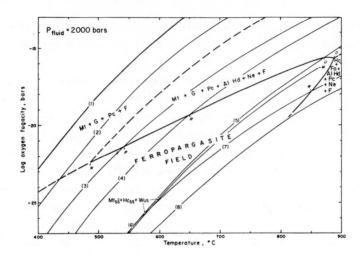

Figure 23. The f_{O_2}-T diagram for the bulk composition, $NaCa_2Fe_4^{2+}Al^{VI}Si_6Al_2^{IV}O_{22}(OH)_2$ (ferro-pargasite), + excess H_2O. Mt = magnetite, G = andraditic garnet, Pc = plagioclase, AlHd = aluminous hedenbergite, Ne = nepheline, Hc = hercynite, Fa = fayalite, F = fluid, (3) = Ni+NiO buffer, (4) = FMQ buffer, (5) = WM buffer, (7) = IW buffer, (8) = IQF buffer. From Gilbert (1966).

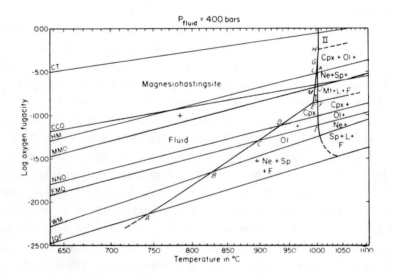

Figure 24. The f_{O_2}-T diagram at 400 bars fluid pressure for the bulk composition $NaCa_2Mg_4Fe^{3+}Si_6Al_2O_{22}(OH)_2$ + excess H_2O. The temperature axis is linear for 1/T (°K). From Semet and Ernst (1981, Fig. 6).

252

before even minimal charges can be discerned. Additional experiments probably should be undertaken. Charles (1980) has synthesized pargasite and ferro-pargasite and three intermediate compositions on that join (Mg_3Fe, Mg_2Fe_2, $MgFe_3$). The unit cell parameters were found to vary in an acceptably linear way, suggesting disorder of Mg and Fe over the M_1, M_2, and M_3 sites, although Al is presumed to fill half of the M_2 sites.

All these quadrilateral members are nepheline-normative and experimentally unstable with excess SiO_2. Since compositions not far removed from these are reported to exist with quartz, it is clear that steep gradients in silica activity must exist in compositional space between the quad and most of the horn-blendes. This space has not yet been closely bracketed experimentally.

A few experiments are available on pargasite and hastingsite compositions above 10 kbar (Gilbert, 1969) (Fig. 25). Holloway (1973) followed the pargasite curve to about 8 kbar, where it is essentially vertical. It would appear to have a negative slope above 10 kbar due to compressibility of the fluid and liquid phases. Since the high-pressure assemblage involves garnet, the slope must be considerably more negative. A few experiments are available to show in what space the breakdown must lie, but the curve is not well bracketed. Has-tingsite breaks down to magnetite + garnet + clinopyroxene at 12 kbar, 700°C, and an oxygen fugacity controlled by fayalite + ferrosilite + magnetite. With this buffer at 650°C, 20 kbar, hastingsite is not stable, so that the curve has a negative slope. Plagioclase is not stable over this higher pressure range. Figure 25 links the high pressure experiments directly with the low pressure ones of Thomas (1982), but this is not strictly correct, since they were deter-mined under close, but different oxidation states.

The stability of hydrous phases which melt is partly controlled by water solubility in that melt (see Yoder and Kushiro, 1969, for a discussion and data on this point). As with any phase, an amphibole has its maximum thermal sta-bility on its own bulk composition. In simple dehydration reactions where fluid (vapor) is released but no melt forms, H_2O-excess conditions may be used, and commonly are, in the experimental determination of stability limits. How-ever, where melt forms and the amount of H_2O which can dissolve in that melt is a function of total pressure, the thermal maximum changes with fluid composition at each different total pressure. Holloway (1973) was able to show this effect well in a study of pargasite stability as a function of fluid composition in a H_2O-CO_2 system. Figure 26 shows that above 3 kbar, maximum thermal stability is no longer achieved in fluids of 100% H_2O. By 10 kbar, the extrapolated, maximum stability would be about 1110°C at $H_2O/(H_2O + CO_2) = 0.40$-$0.45$, but

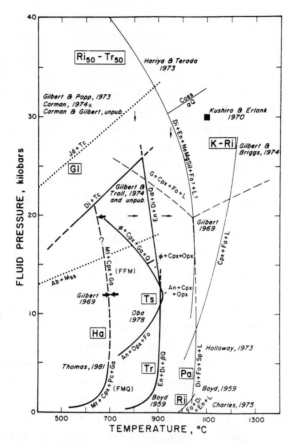

Figure 25. P-T diagram for OH-amphibole end member and/or specific compositions, labeled by boxes, determined experimentally above 10 kbars. Some of these equilibria are only modestly constrained by the data. Curves in heavy lines, dashed, and dots are essentially subsolidus. Curves in lighter weight involve a melt phase. Tr = tremolite, Ha = hastingsite, Ri = richterite, Pa = pargasite, Ts = tschermakite, Gl = glaucophane, K-Ri = potassium-richterite, Ri_{50}-Tr_{50} = richterite$_{50}$-tremolite$_{50}$ solution. All fields have an H_2O-rich fluid present. Small vertical and horizontal arrows mark experiments of Gilbert (1969) bracketing pargasite stability. The solid box confirms K-richterite's high pressure stability. Heavy arrows partly limit hastingsite stability at buffered conditions of fayalite + ferrosilite + magnetite.

only 1062°C at 100% H_2O. Thus, fluid compositions must be carefully controlled in amphibole melting studies (see Helz's discussion below). Figure 27 shows the shallower slopes of curves at lower H_2O activity. Most of the data on amphibole end members were generated in simple fluid systems, usually H_2O-excess. Extrapolation of low-pressure stability data to higher pressures must be done cautiously.

Oba (1980) studied the join tremolite-pargasite at P_{H_2O} of 1 and 5 kbar (Figs. 28 and 29). Starting materials consisted of phases synthesized at 1000°C and 1 atm from oxide mixes. A few reversal runs are reported for both pressures

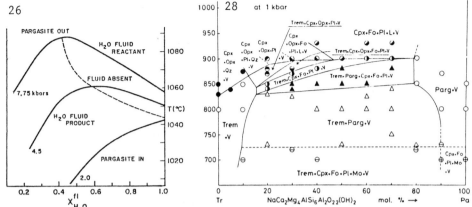

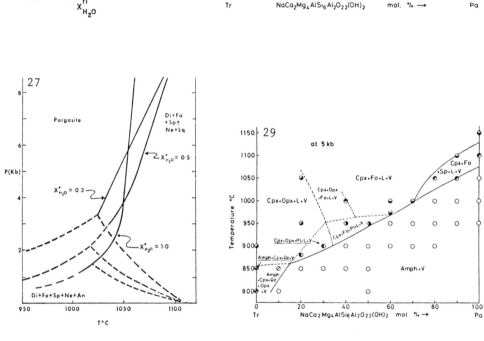

Figure 26 (upper left). T-X (H_2O-CO_2 fluid) diagram for pargasite stability after Sykes (1979, Fig. 6) and Holloway (1973, Fig. 3). Incongruent melting of pargasite is shown at several total pressures as a function of fluid composition, based on experimental data. Positive slopes (left of dashed line) correspond to H_2O as a product; negative slopes (right of dashed line) correspond to H_2O fluid reactant; "fluid-absent" melting occurs at curve maxima (dashed line).

Figure 27 (lower left). P-T projections of upper thermal stability of pargasite for various mole fractions of H_2O in an H_2O-CO_2 fluid. From Holloway (1973, Fig. 4).

Figure 28 (upper right). T-X section at 1 kbar for the join tremolite-pargasite. From Oba (1980, Fig. 2).

Figure 29 (lower right). T-X section at 5 kbar for the join tremolite-pargasite. From Oba (1980, Fig. 3).

and lend credence to the general placement of the boundaries. However, many
of these runs are only half-reversals and not all fields (assemblages) can be
considered established as stable. The greatest importance of this work is its
discovery of a miscibility gap on the join and its attempt to delineate this
gap. Electron microprobe data on the coexisting amphiboles at 1 kbar were used
to set solubility limits. Although X-ray and optical data were apparently collected, they were not reported except for the end members. An unusual aspect
of study was the apparent suppression of miscibility at 5 kbar. Inability to
locate this gap at 5 kbar was attributed to sluggishness of reaction, yet the
reversal runs listed for that pressure are shorter by factors of 4 to 10 compared to the 1 kbar runs. It is common experience that runs at 2 kbar or above,
for the same temperature, react more rapidly than those at 1 kbar or less.
Some unresolved anomalies appear to exist in the work. No two-amphibole runs
are listed in the reversal attempts in the higher pressure data set. Closure
of two amphibole compositions should be attempted at 5 kbar.

c. Edenite

Edenite, $NaCa_2Mg_5Si_7AlO_{22}(OH)_2$, was reported synthesized as early as 1954;
reconnaissance work indicated that its stability would be about 25°C greater
than tremolite (Boyd, 1954). Yet since that time no comprehensive study has
been published on this amphibole, and its stability and phase relations are
not well understood (Table 2). Colville et al. (1966) synthesized edenite at
850°C, 2 kbar, and 3 days run time, from an oxide mix for the purpose of
determining its unit cell parameters. Gilbert (1969) synthesized edenite from
one of Boyd's mixes at 900°C, 39 kbar. Petö (1976) reported that edenitic
amphibole changed to a richteritic one at higher temperature (Fig. 30). The
significance of the field boundary for edenite is unclear, inasmuch as the
criteria for discriminating changes in amphibole composition or type are
unstated. Oba (1980) reported, in passing, the determination of the upper
stability limit of edenite, on composition, at 825°C, 1 kbar. The decomposition assemblage was plagioclase + nepheline + diopside + forsterite + fluid.
Discrepancies on the order of 50°C or more exist in these data from various
workers in the H_2O fluid system.

The situation is no better in CO_2-H_2O systems. Widmark (1974) reported a
study on the reaction plagioclase + dolomite + quartz + H_2O = edenite + calcite
+ CO_2. Greenwood (1979) attempted to use thermodynamic data computed from this
work to calculate other equilibria and found poor agreement between supposed
and actual tremolite–edenite relations. Greenwood's own attempts to produce

TABLE 2.   Summarized experimental data on edenite stability.

Bulk Chemistry	Starting Material	Amphibole Formed: on Composition	T, °C	P, kbar	Duration	Report
Ed + excess H$_2$O	Glass or oxide mix	Yes:Yes?	800–900	0.4–1.0	∿ 2 weeks	Boyd, 1954
Ed + excess H$_2$O	Oxide mix	Yes:Yes?	850	2	3 days	Colville, et al., 1966
Ed + excess H$_2$O	Oxide	Yes:?	900–950	20–39	∿ 1 day	Gilbert, 1969
Ed + CaCO$_3$ + CO$_2$	Natural labradorite, dolomite, calcite, quartz, edenite	Yes:Yes?	540	6	1–2 months	Widmark, 1974
Ed + excess H$_2$O	Glass or gel	Yes:No	875–890–925	0.5–1.0–2.0	6–12 days	Petö, 1976
Ed + excess H$_2$O Ed + CO$_2$ Ed + quartz	Glass or oxide mix	Yes:No	450–825	1–4	1–5 weeks	Greenwood, 1979
Ed + excess H$_2$O	Ne+Pc+Di+Fo	Yes:Yes?	800–<825	1	3–6 months	Oba, 1980

$$Ed_{ss} + Ab = Rc_{ss} + Di_{ss} + Fo.$$

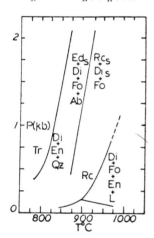

Figure 30.   From Petö (1976). Tremolite (Tr) curve from Boyd; richterite (Rc) curve from Forbes (1971b) but see Charles (1975, 1977). Edenitic amphibole (Ed) + albite with excess H$_2$O is thought to react to richteritic amphibole above the boundary shown.

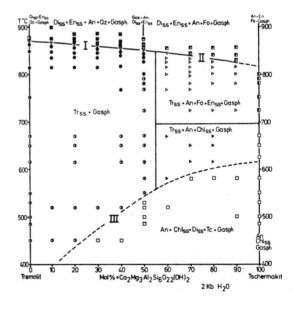

Figure 31.   Tremolite-tschermakite join at P$_{H_2O}$ = 2 kbar from Jasmund and Schäfer (1972). As the experiments were not individually tabulated, degree of reversibility for boundaries cannot be established.

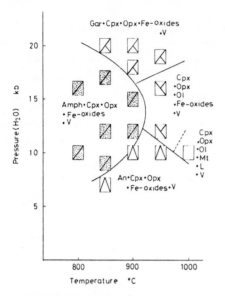

Figure 32. P-T synthesis diagram for ferri-tschermakite, $Ca_2Mg_3Fe_2^{3+}Si_6Al_2O_{22}(OH)_2$. Starting material was anorthite + clinopyroxene + orthopyroxene + hematite. From Oba (1978).

on-composition edenite were not success-ful. He did report sufficient X-ray powder data to characterize the amphi-boles synthesized as rich in tremolite component with no edenite or richterite. It is clear that experimental work on this end member will require careful attention to characterization of all phases involved in the experiments.

d. Tschermakite and other compositions

Oba (1978) has studied tschermakite, $Ca_2Mg_3Al_2Si_6Al_2O_{22}(OH)_2$, on its own bulk composition with excess vapor and deter-mined a stability field at intermediate pressures (Fig. 25). A piston-cylinder apparatus was utilized. The amphibole appeared to exist stably at 800°C be-tween 7 and 17 kbar. The low-pressure decomposition assemblage was anorthite + orthopyroxene + forsterite + fluid, while the high-pressure assemblage was amphibole solid solution + clinopyroxene + garnet + quartz + fluid. One-sided reversals for each of these reactions from amphibole to breakdown assemblage were accomplished. As the starting materials were anorthite + forsterite + enstatite, synthesis of tschermakite completes the reversal for the low-pres-sure decomposition reaction. The very shallow, positive slope on the low pres-sure stability may explain why Jasmund and Schäfer (1972), in their study of the join tremolite + tschermakite, were unable to synthesize this amphibole over the pressure range to 3 kbar (Fig. 31). Their 10 kbar reconnaissance run also failed to yield tschermakite. They did not report the same low pressure assemblage as Oba. It is not clear how much of their work was reversed.

Oba (1978) characterized his tschermakite using refractive indices, unit cell dimensions, and microprobe analyses. Only compositions in equilibrium with garnet were reported, however. Such amphiboles were slightly enriched in Mg and deficient in Ca and Al, compared to the ideal tschermakite formula.

Ferri-tschermakite composition, $Ca_2Mg_3Fe_2^{3+}Si_6Al_2O_{22}(OH)_2$, and the join between this and tschermakite were also studied by Oba. Iron-bearing samples were placed in gold capsules, presumably to avoid Fe loss to platinum. However, since Fe is also soluble in Au, similar Fe loss can be expected. This problem

was not addressed, nor were microprobe data on the Fe-bearing amphiboles presented, although optical and X-ray data were. If experience in other systems
is applicable, the crystal sizes should have been larger and more amenable to
probe analysis in the Fe-bearing experiments. The end member experiments
yielded hematite + magnetite, thus fixing oxygen fugacity. Ferri-tschermakite
was not found stable. The solubility limit for the ferri-end member was about
35 mole percent at 850°C, 12 kbar. Figure 32 is Oba's diagram. Interestingly,
garnet joins the decomposition assemblage at about the same pressure in this
system for Fe-compositions as for Mg-ones. In contrast, garnet enters at pressures below 12 kbar for the Fe-rich end members of the pargasite-hastingsite
quad. This presumably reflects both the lower pressure stability of Fe-rich
garnets and the intersection of the positive sloped curves at lower temperatures, and thus at lower pressures.

Tschermakite has one of the most restricted stability fields of any end
member amphibole yet investigated. This apparently explains, along with the
rather restricted chemical environments necessary (lack of alkalies), why there
are few occurrences of amphiboles approaching this composition.

Sodic-calcic amphiboles

a. Richterites

Rather complete data exist on the richterites (Charles 1975; 1977) (see
Fig. 33). An earlier determination of the low-pressure stability of Na_2CaMg_5
$Si_8O_{22}(OH)_2$ by Forbes (1971b) has been superceded by Charles' more extensive
work. Under conditions of the FMQ buffer, all richterite breakdown involves
clinopyroxene + olivine. All those compositions as magnesian as Mg_2Fe_3 melt
incongruently above several hundred bars. Pure richterite also reacts to
orthopyroxene. All the other members of the series produce magnetite, while
those as Fe-rich as Mg_1Fe_4 yield quartz as well. Finally, at all f_{O_2} above
IW, Charles believes clinopyroxene is stable along with the richterite solution in the "amphibole" field. Compositions of amphibole and pyroxene could
not be determined but cell prameter data were presented.

The magnesian members have high thermal stabilities, and pronounced lower-
ings are exhibited only after compositions become more Fe-rich than Mg_2Fe_3
(Figs. 34 and 35). Charles offered two explanations for this behavior: one
involved preferential filling of the larger two M_1 and one M_3 sites with Fe^{2+}.
When the smaller two M_2 sites contain Mg, more favorable linking of the double
chains of SiO_4 tetrahedra is provided. Occupation of M_2 by the larger Fe^{2+}
would significantly decrease the quality of this linkage and thus the stability.

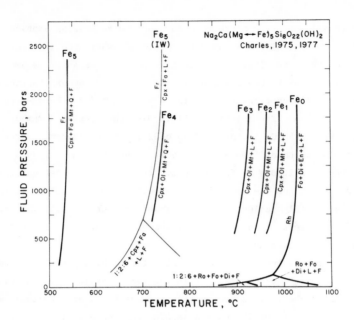

Figure 33. P-T diagram for the series richterite-ferro-richterite. Compositional steps are shown in terms of Fe-atom substitutions for Mg in the formula unit. Clinopyroxene is interpreted to coexist stably with the amphibole below each of these curves. Stabilities of the Fe-bearing solutions are shown at oxygen fugacities equivalent to the FMQ buffer, in heavy lines. The Fe-end member stability is near maximum on the IW buffer and is shown in a light line for comparison with the FMQ-determined curve. The phase designation 1:2:6 = Na-Mg silicate, and Ro = roedderite.

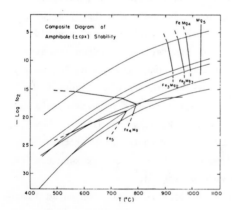

Figure 34. The composite fO_2 -T diagram at 1 kbar fluid pressure of the richterite-ferro-richterite series ± clinopyroxene. From Charles (1977, Fig. 10).

The second effect presumes solid solutions toward magnesio-riebeckite with Fe^{3+} concentrated in M_2 and compensating loss of Na from the A-site in the Mg-rich richterites, and a similar solution toward riebeckite, with its low-temperature stability, in the Fe-rich richterites.

Hariya and Terada (1973) studied the intermediate composition richterite$_{50}$-tremolite$_{50}$ at high pressure (Fig. 25). Their data seemed to indicate this

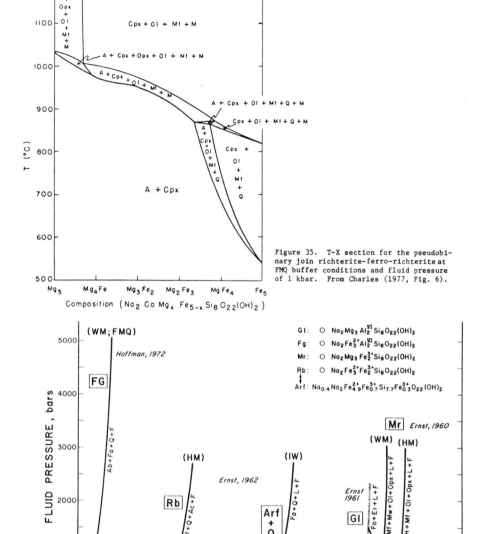

Figure 35. T-X section for the pseudobinary join richterite-ferro-richterite at FMQ buffer conditions and fluid pressure of 1 kbar. From Charles (1977, Fig. 6).

Figure 36. P-T plot of the reported end-member stabilities of alkali amphiboles. Glaucophane stability as originally determined by Ernst (1961) is probably incorrect and shown as a fuzzy line. See Figure 25 for the upper and lower pressure limits on glaucophane. The effect of variation in oxygen fugacity on stability limits is shown for magnesio-riebeckite, riebeckite-arfvedsonite, and ferro-glaucophane. See also Figures 37 and 38. Phase symbols: Mf = magnesioferrite, Mw = magnesiowüstite, N = $Na_2(Mg,Fe)_2Si_6O_{15}$, Ma = $Na_2(Mg,Fe)_5Si_{12}O_{30}$; Ae = aenigmatite, and Ac = acmite. o in the endmember formulae indicates vacant A-site.

phase stable to at least 40 kbar.   If so, this would be the highest pressure
stability at melting of any single amphibole composition studied.

b.   Potassium-richterites

The composition $KNaCaMg_5Si_8O_{22}(OH)_2$ and related phases were synthesized
by Huebner and Papike (1970) and subjected to extensive crystal chemical analysis. No direct experimentation on stability relations or breakdown reactions
was done. However, the study yielded the prediction that K-amphiboles might
be stabilized with pressure.

Gilbert and Briggs (1974) reported a preliminary determination of potassium-richterite stability (Fig. 25) from 10 to 25 kbar. Extrapolation to lower
pressures indicates a thermal stability less than richterite, while the high
pressure thermal stability appears to be the highest of any end member yet
investigated, over 1200°C at 25 kbar. A single reconnaissance run at 30 kbar,
1100°C, reported by Kushiro and Erlank (1970), confirms the extensive stability
field of this amphibole. This is in accord with the predictions of Huebner
and Papike (1970).

Alkali amphiboles

The alkali amphibole quadrilateral members are glaucophane, ferro-glaucophane, magnesio-riebeckite, and riebeckite (Fig. 36). Some of these were among
the first end member compositions studied (Ernst, 1960, 1961, 1962). Because
of special problems associated with glaucophane, that phase will be reviewed
last in this section.

a.   Fe-bearing end members

Ferro-glaucophane was synthesized and a breakdown reaction determined
reversibly by Hoffman (1972) (Fig. 36). This is the lowest upper thermal
stability found for any amphibole as it probably does not exceed 400°C at any
pressure. The decomposition assemblage is albite + fayalite + quartz + fluid
over the oxygen fugacity range represented by the WM to FMQ buffers with no
measurable temperature dependence. No stability at higher oxygen fugacities
was found. Its natural rarity was ascribed to its restricted thermal and oxygen fugacity bounds.

In sharp contrast, Ernst (1960) determined that magnesio-riebeckite has a
high thermal stability and an extreme oxygen fugacity range (Figs. 36 and 37).
In fact, only richterite and magnesio-hastingsite have higher stabilities in
the range of crustal pressures. The dramatic effect of substituting Mg for
Fe^{2+} and Fe^{3+} for Al is clear. The relatively minor control of oxygen fugacity

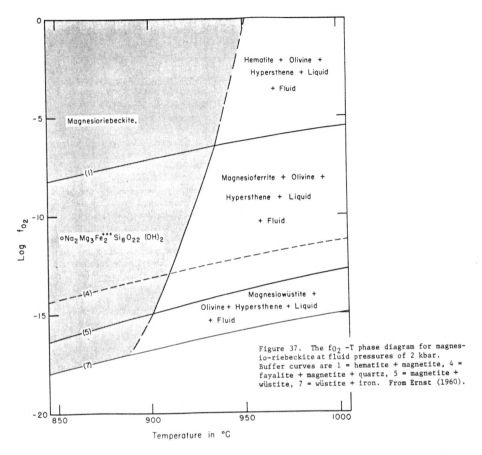

Figure 37. The f_{O_2} -T phase diagram for magnesio-riebeckite at fluid pressures of 2 kbar. Buffer curves are 1 = hematite + magnetite, 4 = fayalite + magnetite + quartz, 5 = magnetite + wüstite, 7 = wüstite + iron. From Ernst (1960).

is interesting in comparison to the much stronger effect in magnesio-hastingsite (Fig. 24). Magnesio-hastingsite stability falls about 200°C, where magnesio-riebeckite only falls about 35°C for the same change in buffers.

Riebeckite bulk composition was studied by Ernst (1962). That composition yielded a single phase amphibole under the oxygen fugacities of the HM buffer. As the composition was subjected to the lower oxygen fugacities of more reduced buffers, the temperatures of stability rose progressively to the IW buffer as the amphibole's composition also changed toward arfvedsonite (Figs. 38 and 39). Incongruent melting was encountered at about 700°C on the WM and IW buffers. As the change toward arfvedsonite begins to fill up the A-site with Na and generate some tetrahedral Fe^{3+}, the amphibole-stable field becomes amphibole + quartz. This study indicated that pure OH-riebeckite was probably *not* stable with granitic liquids and that riebeckite in granites previously identified as primary must have one of the following explanations: (1) riebeckite was really

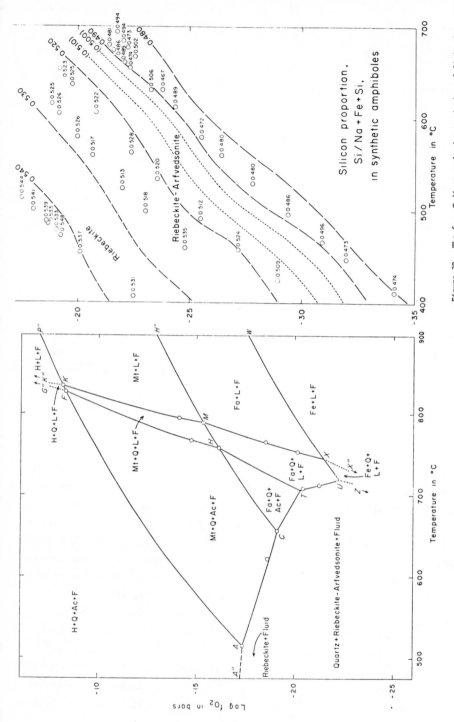

Figure 39. The f_{O_2}–T diagram showing variation of Si in the amphibole formula unit for riebeckite-arfvedsonite. As total pressure produces no variation, data plotted represent experiments over the pressure range to 2 kbar. From Ernst (1962).

Figure 38. The f_{O_2}–T phase diagram for riebeckite bulk composition at fluid pressure of 2 kbar. From Ernst (1962).

264

an arfvedsonite, (2) riebeckite was subsolidus, or (3) riebeckite was F-rich.

The range of thermal stability under different buffer conditions is greater for riebeckite-arfvedsonite than either of the other iron-end members of the alkali amphiboles. The Fe-rich end members free quartz on breakdown. As a final noteworthy point, riebeckite is apparently the only amphibole whose lower thermal stability range includes sedimentary authigenic environments (e.g., see Eugster, 1969).

b. Glaucophane

The first experimental study of glaucophane yielded a high temperature of stability, surprising because of the amphibole's suspected low-temperature paragenesis (Ernst, 1961) (Fig. 36). While yields of glaucophane from oxide mixes were always low, it appeared that longer runs with presumed breakdown products showed growth of glaucophane. Micrometric counts of run products also were interpreted to show constant and correct amphibole composition. As it turned out, the experiments involved albite + a Na-montmorillonite-like phase, which played a role more crucial than expected at that time. Ernst interpreted his data to show the sheet silicate to be metastable. However, no experiments listed in his data tables were really designed to ascertain its role as a possible stable reaction member. The sequence of X-ray patterns offered in his Figure 1 to document Na-montmorillonite metastability can be analyzed in other ways. Later work was to show how crucial this assumption of metastability was. Once it was assumed that the Na-clay was metastable, the rest of Ernst's interpretation followed reasonably.

Ernst had noticed a somewhat larger cell volume for his synthetic glaucophane compared to Fe-poor natural specimens, as well as to an extrapolated end member phase. This led to the first high-pressure study of amphiboles (Ernst, 1963) wherein members of this quad were taken to pressures up to 40 kbar, all in the subsolidus. For some of the intermediate compositions, crossites as well as glaucophane, these experiments showed a reversible contraction in cell volume from low-pressure synthesis or annealing, to high-pressure annealing. This change was interpreted to mean that the high-pressure forms were ordered polymorphs of the low-pressure, disordered ones. The glaucophane I-II polymorphic boundary reported by Ernst (1963) is subparallel to the low-pressure stability limit of glaucophane as subsequently determined by Gilbert and Popp (1973) and Carman (1974a) (Fig. 25).

Carman (1969) was unable to find a field of stability of glaucophane in experiments ranging up to 5 kbar in the system $NaAlSiO_4$-Mg_2SiO_4-SiO_2-H_2O but did find an extensive field for Na-phlogopite and its hydrates (Carman, 1974b).

Subsequently several investigators reported additional data which considerably changed our understanding of the phase relations (Gilbert and Popp, 1973; Maresch, 1973, 1977; Carman, 1974a). Figure 25 shows two probable reactions which provide the upper and lower pressure stability bounds of glaucophane. The solid disproportionation reaction glaucophane = 2 jadeite + talc (gl on the high-temperature, low-pressure side), has been reversed and limits glaucophane to pressures below about 33 kbar. One of Ernst's (1963) experiments ordering glaucophane at 600°C, 30 kbar in his polymorphic study falls above the pressure stability of glaucophane at that temperature. As the breakdown products were not present to nucleate the reaction, as the duration of the experiment was relatively short, and as this reaction is sluggish, it is likely that the amphibole gave no hint that its stability was exceeded.

Glaucophane = albite + Na-phlogopite$_{ss}$ limits glaucophane on the low-pressure side to about 14 kbar at 500°C. Above about 650°C, liquid is also formed on the low-pressure side. The upper thermal stability limit involves melting and glaucophane is gone by about 900°C. A more detailed presentation of glaucophane data is now in preparation by Carman and Gilbert.

The conclusion now seems increasingly likely that Ernst's (1961) determination needs to be re-interpreted. Several possibilities exist. One is that the reported breakdown curve is essentially a metastable extension of a higher-pressure thermal stability curve which terminates at about 18 kbar, at its *low*-pressure end. Another is that the amphibole in Ernst's experiments was not glaucophane but one with solution of other components, especially rich in Na and Mg. On the other hand, Ernst had reason to suggest that the amphibole synthesized was a disordered form and that it could be reversibly ordered with pressure. While the ordered cell volume he produced is still somewhat large, this argues for a composition not far from stoichiometric glaucophane. Finally, there may be a remote possibility of two different stability fields for a glaucophane amphibole -- a high-pressure one and a lower-pressure one -- because of variations in ΔV of reaction due to compressibility of the sheet silicate. [See also the discussion by Thompson in Chapter 3, Volume 9A.]

Fluorine amphiboles

F has been known to substitute for OH in amphiboles for many years. In fact, some of the first syntheses of amphiboles were as the fluorinated species (e.g., Bowen and Schairer, 1935; Grigoriev and Iskuld, 1937). The U.S. Bureau of Mines carried out an extensive program of F-amphibole synthesis aimed toward possible production of asbestos. This work has been summarized in Comeforo and Kohn (1954), Kohn and Comeforo (1955), Shell et al. (1958), and Gibbs et al.

(1962). Over 150 reactions were studied and about 75 different amphiboles were manufactured. Most of the runs used large charges (volumes of cm^3 to m^3), passed through temperature cycles and temperature gradients. Interestingly, F-anthophyllite was never made by this group or others (e.g., Van Valkenburg, 1955). It was early inferred that F substituting for OH would raise the thermal stability of amphiboles dramatically. However, there is very little in the published literature actually documenting breakdown reactions and stability fields. In fact, some of the suggested temperatures of stability are probably 50°-100°C too high and the breakdown reactions incorrect.

a. Fluor-tremolite

This is the only amphibole whose 1 atm stability has been reversibly determined, and this was only reported in abstract form (Troll and Gilbert, 1974; Gilbert and Troll, 1974). The decomposition reaction is fluor-tremolite = diopside + enstatite + tridymite + fluorite, entirely solid-state. The equilibrium temperature was demonstrated to be 1136 ± 3°C using sealed capsules. The pressure stability of this phase was followed using a piston-cylinder apparatus. Reversed curves limiting fluor-tremolite are shown in Figure 40. The upper thermal stability curve has a negative slope (-201 bars/°C) above the tridymite-β quartz inversion. It further flattens after the α-β quartz inversion to -30 bars/°C. Finally, after the α quartz-coesite inversion, the stability limit curve is presumed to reverse sign and become positive, although the reaction was too sluggish to monitor with the techniques employed. Comparison with OH-tremolite (Fig. 25) shows that F raises the pressure limit by only 5 kbar. While the 1 atm stabilities of F- and OH-tremolite differ by 584°C (1136°C and 552°C, respectively), higher pressure *reduces* this difference markedly.

b. Fluor-potassium-richterite

This amphibole was studied by Gilbert and Briggs (1974) (Fig. 40). At one atmosphere, this phase begins to melt to about 1130°C to amphibole + forsterite + silicate liquid. Data on the composition of this latter amphibole were not obtained. By 10 kbar the amphibole melted to mica + liquid with this reaction persisting to 1375°C at 25 kbar. Again, the low-pressure difference in the F- and OH-stabilities (~300°C) is diminished with increasing pressure (~150°C). The upper pressure limit on this amphibole has not been determined.

c. Fluor-pargasite

Holloway and Ford (1975) studied a pargasite of intermediate F-OH content

267

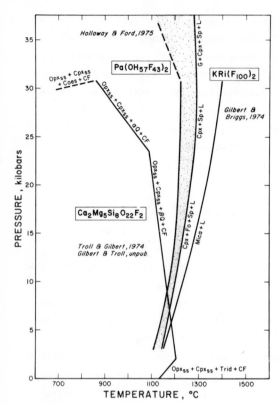

Figure 40. P-T diagram for F-amphibole end mem-
bers, CF = CaF_2; $Pa(OH_{57}F_{43})_2$ = $NaCa_2Mg_4Al^{VI}Si_6$
$Al_2^{IV}O_{22}[(OH)_{57}F_{43}]_2$, fluorohydroxy-pargasite;
$KRi(F_{100})_2$ = $KNaCaMg_5Si_8O_{22}F_2$ (fluor-potassium-
richterite).

(43% of O_3 site was F). This composition was synthesized as a single-phase
amphibole and then used on its own bulk composition in runs to 35 kbar (Fig.
40). The location of the solidus is only approximate due to the small amount
of glass occurring over a temperature zone. Limited microprobe data were said
to suggest that cation ratios did not change significantly until breakdown,
implying that the major compositional variation was an increase of F/OH with
increasing temperature. The presence of F extends the pressure stability of
pargasite by 10-15 kbar, somewhat more than in the case of tremolite noted
earlier. Presumably pure fluor-pargasite would be stable to a higher temperature than fluor-potassium-richterite.

AMPHIBOLES IN METAMORPHIC ROCK COMPOSITIONS (*FSS, MCG*)

This section describes experimental studies involving amphibole stability
where either rock compositions or other mineral compositions have been used as
starting materials. The advantage of this type of study over the study of end-
member mineral stabilities is that it is easier to extrapolate from the

268

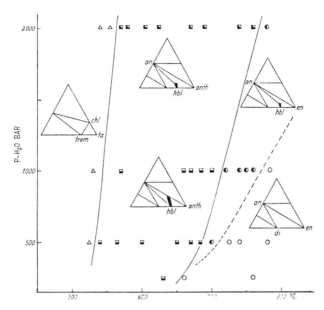

Figure 41. P(H$_2$O) -T diagram from Choudhuri and Winkler (1967) showing plotted run data for amphibole stability in an "ultrabasic" bulk composition. Note text discussion that reactions shown are continuous.

experimental system to the interpretation of real rocks. The disadvantage is that the reactions investigated are highly dependent on bulk composition and it is generally not possible to derive basic thermochemical data from the experimental results.

Choudhuri and Winkler (1967) investigated three reactions in a rock of approximately "ultrabasic" composition. These are

$$\text{chlorite} + \text{talc} + \text{tremolite} + \text{quartz} =$$

$$\text{hornblende}_2 + \text{anthophyllite} + \text{anorthite} + \text{H}_2\text{O},$$

$$\text{hornblende}_1 + \text{anthophyllite} = \text{hornblende}_2 + \text{enstatite} + \text{anorthite} + \text{H}_2\text{O},$$

$$\text{hornblende} = \text{enstatite} + \text{diopside} + \text{H}_2\text{O}.$$

The starting material consisted of a mixture of natural chlorite, talc, tremolite, and quartz in proportions that yielded a bulk rock Fe^T/(Fe^T + Mg) = 0.16, where Fe^T is total iron. The stability fields of the different assemblages produced and the reactions bounding these assemblages are shown in Figure 41.

The paragentic sequence observed on this bulk composition with increasing temperature is

$$\text{tremolite} + \text{talc} + \text{chlorite} + \text{quartz},$$

$$\text{hornblende} + \text{anthophyllite} + \text{anorthite} + \text{quartz},$$

269

hornblende + enstatite + anorthite + quartz,

enstatite + diopside + anorthite + quartz.

Anorthite was observed in association with anthophyllite + hornblende at 2 kbar and above, presumably because the hornblende formed at this pressure has a lower Al content, thus enabling the bulk composition to "see" anorthite. Dehydration of anthophyllite and hornblende begins at approximately the same temperature at pressures below 2 kbar, whereas at 2 kbar and above, Choudhuri and Winkler claim that it is probable that only anthophyllite begins to dehydrate at the enstatite-in reaction, because of the low Al content of the hornblende. The maximum thermal stability of hornblende is higher than that of anthophyllite by 20-50°C.

Although not explicitly stated by Choudhuri and Winkler, all of these reactions must be continuous reactions, with the phases changing in modal abundance and composition over the paragenetic interval. It should also be noted that in natural and experimental systems of basaltic composition, clinopyroxene typically appears at lower temperatures than orthopyroxene (see Chapter 1, this volume). The appearance of enstatite first in these experiments is undoubtedly a function of the Ca-poor bulk composition.

Akella and Winkler (1966) investigated the upper and lower stability limit of gedrite using natural starting minerals consisting of chlorite + quartz + ferrogedrite with an Fe/(Fe + Mg) ratio of 0.44. The reactions were unbuffered, but presumably near the FMQ buffer curve. Two reactions were bracketed by reversals:

chlorite + quartz = gedrite + cordierite + H_2O

and

gedrite + quartz = hypersthene + H_2O

The P-T boundaries for these reactions are shown in Figure 42. The assemblage gedrite + cordierite + quartz is thus stable over a temperature interval of 150-200°C at pressures of 1-2 kbar.

No composition data on phases produced from the experiments were presented by these authors except that the gedrite seed contained 2.0 wt % Na_2O. Inasmuch as the components SiO_2-Al_2O_3-MgO-FeO-Na_2O-H_2O are necessary to describe the phases in this system, the reactions investigated must be at least bivariant and thus sweep out a P-T region over which the Fe/Mg ratios of the phases change with reaction progress. Based on other work involving Fe-Mg-amphiboles, it is probable that the Fe-rich components break down first and the Mg-rich components last.

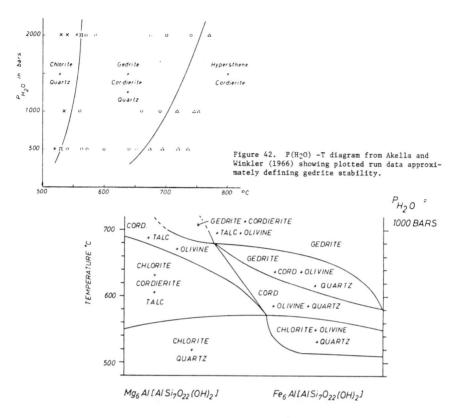

Figure 42. P(H$_2$O) –T diagram from Akella and Winkler (1966) showing plotted run data approximately defining gedrite stability.

Figure 43. T-X diagram from Hinrichsen (1968) showing results of hydrothermal experiments at 1 kbar fluid pressure and oxygen fugacities below FMQ, for the system (Mg,Fe)$_6$AlSi$_7$AlO$_{22}$(OH)$_2$.

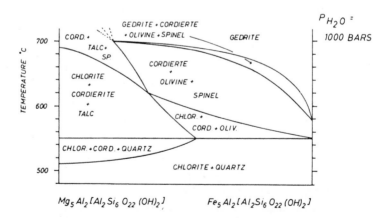

Figure 44. T-X diagram from Hinrichsen (1968) showing results of hydrothermal experiments at 1 kbar fluid pressure and oxygen fugacities below FMQ, for the system (Mg,Fe)$_5$Al$_2$Si$_6$Al$_2$O$_{22}$(OH)$_2$.

Hinrichsen (1968) investigated the stability of gedrites along two pseudo-binary Fe-Mg joins: $(Fe,Mg)_6Al(Si_7Al)O_{22}(OH)_2$ and $(Fe,Mg)_5Al_2(Si_6Al_2)O_{22}(OH)_2$. Oxygen fugacity was controlled by the magnetite-iron and magnetite-wüstite buffers. Hinrichsen found that it was not possible to synthesize gedrites of any Fe-Mg ratio without the addition of small amounts of Na_2O (0.8 - 1.2 wt percent). Natural gedrites invariably contain Na, so it is possible that it is required for the stability of this mineral. Figures 43 and 44 are T-X (Fe-Mg) diagrams showing the results of the hydrothermal experiments.

Under no conditions was Hinrichsen able to synthesize pure Mg-gedrite. In contrast, there have been limited, but persistent, reports (e.g., Yoder, 1971) that gedrites or "aluminous anthophyllite" could be synthesized in the presence of liquids at higher pressures, such as 10 kbar (Fig. 45). Mg-gedrites have not been reported from natural assemblages, so that the special chemical and physical conditions which may be necessary for its formation are evidently not realized in nature. According to Hinrichsen, gedrite has a rather limited stability field that gets smaller with increasing aluminum content. Fe-rich gedrites are stable at lower temperatures than Mg-rich varieties. There is a discrepancy between this work and that of Akella and Winkler (1966) regarding the low-temperature assemblage of gedrite composition. Both authors show chlorite + quartz to be stable at lowest temperatures up to approximately 570°C. Akella and Winkler show this assemblage giving way to gedrite, whereas Hinrichsen shows several fields containing cordierite ± chlorite ± olivine ± spinel ± talc ± quartz, with gedrite relegated to a higher temperature paragenesis. Natural gedrites are certainly encountered at temperatures lower than those indicated by the work of Hinrichsen; moreover, gedrite should be more hydrous (and hence have a lower thermal stability) than assemblages such as olivine + cordierite + quartz. Thus, it is difficult to rationalize these experimental results. One possibility is that total pressure controls which of these two types of assemblages is stable. Studies emphasizing chlorite bulk compositions (e.g., James et al., 1976) do show chlorite reacting to cordierite below 4 kbar and gedrite above (Fig. 46). Another possibility is that Na strongly influences the thermal stability of gedrite and that the differences may be attributed to differences in bulk Na content. It is also possible that differences in f_{O_2} could account for some of the discrepancy.

Binns (1968) studied the reaction

$$hornblende_1 + quartz = hornblende_2 + orthopyroxene +$$

$$Ca\text{-clinopyroxene} + plagioclase + H_2O$$

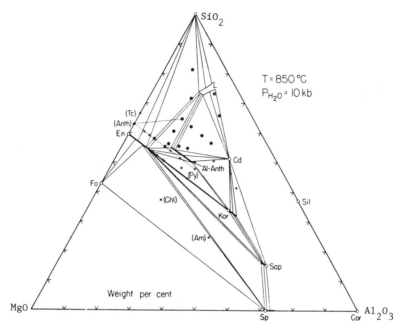

Figure 45. Preliminary section of the MgO–Al$_2$O$_3$–SiO$_2$–H$_2$O system at 850°C and 10 kbar (from Yoder, 1971). Phases in parentheses are absent. X = crystalline phases + gas; circled X indicates liquid also present. Dotted lines indicate possible solid solution in anthophyllite toward Mg$_4$Al$_2$Si$_8$O$_{22}$(OH)$_2$ and Mg$_5$Al$_4$Si$_6$O$_{22}$(OH)$_2$.

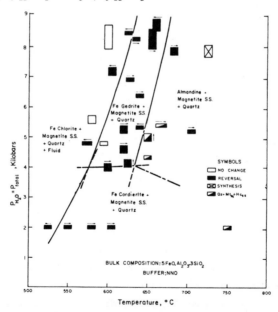

Figure 46. P$_{fluid}$–T diagram for daphnite + excess H$_2$O (James et al., 1976). Note that Fe-chlorite breaks down to Fe-gedrite above 4 kbar.

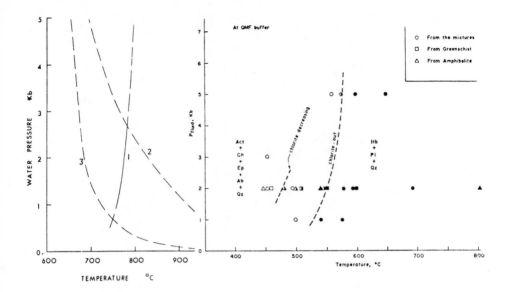

Figure 47 (to the left). $P_{H_2O} = P_{total}$ versus T diagram showing breakdown of "common" hornblende + quartz = opx + cpx + plag + vapor (1) with dashed portions of curve extrapolated. Curve (2) is beginning-of-melting curve for quartz-bearing amphibolite and hornblende gneiss, and curve (3) is beginning-of-melting curve for granite. From Binns (1968, Fig. 1).

Figure 48 (to the right). P_{fluid}-T diagram for the decomposition of chlorite in a basaltic system. Open symbols = growth of chlorite; solid symbols = disappearance; half circles = no change in chlorite/amphibole; half squares and triangles = decrease in chlorite/amphibole, and incipient growth of chlorite, respectively. From Liou et al.(1974).

at pressures of 1.0 and 2.7 kbar and f_{O_2} defined by the FMQ buffer as a simplified model for the amphibolite-granulite facies boundary. He used natural phases as starting materials and thus the reaction investigated is multivariate. The bulk rock Fe/(Fe + Mg) was approximately 0.55–0.60. The P-T conditions for this reaction are shown in Figure 47. The temperature for the incoming of orthopyroxene was established at 760°C, 1 kbar and 780°C, 2.7 kbar.

Two studies utilized natural rocks of basaltic composition as starting materials. Liou et al. (1974) investigated the greenschist to amphibolite facies transition with starting materials of natural greenschist [(albite + quartz + epidote + chlorite + actinolite + magnetite + titanite (sphene)] and amphibolite [(plagioclase + quartz + hornblende + magnetite + titanite (sphene)]. The bulk $Fe^T/(Fe^T + Mg)$ ratios of the greenschist and amphibolite starting materials were 0.41 and 0.50, respectively. All experiments were run on the FMQ buffer and the results are shown in Figure 48.

The transition from greenschist to amphibolite is characterized by the replacement of the assemblage albite + chlorite + epidote + actinolite by the

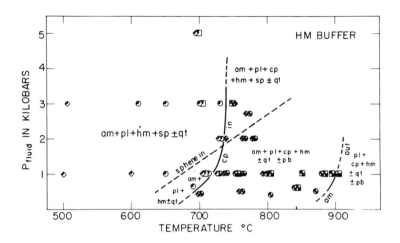

Figure 49. P_{fluid}-T relations at oxygen fugacities defined by the hematite-magnetite buffer for basalt V25-RD1-T2 from the Mid-Atlantic ridge. All starting assemblages include plagioclase + ilmenite or hematite: square = clinopyroxene + olivine (basaltic assemblage); circle = clinopyroxene + amphibole ± orthopyroxene (granulite); diamond = amphibole (amphibolite). Phases present in resulting assemblage are indicated by filled quadrants: NW quad = amphibole; NE = orthopyroxene; SE = clinopyroxene; SW = olivine. Some other abbreviations are hm = titanohematite; pb = pseudobrookite. From Spear (1981).

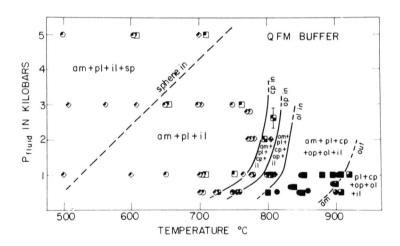

Figure 50. P_{fluid}-T relations at oxygen fugacities defined by the fayalite-magnetite-quartz buffer for the basalt with symbols as in Figure 49. From Spear (1981).

assemblage plagioclase + hornblende. Liou et al. found that chlorite begins
to decrease in modal amount at approximately 475°C, 2000 bars P_{fluid} and disappears from the assemblage at approximately 550°C, 2000 bars P_{fluid}. They
described the transition as a multivariant reaction with phases changing in
proportion and composition across the transition zone. Electron microprobe
analyses of experimentally produced phases indicated that the composition of
the plagioclase changes from approximately An_8 to An_{48} over the transition
zone, and the amphiboles change in composition from actinolite to hornblende
(i.e., Al_2O_3, TiO_2, Na_2O, and FeO/MgO increase, whereas SiO_2 decreases). In
addition to demonstrating the feasibility of replicating natural facies transitions in the laboratory, this study placed temperature and pressure limits
on the greenschist to amphibolite facies transition under conditions where
$P_{fluid} = P_{total}$.

Spear (1981) used a natural olivine tholeiite as a starting material and
investigated the phase relations and changes in mineral chemistry in this rock
from 500-900°C and 0.4 - 5 kbar. P-T diagrams summarizing the phase equilibria
for experiments run on the FMQ and HM buffers are in Figures 49 and 50. Phase
relations on the WM buffer are similar to those on the FMQ buffer (not shown);
f_{O_2}-T relations are given in Figure 51.

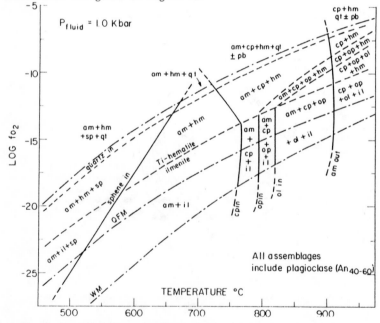

Figure 51. The f_{O_2}-T plot for basalt V25-RDI-T2. Solid lines are measured phase boundaries;
dashed lines are inferred; and dot-dash lines are buffer curves. All assemblages include plagioclase. From Spear (1981).

Phase relations for this olivine tholeiite are characterized by a series of multivariate, continuous reactions that change the modal mineralogy and mineral compositions. On the FMQ buffer, the assemblage hornblende + plagioclase + ilmenite + titanite (sphene) is stable at the lowest temperatures and pressures. This assemblage persists up to the titanite-in reaction boundary, above which titanite is replaced by ilmenite and the assemblage is hornblende + plagioclase + ilmenite. This assemblage persists up to temperatures of approximately 770°C, 1 kbar and 785°C, 2 kbar where amphibole begins to break down in a series of continuous reactions, first to clinopyroxene, then to clinopyroxene + orthopyroxene, and finally to clinopyroxene + orthopyroxene + olivine. Throughout this paragenetic interval amphibole changes in composition and modal abundance. Final dehydration of amphibole occurred at approximately 910°C, 1 kbar.

On the HM buffer, phase relations are similar with the following notable exceptions: (1) orthopyroxene and olivine are never observed as breakdown products of hornblende; (2) the titanite-in reaction boundary is displaced to considerably higher temperatures; (3) the Fe-Ti oxide phase is hematite with approximately 0.25 percent ilmenite component; (4) the proportion of amphibole is smaller; and (5) the temperature of the first appearance of clinopyroxene is approximately 50°C lower than on the FMQ buffer. The temperature of the final dehydration of amphibole is not significantly reduced, however (i.e., 902°C, 1 kbar).

The compositions of amphiboles from the run products were analyzed by electron microprobe using a technique for small particle analysis. At constant P_{fluid} and on a given f_{O_2} buffer, the amphiboles are enriched in Na, K, Ti, and Al and depleted in Si with increasing T. The *same trend* is observed at constant T and P_{fluid} with *decreasing* f_{O_2}. That is, reduction has a similar effect on amphibole composition in this rock as increasing temperature. The other notable change with increasing f_{O_2} is that amphiboles synthesized on the HM buffer have a considerably higher $Fe^{3+}/(Fe^{3+} + Fe^{2+})$ than those synthesized on the FMQ buffer (i.e., 0.40 versus 0.12, respectively, as determined by Mössbauer spectroscopy), and the oxidized amphiboles have a considerably higher Mg/Fe. Increasing oxygen fugacity therefore enriched the amphibole in components that are either stabilized by high f_{O_2} (e.g., the Fe^{3+} components) or not affected by f_{O_2} (e.g., the Mg components). This explains why the upper thermal stability of hornblende in this system is not more strongly influenced by f_{O_2}, as are Fe-amphiboles synthesized on their own bulk compositions (e.g., ferro-actinolite and ferro-pargasite). The effects of pressure were not as well determined, but there is a tendency for Al(IV), Al(VI), and Al(total) to increase with increasing pressure.

The results of the experimental studies outlined above can be used (1) as a guide to the thermal stability of different types of amphiboles in bulk compositions similar to those found in natural environments; (2) as an indication of the P-T conditions of metamorphic facies boundaries; and (3) as a model for the behavior of amphibole in complex chemical systems.

The beginnings of thermal breakdown of amphiboles in rocks of basaltic composition estimated from the experimental results indicate a temperature of 750-800°C for this transition where $P_{fluid} = P_{total}$. Bulk composition clearly affects the details of this transition. For example, quartz saturation probably lowers the temperature for the first appearance of orthopyroxene (compare Binns, 1968, and Spear, 1981), as does a higher bulk rock Fe/Mg.

One obvious limitation to directly applying the experimental results to metamorphic facies transitions is that all of the experimental studies were conducted under conditions where $P_{H_2O} = P_{total}$, a condition that is certainly not applicable in the granulite facies and possibly not applicable in the amphibolite facies. Under conditions where $P_{H_2O} < P_{total}$, all of the stability curves will shift to lower temperatures. Calculations by Binns (1968) and Spear (1981) indicate that amphibole will begin to dehydrate to pyroxene at a temperature 30-50°C lower than the maximum thermal stability where $P_{H_2O} = 0.5 \; P_{total}$ and that complete dehydration of amphibole can be achieved at approximately 700°C where $P_{H_2O} = 0.1 \; P_{total}$.

The compositional variations observed by Liou et al. (1974) and Spear (1981) provide experimental verification of trends observed in studies of natural systems. All amphiboles studied show increases in Na, Al, and Ti and depletion in Si with increasing T, which can be described in terms of increases in the pargasite (edenite + tschermakite) and Ti-tschermakite substitutions. Again, bulk composition plays the dominant role in determining the composition of the amphibole observed, but these changes should be valid for an isochemical system with increasing temperature. Oxidation has an effect that works in the opposite direction from temperature, as pointed out by Spear (1981). Pressure undoubtedly also plays a major role, especially at low temperatures, but no experimental studies of the greenschist-blueschist facies transition on natural rock compositions have been reported in the literature.

PHASE RELATIONS AND COMPOSITIONS OF AMPHIBOLES PRODUCED IN STUDIES OF THE MELTING BEHAVIOR OF ROCKS *(RTH)*

Introduction

Numerous studies of the melting relations of natural rock compositions have been made in the last 25 years. There are several dozen such studies in which amphibole has been reported to occur in equilibrium with a silicate liquid. The rock compositions in which amphibole occurs are almost all igneous, ranging from rhyolite to basanite and nephelinite. Non-igneous compositions studied include six peridotites (Kushiro, 1970; Mysen and Boettcher, 1975a,b; Millhollen et al., 1974) and two pyroxenites (Merrill and Wyllie, 1975; Mysen and Boettcher, 1976). Also, Killinc (1969) reports amphibole as a refractory phase in partial melting experiments on a graywacke. This appears to be the only report of amphibole in a fused sedimentary rock, however; the usual mafic phases in sedimentary compositions are biotite, cordierite, and garnet (see e.g. Winkler and von Platen, 1961; von Platen and Holler, 1966).

In addition to melting experiments on rock compositions, there are a few experimental studies of synthetic "rocks" (Green, 1973; Green and Ringwood, 1968; Naney, 1977; Naney and Swanson, 1980) and of complex synthetic systems containing amphibole (Cawthorn, 1976a) which are relevant to the present discussion.

P-T conditions in these thirty-odd studies cover the range from 1 to 30 kbar and from 700 to 1100°C. Most of the experiments done to date have been carried out in the presence of a vapor phase of nearly pure H_2O ($P_{H_2O} \cong P_{total}$). There are two methods which have been used to study the phase relations of rocks at $P_{H_2O} < P_{total}$. The first is to add to the fluid a (presumably inert) dilutant such as CO_2 or N_2 (Holloway et al., 1968; Holloway and Reese, 1974). A fluid phase is thus always present, and it is possible to estimate X_{H_2O} in the fluid and melt. This method has been used by Holloway and Burnham (1972), Allen and Boettcher (1978), and Sykes (1979). In other studies, lower water activities were achieved by adding insufficient H_2O to saturate the system ("vapor-absent" experiments). Examples here include Robertson and Wyllie (1971) and Naney (1977).

Most workers have chosen to control the oxygen fugacity (f_{O_2}) of their charges with one of several solid-solid buffers originally developed by Eugster and coworkers (Eugster, 1957; Eugster and Wones, 1962); the use of these has been extensively reviewed by Huebner (1971). Buffers used included (in order of decreasing f_{O_2}) the hematite-magnetite (HM), nickel-nickel oxide (NNO), fayalite-magnetite-quartz (FMQ), and magnetite-wüstite (MW) assemblages, plus water. Among the earliest of the present group of studies to use f_{O_2} buffers were those of Tuthill (1968) and Holloway (1970). Other workers have imposed similar f_{O_2} values on their charges using a hydrogen membrane developed by Shaw (1963) instead of solid buffers (Eggler, 1972a,b; Eggler and Burnham, 1973; Nesbitt and Hamilton, 1970). In many other cases, however, the experiments were allowed to equilibrate at whatever oxygen fugacity was imposed by the experimental apparatus. In cold seal vessels made with a nickel or cobalt alloy (Rene, Stellite) the resulting f_{O_2} is near the NNO buffer, as in, e.g., Piwinskii (1968). In at least one type of furnace assembly used in solid-medium (piston-cylinder) apparatus, the combination of packing materials used and the graphite furnace also produce redox conditions near the NNO buffer, as reported by Allen et al. (1975). This need not be true for different furnace assemblies, however, nor even for that used by Allen et al. (1975), if the composition of materials used were to change appreciably. Unbuffered runs in internally heated pressure vessels (as in e.g., Yoder and Tilley, 1962) have f_{O_2} values only slightly lower than the HM buffer (see discussion in Helz, 1973, pp. 290-291).

One recurring weakness in this area of the literature is that phases produced experimentally are often not well characterized. Incomplete characterization of mafic phases is most conspicuous in studies of granitoid rocks, where most authors concern themselves principally with quartz-feldspar-melt relations. Only one-third of the three dozen rock melting studies reporting amphibole include even one amphibole analysis. The analyzed amphiboles (all hornblendes) are mostly from andesites, basalts, or ultramafic rocks, with the exception of those of Naney (1977) and Sykes (1979), who present a few analyses of hornblende from granodioritic compositions. Further data are generally lacking; though 120 or so experimentally produced igneous hornblendes have been analyzed, the coexisting liquid has been analyzed for only a third of them. And, although authors frequently state that amphibole was identified using petrographic or X-ray criteria, there are virtually no optical or cell parameter data for experimental igneous hornblendes in the literature outside of Helz (1973, 1979).

In summary, the available experimental studies reporting amphibole coexisting with liquid vary greatly in methodology, scope, and quality. It is the purpose of this section to review this highly diverse literature, to see what we know, and what we still do not know, about amphibole in igneous rocks.

Before doing so, however, it might be useful to indicate what one might expect to learn from rock melting experiments that cannot be learned from studies of the P-T stability relations of amphibole end members. First, for any rock composition amphibole can coexist with liquid only above some minimum pressure, at $P_{H_2O} = P_{total}$. Therefore, if amphibole in a rock appears to have crystallized from a melt, a minimum pressure of crystallization for the amphibole can be recovered by performing appropriate melting experiments.

Second, if pressure can be estimated independently, and igneous amphibole is present, one can determine experimentally the minimum water activity necessary to stabilize amphibole and liquid at that pressure.

Third, as is well known, the crystal chemistry of amphiboles is extremely complex. Some amphiboles, notably hornblendes, rarely have the composition of any of their established end members, so that applying studies of the P-T relations of end members to natural hornblendes often requires considerable extrapolation. By analyzing amphiboles synthesized in rock melting experiments, at known values of T, P, f_{O_2}, etc., it should be possible to determine the ways in which the compositions of complex hornblendes, essentially identical to natural ones, vary with T or P or whatever.

Last, for studies of trace element partitioning between amphibole and coexisting liquid, pyroxene, etc., it seems that it would be desirable to use whole rock compositions, doped with the appropriate trace elements. This would ensure that the compositional matrix in which the experimental partitioning occurs is reasonably close to natural, even though the level of the trace element under investigation would be artificially high.

Generalized phase relations of igneous amphiboles

The field of stability of hydroxyamphibole in a rock composition is shown schematically in Figure 52, bounded on the high-temperature side by a curve labelled AMPH-IN, and on the low-temperature side by a curve labelled AMPH-OUT. This field is transected by the solidus of the rock. The shaded area is the field in which amphibole coexists with a silicate liquid (AMPH + L).

The geometry of this diagram is somewhat arbitrary, but certain features of it are not. Point b, the thermal maximum, always exists. For most igneous compositions point a exists and, where present, represents the lowest pressure at which amphibole + liquid can coexist. If a exists, then point d, the high-pressure crossover of AMPH-IN and the solidus, also exists. There may be bulk compositions in which amphibole occurs above the solidus but reacts out before the solidus is reached. In such cases, neither point a nor point d would exist, and point f would be the lowest pressure at which amphibole + liquid could

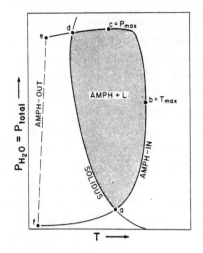

Figure 52. Schematic diagram showing the stability field of hydroxyamphibole (AMPH) in an igneous rock, where $P_{H_2O} = P_{TOTAL}$. The labelled points are:

a = low-pressure intersection of AMPH-IN and SOLIDUS. The pressure at this point is the lowest pressure at which amphibole can coexist with a liquid in this bulk composition.

b = the temperature maximum on AMPH-IN.

c = the pressure maximum on AMPH-IN.

d = high-pressure intersection of AMPH-IN and SOLIDUS.

e,f = intersections of AMPH-IN and AMPH-OUT (the upper and lower thermal stability limits of amphibole, respectively).

Any real rock will contain other crystalline phases in addition to amphibole and liquid.

coexist. Other arbitrary features of the diagram include point c, the pressure maximum, which may be either above or below the solidus, and may coincide with points d and/or e. Similarly, the shape of AMPH-IN, which has been drawn so as to be always convex toward higher temperatures and nearly vertical over a significant range of pressures, though a commonly observed shape, is by no means universal. The shape of AMPH-OUT in Figure 52 is purely schematic.

If, as a result of changes in temperature or pressure, one moves from within the amphibole stability field across AMPH-IN, the amphibole breaks down as follows:

1. Between f and a, the reaction is a subsolidus dehydration reaction, with amphibole breaking down as pressure decreases and/or as temperature increases.

2. Between a and c amphibole melts incongruently, producing liquid plus crystalline phases such as pyroxenes, olivine, and spinel, if they are stable in the bulk composition involved.

3. Between c and d, amphibole is replaced by garnet + cpx $\pm$ biotite. Liquid is present and may be either produced or consumed in the reaction, depending on P-T path and the slope of the solidus.

4. Between d and e, the reaction is as in (3) except no liquid is present. If the temperature decreases, so that AMPH-OUT is crossed, amphibole is replaced by sheet silicates.

In this section on rock-melting behavior, we will be concerned only with that part of the amphibole stability field which lies above the solidus, especially with the location and shape of curve a-b-c-d and the width of the field AMPH + L. The width of AMPH + L is of particular interest, as it controls the extent to which amphibole can participate in igneous processes, whether as a residual phase during partial melting or as a fractionating phase during any sort of crystal-liquid fractionation process.

Phase relations of igneous amphiboles where $P_{H_2O} \cong P_{total}$

The actual shape of curve a-b-c-d in any given rock composition is quite variable. Figures 53-60 summarize the data on water-saturated amphibole-in curves in rocks published to date, grouped by bulk composition. Very few of these studies include estimates of the location of points a or d, or c, and some do not even cover enough of a pressure range to locate point b. We will consider the rock compositional groups studied in order of decreasing silica content, from granites to periodotites.

a. Amphiboles in experiments on granites and other alkali-feldspar-rich rocks at $P_{H_2O} = P_{total}$

Amphiboles are relatively rare in calc-alkaline granites and quartz monzonites. They occur more commonly in peralkaline granites and in syenites. The implied compositional restrictions (amphibole favored by lower silica activity and/or peralkalinity) are reflected in the occurrence of amphibole in experiments on felsic rock compositions as well.

Of the felsic rocks which have been studied so far, amphibole was not observed either above or below the solidus at $P_{H_2O} \cong P_{total}$ in two biotite granites (Piwinskii, 1968, 1973a; Piwinskii and Wyllie, 1970), three biotite quartz monzonites (Piwinskii, 1973b; Piwinskii and Wyllie, 1970), two syenites and one riebeckite-aegirine granite (McDowell and Wyllie, 1971), and one biotite nepheline syenite (Millhollen, 1970). In addition Naney's (1977) synthetic "granite" contains no field of amphibole at any of the conditions studied.

Felsic rocks in which some amphibole has been observed include two quartz monzonites and four samples of a riebeckite-bearing rhyolite (Gibbon and Wyllie, 1969), three biotite-hornblende syenites (McDowell and Wyllie, 1971; Robertson and Wyllie, 1971), one riebeckite granite (McDowell and Wyllie, 1971), and one calcite-bearing nepheline syenite (Millhollen, 1970). The available P-T curves for amphibole in these rocks are shown in Figure 53. In order for a published curve to be included in Figure 53, it had to be bracketed at one pressure at least, as described in the figure caption.

It is evident from Figure 53 that the field of amphibole stability in these

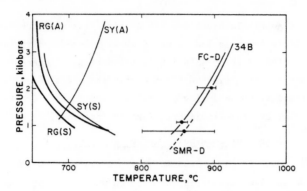

Figure 53. AMPH-IN and solidus curves for granites and other felsic rocks, at $P_{H_2O} = P_{TOTAL}$, as follows:

RG(A) and RG(S) = AMPH-IN and solidus for "riebeckite" granite 26272 (McDowell and Wyllie, 1971);
SY(A) and SY(S) = AMPH-IN and solidus for syenite 26005 (McDowell and Wyllie, 1971);
FC-D = AMPH-IN for quartz monzonite FC-D (Gibbon and Wyllie, 1969);
SMR-D = estimated position of AMPH-IN for alkaline rhyolite SMR-D, using data of Gibbon and Wyllie (1969);
34B = AMPH-IN for syenite 34B (Robertson and Wyllie, 1971).

The AMPH-IN curves for RG and SY are bracketed at several pressures. The other three AMPH-IN curves have been bracketed at only one pressure, as shown (eg. the two bounding runs for FC-D are at 850° and 862°C at 1 kbar). The solidus curves for the latter three rocks nearly coincide with curve SY(S).

very felsic rocks is virtually undefined. Data exist only at 1-3 kbar. Several of the curves are bracketed only once so their slopes are really unknown, though the authors generally assume them to be positive. The data appear to fall into a low-temperature group and a high-temperature group, which we will consider in turn.

The low-temperature group comprises syenite 26005 and riebeckite granite 26272 from the Kungnat alkaline complex. These rocks are the only two for which the amphibole-in curves have been bracketed more than once. The hornblende-in curve in the syenite has a positive slope and crosses the solidus at 700°C, 1.6 kbar P_{H_2O}. This is the only instance in the entire literature in which the location of point a has been determined in a rock composition. By 3 kbar, the field of hornblende + melt in syenite 26005 is 80°C wide. In contrast, the amphibole-in curve in the granite parallels the solidus and lies no more than 10-15°C above it. This amphibole, identified as riebeckite, is the only amphibole other than hornblende yet reported in a rock melting experiment. The shape of the curve (strongly convex upward) is also unique, resembling the melting curve of an anhydrous solid. If the phase really is riebeckite (or some other sodic amphibole, such as arfvedsonite or magnesium-bearing riebeckite), we still do not know whether "riebeckite"-in always has this form in a rock, or whether the curve for "riebeckite" in granite 26272 is peculiar to that rock, or whether (as seems most likely) the shape of this curve is an artifact of the particular experimental configuration or procedure used.

284

The high-temperature group includes curves for a syenite, a quartz monzonite, and an alkaline rhyolite. Each of these is bracketed at only one pressure, and the amphibole is described as hornblende. What is remarkable about
these is the great width of the hornblende + melt field, being ∿100°C at 1 kbar,
and 200°C at 2 kbar. The syenite is a fairly mafic rock (MgO = 4.28 percent),
so the high thermal stability of hornblende in this rock relative to syenite
26005 is quite plausible.

However, the quartz monzonite and alkaline rhyolite are no more mafic than
syenite 26005; furthermore, the amphibole in the original rhyolite was identified as riebeckite, not hornblende (Gibbon and Wyllie, 1969, p. 233). As these
authors appear not to have considered the possible occurrence of quench amphibole, it may be that much of the great width of the AMPH + L field in these two
compositions is due to failure to distinguish between stable and quench amphibole.

The contribution of these rock melting experiments to our knowledge of the
stability relations of amphibole in very felsic rocks is limited to the following:

(1) Both hornblende and a sodic amphibole [probably not end member
    riebeckite, see Ernst (1962) or discussion earlier in this chap-
    ter] can occur in equilibrium with a granitic liquid.

(2) If the position of AMPH-IN for compositions 34B, FC-D, and SMR-D
    are even approximately correct, then the position of point a (the
    AMPH-IN/solidus crossover) varies over a range of 150°C and 1
    kbar within this group of rock compositions.

(3) "Riebeckite"-bearing assemblages are difficult to duplicate in
    unbuffered cold seal runs. Two of the three "riebeckite"-bear-
    ing samples investigated [granite 58303 of McDowell and Wyllie
    (1971) and the SMR rhyolite of Gibbon and Wyllie (1969)] appar-
    ently failed to crystallize any riebeckite, even below the soli-
    dus. This suggests that these rocks might be more appropriately
    studied at some oxygen buffer other than NNO, or (in the case of
    granite 58303, which contains virtually no MgO) that the riebeck-
    ite in the rock formed at temperatures well below the solidus of
    that composition.

(4) More than half of the very felsic rocks studied to date (9 out
    of 17) crystallize no amphibole at all, suggesting that the most
    important control on the presence or absence of amphibole in
    these rocks is not P, T, X_{H_2O}, or f_{O_2}, but simply their bulk

285

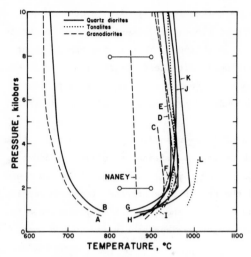

Curve labelled "NANEY" is the approximate location of AMPH-IN for a synthetic "granodiorite" (Naney, 1977). The curve is bracketed only at 2 and 8 kbar; the bracketing runs are shown by the open circles. The dashed line connecting the midpoints of the two brackets has a slight negative slope; the actual slope of AMPH-IN in this composition is unknown.

Figure 54. AMPH-IN and selected solidus curves for intermediate granitoid rocks, at P_{H_2O} = P_{total} as follows:

A = solidus for granodiorite 103 (Piwinskii, 1973a);
B = solidus for quartz diorites CP2-1, DR510, DR126 (Piwinskii, 1973b);
C = AMPH-IN for granodiorite DR321-B (Piwinskii, 1974);
D = AMPH-IN for granodiorite DRV-4 (Piwinskii, 1974);
E = AMPH-IN for granodiorite 103 (Piwinskii, 1973a);
F = AMPH-IN for granodiorites 102, 678 (Piwinskii, 1968; Piwinskii and Wyllie, 1968);
G = AMPH-IN for quartz diorite DR126 (Piwinskii, 1973b);
H = AMPH-IN for quartz diorite CP2-1 (Piwinskii, 1973b);
I = AMPH-IN for tonalite 101 (Pinwinskii, 1973a);
J = AMPH-IN for quartz diorite DR109 (Piwinskii, 1974);
K = AMPH-IN for quartz diorite DR510 (Piwinskii, 1973b);
L = AMPH-IN for tonalites 1213, 751 (Piwinskii and Wyllie, 1968).

compositions.

b. Amphibole stability in intermediate granitoid rocks at P_{H_2O} = P_{total}

Hornblende is very widespread in the more calcic and mafic granitoid rocks. Included here are granodiorites, tonalites and quartz diorites plus one syenodiorite. Of the nineteen such rocks investigated experimentally, only two granodiorites [JSP6-2 in Piwinskii (1973a) and 768 in Piwinskii and Wyllie (1968)] do not contain hornblende. Amphibole is correspondingly common in the melting experiments on these same rocks: Figure 54 presents AMPH-IN curves for thirteen of them. The experimentally produced amphibole is stated to be hornblende and is the first silicate phase on the liquidus from 2 kbar to at least 10 kbar, in all samples.

The curves in Figure 54 are remarkably similar for all compositions investigated. Each increases rapidly in temperature from 1 to 2 kbar, and passes through a temperature maximum (point b in Fig. 52) between 2 and 4 kbar. Above point b the curves have slight negative slopes to 10 kbar, but show no tendency to roll over as the *c-d* segment does in Figure 52.

All thirteen curves lie within 70° of each other over this entire pressure range. Typical solidus curves are shown on the left hand side of the diagram to give some indication of the width of the AMPH + L field: AMPH + L is 200-250° wide over most of the pressure range studied, except below 2 kbar. In no case has point *a* (the AMPH-IN/solidus crossover) been determined. It must be well below 1 kbar at $P_{H_2O} = P_{total}$, however, as the width of AMPH + L at 1 kbar is typically 100°C or so.

Compared with the curves for more felsic rocks shown in Figure 53, the AMPH-IN curves in these intermediate compositions lie at conspicuously higher temperatures (925-1000°C versus 715-895°C, at 2 kbar). Within Figure 54, there is little separation of AMPH-IN curves by rock composition at 1-2 kbar; however, by 10 kbar the AMPH-IN curves for the granodiorites, as drawn in the literature, lie at slightly lower temperatures than do those in quartz diorite or tonalite compositions.

The most interesting feature of Figure 54 is the negative slopes exhibited by almost all of the curves at P > 2 kbar. The significance of these slopes is problematical for two reasons:

(1) All of Piwinskii's runs from 2-10 kbar were made in an internally heated pressure vessel. Only in the runs at 2 kbar was f_{O_2} constrained to NNO conditions by use of a hydrogen membrane. The higher pressure runs were unbuffered (Piwinskii, 1973a,b; 1974) and hence probably had f_{O_2} values only slightly below the HM buffer. Hornblende is less stable on the HM buffer than under more reducing conditions, at least in some rock compositions (see discussion below). Hence it is possible that the negative slopes are an artifact of inconsistent oxygen fugacity levels.

(2) With the exception of the curves for tonalite 101 (Piwinskii, 1973a), quartz diorite DR510 (Piwinskii, 1973b) and of granodiorite DR321-B (Piwinskii, 1974), none of the other curves are required by the data to have negative slopes. They could be drawn vertically without violating the observed assemblage of any run.

The only other data available are those of Naney (1977) on a synthetic "granodiorite." Unfortunately, as indicated in Figure 54, his AMPH-IN curve is so loosely bracketed that it sheds no light on the question of whether the negative slopes in Figure 54 are real or not.

In summary, then, the investigations on intermediate rocks tell us

287

(1) Hornblende is more widespread, more abundant, and stable to higher temperatures, at constant pressure, water activity, and f_{O_2}, in intermediate rocks than it is in granites.

(2) The AMPH + L field is therefore wider, at given P, f_{O_2}, X_{H_2O}, in intermediate rocks than in granites.

(3) There is little obvious bulk compositional control on the thermal stability of hornblende within this group: the curves at 1-2 kbar, where f_{O_2} is controlled, all cross each other.

The validity of other features of the published curves, including the negative slopes between 2 and 10 kbar and the lower thermal stability of hornblende in grandiorites versus quartz diorites and tonalites at 10 kbar, remain problematical, pending the availability of buffered runs above 2 kbar on these same rocks.

c. Hornblende stability in andesites at $P_{H_2O} = P_{total}$

The experimental work on andesites (and basalts) has been rather different in style and focus from that on the more differentiated rocks. Few of the andesites (or basalts) in which amphibole has been produced experimentally contained amphibole initially. With the exception of the work of Cawthorn et al. (1973) on the Grenada suite, the intent has not been to reproduce observed assemblages but to investigate in a more general way the possible variations in crystallization behavior that may be induced by varying P, T, f_{H_2O}, and f_{O_2}. In several studies, the amphibole produced in the melting experiments has been analyzed and was found to be hornblende in all cases (Eggler, 1972a; Allen et al., 1975; Allen and Boettcher, 1978).

Figure 55 presents the available AMPH-IN curves for andesites. The Mt. Hood andesite has been studied the most intensively. Two different curves are shown for it: the upper curve defines the stability limits of hornblende on the HM buffer (Allen and Boettcher, 1978), while the lower curve is a composite curve[2] based on the data of Eggler and Burnham (1973) and Allen et al. (1975). Eggler (1972a,b) also determined a short segment of the amphibole-in curve for a Paricutin andesite as shown.

These curves are extremely steep between 2 and 18 kbar, the Mt. Hood curves in particular being isothermal between 10-15 kbar (NNO buffer) and 10-20 kbar

- - - - - - - - - -

[2]In favorable cases, it has been possible to construct composite amphibole-in curves for certain compositions, using data from more than one study. Consequently, many of the curves in Figures 55-57 are not reproduced from the literature but are best-fit curves for all of the available runs on a given bulk composition, as described in the figure captions.

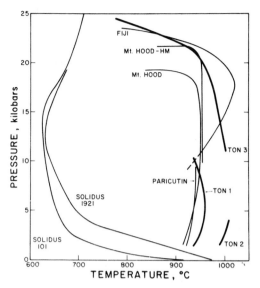

Figure 55. AMPH-IN curves for andesites and one tonalite, at $P_{H_2O} = P_{total}$, as follows:

Paricutin = AMPH-IN for a Paricutin andesite (Eggler, 1972a,b);
Mt. Hood = AMPH-IN for a Mt. Hood andesite compiled from the data of Eggler and Burnham (1973)
    at 1-6.5 kbar, FMQ buffer and of Allen et al. (1975) at 10-20 kbar, NNO buffer;
Mt. Hood-HM = AMPH-IN for the same Mt. Hood andesite at redox conditions of the HM buffer
    (Allen and Boettcher, 1978);
Fiji = AMPH-IN for a Fijian andesite + 10 percent water (Green, 1973);
TON 1 = AMPH-IN for tonalite 101 (Piwinskii, 1973a);
TON 2 = ditto (Piwinskii, 1968);
TON 3 = ditto (Lambert and Wyllie, 1970).
Solidus 101 = the solidus for tonalite 101 (Lambert and Wyllie, 1974);
Solidus 1921 = the solidus for the 1921 Kilauea olivine tholeiite, compiled as described in the
    caption for Figure 56.
Bulk rock analyses are given in Table 3.

Table 3. Chemical analyses of andesites and one tonalite
used in the experimental studies summarized in Figure 55.

	1 Mt. Hood	2 Paricutin	3 Fiji	4 Tonalite 101
SiO_2	59.10	60.5	60.27	59.14
TiO_2	.94	.91	.67	.79
Al_2O_3	17.8	17.3	16.95	18.23
Fe_2O_3	1.78	---	.87	2.32
FeO	4.83	4.3	5.28	3.62
MnO	.10	---	.13	.11
MgO	3.05	3.8	3.30	2.50
CaO	6.85	6.3	7.34	5.92
Na_2O	4.27	4.3	3.91	3.81
K_2O	1.08	1.69	1.26	2.19
P_2O_5	.22	---	.20	.30
Sum	100.02	99.10	100.18	98.93

(1) Wise (1969, p. 1002, p. 155). Cited in Allen et al.
        (1975, Table 1a, Col. 1)
(2) Eggler (1972a, Table 1, Col. 1)
(3) Green (1972, Table 1, Col. 2)
(4) Piwinskii (1968, Table 2, Col. 1)

(HM buffer). Thus T_{MAX} is well-defined, but there is no one pressure corresponding to point b in Figure 52 at which it occurs. Point a of Figure 52 has
not yet been determined for these andesites because their solidi have not yet
been determined.[3]

Allen et al. (1975) sketched in a pressure maximum for the Mt. Hood andesite at NNO conditions. However, their curve as drawn would exclude a run at
19 kbar, 850°C in which they report amphibole. The curve shown in Figure 55
has been drawn flat in order to include that run. The more recently-determined
curve for HM-buffered runs [shown as given by Allen and Boettcher (1978)] was
drawn flat at 21.5 kbar, 850-900°C, but is not defined at lower temperatures.
Consequently, we do not yet know whether there is a pressure maximum on the
hornblende-in curve in the Mt. Hood andesite, and if so, whether it lies above
or below the solidus.

It is interesting to note that amphibole is stable to higher pressures on
the HM buffer than on the NNO buffer. This may be because the more magnesian
garnet stable on the HM buffer requires higher pressures for its stabilization,
rather than because amphibole stability *per se* is enhanced by higher f_{O_2}.

The last andesite curve shown in Figure 55 is for a Fijian andesite + 10
percent H_2O (Green, 1973). Its shape between 10 and 17 kbar is very different
from the steep, almost isothermal curves for the Mt. Hood andesite in this same
pressure interval. A possible explanation for the marked difference in slope
is this: the runs bracketing AMPH-IN in the Fijian andesite appear to be vapor-
absent except for the runs at 10 kbar (Green, 1973, p. 153), so that water activity varies continuously along the curve, decreasing as P and T increase. This
would explain why this curve lies at so much higher temperatures ($\sim$1020°C) than
the 950°C observed in the water-saturated experiments on the other andesites
(see discussion below; also discussion earlier in this chapter on the effect of
a_{H_2O} on pargasite stability).

Superimposed on the andesite curves is the AMPH-IN curve for tonalite 101
from the Sierra Nevada as reported by Piwinskii (1973a). The tonalite curve is
quite different from the linear andesite curves: it has a fairly well-defined
T_{MAX} at 5 kbar and a negative slope above that. As discussed above, the negative slope is suspect because of variable redox conditions in runs at different

- - - - - - - - - - -

[3]The solidus curve shown in Eggler (1972a,b) and Eggler and Burnham (1973) is
actually that of Sierra Nevada tonalite number 101, studied by Piwinskii (1968,
1973a). That curve, plus the solidus curve for the 1921 Kilauea olivine
tholeiite, are shown in Figure 55. The solidi of the andesites would be expected to lie somewhere between these two curves.

pressures. However, the relative position of the curves at 1-2 kbar should be accurate, and it is interesting to note that, at those pressures where all runs are buffered, hornblende is stable to considerably higher temperatures in the tonalite (25°C at 2 kbar) than in the andesites.

There are two other segments of hornblende-in curves for this same tonalite reported in the literature. The small segment at 1000°C, 2 kbar was given by Piwinskii (1968); the publication of the lower curve in 1973 probably implies that the trace of amphibole present in the 2 kbar, 1000°C run of Piwinskii (1968) was later judged to be a quench phase.

The other segment, at 10-23 kbar, was presented by Lambert and Wyllie (1970). It too was subsequently revised: the high-pressure limb of the curve (below 900°C) is shown lying 2-3 kilobars lower in a later paper (Lambert and Wyllie, 1974). The high-temperature limb of the 1970 curve (for pressures < 20 kbar) was completely abandoned in the 1974 paper, for reasons which are not obvious, and the near-liquidus phase relations of the Mt. Hood and Paricutin andesites spliced on instead (see Fig. 1, Lambert and Wyllie, 1974). Both andesites are distinctly richer in CaO, MgO, and FeO than the tonalite (see Table 3). In consequence, they both crystallize augite and hypersthene with or without hornblende, over a wide temperature interval. By contrast, Piwinskii (1973a) reports no pyroxene whatever in the tonalite. Thus the revised Lambert and Wyllie figure is rather curious: their original phase relations, which show AMPH-IN at higher temperatures than those observed for the andesites and show no stability field for pyroxene, are in those respects more compatible with the new (1973a) Piwinskii data on this tonalite than with the andesite data.

In summary, the data available on andesites, and particularly on the Mt. Hood andesite, are the most comprehensive yet considered. The conclusions which can be drawn from Figure 55 and the earlier figures include:

(1) The width of the AMPH + L field is no wider in andesites than it is in granodiorites, tonalites, and quartz diorites, on the average.

(2) Several of the AMPH-IN curves roll over at high pressures, as garnet becomes stable, bearing out the prediction of Green and Ringwood (1967) that amphibole would become unstable at sufficiently high pressures, regardless of water pressure. (See Essene et al., 1970, for a discussion of this point; also the earlier discussion and Fig. 25 of this chapter for the most recent data on the upper pressure stability of end-member amphiboles.)

(3) Variations in oxygen fugacity significantly alter the size and/or shape of the AMPH + L field. In the Mt. Hood andesite, the upper

pressure limit of amphibole is raised at higher f_{O_2}, while maximum
thermal stability is virtually unaffected.

(4) Although data are limited, it appears that hornblende may be stable
to higher temperatures in some tonalites and quartz diorites than it
is in the andesites, at least at pressures of 1-2 kbar.

d. Hornblende stability in basalts and other mafic lavas as a function of f_{O_2}
at $P_{H_2O} = P_{total}$

There has been more work done to determine the field of stability of amphibole in basalts than on any other type of igneous rock. However, none of
the basalts studied contains amphibole in the starting assemblage. Even more
than in the case of andesites, the investigation of the phase relations of
basalt + H_2O has been justified on very broad petrogenetic grounds, namely, the
need to determine H_2O-saturated phase relations because they are one end member
of the possible range of water activity. Few individual rock compositions have
been studied, but these have been studied more intensively (often by more than
one investigator), so that the phase relations of these few compositions are
known over much greater ranges of P, T, f_{O_2}, and X_{H_2O} than those of any rock
other than the Mt. Hood andesite discussed in the preceding section. As was
the case for experimental amphiboles in andesites, many have been analyzed,
and all are hornblendes (Holloway and Burnham, 1972; Helz, 1973, 1976, 1979;
Allen et al., 1975; Allen and Boettcher, 1978; Cawthorn et al., 1973; Nesbitt
and Hamilton, 1970).

Figures 56 and 57 present AMPH-IN curves for the basalts which have been
studied to date. Those in Figure 56 are for runs held at redox conditions of
the FMQ or NNO buffers; the curves in Figure 57 are for runs on or near the HM
buffer. Only one solidus curve, that for the 1921 Kilauea olivine tholeiite,
is shown. The solidus curve determined by Lambert and Wyllie (1972) for a
high-alumina olivine tholeiite from Soay is essentially identical.

The AMPH-IN curves shown for the Picture Gorge, 1921, and Hualalai basalts
in Figures 56 and 57 are composites, as described in the figure captions. These
curves have been drawn (1) to be compatible with as many of the available runs
as possible and (2) to be as simple in shape as possible. In compiling the
data, it was discovered that in four cases, the slopes of AMPH-IN between 10-
13 kbar as reported by Allen et al. (1975) cannot be extrapolated to lower
pressures without violating large numbers of well-documented lower-pressure
runs. Curves affected include the PG, 1921, and Hualalai curves in Figure 56,
and the Hualalai curve in Figure 57. Only the 10 kbar data are problematical,

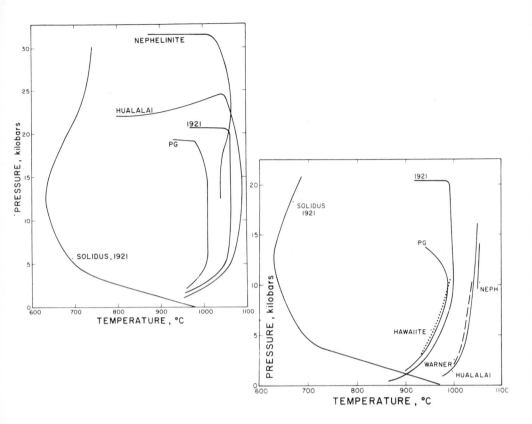

Figure 56. AMPH-IN curves for basalts, at $P_{H_2O} = P_{TOTAL}$, at the redox conditions of the FMQ and NNO buffers, as follows:

PG = AMPH-IN for the Picture Gorge tholeiite, compiled from the data of Helz (1973) at 5 kbar, FMQ, and of Allen et al. (1975) at 13-20 kbar, NNO.
1921 = AMPH-IN for the 1921 Kilauea olivine tholeiite, compiled from the data of Eggler (1972b) at 2 kbar, FMQ; of Helz (1976) at 5 kbar, FMQ; of Holloway (unpublished data, 1981) at 8 kbar, FMQ; and of Allen et al. (1975) 13-21 kbar, NNO.
Hualalai = AMPH-IN for a Hualalai alkali basalt from data of Nesbitt and Hamilton (1970) at 2 kbar, FMQ; of Helz (1973) at 5 kbar, FMQ; and of Allen et al. (1975) at 13-25 kbar, NNO.
Nephelinite = AMPH-IN for the Nuuanu nephelinite, NNO (Allen et al., 1975).
Solidus 1921 = the solidus for the 1921 Kilauea olivine tholeiite, from the data of Holloway (1970) at 2 and 3 kbar; of Tuthill (1968) at 5 kbar and of Hill and Boettcher (1970) at 10-30 kbar. The temperature of the solidus at 1 atm (970°C) is that observed in Kilauean lava lakes (Wright and Okamura, 1977; Wright and Peck, 1978).

Figure 57. AMPH-IN curves for basalts, at $P_{H_2O} = P_{TOTAL}$, at or near the redox conditions of the HM buffer, as follows:

PG = AMPH-IN for the Picture Gorge tholeiite, compiled from the data of Helz (1973) at 5 kbar and of Allen et al. (1975) at 10-13 kbar.
1921 = AMPH-IN for the 1921 Kilauea olivine tholeiite, from the data of Yoder and Tilley (1962) at 1-10 kbar, of Helz (1973) at 5 kbar, and of Allen and Boettcher (1978) at 10-21 kbar.
Hualalai = AMPH-IN for a Hualalai alkali basalt, from the data of Yoder and Tilley (1962) at 1-10 kbar, of Helz (1973) at 5 kbar, and of Allen et al. (1975) at 13 kbar.
Hawaiite = AMPH-IN for an oxidized hawaiite (Yoder and Tilley, 1962).
Warner = AMPH-IN for the Warner high-alumina basalt (Yoder and Tilley, 1962).
Nephelinite = AMPH-IN for the Nuuanu nephelinite (Allen et al., 1975).
Solidus 1921 = the solidus of the 1921 Kilauea olivine tholeiite, as in Figure 56. The position of the solidus does not vary significantly with f_{O_2}, at least at 5 kbar (Tuthill, 1968; Helz, 1976).

293

however; AMPH-IN can be drawn as vertical or as smoothly convex between 2 and 20 kbar, in all cases, if Allen's 10 kbar runs are ignored. To include all runs would entail drawing a substantial temperature minimum (35-50°C below the position of AMPH-IN in Figs. 56 and 57) at 10 kbar.

This was not done. Instead, the few 10 kbar runs of Allen et al. were ignored. The reasons for preferring simple vertical or convex curves were:

(1) The slope of the AMPH-IN curve for the amphibole end member pargasite is very steep, and without significant curvature, from 5-20 kbar (Holloway, 1973; Holloway and Ford, 1975; see discussion earlier in this chapter by Gilbert and Popp).

(2) The extent to which amphibole persists metastably beyond AMPH-IN at high temperatures in the presence of a liquid has been demonstrated to be slight. Holloway (1973) reports a 6° overlap for the assemblages pargasite versus its breakdown products in certain two-stage runs, but there is no discernible problem in that study with the finer-grained amphibole which grows during heat-up in single-stage runs.

(3) AMPH-IN curves in five basalts studied by Yoder and Tilley (1962) are all steep, with positive slopes from 3-10 kbar with no indication of negative slopes as 10 kbar is approached.

(4) In three cases, the data of Allen et al. (1975) also permit AMPH-IN to be drawn as vertical or convex. These are the curves for Mt. Hood (Fig. 55) and for the PG and 1921 tholeiites on the HM buffer (Fig. 57).

(5) In the other four cases, the best inferred position of AMPH-IN at 5-10 kbar, based on all other available data, is at essentially the same temperature as that reported by Allen et al. for AMPH-IN between 13 and 20 kbar.

On balance, therefore, the available data tend to support the relatively simple shapes of the AMPH-IN curves as drawn in Figures 56 and 57. Further work in the range 8-12 kbar is certainly indicated in order to verify or reject the possibility of a sharp temperature minimum at 10 kbar suggested by some of the data of Allen et al. (1975), however, because there are no obvious deficiencies of technique in the Allen experiments.

Regardless of the exact shape of these curves at 10 kbar, it is obvious that the field where hornblende and liquid coexist is very much larger in basalts than in the more silicic rocks: it is 300-450°C wide in the 5-20 kbar pressure range, versus 200-300°C for intermediate granitoids and andesites. Furthermore, as noted by Allen et al. (1975) the hornblende stability field expands steadily as the basalt becomes more undersaturated, being smallest in the quartz-normative Picture Gorge tholeiite, intermediate in the 1921 Kilauea olivine tholeiite, and largest in the nepheline-normative rocks. Extreme SiO_2 undersaturation (as in the Nuuanu nephelinite) enhances pressure stability very markedly, but maximum thermal stability is reached in the slightly Ne-normative Hualalai basalt. A similar pattern, with maximum thermal stability of amphibole occurring in slightly Ne-normative compositions, was observed by Cawthorn (1976a) in the CMAS + Na_2O + H_2O system.

As discussed above, the shapes of the best-fit AMPH-IN curves are broadly similar to AMPH-IN for the Mt. Hood andesite: very steep between 2 and 20 kbar and turning over sharply at some higher pressure. The pressure of point b is consequently ill-defined, though T_{max} itself is well determined. One of these curves (for the Hualalai basalt) has a well defined pressure maximum (point c) as well. The others have not yet been investigated sufficiently at lower temperatures and high pressures to locate point c. [The reversal brackets of Essene et al. (1970) for a synthetic quartz tholeiite are unfortunately too broad to define the slope of the upper limb of AMPH-IN in that type of composition as being either positive or negative: the best one can say is that AMPH-IN in quartz-normative tholeiites appears to be nearly flat between 700 and 950°C, at 19 $\pm$ 1 kbar.]

One unique feature of the experimental data available for basalts is that several rocks have been studied at more than one set of redox conditions, so that the effects of varying f_{O_2} on hornblende stability can be evaluated. In general, hornblende is stable to higher temperatures at lower f_{O_2} in basalts (cf. curves for the Picture Gorge, 1921, and Hualalai basalts in Figs. 56 and 57). The size of the effect is quite variable, however: AMPH-IN in the Picture Gorge and Hualalai basalts is lowered only 40-50°C, while in the 1921 Kilauea basalt it drops 70°C at the higher oxygen fugacities of the HM buffer. The explanation for this larger effect may be found in the observation of Helz (1973, p. 250) that whereas the Picture Gorge tholeiite is quartz-normative and the Hualalai basalt nepheline-normative on both the FMQ and HM buffers, the 1921 Kilauea olivine tholeiite changes from olivine-normative at FMQ conditions to quartz normative at HM conditions. This shift in normative components correlates well with the shift in relative position of the 1921 AMPH-IN curve, which is near the Hualalai curve in Figure 56, but close to the PG curve in Figure 57.

Although increasing f_{O_2} significantly decreases the thermal stability of amphibole in basalt, it appears not to affect the upper pressure limit. This is precisely the opposite of the case of the Mt. Hood andesite, where the high-pressure limb of AMPH-IN was raised significantly, but maximum thermal stability was not affected. Clearly the effects of varying f_{O_2} on the size and shape of the AMPH + L field in an igneous rock, though substantial, are not readily predictable.

In summary, then, the AMPH + L field in basalts is the largest yet encountered, and it expands appreciably as SiO_2 activity decreases in the host rock. Several rocks have been studied over a sufficient range of pressures for the high-pressure limb of AMPH-IN to be located. Point c (P_{max}) has been determined in one case (the Hualalai basalt). At low pressures, however, the situation is as for the other rock types studied: point a is not determined for any of these curves, with the possible exception of the 1921 Kilauea basalt at HM conditions. Yoder and Tilley (1962, p. 449) show the AMPH-IN/solidus crossover at 915°C, 1.4 kbar. The revised solidus shown in Figure 57 moves this point down to 900°C, 1.0 kbar, however, so even in this case the definitive runs have not been made.

e. Hornblende stability in ultramafic compositions at $P_{H_2O} = P_{total}$

The final category of rock compositions to be considered is ultramafic rocks. These include hornblende itself, hornblendite, two pyroxenites and seven peridotites, none of which are, strictly speaking, igneous rocks. In contrast to the basalts, however, many of these compositions were investigated precisely because the samples contained so much amphibole. Available analyses of experimental amphiboles (Mysen and Boettcher, 1975b, 1976; Green, 1973) are all hornblende. Apparently none of the bulk compositions investigated so far is sufficiently poor in Al_2O_3 for richterites of the sort studied by Kushiro and Erlank (1970) and Gilbert and Briggs (1974) to be stable.

In contrast to the experimental work for andesites and basalts, that on the ultramafic rocks is mostly unbuffered and the prevailing oxygen fugacities only vaguely known. Merrill and Wyllie (1975) suggest that redox conditions for their unbuffered solid-medium runs were more reducing than the NNO buffer. Millhollen and Wyllie (1974) and Millhollen et al. (1974) presumably used the same furnace assembly as Merrill and Wyllie. Mysen and Boettcher (1975a, 1976) claim NNO conditions for their furnace assembly. Kushiro (1970) and Green (1973) do not offer any estimate of f_{O_2}. This lack of concern is unfortunate, because, as we have seen from the work on andesites and basalts, f_{O_2} is a significant variable in these iron-bearing systems.

Figure 58 presents AMPH-IN curves for the less magnesian ultramafic compositions. Not surprisingly, hornblende attains its maximum thermal stability

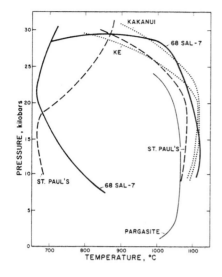

Figure 58. AMPH-IN and solidus curves for hornblendes and garnet pyroxenites, at P_{H_2O} =
P_{TOTAL}, as follows:

St. Paul = AMPH-IN and solidus for brown horn-
    blende mylonite from St. Paul's Rocks
    (Millhollen and Wyllie, 1974).
Kakanui = AMPH-IN for the Kakanui hornblende
    (Merrill and Wyllie, 1975).
Pargasite = AMPH-IN for pargasite (Holloway,
    1973; Holloway and Ford, (1975).
KE = AMPH-IN for kaersutite "eclogite" from
    Kakanui (Merrill and Wyllie, 1975).
68 SAL-7 = AMPH-IN and solidus for garnet web-
    sterite from Salt Lake Crater, Oahu (Mysen
    and Boettcher, 1976).

at P_{H_2O} = P_{total} in this bulk compositional range, with T_{max} > 1100°C for all
but the St. Paul's hornblendite mylonite. The curves are all quite steep from
10-20 kbar. They have markedly negative slopes at higher pressures but do not
exhibit the abrupt "corner" usually seen in the basalts: the change in slope
is in all cases much more gradual.

It is interesting to note (1) that hornblende is only slightly more stable
where the bulk composition is that of the Kakanui hornblende than it in the
pyroxenites, and (2) that the amphibole present in the Kakanui hornblende runs
is stable to higher temperatures than is the end member pargasite. Apparently
the presence of TiO_2, Fe, and K_2O in the amphibole structure enhances its thermal stability considerably.

Solidus curves have been determined and point d (the high-pressure crossover of the solidus and AMPH-IN) has been located, for two of these compositions.
The brown hornblende mylonite appears to be a case in which point c (P_{max}) lies
at subsolidus temperatures. In contrast, point c for garnet websterite 68SAL-7
lies above the solidus, at roughly 875°C, 29 kbar.[4] The low-pressure crossover
(point a) has again not been determined in any case.

The shapes of these two solidus curves are radically different. The abrupt
change in slope of the hornblendite solidus at 17 kbar correlates with the loss
- - - - - - - - - -
[4]The position of AMPH-IN for 68SAL-7 as shown in Figure 58 was determined using
the published run table (Mysen and Boettcher, 1976, p. 5). This curve differs
in some unexplained ways from the AMPH-IN curve shown on the facing page (p. 4)
in that same paper.

TABLE 4.   Chemical analyses of peridotites used in the experimental studies summarized in Figures 59 and 60.

Sample:	1 K	2 M	3 A	4 B	5 C	6 D	7 G
SiO_2	48.3	44.78	45.7	43.7	45.1	44.82	47.8
TiO_2	.2	.32	.05	.20	.13	.52	1.2
Al_2O_3	4.9	4.69	1.6	4.0	3.92	8.21	5.9
Fe_2O_3	-	3.03	.77	.89	1.00	2.07	0.8
FeO	10.0	4.72	5.21	8.09	7.29	7.91	8.2
MnO	-	-	-	-	-	-	-
MgO	32.5	36.71	42.8	37.4	38.8	26.53	28.7
CaO	3.0	4.16	.70	3.50	2.66	8.12	5.1
Na_2O	.7	.46	.09	.38	.27	.89	.95
K_2O	.07	.12	.04	.01	.02	.03	.22
P_2O_5	-	.05	-	-	-	-	-
Cr_2O_3	.30	.53	.41	.40	.31	.20	.70
	99.97	99.57	97.37	98.57	99.50	99.30	99.57
$Mg/Mg+Fe$	.85	.90	.93	.88	.89	.83	.89

------

(1) Kushiro et al. (1968, Table 1)

(2) Millhollen et al. (1974, Table 4)

(3) - (6) Mysen and Boettcher (1975a, Table 1)

(7) Green (1973, Table 1, Col. 1). Pyrolite minus 40 percent olivine.

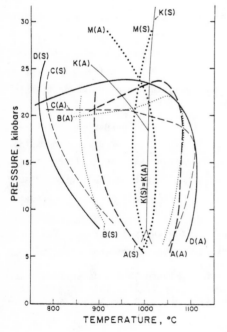

Figure 59. AMPH-IN and solidus curves for peridotites, at $P_{H_2O} = P_{TOTAL}$. Curves designated (S) are solidi and curves designated (A) are AMPH-IN, for individual peridotites, as follows:

K(S) = K(A) are for a spinel lherzolite (Kushiro, 1970). Amphibole and liquid coexist only at the solidus between 6 and 17 kbar in this composition.
M(S), M(A) are for a pargasite-rich spinel peridotite from St. Paul's rocks (Millhollen et al., 1974).
A(S),A(A) are for peridotite A;
B(S),B(A) are for peridotite B;
C(S),C(A) are for peridotite C;
D(S),D(A) are for peridotite D.
[Data last four samples from Mysen and Boettcher (1975a).]
Bulk rock analyses utilized in these experiments are in Table 4.

298

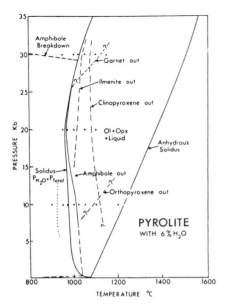

Figure 60. Experimental determination of the water-saturated near-solidus relations for pyrolite. Reproduced from Green (1973, Fig. 1). See Table 4 for analysis of starting material.

of plagioclase and the incoming of garnet in near- and subsolidus assemblages in that composition. This suggests that plagioclase is the principal phase melting along the lowest-temperature part of the solidus, below 17 kbar. In contrast, the minimum in the solidus of 68SAL-7 does not coincide with any obvious change in reported crystalline assemblage. Furthermore, significant changes in assemblage in that rock (e.g., garnet-in, which intersects the solidus at 10 kbar, and AMPH-IN, which intersects it as shown in Fig. 58) produce no deflection in the solidus whatever. It would be interesting to know, for 68SAL-7, what phases are melting at the solidus, since its reported phase relations correlate so poorly with the shape of the solidus.

Because of the widely varying positions of the solidi, the width of AMPH + L varies greatly. Generalizations are difficult to make except that the field widths are comparable to those observed for AMPH + L in basalts (300-400°C). The maximum thermal stability of amphibole in these low-MgO ultramafic compositions is higher than that in basalts, but the solidus temperatures are higher also.

Figure 59 presents AMPH-IN and solidus curves for six peridotites. Figure 60 shows the reported phase relations for a seventh. Analyses of the seven rocks are given in Table 4. They are very similar in composition except for peridotites A and D (Cols. 3 and 6, Table 4, respectively).

In spite of the narrow range of bulk compositions represented, the AMPH-IN and solidus curves reported in the literature vary greatly, both in their shapes and in their absolute positions in P-T space. The high temperature limb is steep in all cases, from 6 to >20 kbar, as was true for the curves shown in Figure 58. However, T_{max} varies over a range of 100°C (from 1000 to 1100°C) in Figure 59, versus only 40°C (from 1080-1120°C) in Figure 58.

The high-pressure limb of the AMPH-IN curves in Figure 59 is even more variable. The slope of AMPH-IN becomes negative at high pressures always, but in two cases (Kushiro, 1970; Millhollen et al., 1974) the curve remains very

299

steep. In contrast, Mysen and Boettcher (1975a) report that AMPH-IN rolls over
and becomes flat (in peridotite C) or passes through a pressure maximum (peridotites A, B, D).

The positions of the reported solidi also vary greatly. The most striking
feature of Figure 59 is that, as reported AMPH-IN moves to higher temperatures,
the reported solidus moves to lower temperatures, so that the width of the AMPH
+ L field varies from nil (Kushiro, 1970) to >300°C (peridotite D of Mysen and
Boettcher, 1975a). The position of point d (the high-pressure AMPH-IN/solidus
crossover) has been determined for all six compositions, and is likewise highly
variable. One can say, however, that point d always occurs between 18 and 23
kbar, though the temperature ranges over 225°C.

The phase relations in Figure 60 (Green, 1973) tend to resemble those of
Kushiro and Millhollen et al. in that the reported solidus temperature is high
and the field AMPH + L narrow. This AMPH-IN curve (labelled "amphibole-out"
in Fig. 60) has a unique shape, however, with a negative slope from 1–20 kbar,
an inflection point at ∿14 kbar, and a positive slope from 20–30 kbar. (The
only other concave AMPH-IN curve reported in the literature is that for "riebeckite" in a granite, as discussed earlier.) Unfortunately most of the unique
features of this curve are not required by the limited run data shown in Figure
60, nor otherwise justified in the accompanying text, so further discussion of
them appears to be unwarranted.

Possible causes for these extreme variations in phase relations include:

(1) observed variations in bulk composition of the starting materials,
as shown in Table 4,

(2) inadequate or variable criteria used to determine the presence of
amphibole and glass,

(3) other variations in experimental techniques or parameters (f_{O_2}, iron
loss) inadequately controlled and/or ignored, and

(4) significant differences between the composition of the starting material actually used and that of the split analyzed.

As can be seen by inspection of Figure 59 and Table 4, very few of the
differences in phase relations can be correlated with significant variations
in bulk composition. The very "fertile" composition of peridotite D of Mysen
and Boettcher (1975a) makes it reasonable for that rock to have the lowest
solidus, the highest AMPH-IN curve, and hence the largest AMPH + L field, as
indeed it does (Fig. 59). If there were any modal data available, peridotite
D would undoubtedly be found to contain more hornblende than any of the other
peridotites.

With that exception, however, there is no correlation at all between reported bulk composition and phase relations. Particularly curious are the phase relations for peridotite A: the reported AMPH + L field is 150-200°C wide. The amphibole coexists with clinopyroxene in addition to olivine + opx, throughout its stability range (Mysen and Boettcher, 1975a). Yet the rock contains only 0.70 percent CaO and only 0.09 percent Na_2O, and could contain at most 2-3 percent hornblende, even if the ubiquitous cpx is a low-Ca pigeonite. It seems unreasonable for trace amounts of amphibole to melt over a 200° interval. One would expect this peridotite to exhibit the phase relations reported by Kushiro (1970), where AMPH-IN and solidus coincide, so that amphibole breaks down completely at the solidus.

The other five peridotites (B, C, and those used by Millhollen et al., Green, and Kushiro) are so similar in bulk composition that the considerable differences in phase relations reported must be caused by factors (2), (3), or (4) listed above. A similar conclusion, that experimental problems were behind the great variability of reported phase relations for peridotite + H_2O, was reached by Millhollen et al. (1974).

Possible experimental factors herein include:

(a) Variation in capsule material. Green and Mysen used PdAg; all others used Pt. Iron loss may have been more severe in Pt capsules. Also, it is conceivable that differences in catalytic properties of the two materials might affect the appearance of runs that had not reached equilibrium.

(b) Differences in the amount of H_2O added and/or in the manner in which H_2O was bound in the starting materials. Millhollen et al. (1974) added no H_2O: the 5.7 percent water in their sample was presumably mostly bound in serpentine, talc, etc. This might tend to retard reaction rates. Green (1973) added 10 percent H_2O, Kushiro (1970) added 5.8-9.3 percent H_2O, while Mysen and Boettcher (1975a) added 10-37 percent H_2O, with most of their capsules containing 16-25 percent H_2O. More vapor means more quenched vapor solute, a glass-like material that under unfavorable circumstances can be confused with near solidus liquids. From Figures 58 and 59, it is clear that solidus temperatures do tend to be lower in the Mysen experiments, which contain the most excess water. However, Mysen reports a large difference in refractive index between his quenched vapor solute (R.I. < 1.49) and what he interpreted as melt (R.I. = 1.57-1.55). It is conceivable that more than one phase may have precipitated from the vapor solute [Helz (1973) reports three: cordierite, mica, and the glassy "fishroe"]; however, it would be surprising for there to be more than one isotropic "glassy" phase.

(c) Variation in length of runs. Only two of these papers include run tables, but for those the contrast is suggestive: Mysen and Boettcher (1975a) report run times of 24-51 hours for solidus-bracketing runs, with runs 3-15 hours long near AMPH-IN. Run times of Millhollen et al. (1974) were mostly 2-4 hours. Kushiro's runs were also apparently quite short: Mysen and Boettcher (1975a, p. 533) report them to be less than 1 hour. Mysen's runs ought, therefore, to be the best-equilibrated and his curves, especially the solidi, better located. This does not explain why the solidi for Mysen's peridotite B and C are so different, however.

(d) Variation in the criteria used to identify hornblende. Millhollen et al. (1974) relied on X-ray diffraction patterns, which cannot detect small quantities of any phase and cannot distinguish between stable and quench amphibole. Mysen's criteria were optical, mainly the extinction angle ($Z \wedge c$ = 15-25°). This is somewhat hazardous as a main criterion, as oblique sections of pyroxene can also give extinction angles in this range. Also it assumes the absence of orthorhombic amphiboles.

The last possibility in the earlier list, that some of the analyses of Table 4 do not correspond to the bulk composition actually present in the experimental charges, is exceedingly difficult to evaluate. Xenoliths, as in Columns 1 and 3-6, Table 4, can be quite heterogeneous on a small scale, more so than most lavas and intrusive rocks; also they may be slightly contaminated by their host rock (nephelinite or kimberlite in all cases shown). Accordingly, these samples are unusually vulnerable to being "off composition." This possibility is particularly attractive in trying to rationalize the phase relations reported by Mysen and Boettcher (1975a) for peridotite A, if there is amphibole present and if the amphibole is hornblende. Yet another possibility would be that the amphibole in peridotite A is cummingtonite-like, rather than being a calcic amphibole. (No analyses of amphibole from peridotite were presented.)

In summary, amphibole attains its maximum thermal stability in hornblende-rich ultramafic compositions of the sort represented in Figure 58. The available data on AMPH-IN in these compositions are quite consistent and show that natural hornblendes with some TiO_2, Fe, and K_2O are stable to higher temperatures than end-member pargasite is. The available amphibole stability fields in peridotites are highly variable, however, with bulk compositional variations contributing very little to the observed variation. Evidently there are more than the usual number of unresolved experimental difficulties in this part of the literature. The only thing that seems certain is that amphibole coexists with liquid in some peridotites and occasionally does so over a considerable

302

temperature range.

The effect on hornblende stability of $P_{H_2O} < P_{total}$

The effect on hornblende stability of lowering water activity is complex. Several discussions of the theory of melting of amphibole are available in the literature (Eggler, 1972a, 1973; Sykes, 1979). Of these the most thorough analytical treatment is given by Sykes, who derives a reaction similar to the following:

$$n_{H_2O}^{fl} = 1 - n_{H_2O}^{m} \tag{1}$$

This equation says simply that, when one mole of a hydrous phase (here amphibole) melts, and the crystalline phases produced in the melting reaction are all anhydrous (which is usually the case for amphibole), that the number of moles of H_2O added to the fluid phase $n_{H_2O}^{fl}$ plus the number of moles of H_2O in the melt $n_{H_2O}^{m}$ equals the 1 mole of water contained in the amphibole.

Complications arise from the fact that the amount of H_2O which the melt, produced as hornblende breaks down, can dissolve depends on pressure and water activity (a_{H_2O}). Hence, the partitioning of water between fluid ("vapor") and melt is also a function of pressure and a_{H_2O}. To paraphrase Sykes (1979, p. 26), at constant a_{H_2O} and at low pressures (P < 4 kbar), the solubility of water in the melt is relatively low, $n_{H_2O}^{m}$ is less than one, and $n_{H_2O}^{fl}$ is positive (i.e., water is added to the vapor phase as a product of the melting of amphibole). As pressure increases, at the same a_{H_2O}, $n_{H_2O}^{m}$ reaches 1, and the amphibole melting reaction is "vapor-absent", i.e., H_2O is neither added to nor removed from the vapor as amphibole melts. At still higher pressures, $n_{H_2O}^{m}$ can become greater than 1, i.e., the melt can dissolve more water than is produced by the melting of amphibole, and $n_{H_2O}^{fl}$ becomes negative. Then, H_2O is extracted from the vapor phase as amphibole melts or, to phrase it another way, H_2O acts as a reactant rather than as a product in the melting reaction. Thus, the slope of an amphibole melting curve, as a function of a_{H_2O}, can be positive, zero, or negative. Figure 26, given earlier in the chapter and modified from Sykes (1979, Fig. 6), summarizes the possibilities for pargasite using the phase relations of Holloway (1973).

As discussed in the introduction, there are two methods by which the $P_{H_2O} < P_{total}$ region has been studied. The first, including the work of Holloway cited above, involves using mixed fluids (H_2O-CO_2 or $H_2O-CO_2-N_2$) to dilute H_2O. The second method is simply to add to the system less water than needed to saturate it. The two types of experiment are difficult to compare, so will be discussed separately.

a. Mixed-volatile studies

Mixed volatile studies of the melting relations of hornblende in natural rocks include the work of Eggler (1972a,b) on a Paricutin andesite, Eggler and Burnham (1973) and Allen and Boettcher (1978) on a Mt. Hood andesite, and Ritchey and Eggler (1978) on a Crater Lake andesite, plus that of Hill and Boettcher (1970), Holloway and Burnham (1972), and Allen and Boettcher (1978) on the 1921 Kilauea olivine tholeiite. Mixed-volatile studies of other hornblende-bearing rocks have been made (Sykes, 1979; Mysen and Boettcher, 1975a), but the effect of $P_{H_2O} < P_{total}$ on hornblende melting was not determined.

The earliest work, on a Paricutin andesite, established that, at 5.5 kbar, one could lower the mole fraction of water in the vapor phase $(X_{H_2O}^{fl})$ from 1.0 to 0.5 without affecting the thermal stability of amphibole (Eggler, 1972a,b). Further decrease in $X_{H_2O}^{fl}$ resulted in amphibole melting at a lower temperature. Results on the Mt. Hood andesite at 5.5 kbar were similar (Eggler and Burnham, 1973). For this same Mt. Hood andesite Allen and Boettcher (1978, Fig. 1) showed that AMPH-IN passes through a temperature maximum somewhere between $X_{H_2O}^{fl} = 1.0$ and 0.5 for pressures between 10 and 20 kbar. Below $X_{H_2O}^{fl} = 0.5$ amphibole stability drops rapidly, such that amphibole is not present even as a subsolidus phase at $X_{H_2O}^{fl} = 0.25$. This pattern is broadly consistent with the pattern shown by pargasite in Figure 26, in which amphibole melting curves are relatively flat at moderate pressures and develop a pronounced T_{max} only at higher pressures.

Mixed-volatile work on basalts has involved only the 1921 Kilauea olivine tholeiite. The earliest one, of Hill and Boettcher (1970), demonstrated that amphibole stability increased at $X_{H_2O}^{fl} \cong 0.5$ relative to $X_{H_2O}^{fl} \cong 1$ at pressures of 10-25 kbar. These workers reported that amphibole was stable at higher pressures as well as at higher temperatures, at $X_{H_2O}^{fl} = 0.5$.

Results on AMPH-IN in this basalt at pressures below 10 kbar are ambiguous. Eggler (1972b) bracketed AMPH-IN at 968 $\pm$ 6°C, 2 kbar at $X_{H_2O}^{fl} = 1$ at FMQ conditions. Helz (1976) presented data showing that AMPH-IN is above 1045°C, 5 kbar at $X_{H_2O}^{fl} = 1$, also at FMQ conditions. Holloway and Burnham (1972) report AMPH-IN at 975 $\pm$ 25°C, 2 kbar and 1025 $\pm$ 25°C, 5 kbar, both at $X_{H_2O}^{fl} \cong 0.6$. The NNO buffer was used, as it should impose an oxygen fugacity near that of the FMQ buffer at $X_{H_2O}^{fl} \cong 0.6$. Unfortunately, most of these charges are considerably more oxidized than that (Holloway and Burnham, 1972; plus unpublished data on the Fe-Ti oxides in some of the charges, i.e., those analyzed for Helz, 1979). Thus, it is not certain whether the absence of an effect at 2 kbar and the apparent decrease in hornblende stability at 8 kbar are the result of lower

304

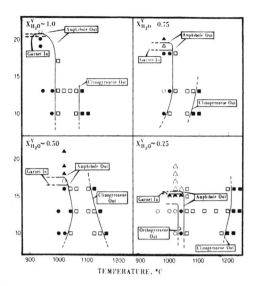

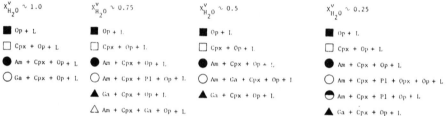

Figure 61. Crystallization sequence for the 1921 Kilauea olivine tholeiite at $X_{H_2O}^{fl}$ = 1.0, 0.75, 0.5 and 0.25. All assemblages coexist with vapor. Reproduced from Allen and Boettcher (1978, Fig. 2).

$X_{H_2O}^{fl}$ or higher oxygen fugacity, as the stability of hornblende in this basalt decreases markedly as f_{O_2} increases above NNO conditions (cf. Figs. 56 and 57 above). This ambiguity has already been noted by Holloway (1973, p. 654).

The best and most complete study of the effect of lowering $X_{H_2O}^{fl}$ on the phase relations of the 1921 Kilauea basalt is that of Allen and Boettcher (1978). Their results are reproduced here as Figure 61. Unfortunately they used yet another buffer, the HM buffer, so their results are not comparable to any of the preceding work. Also, since the f_{O_2} of the charge in the inner capsule decreases as $X_{H_2O}^{fl}$ decreases, at constant f_{H_2}, oxygen fugacity must vary somewhat from one $X_{H_2O}^{fl}$ level to the next in Figure 61. Only the H_2O-saturated runs should be at HM buffer conditions.

The data of Figure 61 show a marked maximum in the thermal stability of hornblende between $X_{H_2O}^{fl}$ = 0.75 and 0.25, again compatible with the results of Figure 26 for pargasite. Equally striking is the steady decrease in the

305

pressure at which hornblende is replaced by garnet as the high-Al_2O_3 phase, as $X_{H_2O}^{fl}$ decreases, an effect also seen in the Mt. Hood andesite. This latter effect is exactly the opposite of what Hill and Boettcher (1970) reported; in the earlier study (which also used the 1921 Kilauea basalt), the high-pressure limb was reported to shift to higher pressures at low $X_{H_2O}^{fl}$. However, if the breakdown of hornblende along this high-pressure limb is basically a dehydration reaction, with H_2O as a product, it seems more reasonable for the high pressure stability limit of amphibole to decrease as $X_{H_2O}^{fl}$ decreases. Hence the later results of Allen and Boettcher seem more plausible.

As mentioned earlier, f_{O_2} should decrease as $X_{H_2O}^{fl}$ decreases in these runs at constant f_{H_2}. Thus it is often not possible to resolve whether reported shifts in position of AMPH-IN are caused exclusively by changes in $X_{H_2O}^{fl}$ or may in part result from changes in f_{O_2}. For example, the high-temperature limb of AMPH-IN in the 1921 basalt is very f_{O_2}-dependent (see Figs. 56 and 57). Its position moves up almost 100° as f_{O_2} decreases from HM to NNO conditions, a decrease of 5 orders of magnitude in f_{O_2}. If one assumes that this f_{O_2} dependence of AMPH-IN is linear and continuous, this works out to an increase of 20°C per log unit decrease in f_{O_2}. From the stoichiometry of the water dissociation reaction, one can calculate that f_{O_2} will decrease roughly 0.3 log unit for a decrease of 0.25 in $X_{H_2O}^{fl}$. Thus, at $X_{H_2O}^{fl}$ = 0.5-0.25, AMPH-IN in the 1921 basalt should lie 12-20°C higher than at $X_{H_2O}^{fl}$ = 1.0, from the f_{O_2} effect alone. It in fact lies about 50°C higher, so there is an effect of decreasing $X_{H_2O}^{fl}$ beyond that of decreasing f_{O_2}, but it is not necessarily as large as might appear at first glance.

b. "Vapor-absent" studies

Vapor-absent studies of amphibole stability in natural rocks include the work of Green (1972) on a Fijian andesite and that of Green (1973), Millhollen and Wyllie (1974), and Merrill and Wyllie (1975) on ultramafic rocks. In addition, Naney (1977) has studied a synthetic "granodiorite." The work of Robertson and Wyllie (1971), one of the earliest published studies of "vapor-absent" melting, does not extend to high enough temperatures to determine the effect on hornblende stability.

There are many drawbacks to this type of experiment. The first is that the small amount of H_2O added usually does not distribute itself uniformly throughout the charge; instead one gets a rind of H_2O-saturated material on the outside of the charge, with the core of the charge nearly unreacted (Robertson and Wyllie, 1971; Eggler, 1972b).

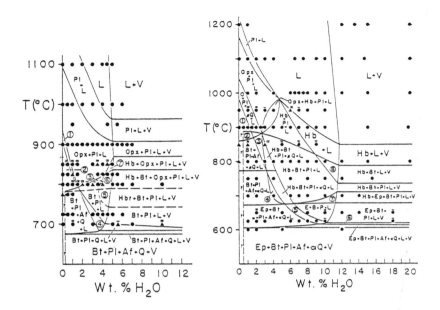

Figure 62a (to the left). Temperature versus weight percent H_2O phase assemblages for the synthetic granodiorite composition (R5 + 10Ml) at 2 kbar. Numbered fields shown in this diagram represent the phase assemblages indicated below:
1. Opx + Pl + Af + L
2. Opx + Pl + Af + Q + L
3. Opx + Bt + Pl + L
4. Bt + Pl + Q + L
5. Hb (?) + Bt + Pl + L
6. Hb + Bt + Opx + Pl + L
7. Hb + Opx + Pl + L

Figure 62b (to the right). Temperature versus weight percent H_2O phase assemblage diagram for the synthetic granodiorite composition (R5 + 10 Ml) at 8 kbar. Numbered fields represent the phase assemblages listed below:
1. Opx + Pl + Af + 3Q + L
2. Opx + Bt + Pl + Af + βQ + L
3. Bt + Pl + βQ + L
4. Hb + Bt + Pl + Af + αQ + L
5. Ep + Bt + Pl + αQ + L
6. Ep + Bt + Pl + αQ + L + V
7. Hb + Ep + Bt + Pl + L
8. Hb + Bt + L
This and Figure 62a have been reproduced from Naney (1977, Figs. 4 and 5). See Naney and Swanson (1980, p. 644, Fig. 2) for explanation of symbols and abbreviations.

A second problem is that it can be difficult to discuss the variation of water content in terms of thermodynamically significant variables. $X_{H_2O}^{fl}$ is undefined, because there is no fluid phase. $X_{H_2O}^{melt}$ could be determined (with difficulty) but in practice has not been determined in any of these studies, so estimates of water activity are not possible. What is usually done is to present a T-X section in which X is the weight percent H_2O added to the charge. An example of such a diagram is shown in Figure 62a,b.

A third drawback is that it is impossible to buffer the oxygen fugacity of a vapor-absent charge by any method which depends on equilibration of H_2 in two different fluids. Hence, the oxygen fugacity of all of these runs is uncontrolled, unknown, and probably not constant within a set of runs anyway.

A fourth, presumably minor, difficulty is that all of the capsules will usually contain some trapped air. The O_2, CO_2, and H_2O in the air may react with or dissolve in the melt, but the remainder (N_2 + Ar) should remain present as a vapor phase. So technically, there is no such thing as a "vapor-absent" run unless the sample capsules were evacuated prior to welding.

The best of these studies is that of Naney (1977), whose results are summarized in Figure 62a,b. These T-X projections display the effect of decreasing water content on the phase relations of the "granodiorite" at a given isobar, and it is evident that Naney's results are broadly compatible with those that would be predicted from the stability relations of pargasite in Figure 26. At 8 kbar (Fig. 62b) the thermal stability of hornblende increases from 850 $\pm$ 50°C at $P_{H_2O} = P_{total}$ to 975 $\pm$ 25°C at 5 percent H_2O added, declining precipitously thereafter. Hornblende is completely absent below 2.5 percent H_2O added. This resembles the stability results for pargasite fairly closely, except that the abscissas in Figures 26 and 62b are not exactly comparable.

At 2 kbar (Fig. 62a), by contrast, the upper stability limit of hornblende decreases as soon as $P_{H_2O} < P_{total}$, as is true for pargasite at 2 kbar. Pargasite does persist to intermediate $X_{H_2O}^{fl}$ values, however, whereas hornblende in the "granodiorite" has an extremely restricted field in the "vapor-absent" region, occurring only at what are probably very high water activities.

Interestingly, in neither case is amphibole stable in the subsolidus region, which is all vapor-present. This not true for natural granodiorites; all of the rocks whose hornblende stability curves are included in Figure 54 contain amphibole as part of the subsolidus assemblage, and indeed contain hornblende in the starting material. The absence of hornblende in the synthetic mix is a consequence of the artificial bulk composition used, as will be discussed in a later section. Here, it is sufficient to point out that this mix does *not* model the near-solidus and subsolidus relations of natural granodiorites very closely.

Green (1972) presents a series of P-T diagrams for a Fijian andesite at "anhydrous" conditions and with 2, 5, and 10 percent H_2O added. The size of AMPH + L expands steadily as H_2O content increases, but the maximum temperature stability of hornblende at a given pressure does not always increase as H_2O content increases. At 10 kbar, AMPH-IN lies at 965°C at 5 percent H_2O and 950°C at 10 percent H_2O, for instance. Green reports the presence of a vapor in the 10 percent, 10 kbar subliquidus runs (p. 153), so this implies the presence of a T_{max} in T-X space at intermediate water contents for AMPH-IN at 10 kbar. This is in agreement with the results for pargasite (Fig. 26). Green's data do not extend to high enough water contents to verify the presence of a T_{max} at higher pressures. As mentioned in an earlier section, the peculiar shape of the AMPH + L field in these diagrams is presumably caused by continuous variation in a_{H_2O} as P and T change along AMPH-IN.

The remaining "vapor-absent" experiments on hornblende stability involve a series of ultramafic compositions: hornblendite (Millhollen and Wyllie, 1974), Kakanui hornblende and hornblende eclogite (Merrill and Wyllie, 1975), and "pyrolite" (Green, 1973). Each of these compositions was studied (1) H_2O-saturated (AMPH-IN curves shown in Figs. 58 and 60) and (2) with little or no H_2O added. In the second case, the only water in the natural rocks was presumably that in the hornblende present in the starting materials, while the pyrolite had 0.2 percent H_2O added to it.

In the three hornblende-rich samples, the thermal stability of amphibole in the vapor-absent experiments increased 70-100°C over that in the H_2O-saturated runs. Maximum temperatures of 1150-1200°C at 15-20 kbar are reported, making the amphiboles in these experiments the most refractory hydroxy amphiboles known from rock compositions. The water activity at which these temperatures were achieved is not known, but obviously there is a T_{max} in T-X space along AMPH-IN in these bulk compositions, at least at high pressures.

Although the high-temperature limb of AMPH-IN is affected by the decrease in a_{H_2O}, the high-pressure limb of AMPH-IN is not shifted very much in the "vapor-absent" runs in these compositions. This is in notable contrast to the results reported by Allen and Boettcher (1978) (see Fig. 61 for andesite and basalt).

The results of Green (1973) on amphibole stability in pyrolite are somewhat different from the above. The amphibole is stable to higher temperatures, but Green reports that solidus temperature rises faster, so that amphibole is stable only in the subsolidus region, and the narrow field of AMPH + L shown in Figure 60 has disappeared. In the other three ultramafic compositions AMPH + L may have narrowed (the solidus was not determined closely for any of the three in the "vapor-absent" experiments), but it is still substantial (200-300° C).

In summary, almost all of the data on amphibole stability at pressures of 10 kbar or more show that amphibole melts at higher temperatures when $P_{H_2O} < P_{total}$ than when $P_{H_2O} = P_{total}$. Between 5 and 10 kbar, amphibole thermal stability is insensitive to decreasing $X_{H_2O}^{fl}$, down to $X_{H_2O}^{fl} = 0.3$ or 0.4. At pressures below 5 kbar, amphibole achieves its maximum thermal stability at water-

saturated conditions. Thus all of the data appear to be in general agreement
with the phase relations for pargasite (Fig. 26) and with the conclusion of
Holloway (1973) that pargasite + H_2O + CO_2 may be a reasonable model for igneous
amphiboles.

More detailed interpretation of this part of the literature is hampered by
the general lack of f_{O_2} control. Because a_{H_2O}, f_{H_2}, and f_{O_2} are interrelated,
it is very difficult to lower a_{H_2O} while maintaining f_{O_2} constant. Thus, most
experimental studies in which water activity (content, etc.) has been varied
will include concomitant variations in f_{O_2}. As the stability of hornblende in
an iron-bearing system depends on f_{O_2}, this uncontrolled double variation makes
the results of most of these studies somewhat ambiguous at best, uninterpretable
at worst. Isolation of the two effects for a natural rock remains to be done.

Compositions of experimentally produced igneous hornblendes

All of the experimentally produced amphiboles which have been analyzed to
date are hornblendes. There are no reports of richterites, though richterite
is intrinsically stable at temperatures in the melting range of most igneous
rocks (Charles, 1975, 1977; and earlier discussion in this chapter). The reason appears to be that none of the rocks investigated, even the peridotites,
are sufficiently low in Al_2O_3 for richterite to be stable: Kushiro and Erlank
(1970) have established that richterite is unstable in the presence of aluminous
phases. Similarly, the absence of representatives of the tremolite-actinolite
series is not the result of their intrinsic instability at temperatures in the
melting range: tremolite is stable to well over 850°C at $P_{H_2O} = P_{total} = 2$ kbar
(see discussion earlier in this chapter). The absence of tremolite-actinolite
is probably also due to the inability of Al_2O_3-poor amphibole to coexist with
liquids of normal (10-25 percent) Al_2O_3 content.

The absence of analyses of riebeckite and other alkali amphiboles, by contrast, reflects the fact that the appropriate peralkaline rock compositions have
received very little attention from experimentalists so far. The only "riebeckite" reported in a rock melting experiment (McDowell and Wyllie, 1971) was not
analyzed.

The absence of cummingtonite from the population of analyzed amphiboles is
more problematical. Cummingtonite occurs, apparently stably, in glassy volcanic
rocks as the only amphibole or coexisting with hornblende (Ewart et al., 1971;
Klein, 1968). The analysis of Wood and Carmichael (1973) supports the idea that
it is stable in these rocks, yet it has not been reported in any rock-melting
experiment. It is not clear, however, whether this is because rocks of the
appropriate compositions have not been studied, or because in the absence of

microprobe analyses, cummingtonite has been misidentified as hornblende, which it might closely resemble in rapidly quenched experimental run products.

The experiments thus confirm that hornblende is by far the most important igneous amphibole. Experimental conditions for most of the analyzed experimental amphiboles in the literature are summarized in Table 5. Bulk compositions represented range from granodiorite to peridotite, but the bulk of the analyses are of hornblendes from andesite or basalt. These 104 amphiboles, plus three from the CMAS + Na_2O + H_2O system (Cawthorn, 1976a) are displayed in Figures 63-70. The only significant block of data not included are twelve analyses of hornblendes from the Fijian andesite (Green, 1972) and four analyses from assorted pyrolite mixes (Nicholls, 1974). Both authors mentioned the existence of analyses, but chose not to publish their data, which therefore could not be included here.

a. Plotting conventions and limitations of the data

The amphibole compositional parameters plotted in Figures 63-70 are calculated on the basis of 23 oxygens, with the ideal amphibole structural formula assumed to be $A_{0-1}X_2Y_5Z_8O_{22}(OH)_2$. Only Si and Al were assigned to Z (the tetrahedral sites). Remaining Al was assigned to the Y, or octahedral, sites as Al(VI). Any excess in the Y cations [Al(VI) + Ti + Fe + Mn + Mg] above 5 was assigned to X (the M_4 site, nearly filled by Ca in most hornblendes). This excess will be referred to as $Fe(M_4)$, because the larger Fe^{+2} cation generally occupies the M_4 site more readily than any of the other common Y cations but Mn^{+2} (Ross et al., 1969). The notation is not meant to imply the total absence of other ions, only the probable predominance of Fe^{+2}. The X (or M_4) site is filled with Ca, $Fe(M_4)$ and $Na(M_4)$, to its limit of 2.0 cations. Any Na^+ remaining after the M_4 site is filled has, with all K^+ present, been assigned to the A-site.

In Figures 63-70, the symbols identify hornblendes by the bulk composition in which they were synthesized and by the f_{O_2} buffer, if any, used during the synthesis experiment. No attempt was made in these figures (or in Table 5) to include information on the nature of the coexisting crystalline assemblage, for three reasons. First, the assemblages are too variable in detail for this to be practical. (The hornblendes from Helz, 1973, 1976 would require 12 symbols instead of four, for example.) Second, in many cases the coexisting assemblages are incompletely characterized. Third, very few compositional parameters of hornblende are much affected by changes in coexisting crystalline assemblage, so long as bulk composition is constant and a melt is present. (The most conspicuous exception, TiO_2 content of hornblende, will be discussed below.)

311

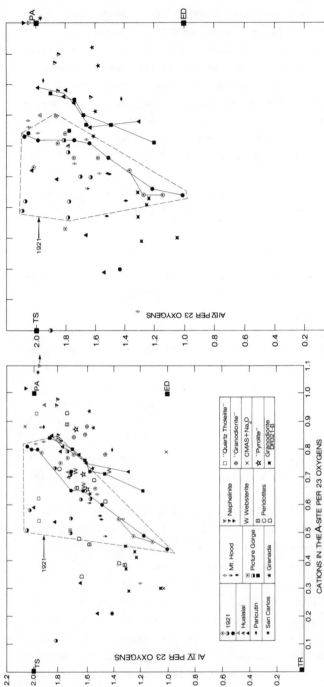

Figure 63a. Al(IV) versus cations in the A-site per 23 oxygens for experimentally produced igneous hornblendes (Fe$_2$O$_3$ = 0.0). The positions
of hornblende endmembers tremolite (TR), edenite (ED), tschermakite
(TS), and pargasite (PA) are indicated by the large solid squares. Rock
names used in the key are the same as those used in Table 5; the sources
of the analyses are given in that table. Multiple symbols beside a single rock name signify as follows: solid symbols = QFM or MW buffer;
half-filled symbols = NNO buffer; open symbols with dot = HM buffer. B,
C and D refer to specific peridotites used by Mysen and Boettcher
(1975b), as indicated in Table 5. Certain hornblendes from the 1921,
Picture Gorge and Hualalai basalts (the data of Helz, 1973, 1976) have
been connected by lines, in order to emphasize how hornblende within a
given rock changes compositionally as temperature varies, at constant
pressure and redox state. The dashed line encloses all hornblendes from
the 1921 Kilauea basalt except the two with A-site occupancy <0.2. The
hornblende plotted on the right ordinate (with arrow) plots outside the
figure, with cations in A = 1.3, at Fe$_2$O$_3$ = 0.0.

Figure 63b. Al(IV) versus cations in the A-site for experimentally produced igneous hornblendes, with Fe$_2$O$_3$ contents as described in the text.
Symbols for endmembers and individual analyses as in (a). Note that
hornblendes from synthetic mixes and ultramafic rocks included in (a)
are omitted from this figure. Lines connect hornblendes from Helz
(1973, 1976), and the dashed line encloses analyses of hornblendes from
the 1921 Kilauea olivine tholeiite, as in (a).

312

As can be seen by inspection of Figure 63a, the experimental hornblendes cover a very broad compositional range. Before we can discuss the significance of the observed variations we must first consider some limitations on the quality and significance of the data caused by (1) problems of experimental technique, (2) occasional peculiarities in the microprobe analyses, and (3) the absence of separate analyses for ferric and ferrous iron in almost all of the available analyses.

As should be evident to the reader by now, difficulties and defects in experimental technique limit the value of much of the published work on the phase relations of amphibole in igneous rocks. The same is true for the significance of an analysis: if the reported temperature is not the true one, or the reported pressure is off (as may be the case for experiments in piston-cylinder apparatus), or the water activity is unknown and/or uncontrolled, or oxygen fugacity is unknown and/or uncontrolled, the value of the analysis is correspondingly diminished, no matter how excellent the analysis itself may be. The commonest of these problems, as is evident from Table 5, is poor f_{O_2} control.

An additional problem is internal disequilibrium of the phase assemblage because of inadequate run time or because of drift in some experimental parameter (e.g., progressive loss of iron to Pt or PdAg capsules, drift in f_{O_2}, etc.). This problem seems to be fairly widespread, for example, in the work of Allen et al. (1975) and Allen and Boettcher (1978). These authors often present 2-6 individual analyses of amphibole, ostensibly from a single charge, certainly from a single set of run conditions. The individual analyses often differ by a percent or more in Al_2O_3, FeO, MgO, or CaO, and perhaps by half a percent or more in Na_2O or TiO_2 (see, e.g., Columns 1 and 2, Table 6). These variations exceed the expected uncertainty of a microprobe analysis, often by a factor of 2 or 3.[5] In the absence of any expressed preference by the authors for one composition over another, these multiple analyses have been averaged (as indicated in Table 5) and the averages plotted in Figures 63-70. The significance of the averages is problematical, however.

Further evidence for imperfect equilibration in the results of experienced and reasonably careful experimentalists can be seen in comparing columns 3-5,

- - - - - - - - - -

[5]In contrast to this heterogeneity, the amphibole analyses reported by Helz (1973, 1976) represent averages of 10-40 points each, and in most cases the dispersion of those data lies within the reported uncertainty of the microprobe analyses: ±2 percent for SiO_2, Al_2O_3, and CaO; ±3 percent for FeO, MgO, and TiO_2; and $\pm$ 5 percent for MnO, Na_2O, and K_2O (Helz, 1973, p. 297).

Table 5 Summary of experimental conditions for published analyses of hornblendes produced in rock compositions in the presence of a melt.

	Starting material	Reference	Pressure range (kb)	Temperature range (°C)	X_{H_2O} in vapor phase	Oxygen buffer used	Number of analyses	Comments
I.	Granodiorite							
	synthetic granodiorite	Naney (1977)	8	800, 900	no vapor	none	4	H_2 membrane used, but in the the absence of a vapor phase, water activity, oxygen fugacity are unknown.
	"granodiorite" DR321-B	Sykes (1979)	2 2	825-914 765-800	1.0 0.5	QFM none	3 3	Oxygen fugacity maintained by H_2 membrane near QFM for unbuffered cold-seal runs.
II.	Andesite							
	Mt. Hood	Allen et al. (1975)	13 10-18 10,13	880, 920 900-920 900, 940	1.0 1.0 1.0	HM none MW	2 3 2	Unbuffered runs close to NNO Multiple analyses reported from a single run have been averaged
	Same	Allen and Boettcher (1978)	13, 17 13 13	920 900 925, 940	1.0 0.75 0.50	HM HM HM	2 1 2	Multiple analyses reported from a single run have been averaged.
	Paricutin	Eggler (1972b)	5.5 5.8	900 930	1.0 0.5	QFM QFM	1 1	Oxygen fugacity maintained by H_2 membrane.
III.	Basaltic andesite							
	Grenada	Cawthorn et al. (1973)	5	961	1.0	NNO	1	
IV.	Quartz tholeiites							
	Picture Gorge	Allen et al. (1975)	13 10 10	910 920 960	1.0 1.0 1.0	HM none MW	1 1 1	Unbuffered run close to NNO. Multiple analyses reported from a single run have been averaged.
	Same	Helz (1973)	5	700-1000	1.0	QFM	6	
	synthetic "quartz tholeiite"	Green and Ringwood (1968)	9-10	920-1040	unknown	none	5	Water from talc in furnace assembly allowed to enter open capsule. Three runs in Pt, two in graphite capsules. F_{O_2} conditions unknown.
V.	Olivine tholeiite							
	1921 Kilauea	Allen et al. (1975)	13 18 13	950 1000 980	1.0 1.0 1.0	HM none MW	1 1 1	Unbuffered runs close to NNO. Multiple analyses reported from a single run have been averaged.

--continued

Table 5 Summary of experimental conditions for published analyses of hornblendes produced in rock compositions in the presence of a melt (cont.).

Starting material	Reference	Pressure range (kb)	Temperature range (°C)	X_{H_2O} in vapor phase	Oxygen buffer used	Number of analyses	Comments
Same	Allen and Boettcher (1978)	13 18 13 13	960 980 1010 1025	1.0 0.75 0.50 0.25	HM HM HM HM	1 1 1 1	Multiple analyses reported from a single run have been averaged.
Same	Helz (1973)	5 5	725-925 700-1000	1.0 1.0	HM QFM	3 6	
Same	Helz (1976)	5	1015-1045	1.0	QFM	2	Runs made by J.R. Holloway
Same	Helz (1979)	5, 8	995-1050	0.6	NNO	4	Runs made by J.R. Holloway
Same	Holloway and Burnham (1972)	5, 8	875-1050	0.6	NNO	4	

VI. Alkali basalts

Starting material	Reference	Pressure range (kb)	Temperature range (°C)	X_{H_2O} in vapor phase	Oxygen buffer used	Number of analyses	Comments
Hualalai (prehistoric)	Allen et al. (1975)	13 10	1040 980 980	1.0 1.0 1.0	HM none MW	1 1 1	Unbuffered run close to NNO. Multiple analyses reported from a single run have been averaged.
Hualalai (prehistoric)	Nesbitt and Hamilton (1970)	2	930	1.0-0.0	QFM	3	Oxygen fugacity maintained by H2 membrane. Charges vary in H2O content. Multiple analyses reported from a single run have been averaged.
1801 Hualalai	Helz (1973)	5	725-1000	1.0	QFM	6	
Grenada	Cawthorn et al. (1973)	5	961, 1001	1.0	NNO	2	

VII. Basanite/oid

Starting material	Reference	Pressure range (kb)	Temperature range (°C)	X_{H_2O} in vapor phase	Oxygen buffer used	Number of analyses	Comments
Grenada	Cawthorn et al. (1973)	5	1031	1.0	NNO	1	
San Carlos	Helz (1979)	5	1000	1.0	NNO	1	Run made by J.R. Holloway.

—continued

Table 5 Summary of experimental conditions for published analyses of hornblendes produced in rock compositions in the presence of a melt (cont.).

Starting material	Reference	Pressure range (kb)	Temperature range (°C)	X_{H_2O} in vapor phase	Oxygen buffer used	Number of analyses	Comments
VIII. Nephelinite							
Nuuanu flow	Allen et al. (1975)	13 13-28 13	1020 1015-1060 1020	1.0 1.0 1.0	HM none MW	1 4 1	Unbuffered runs close to NNO. Multiple analyses reported from a single run have been averaged.
IX. Garnet Websterite							
68SAL-7	Mysen and Boettcher (1976)	7.5, 15	850, 950	1.0	none	3	Unbuffered runs close to NNO.
X. Peridotites							
Spinel lherzolite 618.138b.1 (B)	Mysen and Boettcher (1975b)	10, 15 15	890, 1050 910, 950	1.0 0.75	none HM	2 2	Unbuffered runs close to NNO.
Garnet lherzolite 66SAL-1 (Δ)	Mysen and Boettcher (1975b)	7.5-20	820-110	1.0	none	6	Unbuffered runs close to NNO.
Lherzolite (C) + 2.7 pct. phlogopite	Mysen and Boettcher (1975b)	15	1000	1.0	none	1	Unbuffered runs close to NNO.
"Pyrolite"—40 pct. olivine	Green (1973)	10, 20	950-1000	1.0	none	3	

316

TABLE 6.　Hornblende analyses selected from the literature.

	1	2	3	4	5
Rock used	Mt. Hood	Mt. Hood	1921	1921	1921
Pressure (kb)	17	17	5.2	5.1	4.95
Temperature (°C)	920	920	999	1001	999
X_{H_2O}	1.0	1.0	~0.57	~0.57	~0.57
f_{O_2}	HM	HM	NNO	NNO	NNO
Coexisting phases	L	L	L	L	L
	V	V	V	V	V
	opaques	opaques	Ol	Cpx	Cpx
			Cpx	Il	Psb
			Mt(?)	Mt	Hm
				Ap	Ap
				Plag (relict)	
Duration of run (hr)	not given	not given	30	6	6
SiO_2	45.16	44.30	43.3	41.7	43.6
TiO_2	0.81	0.46	2.9	3.46	2.82
Al_2O_3	11.71	14.07	11.5	12.6	12.4
FeO	12.53	9.73	12.2	12.3	12.2
MnO	0.26	0.12	--	0.14	0.18
MgO	13.62	15.24	13.2	13.6	14.3
CaO	10.67	11.90	10.8	10.8	9.94
Na_2O	1.66	2.24	2.4	2.25	2.10
K_2O	0.41	0.48	0.3	0.51	0.47
Sum	96.83	98.54	96.6	97.36	98.01

Cols. 1 and 2.　Analyses from Allen and Boettcher, 1978, Table 5a, Nos. 4 and 5.

Col.3　Analysis and phase assemblage from Holloway and Burnham, 1972, Table 4, Col. 20.　Starting material for this experiment was previously run at 7.8 kb, 995°C.

Col. 4.　Analysis from Helz, 1979, Table 5, Col. 1.　Phase assemblage as determined by Helz.　Run conditions in Holloway and Burnham (1972), Table 3. 1921 powder was used as starting material.

Col. 5.　Analysis from Helz, 1979, Table 5, Col. 2.　Phase assemblage as determined by Helz.　Run conditions in Holloway and Burnham (1972), Table 3. Glass made by fusing 1921 powder was used as starting material.

Table 6. The charges these three hornblendes are from should be identical, and
are not, differing significantly in the proportions and compositions of other
phases present (Holloway and Burnham, 1972, Table 3; Helz, unpublished data),
as well as in amphibole composition (shown here). Furthermore, amphiboles
within the charges of columns 4 and 5 are appreciably more variable in composition than those analyzed by Helz (1973) from water-saturated runs. There are
two possible contributing factors: first, reaction rates appear to decrease
greatly as $X_{H_2O}^{fl}$ decreases from 1.0 to 0.57. Second, it is known that oxygen
fugacity was drifting upward during these runs, presumably because the buffer
capsules ran dry (J.R. Holloway, oral comm.). The effects of this f_{O_2} drift
can be seen in the compositions of the Fe-Ti oxides present. The run corresponding to the analysis in column 4 contains magnetite + ilmenite, which have compositions of 28.3 percent Usp and 35.7 percent Hm respectively. This pair cannot
have coexisted stably at the run temperature of 1000°C. However, the analysis
of Lindsley and Rumble (1977) suggests that the presence of ilmenite of this
composition at 1000°C would require f_{O_2} of the order of 10^{-8}, 2-3 orders of
magnitude higher than the intended f_{O_2} of the run, which should have been near
the FMQ buffer. The charge corresponding to the analysis in column 5 contains
hematite + pseudobrookite, and was essentially at HM conditions.

By contrast with the many experimental difficulties evident in the literature, it appears to be relatively easy to obtain an acceptable microprobe analysis of an amphibole, providing that the charges are coarse-grained enough to
analyze. Virtually all of the analyses reported in the literature are indeed
possible hornblendes, with reasonable summations (94.2-99.7, with most between
96 and 98 percent) and without obvious analytical flaws (e.g., Si + Al $\geq$ 8.00
in all cases). There are two small groups of hornblendes the analyses of which
appear somewhat strange, however. The first group is the three analyses in
Figure 63 that have 0.30 cations in the A-site. These hornblendes, from the
1921 Kilauea and a prehistoric Hualalai basalt, plot far away from other hornblendes from the same rocks, synthesized at very similar conditions, by the
same workers. It seems reasonable to suppose that these three analyses are
defective in some way.

The second group includes two hornblendes from a peridotite (Mysen and
Boettcher, 1975b, Table 4, columns 7 and 8), three of the analyses of hornblendes
from the Grenada suite (Cawthorn et al., 1973) and one from the 1921 Kilauea
basalt (Allen et al., 1975, Table 6a, column 22). The peculiarity of these
analyses is that they contain so much CaO that Ca in the structural formula
exceeds 2.00. Most of these analyses have Ca in the range 2.00-2.32, and have

been included here, as this range of Ca content exceeds the stoichiometric limit by only 10-15 percent of the amount present, an amount possibly dismissible as within the analytical uncertainty of a (rather poor) microprobe analysis. The analysis from the 1921 basalt, however, contains 17.14 percent CaO, or 2.7 Ca per 23 oxygens, a Ca content difficult to reconcile with the traditional amphibole unit cell containing no more than 2 Ca ions. This analysis, presumably a mixture of hornblende + augite, has been excluded from Figures 63-70.

As is well known, ferric and ferrous iron cannot be distinguished on the microprobe. The presence of the A-site in amphibole, which may be partially vacant, makes it impossible to calculate the ferric iron content of an amphibole from stoichiometric considerations. Therefore the ferric iron content of an amphibole for which only a microprobe analysis is available is unknown.

Nevertheless, many suggestions have been made as to how ferric iron might be estimated; these have been reviewed elsewhere in Volumes 9A,B. These methods hinge on making simplifying assumptions about hornblende stoichiometry, such as (1) assuming the $Fe(M_4)$ should be zero or (2) assuming that A-site occupancy cannot exceed $\frac{1}{3}[Al(IV)]$. However, hornblendes do contain $Fe(M_4)$ [see, e.g., Goldman and Rossman, 1977] and they may contain a richterite component, especially in high-alkali bulk compositions (see Helz, 1973).

The most important question here, given the absence of real analyses of ferric iron in almost all of these hornblendes, is how severely does the presence of variable amounts of ferric iron affect the distribution of these analyses in plots of *other* compositional parameters. One of the parameters most strongly affected is A-site occupancy (the worst case is $Na(M_4)$, to be discussed later). The nature of the effect of varying Fe^{+3} on A-site occupancy can be seen by comparing Figures 63a and 63b.

In Figure 63a, the amphibole structural formulas used had $Fe_2O_3 = 0.0$. In Figure 63b, estimated ferric iron contents were used in calculating the structural formula. Ferric iron as a percentage of total iron present was assumed to be 40 percent for amphiboles on the HM buffer, 12 percent for amphiboles on the FMQ, and 11 percent for those on the MW buffer, in accordance with the ferric iron determinations of Spear (1981). Amphiboles on the NNO buffer were assumed to contain Fe_2O_3 equal to 25 percent of total iron, in accordance with the ferric iron analyses of Holloway and Burnham (1972). (This assumption, that Fe^{+3}/Fe^{+2} is the same for all amphiboles synthesized on a given buffer, is probably a gross oversimplification: it implies that Fe^{+3}/Fe^{+2} is completely independent of T, P, X_{H_2O}, and of changes in bulk composition as great as the difference between andesite and nephelinite. Nevertheless it is the best guess

that can be made with the available data.) The only amphiboles included in
Figure 63b are those from natural rocks with moderate to high Fe/Mg ratios.
Excluded from Figure 63b were amphiboles from synthetic mixes of whatever com-
position and those from ultramafic rocks.

Allowing for some ferric iron increases Al(IV) and decreases A-site occupancy, so that the points in Figure 63b lie somewhat nearer the Ts corner than
they do in Figure 63a. However, the two figures are very similar in appearance.
The field of amphibole compositions from the 1921 basalt has changed shape somewhat, and the paths of amphibole compositions from individual basalts (see caption) are steeper in Figure 63b, but the overall distribution of data is very
similar in the two figures. Most other hornblende compositional parameters are
less sensitive to assumed Fe_2O_3 content than A-site occupancy is. This is
fortunate, because, as is evident from Table 5 and from the discussion above,
many of these runs were unbuffered, and their f_{O_2} is unknown. Even where f_{O_2}
control was attempted, it was not always achieved. In such cases, the Fe_2O_3
ratios assumed in compiling Figure 63b are not likely to be valid. Therefore,
in all subsequent figures, parameters for structural formulas with $Fe_2O_3 = 0.0$
have been used, regardless of whatever estimates of Fe_2O_3 content may have been
made in the original papers.

b. Substitutions active in experimental igneous hornblendes

The chemical substitutions active in experimentally produced hornblendes
are, of course, the same as those occurring in natural hornblendes. These
substitutions include simple cation exchanges such as:

$$Mg \rightleftarrows Fe^{+2} \rightleftarrows Mn^{+2} \text{ in the Y-sites} \tag{2}$$

$$Ca \rightleftarrows Fe^{+2} \quad \text{in the } M_4 \text{ site} \tag{3}$$

$$Na \rightleftarrows K \quad \text{in the A-site} \tag{4}$$

The most important of these are the $Mg \rightleftarrows Fe$ and $Na \rightleftarrows K$ exchanges, in these
hornblendes as well as in natural igneous hornblendes.

Other substitutions which appear to occur in experimental igneous hornblendes include:

$$Mg + Si \rightleftarrows Al(VI) + Al(IV) \quad \text{(tschermakite)} \tag{5}$$

$$Mg + 2Si \rightleftarrows Ti^{+4} + 2Al(IV) \quad \text{(Ti-tschermakite)} \tag{6}$$

$$Mg + Si \rightleftarrows Fe^{+3} + Al(IV) \quad \text{(ferri-tschermakite)} \tag{7}$$

$$\square + Si \rightleftarrows Na(A) + Al(IV) \quad \text{(edenite)} \tag{8}$$

$$\square + Ca \rightleftarrows Na(A) + Na(M_4) \quad \text{(richterite)} \tag{9}$$

This list was found sufficient to describe all the coupled substitutions occurring in the hornblendes studied by Helz (1973, 1976). The number of chemically possible substitutions is larger, however, and includes the glaucophane substitution [Ca + Mg $\rightleftarrows$ Na(M$_4$) + Al(VI)] and its ferric and titanian analogues.

c. Composition-composition diagrams

Figures 63a and 63b show the experimental hornblendes on the familiar Al(IV) versus A-site diagram. They cover virtually the entire field of compositions with Al(IV) > 1.0. More silicic hornblendes, with Al(IV) < 1.0, appear to be confined to subsolidus conditions [see the amphibole compositions reported by Spear (1981) for a midoceanic ridge basalt at comparable temperatures (700-900°C), but at pressures low enough that no melt was present]. Within the field where Al(IV) > 1.0, the analyses cluster on, or slightly to the left of, a line between the end members tremolite and pargasite. Relatively few analyses have fewer than 0.3 cations in the A-site, and those that do are suspect, as discussed above. Fewer still lie near the end member edenite, in spite of the importance of edenite as a substitution.

One of the most interesting features of Figures 63a and 63b is that hornblendes from a single bulk composition, which are related to each other by changes in temperature only, that is, with all other intensive parameters (pressure, $X_{H_2O}^{fl}$, redox state) held constant, show a strong coupling between Al(IV) and A-site occupancy. Both of these parameters increase as temperature increases in almost all cases (see discussion below). Thus amphibole composition within each bulk composition varies along a line whose slope is noticeably steeper than the 2:1 slope of the Tr-Pa join, with amphibole moving toward more Pa-rich compositions as temperature increases. This is illustrated in Figures 63a and 63b by the trends exhibited by hornblendes from the 1921, Picture Gorge, and 1801 Hualalai basalts (Helz, 1973, 1976). These slopes (3:1 to 5:1) are not required by nor explicable in terms of gross charge balance considerations. Presumably they are controlled by detailed structural adjustments made as the various hornblende substitutions proceed, distorting the tremolite structure as they occur. Similar trends have been reported in amphiboles in a variety of natural rock suites (e.g., Robinson and Jaffe, 1969; Robinson et al., 1971), including amphiboles from the Sierra Nevada batholith. It is possible that the trends observed in the natural hornblende suites also result from variation in temperature, at near-constant P, $X_{H_2O}^{fl}$, and redox state.

Figure 64 shows the same population of amphiboles as Figure 63a, but with Al(VI) on the abscissa instead of A-site occupancy. Whereas in Figure 63a

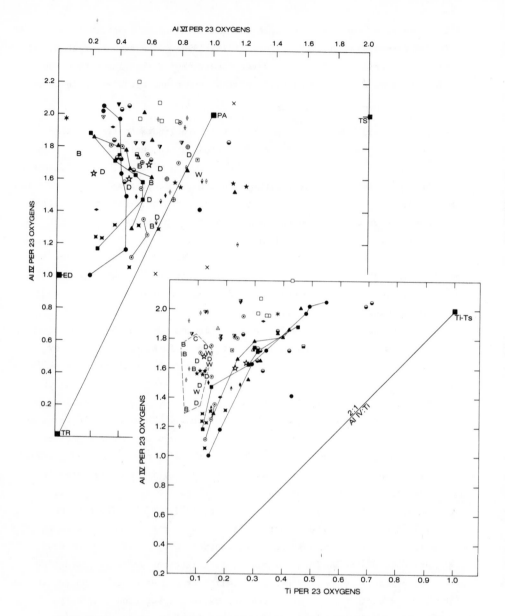

Figure 64 (upper left). Al(IV) versus Al(VI) per 23 oxygens, for experimentally produced igneous hornblendes (Fe_2O_3 = 0.0). Symbols as in Figure 63a; lines connect hornblendes from Helz (1973, 1976). Al($\overline{VI}$) in these hornblendes increases, passes through a maximum and then decreases, as Al(IV) and temperature increase.

Figure 65 (lower right). Al(IV) versus Ti per 23 oxygens, for experimentally produced igneous hornblendes (Fe_2O_3 = 0.0). The 2:1 diagonal line indicates the stoichiometry of the Ti-tschermakite (Ti-Ts) substitution. Symbols as in Figure 63a. Hornblendes from synthetic systems containing no TiO_2 do not appear in this figure (see text). Lines connect hornblendes from Helz (1973, 1976) as in Figure 63a. Ti in these hornblendes increases as temperature of synthesis increases.

almost all analyses lay in the triangle Tr-Pa-Ts, here almost all lie to the left of that compositional space. It is evident that Al-tschermakite is not the only tschermakite substitution active in these amphiboles: the Fe^{+3} and Ti^{+4} analogues must be important, even dominant, in most cases. It is probably significant that the three amphiboles from Cawthorn's (1976a) iron- and titanium-free system are the only group which consistently lies in Tr-Pa-Ts space.

As in Figure 63a, the amphiboles from Helz (1973, 1976) have been connected by lines in order to show how amphibole changes with temperature in this projection. Al(VI) passes through a rough maximum in each case, decreasing at the highest and lowest temperatures, while Al(IV) increases steadily as temperature increases.

Figure 65 shows Al(IV) versus Ti content, for those hornblendes containing TiO_2. [Some of the synthetic mixes (Naney, 1977; Cawthorn, 1976a) do not include TiO_2.] The Ti-tschermakite substitution is clearly important, especially in hornblendes from basalts. It increases as temperature increases and as f_{O_2} decreases. Nevertheless, as none of these hornblendes lies on the line connecting the Ti-tschermakite end member with tremolite, it is evident that Al(IV) is involved in other substitutions in all cases.

The maximum Ti content of 0.7 cations per 23 oxygens (corresponding to 5.5 percent TiO_2) is found in a hornblende synthesized at 1050°C, 8 kbar, $X_{H_2O}^{fl}$ = 0.57 in the 1921 Kilauea olivine tholeiite (Holloway and Burnham, 1972). This TiO_2 content is similar to the TiO_2 contents observed in kaersutite megacrysts (4.5-6.5 percent TiO_2) found at Dish Hill (Wilshire and Trask, 1971), Kakanui (Dickey, 1968), and San Carlos (Mason, 1968), among many known localities. This amphibole was rechecked (Helz, 1979) and its TiO_2 content confirmed. It appears therefore that the belief of Stewart et al. (1979), that kaersutite cannot coexist with a liquid, and *must* be of subsolidus (metasomatic) origin, is not justified.

This diagram shows quite clearly the overriding control that bulk composition can exert on some aspects of hornblende composition. The small field on the left encloses all of the analyses from the ultramafic rocks studied by Mysen and Boettcher (1975a,b; 1976), all rocks with very low TiO_2 contents. Coincidentally, it encloses all of the hornblendes of Cawthorn et al. (1973) from the Grenada suite compositions; these analyses are rather low in TiO_2 for hornblendes from alkali basalts, but then so are the rocks in which they were synthesized (see Table 1, p. 329 in Cawthorn et al., 1973).

Figure 66 shows Al(VI) versus Na(M_4) for some of the amphiboles shown in Figures 63-65. As mentioned above, and as discussed in some detail by Stout

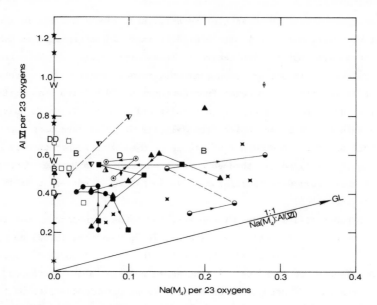

Figure 66. Al(VI) versus Na(M₄) per 23 oxygens, for experimentally produced hornblendes
(Fe_2O_3 = 0.0). The 1:1 diagonal line indicates the stoichiometry of the glaucophane (GL)
substitution. Symbols as in Figure 63a. Only hornblendes with Fe(M₄) <0.25 cations per 23
oxygens at Fe_2O_3 = 0.0 are shown. Most omitted data would plot on the ordinate. Solid lines
connect hornblendes from Helz (1973, 1976), plus those from Holloway and Burnham (1972).
Arrows point in the direction of increasing temperature. Dashed lines connect hornblendes
whose synthesis condition differ only with respect to pressure, from the data of Holloway and
Burnham (1972) and of Allen et al. (1975).

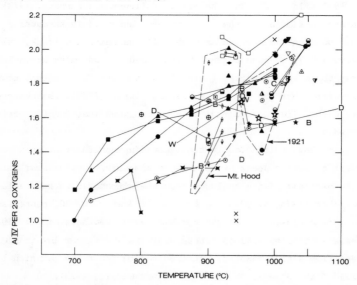

Figure 67. Al(IV) per 23 oxygens versus temperature for experimentally produced igneous hornblendes (Fe_2O_3 = 0.0). Symbols as in Figure 63a. Whenever two symbols are connected by a line
it means that their synthesis conditions differ only with respect to temperature. Dashed lines
enclose all of the hornblendes from the Mt. Hood or 1921 compositions analyzed by Allen et al.
(1975) and Allen and Boettcher (1978).

324

(1972), it is essentially impossible to estimate $Na(M_4)$ in a hornblende without knowing its Fe_2O_3 content, unless $Fe(M_4)$ is small in the structural formula calculated with $Fe_2O_3 = 0.0$. Accordingly, this figure excludes hornblendes with $Fe(M_4) \geqslant 0.25$, plus the few others which appear to be defective analyses. (Most of the hornblendes in the first category plot on the ordinate at $Na(M_4)$ = 0.0 if $Fe_2O_3 = 0.0$.)

The remaining hornblendes are shown in Figure 66. There is very little obvious correlation between $Al(VI)$ and $Na(M_4)$ in the overall distribution. When one looks at the temperature-controlled succession of hornblende compositions from the Picture Gorge, 1921, and Hualalai basalts, one sees that there are few line segments parallel to the line defining the glaucophane substitution. The two that are most conspicuously parallel (connecting the amphiboles from Holloway and Burnham, 1972) have $Al(VI)$ and $Na(M_4)$ both increasing as temperature increases. The dashed lines connect amphiboles synthesized at different pressures, but with all other factors constant. The pressure-related pair from Holloway's work (synthesized at 5 and 8 kbar, 1000°C, $X_{H_2O}^{fl}$ = 0.57) shows $Al(VI)$ and $Na(M_4)$ decreasing as pressure increases from 5 to 8 kbar. Now, the phase relations of glaucophane and the occurrence of glaucophane-rich amphiboles are such (Ernst, 1968) that one would expect to see Al (VI) and $Na(M_4)$ decrease at higher temperatures and increase at higher pressures. The opposite behavior is observed here, as often as not. Therefore, even where $Al(VI)$ and $Na(M_4)$ appear to be correlated, it is difficult to believe that the glaucophane substitution is really active.

Could changing Fe^{+3} contents produce some order in the nearly random pattern of $Al(VI)$ versus $Na(M_4)$ seen in Figure 66? It seems unlikely: most of the amphiboles included were synthesized on the FMQ or NNO buffers, so they should all have similar Fe^{+3} contents. Recalculating $Na(M_4)$ with appropriate Fe^{+3} contents would simply move the whole population to slightly higher $Na(M_4)$ levels, without shifting the amphiboles relative to each other.

There are three hornblendes whose relative positions are consistent with the expected P-T dependence of the glaucophane substitution. These, synthesized in the Nuuanu nephelinite at 13, 19, and 28 kbar, 1015-1020°C (Allen et al., 1975) show $Al(VI)$ and $Na(M_4)$ increasing as pressure increases. The high synthesis pressures are unusual: there is only one other analyzed hornblende in the literature synthesized at pressures $\geqslant$ 19 kbar (from peridotite D at 20 kbar; Mysen and Boettcher, 1975a,b). It may be significant that these extremely high pressure hornblendes are the only ones which can plausibly be said to have the glaucophane substitution occurring in them. It is interesting to note that the possible occurrence of the glaucophane substitution in these three hornblendes is consistent with the lower pressure limits on glaucophane stability presented earlier in this chapter. (Pure glaucophane would be metastable at these temperatures, even at P > 20 kbar, of course; here it is a question of complex amphiboles containing glaucophane as a minor component.)

Without knowing ferric iron content, it is impossible to evaluate the significance of the ferri-tschermakite or riebeckite [$Na(M_4) + Fe^{+3}(VI)$] substitutions. However, there are two observations in the literature which may be relevant here. The first is the data of Spear (1981) which show that, although Fe_2O_3/FeO increases considerably as f_{O_2} increases, that the absolute amount of Fe_2O_3, and hence of Fe^{+3} per formula unit, is much less variable. Hornblendes synthesized on the HM buffer contain roughly 0.1 Fe^{+3} more per formula unit than hornblendes synthesized on the FMQ buffer, not a very big increase considering that these two buffers bracket almost the entire range of f_{O_2} variation observed in terrestrial rocks.

The second is the observation of Helz (1973, p. 299) that the variation of Mg and Fe in hornblende with temperature is almost exactly symmetrical, when expressed in terms of cations or moles. Evidently ferric iron content must not increase or decrease systematically with temperature on a given buffer in those experiments, if every mole of Fe that entered or left hornblende was balanced by one mole of Mg^{+2}.

The limited evidence available thus suggests that although hornblende contains some ferric iron, the amount of ferric iron hornblende will accept may not always be very sensitive to variations in f_{O_2} and temperature. In view of the absence of peralkaline compositions among the rocks listed in Table 5, it seems probable that whatever ferric iron exists is present as ferri-tschermakite rather than riebeckite.

In conclusion, then, three substitutions are dominant in experimentally produced igneous hornblendes: edenite, tschermakite, Ti-tschermakite. The glaucophane substitution appears to occur only in hornblendes formed at very high pressures. Ferri-tschermakite presumably occurs, but its *variation* cannot be assessed with the available data.

One question remains: to what substitution should one attribute minor $Na(M_4)$ observed in some of these hornblendes? The glaucophane substitution appears not to be active in most, and the bulk compositions involved are such that riebeckite seems unlikely. The possibilities remaining are the richterite substitution [$Na(A) + Na(M_4)$] and the titanian analogue of glaucophane [$2Na(M_4) + Ti(VI)$]. Both could be present: the data are not good enough to distinguish between them.

d. Hornblende composition versus intensive variables

In these experiments, as in nature, hornblende composition depends on the intensive variables (temperature, pressure, f_{O_2}, $X_{H_2O}^{fl}$) and on bulk composition. One can determine the dominant substitutions occurring in natural igneous hornblendes without knowing any of the controlling variables. The most valuable feature of the experimental studies is (or ought to be) that these controlling parameters are known. A unique contribution that rock melting studies could (potentially) make to our knowledge of igneous hornblendes, then, would be to quantify the relationships between specific compositional parameters of hornblende and controlling variables such as T, P, or f_{O_2}. Accordingly, in Figures 67-70, the hornblende parameters found most important in the above section are shown plotted against temperature or pressure. Whenever the reported synthesis conditions of two hornblendes differ only with respect to temperature (Figs. 67-69) or pressure (Fig. 70) the symbols for those two analyses have been connected by a line. In this way, the effect of temperature, say, on Al(IV) can be isolated from the effects of varying pressure, f_{O_2}, bulk composition, etc.

Figure 67 shows Al(IV) versus temperature. It is evident that Al(IV) generally increases with increasing temperature, at constant pressure, water activity, oxygen fugacity, and bulk composition. Negative slopes are the exception in Figure 67, and those that occur probably result from disequilibrium (the 1921 NNO pair, see Table 6) or other analytical difficulties (fine grain size may be a factor in the case of the hornblende from 820°C in peridotite D). This relative coherence of the variation of Al(IV) with temperature in part reflects the fact that the only analytical error which affects Al(IV) much is the uncertainty in the SiO_2 analysis. It is important to note that Al(IV) variation is not discernibly affected by presence or absence of plagioclase, garnet, clinopyroxene, etc., in the coexisting phase assemblage.

The fields labelled "1921" and "Mt. Hood" enclose all of the hornblendes from those two rocks reported by Allen et al. (1975) and Allen and Boettcher (1978). Note that the shapes of these fields show no overall correlation between Al(IV) and temperature, even though bulk compositions, analyst and microprobe standards, operating conditions, and data reduction procedures were presumably the same throughout. The conclusion one can draw, I think, is that variations in pressure, f_{O_2}, and $X_{H_2O}^{fl}$ in this data set, plus poor equilibrium in many of the runs analyzed, affect Al(IV) sufficiently to completely obscure the relationship between Al(IV) and temperature. If one is to see the effect of *temperature* on hornblende composition, one needs a set of hornblendes for which temperature is the only variable. The only large data set of this sort currently available is that of Helz (1973, 1976) at P_{H_2O} = 5 kbar.

Figure 68 shows A-site occupancy versus temperature. There is much more scatter in Figure 68 than in Figure 67. This is to be expected, as the estimated A-site occupancy inevitably includes the arithmetic sum of the analytical errors for every oxide in the hornblende analysis. Nevertheless, there is generally a positive correlation between A-site and temperature, especially for hornblendes synthesized below 1000°C. A-site occupancy appears to pass through a rough maximum near 1000°C: most of the hornblendes from T > 1000°C have somewhat lower A-site occupancies than hornblendes in the 950-1000°C range. This apparent reversal in A-site occupancy lies just below AMPH-IN in these rocks; it does not coincide with any other change in phase assemblage. The fields for the 1921 basalt and Mt. Hood andesite again show none of the correlation with temperature that is evident when all variables but temperature are held constant.

Both Al(IV) and A-site occupancy thus tend to increase with increasing temperature, over most of the field of AMPH + L. This provides experimental corroboration for the common observation that natural hornblendes become increasingly pargasite-rich as inferred temperature of paragenesis increases (see following chapter).

Figure 69 shows the Ti content of hornblende versus temperature. This variable shows a strong positive correlation with temperature, with few exceptions. This is again in good agreement with inferences drawn from natural hornblende occurrences: high-Ti-hornblendes tend to be found in high-temperature parageneses, providing bulk TiO_2 content is high enough.

It is fairly obvious from this figure that Ti content also depends strongly on f_{O_2}: Ti is much lower in hornblendes synthesized on the HM buffer than in hornblendes synthesized at NNO, FMQ, or MW conditions. The effect is best seen in hornblendes from the 1921 basalt. In fact the negative slopes connecting the hornblende synthesized at 875°C, NNO (Holloway and Burnham, 1972) with the 1000°C hornblendes probably reflect this f_{O_2} dependence. As discussed earlier (see also Table 6) the runs at 1000°C have f_{O_2} values lying between NNO and HM. This example raises the possibility that some of the apparent incoherence in Ti versus temperature and *nominal* f_{O_2} seen in Figure 69 (especially in hornblendes from low-Ti bulk compositions) is the result of unrecognized f_{O_2} drift.

The variation of Al(VI) with temperature has already been shown to be complex (see Fig. 64; also Helz, 1973, Fig. 4). Figure 70 shows instead how Al(VI) in hornblende varies with pressure, the intensive variable by which it is most

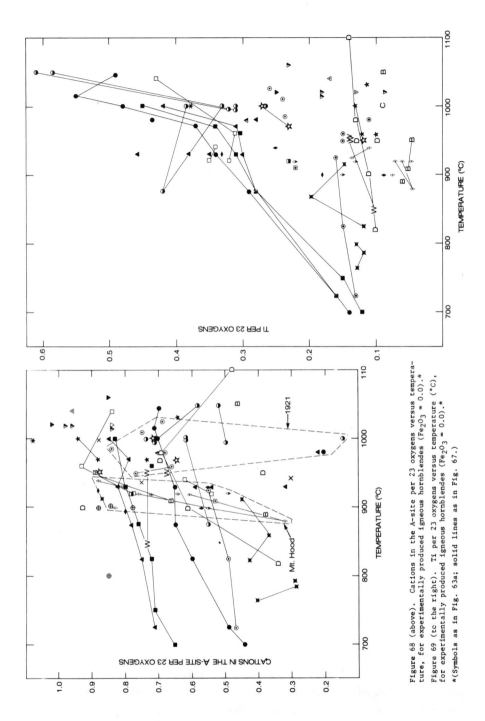

Figure 68 (above). Cations in the A-site per 23 oxygens versus temperature, for experimentally produced igneous hornblendes (Fe_2O_3 = 0.0).*

Figure 69 (to the right). Ti per 23 oxygens versus temperature (°C),
for experimentally produced igneous hornblendes (Fe_2O_3 = 0.0).*

*(Symbols as in Fig. 63a; solid lines as in Fig. 67.)

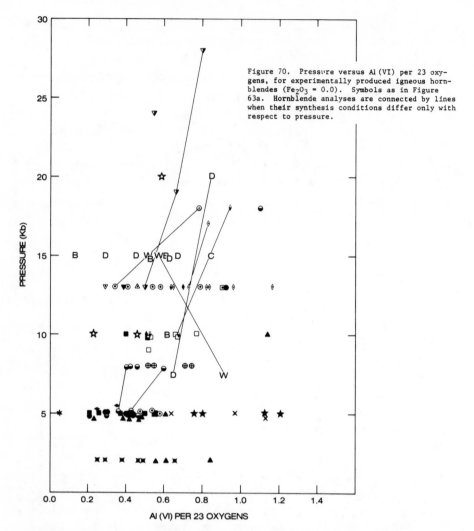

Figure 70. Pressure versus Al(VI) per 23 oxygens, for experimentally produced igneous hornblendes ($Fe_2O_3 = 0.0$). Symbols as in Figure 63a. Hornblende analyses are connected by lines when their synthesis conditions differ only with respect to pressure.

commonly said to be controlled. Again, hornblende pairs in which pressure is the *only* variable show a fairly consistent pattern: Al(VI) increases as pressure increases. Again the overall distribution of data shows nothing so systematic.

At least two different substitutions are involved here. As discussed above, the very high-pressure hornblendes from the nephelinite may have a glaucophane component in them. At the low-pressure end, the hornblende pair from Holloway and Burnham's (1972) work shows a strong decrease in Al(VI) with pressure but a substantial decrease in $Na(M_4)$: here the Al(VI) must be present as tschermakite component. The other pressure-related pairs may involve either or both of these substitutions. What is important here is that the data confirm the idea that Al(VI) in hornblende increases with increasing pressure, all other things being equal.

Of the parameters from the coupled substitutions listed in equations 5-9 earlier, the only ones that have not yet been discussed are $Na(M_4)$ and Fe^{+3}. Helz (1973) noted a decrease in $Na(M_4)$ with increasing temperature in two relatively alkali-rich basalts, but no variation at all in a third basalt. No other authors offer any comments on $Na(M_4)$. Fe^{+3} is, as discussed above, unknown. It should increase somewhat as f_{O_2} increases but its temperature and pressure dependence are presently undetermined.

These single parameters usually are involved in more than one substitution, as already noted for Al(VI). Combining the results from Figures 67-70 with the conclusions reached in the previous section, we can say that the three most important substitutions observed in these hornblendes depend on one or more of the intensive variables as follows: Ti-tschermakite component increases as temperature increases and decreases as f_{O_2} increases above NNO (Fig. 69). Edenite substitution increases as temperature increases except at very high temperatures ($\geq$1000°C, Fig. 68). Tschermakite component increases as pressure increases (Fig. 70) and decreases as temperature increases, except at very low temperatures (<750°C, Fig. 64; also Helz, 1973, Fig. 4). These observations are roughly consistent with the P-T range of stability found for end-member tschermakite (see discussion earlier in chapter).

The P-T dependence of minor substitutions is less well determined. The $Na(M_4)$ variation observed by Helz (1973) would suggest that richterite substitution decreases at higher temperatures, as hornblende becomes more aluminous, if the $Na(M_4)$ can properly be assigned to richterite. The double dependence of the glaucophane substitution on pressure has already been noted: it occurs only in hornblendes synthesized at high pressure and increases as pressure increases.

The coupled substitutions discussed above are not the only compositional variables of hornblende which respond to changes in T, P, f_{O_2}, or $X_{H_2O}^{fl}$. The various simple cation exchanges, of which $Mg \rightleftarrows Fe^{+2}$ is the most important, also depend on these variables. Mg/Fe in hornblende tends to increase as temperature increases. This trend may be reversed in certain temperature intervals by complex solid-solid reactions in assemblages containing Fe- and Ti-rich accessory minerals, such as the Fe-Ti oxides, fayalite, and titanite (sphene) (Helz, 1973, 1976). In assemblages consisting only of ferromagnesian silicates plus liquid, however, Mg/Fe in hornblende always increases with temperature, at constant redox conditions (see, e.g., Green and Ringwood, 1968; Mysen and Boettcher, 1975b).

Mg/Fe in hornblende increases as f_{O_2} increases, at constant temperature, pressure and bulk composition (see Helz, 1973, Fig. 7). This effect can also be seen in the data of Allen et al.(1975, Table 6a, cf. analyses 23 versus 24-26 or 28 versus 36 versus 37).

The Mg/Fe ratio in hornblende is reported to decrease with increasing pressure in the Mt. Hood andesite (Allen et al., 1975; Allen and Boettcher, 1978) and in some peridotites (Mysen and Boettcher, 1975b). While the compositions are much simpler, Gilbert and Popp have noted a similar increase of Fe solubility in Fe/Mg amphiboles at higher pressures, as discussed in an earlier section of this chapter. In other bulk compositions (basalts, nephelinite), however, Allen and coworkers did not observe any pressure dependence of this variable.

This pressure effect may result from the fact that the extent of melting decreases with increasing pressure, as rock solidi at $P_{H_2O} = P_{total}$ have positive slopes in the pressure range Allen and coworkers studied (10-30 kbar). The lower degree of partial melting, at higher pressure and constant temperature, would necessarily mean that the crystalline phases would be more iron-rich, in assemblages where Fe-Ti oxides were not important. It may be significant that the pressure effect is observed in rocks with $TiO_2 = 0.05$-0.94 percent, FeO = 5.9-9.8 percent, and is not observed in rocks with $TiO_2 = 1.7$-2.8 percent and FeO = 11.3-15.5 percent.

A small decrease in $X_{H_2O}^{fl}$ should affect hornblende composition at a given temperature for much the same reason that pressure does: it changes the extent of melting. All things being equal, therefore, a small decrease in $X_{H_2O}^{fl}$ will mimic a decrease in temperature. The effect of large changes in $X_{H_2O}^{fl}$ on hornblende composition cannot be evaluated, because the phase assemblage of a rock at low $X_{H_2O}^{fl}$ is usually different from that in the same rock at high $X_{H_2O}^{fl}$ and low temperature, so that the resulting changes in hornblende composition cannot be ascribed unambiguously to change in $X_{H_2O}^{fl}$. A further difficulty is that, at present, f_{O_2} decreases as $X_{H_2O}^{fl}$ decreases, in all of the available experiments. Because of the low f_{O_2} effect, there are no hornblende pairs in the literature of which one can say that the difference in composition is sole y the result of decreasing $X_{H_2O}^{fl}$, so the effect of this variable on hornblende composition, if any, is unknown.

Compositional Relationships Between Hornblende and Coexisting Phases

Thus far we have discussed the chemical variations of hornblende alone. This section will summarize the available data on element partitioning between hornblende and the phases it coexists with in these experiments. Coexisting phases which have been analyzed include olivine, orthopyroxene, augite, garnet, spinel (Al- or Cr-rich), plagioclase, various Fe-Ti oxides (magnetite, ilmenite, hematite, pseudobrookite, rutile), titanite (sphene), and, of course, a silicate melt. There are as yet no reports of two coexisting amphiboles in any rock melting experiment.

a. Hornblende-olivine relations

There are 19 analyzed hornblende-olivine pairs in the literature. All are from basalts (Holloway and Burnham, 1972; Helz, 1973, 1976; Cawthorn et al., 1973; Allen et al., 1975) or ultramafic compositions (Green, 1973; Mysen and Boettcher, 1975b, 1976). In the basalts $Mg/(Fg + Fe)$ is much higher in olivine than in coexisting hornblende. In a nephelinite and in the ultramafic rocks, $[Mg/(Mg + Fe)_{ol}]/[Mg/(Mg + Fe)_{hbl}]$ varies inconsistently around 1.0.

Minor element partitioning data are sparse. In basalt, Mn is concentrated in olivine relative to hornblende (Mn_{ol}/Mn_{hbl} = 1.7-2.5) at the redox conditions of the FMQ buffer (Helz, 1973). Very limited data (two hornblende-olivine pairs from Mysen and Boettcher, 1975b) suggest that olivine concentrates Mn in ultramafic compositions as well, though less strongly (Mn_{ol}/Mn_{hbl} = 1.2-1.7). Ni is very strongly partitioned into olivine relative to amphibole in an iron-free system (Mysen, 1978a). This is presumably true in rocks as well, but to date no one has analyzed both phases of a coexisting hornblende-olivine pair for NiO in a rock-melting experiment.

b. Hornblende-orthopyroxene relations

There are nine analyzed hornblende-orthopyroxene pairs in the literature, from the Mt. Hood andesite (Allen and Boettcher, 1978), a synthetic quartz tholeiite (Green and Ringwood, 1968), and ultramafic compositions (Green, 1973; Mysen and Boettcher, 1975b, 1976). In the andesite, hornblende is more magnesian than coexisting opx. In the quartz tholeiite and peridotites the two phases have roughly the same $Mg/(Mg + Fe)$ ratios.

Orthopyroxenes are, of course, higher in SiO_2 and much lower in Al_2O_3, CaO, Na_2O, and TiO_2 than coexisting hornblendes. Distribution ratios for Ti_{hbl}/Ti_{opx} are 1.5-1.8 in the andesite, 1.9-6.2 in the basalt and peridotites. The only minor or trace element for which any data are available is Cr in the ultramafic compositions. Cr_{hbl}/Cr_{opx} varies from 1.1 to 4.3; this ratio decreases as temperature increases, all other variables being equal.

c. Hornblende-augite relations

Augite is very widespread in hornblende-bearing experimental assemblages, and analyses of coexisting hornblende-augite pairs are correspondingly abundant.

The 38 published pairs are from andesite (Allen and Boettcher, 1978), basalts (Holloway and Burnham, 1972; Helz, 1973; Cawthorn et al., 1973; Green and Ringwood, 1968; Allen et al., 1975; Allen and Boettcher, 1978), and from ultramafic rocks (Green, 1973; Mysen and Boettcher, 1975b, 1976).

Augite is almost always more magnesian than coexisting hornblende, and usually has the highest $Mg/(Mg + Fe)$ ratio of any phase present. In two hornblende-augite pairs from peridotite D (Mysen and Boettcher, 1975b) three from 1921 basalt, and one from the Mt. Hood andesite (Allen and Boettcher, 1978), hornblende is more magnesian than the coexisting augite. As no common factor in terms of T, P, f_{O_2}, or bulk composition is evident for these six pairs, one suspects either poor analyses or internal disequilibrium.

Augite is higher in SiO_2 and CaO than is hornblende; hornblende is almost always enriched in Al_2O_3, TiO_2, and Na_2O relative to augite. Typical ratios for Ti_{hbl}/Ti_{cpx} are:

in andesite 1.3 (1 pair)
in basalts 1.3-8.6 (29 pairs)
in ultramafic rocks 1.3-7.1 (5 pairs)

The exceptions, with less TiO_2 in hornblende, include two pairs from basalt with $Ti_{hbl}/Ti_{cpx} = 0.9$ (Allen and Boettcher, 1978). Both of these are pairs in which the $Mg/(Mg + Fe)$ distribution is also anomalous.

Values of Na_{hbl}/Na_{cpx} observed experimentally are:

in andesite 7.8 (1 pair)
in basalts 1.4-8.2 (26 pairs)
and 20.0 (1 pair)
in ultramafic rocks 2.0-3.4 (5 pairs)
and 17.1 (1 pair)

There is only one hornblende-augite pair in the literature where the analyses show less Na_2O in the hornblende than in coexisting augite. The analysis of this hornblende (Allen et al., 1975, Table 6a, No. 21), which has an apparent A-site occupancy of 0.1 (see Fig. 63a of this paper), shows only 0.12 percent Na_2O, an amount which appears on several grounds to be unreasonably low.

Curiously, there is very little correlation between Na_{hbl}/Na_{cpx} and pressure in the available data. If the experiments have equilibrated adequately, this result implies that jadeite component does not enter cpx in significant amounts in experiments where amphibole is present, even at pressures of 18-24 kbar at $X_{H_2O}^{fl}$ as low as 0.25.

Minor and trace elements for which data are available include Mn and Cr. Mn_{hbl}/Mn_{cpx} values observed are typically:

in basalts 0.46-0.79 (8 pairs)

in peridotites 0.20-0.80 (4 pairs)

There are two pairs in basalt with values of 1.1 and 1.7 (Allen and Boettcher, 1978), one of which also has anomalous Ti and Mg/Fe distributions. From these data, Mn distribution between augite and hornblende appears to be quite insensitive to f_{O_2}, as values of the distribution ratio observed on the FMQ buffer (0.52-0.61, Helz, 1973) are similar to those most commonly observed on the HM buffer (0.46-0.79, Allen and Boettcher, 1978). Absolute levels of Mn do not vary either, which suggests that Mn^{+2} and Mn^{+3} are accommodated readily in both hornblende and augite.

Chromium partitioning data are available only for the ultramafic compositions. In these, Green's (1973) data give Cr_{hbl}/Cr_{cpx} values of 1.1-1.3, while the data of Mysen and Boettcher (1975b) give values of 0.13-0.60 for this same ratio. There is no obvious explanation for this discrepancy.

d. Hornblende-garnet relations

The stability fields of hornblende and garnet overlap only slightly in most rock compositions studied to date, so it is not surprising that there are only three hornblende-garnet pairs in this experimental literature: one from the Mt. Hood andesite, at 920°C, 19 kbar (Allen et al., 1975) and two from peridotite D at 820°C and 900°C, 15 kbar (Mysen and Boettcher, 1975b). [Mg/ $(Mg + Fe)_{hbl}]/[Mg/(Mg + Fe)_{garnet}]$ ratios are 1.56, 1.05, and 1.10, respectively. Garnet is the most iron-rich ferromagnesian silicate present, and also appears to be highest in MnO, where all other ferromagnesian phases present have been analyzed for MnO.

e. Hornblende versus oxide minerals

Oxide phases (Cr- or Al-rich spinel, magnetite, members of the ilmenite-hematite series, pseudobrookite, and rutile) are very widespread in these experiments. They are reported in all of the experiments summarized in Table 5 except those of Naney (1977) and Green (1973), both of whom worked on synthetic "rocks." Characterization is often limited, however; they may be referred to as "opaques" or "Fe-Ti oxides," or identified as "magnetite" without specifying the criteria used in making the identification. Analyses of oxide phases co-existing with hornblende are reported only by Mysen and Boettcher (1975b, Table 5) who present two analyses of Al-rich spinel, and Helz (1973, Table 6a,b,c), who presents analyses of Fe-Ti oxides and titanite (sphene).

The lack of analyses is not so critical, however, as the lack of mineral identification, as the effects of f_{O_2} and of bulk composition on TiO_2 and on

335

Fe^{+2}/Fe^{+3} in hornblende tend to be determined by the nature of the coexisting oxide phase, if any. For example, if hornblende is in equilibrium with ilmenite ± magnetite, as it is in the 1921, Picture Gorge, and Hualalai basalts, FMQ buffer, from 700–1000°C (Helz, 1973, Table 2), its Ti content is high and increases steadily as temperature increases (see Fig. 69). With increasing temperature, shortly after the last ilmenite melts (as it does at ∿1010°C in the 1921 basalt), the TiO_2 content of hornblende starts to decline. In these same basalts on the HM buffer, the oxide phases are pseudobrookite ± hematite (Helz, 1973, Table 2). The Ti content of the coexisting hornblende in the 1921 basalt is much lower, even though the percentage of TiO_2 in pseudobrookite is very similar to that in ilmenite (Helz, 1973, Table 6a,b). Evidently TiO_2 content of hornblende is very strongly affected by changes in oxide assemblage. Hence, the absence of oxide phase identifications for most of the experiments summarized in Table 5 make it difficult to evaluate the TiO_2 variation in hornblendes from those studies.

Similarly Fe^{+2}/Fe^{+3} variations in hornblende should be affected by the nature of the coexisting oxides. Hematite and pseudobrookite are efficient scavengers of ferric iron, so much so that the absolute ferric iron content of hornblendes synthesized on the HM buffer appears not to be much higher than that in hornblendes synthesized on the FMQ buffer (Spear, 1981; Helz, 1973). It is possible that peak Fe^{+3} contents in hornblende occur at somewhat lower f_{O_2}, where hematite is not stable, as natural igneous hornblendes containing more than 0.3 Fe^{+3} per formula unit are not unknown (see following chapter).

f. Hornblende-liquid relations

Each of the hornblendes considered in this discussion coexisted with a silicate melt at temperature. The melt was quenched, more or less successfully, to a glass at the termination of the experiment. The composition of this glass is of great petrogenetic interest, more so, to many investigators, than the composition of the hornblende and other crystalline phases with which it coexists. Consequently, there are nine analyzed hornblende-glass pairs from granodiorites (Naney, 1977; Sykes, 1979), six from the Mt. Hood andesite (Allen et al., 1975; Allen and Boettcher, 1978), 37 from basalts (Holloway and Burnham, 1972; Helz, 1973, 1976; Cawthorn et al., 1973; Allen and Boettcher, 1978), and two from peridotites (Mysen and Boettcher, 1975b), plus three from Cawthorn's (1976a) CMAS-Na_2O-H_2O system. In addition, Green and Ringwood (1968) present five glass compositions calculated by difference, using modal proportions obtained in an unspecified manner.

This relative abundance of data has not been easy to obtain: it can be difficult to get a good estimate of the composition of the melt present at temperature for an experimental charge. First, the more volatile components in the glass (Na_2O, K_2O, H_2O) tend to evaporate under a focused microprobe beam. The problem becomes more severe as alkali and water contents increase. Significant alkali loss can be avoided by defocusing the beam, if the pools of glass in the charge are large enough (as was done for the PG-1000 and 1921-HM-925 charges of Helz, 1976), or one can calculate alkalies in the glass by difference. The latter method requires (1) that all phases present be analyzed, (2) that the mode be calculated by some least-squares procedure (e.g., that of Wright and Doherty, 1970), and (3) that total alkali content of the vapor phase is negligible. The results of Holloway (1971) suggest that this last assumption is reasonable, at least for basalts.

Calculation of alkalies by difference in this manner has been done in several studies (Holloway and Burnham, 1972; Mysen and Boettcher, 1975b; Helz, 1976). The procedure is fairly straightforward for charges in which (1) the amount of melt exceeds 15 weight percent and (2) there is no more than one phase other than the melt which contains significant alkalies (see Helz, 1976, pp. 183-185).

A second difficulty with glass analyses is that the melt may precipitate some crystalline material during quenching. This problem is particularly severe in peridotites and has been much discussed in interpretation of peridotite melting experiments (see, e.g., Green, 1973; Mysen et al., 1974). In less magnesian compositions, however, quench phase precipitation is easier to recognize, because of the larger contrast in Mg/Fe between, say, stable and quench hornblende (cf. Helz, 1973, Table 8 and Helz, 1976, Table 13a, versus Helz, 1976, Table 12). If quench phases are analyzed, they can be included in the least-squares modal calculations and recombined with the glass to obtain an estimate of melt composition at temperature (see Helz, 1976, pp. 185-191). This method is intrinsically more accurate than trying to calculate liquids by differences, unless the ratio of crystals to liquid is very low. This point has been discussed in some detail by Mysen and Boettcher (1975b).

The petrogenetic significance of the resulting estimated melt compositions has been discussed by almost all of the authors listed in Table 5 and is beyond the scope of this paper. Here we will focus, as in the preceding sections, on distribution of elements between hornblende and coexisting liquid.

The following inequalities hold for all reported analyses or estimates of melt composition:

337

$$Si_{hbl} < Si_{melt} \quad (1\!:\!1.5, \text{ approximately})$$
$$Al_{hbl} < Al_{melt} \quad (1\!:\!1.5, \text{ approximately})$$
$$Fe_{hbl} > Fe_{melt} \quad (1.5\!:\!1 \text{ or more})$$
$$Mg_{hbl} \gg Mg_{melt} \quad (4\!:\!1 \text{ or more})$$
$$Ti_{hbl} > Ti_{melt} \quad (2\!:\!1 \text{ or more})$$

The estimates in parentheses are typical ratios for basaltic to andesitic bulk
compositions at high temperature (900-1050°C). The concentration ratios of
Fe, Mg, and Ti are much higher in the basalts at low temperatures (700-900°C)
and in the granodiorites (750-900°C).

Also, $Ca_{hbl} > Ca_{melt}$ in almost all cases, ranging from 1.1 to 10.0. The
only exception is the hornblende-glass pair reported by Mysen and Boettcher
(1975b) in peridotite D at 1100°C, 15 kbar where $Ca_{hbl}/Ca_{melt} = 0.93$.

Alkali partitioning between hornblende and liquid has been of special concern because hornblende might be a major K- and Na-bearing phase in the upper
mantle, a possibility first broached by Oxburgh (1964). For melts in which
alkalies have been either analyzed using a defocused beam or calculated by
difference, the observed distribution ratios are:

$$Na_{hbl}/Na_{melt} = 0.26\text{--}0.82 \quad (42 \text{ pairs})$$
$$K_{hbl}/K_{melt} = 0.17\text{-}0.68 \quad (41 \text{ pairs})$$

These data are quite consistent, over a fairly broad range of whole-rock compositions. There is no instance of a hornblende containing more Na_2O or K_2O
than the melt it equilibrated with. Apparent exceptions in the literature
(Allen et al., 1975; Allen and Boettcher, 1978) are glasses in which no attempt
was made to restore alkalies lost during analysis.

In some cases, Allen and coworkers have analyzed enough of the silicate
phases present, so that modes can be calculated. The results of these calculations usually indicate that large amounts of Na_2O and lesser amounts of K_2O
are missing from the whole rock compositions. If the amounts missing are assigned to the glass (see Table 7), the resulting alkali distribution ratios
fall within the ranges given above.

Several authors have been interested in the pressure and/or temperature
dependence of the alkali distribution between hornblende and liquid. Nicholls
(1974) and Cawthorn (1976b) both suggested that this exchange might be quite
sensitive to changes in pressure. In analyzing the available data, Helz (1979)
found that the distribution coefficient $K_D = (K/Na)_{hbl}/(K/Na)_{melt}$ increases
markedly as temperature increases. K_D also depends on hornblende composition.
This compositional dependence, which is very complex in detail, appears, to a

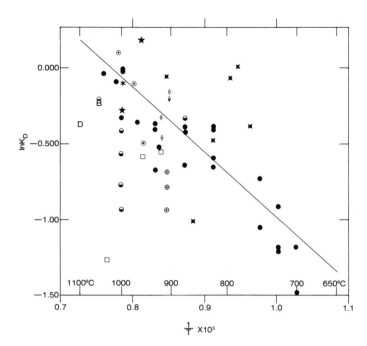

Figure 71. lnK_D [where $K_D \cong (K/Na)_{hbl}/(K/Na)_{melt}$] versus temperature, for coexisting horn-blende-melt pairs from the literature, adapted from Figure 4 in Helz (1979). Solid circles indicate K_D values for all of the hornblende-melt pairs from Helz (1973, 1976). Other symbols as in Figure 63a. The solid line is the best-fit line for the solid circles only.

Table 7. Alkali contents of selected glasses from melting experiments on a Mt. Hood andesite and the 1921 Kilauea basalt.

	1	2		3	4	5	6	7
Reference	Allen et al. (1975)			Allen and Boettcher (1978)				
Rock	Mt. Hood	Mt. Hood		Mt. Hood	Mt. Hood	1921	1921	1921
T(°C)	900	920		920	900	960	980	1010
P(kb)	13	13		13	13	13	18	13
$X_{H_2O}^{fl}$	1.0	1.0		1.0	0.75	1.0	0.75	0.50
Buffer	none	HM		HM	HM	HM	HM	HM
Coexisting	L	L		L	L	L	L	L
phases:	V	V		V	V	V	V	V
	Opx	opaques		opaques	Opx	Cpx	Cpx	Cpx
	Opaques				opaques	opaques	opaques	opaques
Na_2O (probe)[1]	0.8	0.7		0.75	0.70	0.3	3.0	0.9
Na_2O (diff)[2]	5.0	4.7		4.9	5.1	3.0	3.0	3.05
K_2O (probe)	0.8	0.7		0.45	0.58	0.5	1.1	0.9
K_2O (diff)	1.37	1.08		1.27	1.31	0.92	1.1	0.9

[1] "(probe)" indicates Na_2O or K_2O as reported in the microprobe analyses. Usually these values are low because of loss of alkalies under the beam.

[2] "(diff)" indicates the value of Na_2O (or K_2O) in the glass if all the Na_2O (or K_2O) deficiency found when the mode is calculated is assigned to the glass. Note that in some cases (e.g., Col. 6) there is no deficiency.

first-order approximation, to be controlled by the cell volume of the hornblende, with K_D increasing as cell volume increases. Unfortunately, the nature of the data base for the Helz study, twenty-nine hornblende-melt pairs synthesized at 5-8 kbar (Helz, 1973, 1976, 1979), made it impossible to evaluate the effect of pressure on K_D using only those data.

To evaluate the effect of pressure on K_D, Helz (1979) presented K_D data for eleven hornblende-melt pairs from the literature, synthesized at pressures of 5-15 kbar. The higher-pressure pairs did not deviate significantly in K_D from the 5 kbar data (Helz, 1979, Fig. 4). Since then, more hornblende-melt pairs have become available, including three from Naney (1977), five from Allen and Boettcher (1978) and six from Sykes (1979). These are shown in Figure 71. The new data include pairs synthesized at pressures ranging from 2-18 kbar. The expected effect of higher pressure would be to raise K_D, all other things being equal. Nothing of the sort is observed, as can best be seen in the data from the 1921 Kilauea basalt, in which hornblende-melt pairs from pressures as high as 18 kbar do not deviate significantly from the 5 kbar data for the same rock. There is no evidence for a pressure effect of the size postulated by Nicholls (1974) and by Cawthorn (1976b). However, without any cell volume data for hornblendes from andesite and granodiorite compositions, it is still not clear whether this exchange can be calibrated for use as a geothermometer in the bulk compositional range of greatest interest.

Experimental data for the partitioning of minor and trace elements between hornblende and melt are sparse. $Mn_{hbl}/Mn_{melt} = 1.2-2.0$ for eleven pairs from basalts. No other data are available, for other elements or in other rock compositions. The only other information available is that of Mysen (1978a,b), who reports the following partitioning data for amphibole (pargasite)/liquid in a complex synthetic system:

$$Ni_{hbl}/Ni_{melt} = 1.40-3.0$$
$$Ce_{hbl}/Ce_{melt} = 0.04-0.4$$
$$Sm_{hbl}/Sm_{melt} = 0.08-0.8$$
$$Tm_{hbl}/Tm_{melt} = 0.08-0.1$$

The large ranges in concentration ratios correlate with changes in melt composition, with ratios increasing as the melt becomes more siliceous.

Bulk compositional controls on amphiboles

In this section we will consider the extent to which variations in bulk compositional parameters other than water content and f_{O_2} may control the occurrence and composition of amphibole in rock melting experiments. The available experimental work contributes chiefly to our knowledge of the occurrence and composition of hornblende, as other amphiboles (riebeckite, cummingtonite) are rare or absent in experiments reported to date. It is not obvious that this lack is solely because the appropriate bulk compositions have yet to be studied: experimental difficulties (faulty f_{O_2} control, inadequate phase characterization) may also be contributing factors.

The ways in which hornblende composition is controlled by bulk composition are usually straightforward. Mg/Fe in hornblende, for example, increases as Mg/Fe in the bulk rock increases, in all cases. K/Na in hornblende is somewhat dependent on K/Na in the rock. Total alkali content of amphibole correlates roughly with total alkali content of the rock, at least for basalts (Helz, 1973; see also Fig. 63a,b). TiO_2 content of amphibole correlates with bulk TiO_2 content, especially in assemblages where no Fe-Ti oxide phases are present (see Fig. 65). On the other hand, variations in SiO_2, Al_2O_3, CaO, and the sum MgO + FeO appear not to be closely controlled by changes in rock compositions. For example, SiO_2 contents of hornblendes synthesized in the quartz-normative Picture Gorge basalt are very similar to SiO_2 contents of hornblendes produced in the nepheline-normative Hualalai basalt (Helz, 1973).

The bulk compositional limitations on the occurrence of hornblende are more difficult to quantify. It has been observed widely that, in the calc-alkalic rock series, hornblende occurs only in a certain intermediate range of rock compositions, an observation formalized in Bowen's (1928) "discontinuous reaction series." In this model Bowen indicated that pyroxene is normally replaced by hornblende, which is succeeded by biotite, as rock composition otherwise becomes more differentiated. The rock compositions investigated to date illustrate both ends of this range. At low pressures (<5 kbar), the andesites (Fig. 55) contain opx ± cpx and crystallize amphibole only at temperatures well below their liquidi. Tonalites and quartz diorites (Figs. 54 and 55) have hornblende as the first phase on the liquidus and crystallize no pyroxene. Bulk compositional differences are subtle (see Table 3), but the H_2O-saturated phase relations make it clear that there is, at constant $X_{H_2O}^{fl}$, a point where pyroxene reacts out, and pyroxene is completely absent in more differentiated rocks.

It is equally clear from the water-saturated melting relations of the granitoid rocks studied to date (Figs. 53 and 54) that hornblende eventually is replaced by biotite as the dominant mafic phase. In the more mafic granitoids, hornblende is the liquidus phase except at pressures below 2 kbar, where plagioclase is the first phase to crystallize. Biotite is almost always present

341

in the crystallization sequence, but it comes in at much lower temperatures.
In the most differentiated calc-alkalic rocks investigated, hornblende is
reported only in the two quartz monzonites. The other six rocks, quartz monzonite or granite, contain biotite as the only mafic silicate at $P_{H_2O} = P_{total}$,
as discussed earlier in this section.

The phase relations of these rocks agree well with the predictions implicit in Bowen's discontinuous reaction series. The question of interest here
is, why? What is missing from the granites which is necessary to the crystallization of hornblende?

The answer may be found in considering the results of Naney (1977) on the
synthetic granite system. In that study, Naney worked out the phase relations
of a synthetic granite and a synthetic granodiorite, made by adding 10 percent
anhydrous biotite to appropriate compositions in the Ab-An-Or-Qz system. The
compositions differ in CaO, Na_2O, and K_2O, at constant MgO and FeO (see Table
1, p. 641, Naney and Swanson, 1980), a situation not often found in natural
rock series. The "granite" crystallizes no hornblende. The granodiorite crystallizes some hornblende above the solidus, but it reacts out as the solidus
is crossed. The subsolidus assemblage in both compositions is plagioclase +
alkali feldspar + quartz + biotite ± epidote + vapor, an assemblage which fits
almost exactly the bulk compositional constraints imposed by the nature of the
starting mixes.

The presence of hornblende in the "granodiorite" in its melting range
must be the effect of higher CaO and Na_2O/K_2O in that bulk composition relative to the "granite." Its presence further implies that the melt has moved
off the feldspar compositional plane into corundum-normative space, as the
hornblende must be at least somewhat diopside-normative (see hornblende norms
in Helz, 1973, Table 11; Allen et al., 1973, Table 6c; Allen and Boettcher,
1978, Table 5c). This situation cannot persist below the solidus, of course:
as the solidus is approached, the feldspars continue to crystallize and hornblende reacts out completely.[6] As mentioned earlier, natural granodiorites do
not behave this way. Evidently their bulk compositions must include the excess

- - - - - - - - - -

[6]This contrasts with the situation in basalts, in which hornblende also coexists with corundum-normative liquid (Helz, 1976). In basalts the normative
corundum in the liquid is "resorbed" by a slight decrease in the amount of
hornblende and minor changes in hornblende composition, as the solidus is
crossed (see Helz, 1973, Table 9 and discussion on p. 298 ff). As a result,
no aluminous phases other than feldspars and hornblende appear in the subsolidus assemblage, even though the liquids present just above the solidus are
markedly peraluminous.

Ca and Na beyond that required for feldspar, necessary to stabilize hornblende in the subsolidus region as well as in the melting range.

In Bowen's reaction series, the most mafic rocks in a magma series should contain olivines and pyroxenes, not hornblende. It is evident, from the very large AMPH + L fields observed in H_2O-saturated experiments on basalts, pyroxenites, and even some peridotites, that the absence of hornblende in many of these rocks in nature reflects low water activity, rather than inappropriate condensed bulk composition. On the other hand, a total lack of Al_2O_3, CaO, or Na_2O, as in a dunite, effectively precludes hornblende, even at $P_{H_2O} = P_{total}$. So the question remains, what is the minimum level of these three components necessary to stabilize hornblende in the presence of a liquid? Cawthorn (1976a) investigated the role of varying Na_2O and found, in the system $CaO-MgO-Al_2O_3-SiO_2$ (CMAS)$-Na_2O-H_2O$, that amphibole occurred in equilibrium with a liquid only where the liquid contained 3 percent Na_2O or more. It is not entirely obvious how to apply this limitation to rocks containing K_2O as well as Na_2O. There are a few cases of hornblende coexisting with liquids containing 2.4-2.9 percent Na_2O (Holloway and Burnham, 1972; Helz, 1976; Mysen and Boettcher, 1975b). However, there is no instance of a hornblende coexisting with a melt in which total alkalies ($Na_2O + K_2O$) were less than 3 percent. This suggests that the condition delineated by Cawthorn does not require Na_2O per se: K_2O appears to perform the same structural role in the liquid, and, to a lesser extent, in hornblende.

Melting reactions for hornblende

The logical end of an experimental study of the phase relations of hornblende would be to present one or more reactions describing those relations quantitatively. Possibilities include (1) the reactions which occur as hornblende reacts out completely as temperature increases; (2) reactions which occur within AMPH + L, as hornblende undergoes partial melting; and (3) reactions between hornblende and liquid to produce, for example, biotite + feldspar, as temperature decreases.

Reactions describing the incongruent melting of hornblende, in which hornblende melts completely (type 1) are the most easily investigated. These are all variations of the pargasite melting reaction, described by Boyd (1959) as:

$$Pa \rightleftarrows Di + Fo + Sp + L + V \qquad (10)$$

at pressures of 700-1300 bars. Holloway (1973) modified this slightly to

$$Pa \rightleftarrows Di + Fo + Sp \pm Ne + L + V \qquad (11)$$

at pressures of 1-8 kbar, $X_{H_2O}^{fl} = 1.0-0.3$. He noted that the nepheline melts

343

out at temperatures only slightly higher than pargasite-in, so that with slightly broader temperature brackets, the reaction would appear to be that given by Boyd. More important, Holloway remarked that the stoichiometry of the reaction varied as pressure and $X_{H_2O}^{fl}$ changed, so that no single set of numerical coefficients could describe the melting of pargasite.

Melting reactions along hornblende-in curves in rocks are similar to that of pargasite, with this exception: that augite, olivine, spinel, etc. can appear as crystalline products only if they are otherwise stable in that bulk composition at those conditions of P, T, etc. Nepheline has never been reported, as a product, for example, even in the nephelinite (Allen et al., 1975), while aluminous spinel appears only in some of the peridotites (e.g., Mysen and Boettcher, 1975a). Also, the reactions have at least two degrees of freedom.

There are only two instances in the literature where the stoichiometry of the hornblende melting reaction has been determined. The first reaction is that of Holloway and Burnham (1972), describing the change in assemblage between 999°C, 5 kbar and 1051°C, 5 kbar in the 1921 Kilauea olivine tholeiite, at $X_{H_2O}^{fl}$ = 0.6:

$$54 \text{ Hbl} \rightarrow 11 \text{ Cpx} + 42 \text{ Liquid.} \tag{12a}$$

Renormalized to 100 grams of hornblende, this becomes approximately

$$100 \text{ Hbl} \rightarrow 23 \text{ Cpx} + 77 \text{ Liquid,} \tag{12b}$$

the reaction given by Holloway and Burnham (1972, p. 21). Two features of this reaction should be noted: first, the coefficients are weight fractions, not molecular fractions, and second, it describes the *net* change in assemblage over a temperature range of 50°C. It does not describe the stoichiometry of the melting of hornblende exactly at the hornblende-in curve.

Equation (12b) has been widely cited and used in calculations as though it were *the* melting reaction for hornblende in basalts. Unfortunately, this is not so. The only other hornblende melting reaction which has been quantified is for the same 1921 basalt, at the same pressure, and its stoichiometry is very different.

This second reaction describes the change in assemblage between 925°C, 5 kbar and 1000°C, 5 kbar, $X_{H_2O}^{fl} \cong 1.0$, on the HM buffer (Helz, 1973, 1976):

$$49.8 \text{ Hbl} \rightarrow 27.0 \text{ Cpx} + 1.8 \text{ Ol} + 2.0 \text{ Fe-Ti oxides} + 19.1 \text{ Liquid} \tag{13a}$$

Renormalized to 100 grams of hornblende, this becomes:

$$100 \text{ Hbl} \rightarrow 54.2 \text{ Cpx} + 3.61 \text{ Ol} + 4.0 \text{ Fe-Ti oxides} + 38.4 \text{ Liquid} \tag{13b}$$

344

The ratio of clinopyroxene to liquid produced is grossly different in the two cases.

Of the parameters which differ between the two (T, ΔT, f_{O_2}, $X^{fl}_{H_2O}$) the most critical, apparently, is absolute temperature. The temperature interval (ΔT) is wider for reaction (13b) than for (12b), 75°C versus 50°C, so one might expect to see more liquid produced in reaction (13b). Similarly, one might expect more liquid to be produced at higher $X^{fl}_{H_2O}$. Both of these effects are overridden by the difference in absolute temperature: on the HM buffer, hornblende breaks down at much lower temperatures (50-70°C lower) than on the NNO buffer. The amount of melt present at 1000°C, even above hornblende-in, is necessarily less than the amount present in the same basalt at 1050°C. So when hornblende reacts out at 970°C instead of 1025 ± 25°C, a larger fraction of its substance must appear as crystalline phases, clinopyroxene + olivine + hematite in the present instance.

Other melting reactions for hornblende can be described only qualitatively, from the reported P-T relations. The general reaction appears to be

$$Hbl \rightarrow Liquid \pm Cpx \pm Opx \pm Ol \pm Plag \pm Spinel \pm Garnet \pm \text{Fe-Ti oxides} \quad (14)$$

In the granitoid rocks, the only crystalline phases which persist above hornblende-in are plagioclase (at $P_{H_2O} = P_{total} < 2$ kbar) and, perhaps, Fe-Ti oxides. In andesites, clinopyroxene, orthopyroxene, and plagioclase persist above hornblende-in at low pressures (P < 5 kbar). At higher pressures in andesites, as in the granitoid rocks, hornblende is the first phase on the liquidus where $X^{fl}_{H_2O} = 1.0$. This does not mean that the hornblende melts congruently, however: it is dissolving in a liquid the bulk composition of which is very different from hornblende.

In basalts, the crystalline phases produced by incongruent melting of hornblende are clinopyroxene and/or olivine and Fe-Ti oxides. This much is true for all basalts studied, not just the 1921 Kilauea basalt. As is obvious from the earlier discussion, however, the stoichiometry of the reaction is very variable. As the high-pressure limit of AMPH-IN is crossed, hornblende is replaced by garnet + clinopyroxene ± olivine. The absence of mica in the reported assemblages (Allen et al., 1975; Allen and Boettcher, 1978) implies that the melt must become more alkali-rich as amphibole reacts out, even when the amount of melt present is constant.

In the ultramafic compositions of Figure 58 (kaersutite, hornblendite, pyroxenite), the phases produced by the melting of hornblende include clinopyroxene ± olivine ± garnet ± phlogopite. Olivine is produced at lower pressures, garnet at higher pressures with trace amounts of phlogopite reported throughout the pressure range investigated (Merrill and Wyllie, 1975). In some compositions hornblende-in coincides with the liquidus at lower pressures (<15 kbar, Millhollen and Wyllie, 1974). Only in the peridotites is it impossible to discern the melting reaction of hornblende by inspection. In these compositions ol + opx + cpx are present throughout the range studied (Mysen and Boettcher, 1975a, Fig. 1). As no modal data are presented, we cannot tell whether any of these phases increases in amount as hornblende-in is crossed.

The other types of reactions mentioned initially have been little studied. The only detailed work on melting reactions of hornblende within AMPH + L is that of Helz (1973, 1976). There are several noteworthy results of that study. First, in two olivine-normative basalt compositions, the amount of hornblende passes through a maximum at some intermediate point in the melting range, as hornblende reacts out partially, to Fe-Ti oxides + plagioclase, as the solidus is approached. Second, hornblende begins to melt at temperatures of 875°C or so, long before the hornblende-in curve (at 1010-1050°C) is reached, so that the incongruent melting of hornblende takes place over a range of 135-175°C in all basalts studied. Third, the stoichiometry of these reactions is as variable as that of hornblende melting reactions.

There have been no formal studies made of the process by which hornblende reacts with liquid to produce biotite plus feldspar in granitic compositions. That reaction can be inferred to occur in Naney's "granodiorite" (see above discussion); also, Gibbon and Wyllie (1969) mention a reaction relation between hornblende and biotite in two of their compositions. But with those exceptions, this reaction, a conspicuous part of Bowen's discontinuous reaction series, is still known to us almost exclusively from observation of natural assemblages.

Acknowledgments

I (RTH) thank Dr. J. R. Holloway of Arizona State University, for allowing me access to a variety of run materials and unpublished data of his, and for calling my attention to the existence of Sykes' work. I also thank M.T. Naney and M.L. Sykes for permission to use figures from their theses. With those exceptions, however, this review has been compiled from the published record only. I have attempted a reasonably thorough review of the English literature. However, coverage of articles in other western European languages is sketchy, and I have made no attempt to review the Russian, Japanese, or Chinese literature. There are instances in which something appears peculiar about one or another experimental study or analysis. In several cases, I have ventured a guess as to what the problem might be. These guesses should not be taken as definitive by the reader. It is impossible, without examining the actual run material and/or repeating the experiment to determine what, if anything, went wrong. Lastly, and this should go without saying, the author is solely responsible for the contents of this section.

Akella, J., and Winkler, H. G. F. (1966) Orthorhombic amphibole in some metamorphic reactions. Contrib. Mineral. Petrol. 12, 1-12.

Allen, J. C., Boettcher, A. L., and Marland, G. (1975) Amphiboles in andesite and basalt: I. Stability as a function of $P-T-f_{O_2}$. Am. Mineral. 60, 1069-1085.

_____ and Boettcher, A. L. (1978) Amphiboles in andesite and basalt: II. Stability as a function of $P-T-f(H_2O)-fO_2$. Am. Mineral. 63, 1074-1087.

Binns, R. A. (1968) Hydrothermal investigations of the amphibolite-granulite facies boundary. Aust. Geol. Soc. Spec. Pub. 2, 341-344.

Bonnichsen, B. (1969) Metamorphic pyroxenes and amphiboles in the Biwabik iron formation, Dunka River area, Minnesota. Mineral. Soc. Am. Spec. Paper 2, 217-239.

_____ (1975) Geology of the Biwabik iron formation, Dunka River area, Minnesota. Econ. Geol. 70, 314-346.

Bowen, N. L. (1928) *The Evolution of the Igneous Rocks*. Princeton Univ. Press, Princeton, N.J.

_____ and Schairer, J. F. (1935) Grunerite from Rockport, Massachusetts, and a series of synthetic fluor-amphiboles: Am. Mineral. Year Book 47, 75-82.

Boyd, F. R. (1954) Amphiboles. Carnegie Inst. Wash. Year Book 53, 108-111.

_____ (1959) Hydrothermal investigations of the amphiboles. In *Researches in Geochemistry*. P. H. Ableson, ed., John Wiley and Sons, New York, 377-396.

_____ and England, J. L. (1960) Apparatus for phase-equilibrium to pressures up to 50 kilobars and temperatures up to 1750°C. J. Geophys. Res. 65, 741-748.

Butler, P. (1969) Mineral compositions and equilibria in the metamorphosed iron formation of the Gagnon region, Quebec, Canada. J. Petrol. 10, 56-101.

Cameron, K. L. (1971) *An experimental study of coexisting amphiboles: Phase relations along the join* $Mg_{3.5}Fe_{3.5}Si_8O_{22}(OH)_2-Ca_2Mg_{2.5}Fe_{2.5}Si_8O_{22}(OH)_2$. Ph.D. thesis, Virginia Polytechnic Institute and State University, Blacksburg, Virginia, 78 pp.

_____ (1975) An experimental study of actinolite-cummingtonite phase relations with notes on the synthesis of Fe-rich anthophyllite. Am. Mineral. 60, 375-391.

Carman, J. H. (1969) The study of the system $NaAlSiO_4-Mg_2SiO_4-SiO_2-H_2O$ from 200 to 5000 bars and 800°C to 1100°C and its petrologic applications. Ph.D. thesis, The Pennsylvania State University.

_____ (1974a) Preliminary data on the P-T stability of synthetic glaucophane. (Abstr.) EOS, 55, 481.

_____ (1974b) Synthetic sodium phlogopite and its two hydrates: stabilities, properties, and mineralogic implications. Am. Mineral. 59, 261-273.

Cawthorn, R. G. (1976a) Melting relations in part of the system $CaO-MgO-Al_2O_3-SiO_2-Na_2O-H_2O$ under 5 kb pressure. J. Petrol. 17, 44-72.

_____ (1976b) Some controls on igneous amphibole composition. Geochim. Cosmochim. Acta 40, 1319-1328.

_____ Curran, E. B., and Arculus, R. J. (1973) A petrogenetic model for the origin of the calc-alkalic suite of Grenada, Lesser Antilles. J. Petrol. 14, 327-338.

Charles, R. W. (1975) The phase equilibria of richterite and ferrorichterite. Am. Mineral. 60, 367-374.

_____ (1977) The phase equilibria of intermediate compositions on the pseudobinary $Na_2CaMg_5Si_8O_{22}(OH)_2 - Na_2CaFe_5Si_8O_{22}(OH)_2$. Am. J. Sci. 277, 594-625.

_____ (1980) Amphiboles on the join pargasite-ferropargasite. Am. Mineral. 65, 996-1001.

Chernosky, J. V., Jr. (1976) The stability field of anthophyllite -- A reevaluation based on new experimental data. Am. Mineral. 61, 1145-1155.

_____ and Autio, L. K. (1979) The stability of anthophyllite in the presence of quartz. Am. Mineral. 64, 294-303.

Choudhuri, A. and Winkler, H. G. F. (1967) Anthophyllit und Hornblende in einigen metamorphen Reaktionen. Contrib. Mineral. Petrol. 14, 367-374.

Colville, P. A., Ernst, W. G., and Gilbert, M. C. (1966) Relations between cell parameters and chemical compositions of monoclinic amphiboles. Am. Mineral. 51, 1727-1754.

Comeforo, J. E. and Kohn, J. A. (1954) Synthetic asbestos investigations. I. Study of synthetic fluor-tremolite. Am. Mineral. 39, 537-548.

Day, H. W. and Halbach, H. (1979) The stability field of anthophyllite: The effect of experimental uncertainty on permissible phase diagram topologies. Am. Mineral. 64, 809-823.

Dickey, J. S., Jr. (1968) Eclogitic and other inclusions in The Mineral Breccia Member of the Deborah Volcanic Formation, Kakanui, New Zealand. Am. Mineral. 53, 1304-1319.

Eggler, D. H. (1972a) Amphibole stability in H_2O - undersaturated calc-alkaline melts. Earth Planet. Sci. Lett. 15, 28-34.

_____ (1972b) Water - saturated and undersaturated melting relations in a Paricutin andesite and an estimate of water content in the natural magma. Contrib. Mineral. Petrol. 34, 261-271.

_____ (1973) Principles of melting of hydrous phases in silicate melt. Carnegie Institution, Washington Year Book 72, 491-495.

_____ and Burnham, C. W. (1973) Crystallization and fractionation trends in the system andesite - H_2O - CO_2 - O_2 at pressures to 10 kb. Geol. Soc. Amer. Bull. 84, 2517-2532.

Ernst, W. G. (1960) Stability relations of magnesioriebeckite. Geochim. Cosmochim. Acta 19, 10-40.

_____ (1961) The stability relations of glaucophane. Am. J. Sci. 259, 735-765.

_____ (1962) Synthesis, stability relations, and occurrence of riebeckite and riebeckite-arfvedsonite solid solutions. J. Geol. 70, 689-736.

_____ (1963) Polymorphism in alkali amphiboles. Am. Mineral. 48, 241-260.

_____ (1966) Synthesis and stability relations of ferrotremolite. Am. J. Sci. 264, 37-65.

_____ (1968) *Amphiboles*. Springer-Verlag, New York, 125 pp.

Essene, E. J., Hensen, B. J., and Green, D. H. (1970) Experimental study of amphibolite and eclogite stability. Phys. Earth Planet. Inter. 3, 378-384.

Eugster, H. P. (1957) Heterogeneous reactions involving oxidation and reduction at high pressures and temperatures. J. Chem. Phys. 26, 1760-1761.

_____ (1969) Inorganic bedded cherts from the Magadi area, Kenya. Contrib. Mineral. Petrol. 22, 1-31.

_____ and Wones, D. R. (1962) Stability relations of the ferruginous biotite, annite. J. Petrol. 3, 82-125.

Ewart, A., Green, C. D., Carmichael, I. S. E., and Brown, F. H. (1971) Voluminous low temperature rhyolitic magmas in New Zealand. Contrib. Mineral. Petrol. 33, 128-144.

Fonarev, V. I. and Korolkov, G. Ya. (1980) The assemblage orthopyroxene + cummingtonite + quartz. The low-temperature stability limit. Contrib. Mineral. Petrol. 73, 413-420.

_____, _____, and Dokina, T. N. (1976) Stability of the cummingtonite-quartz-magnetite association. Geochim. Int'l 15, 34-35.

_____, _____, and _____ (1977a) Stability fields in the assemblage cummingtonite-olivine-quartz from experimental evidence. Geochem. Int'l 16, 21-32.

_____, _____, and _____ (1977b) Experimental study in the assemblage orthopyroxene-olivine-quartz. In *Problems of Physio-chemical Petrology,* Vol. 1, Nauka, Moscow, 159-171.

_____, _____, and _____ (1977c) Experimental study of the assemblage cummingtonite + magnetite + quartz, $P_T = PH_2O = 1000$ kg/cm^2, NNO buffer. In *Contrib. to Physiochem. Petrol.,* Vol. VI, Nauka, Moscow, 224-235.

Forbes, W. C. (1971a) Synthesis of grunerite, $Fe_7Si_8O_{22}(OH)_2$. Nature 232, 109.

_____ (1971b) Synthesis and stability relations of richterite. Am. Mineral. 56, 997-1004.

_____ (1977) Stability relations of grunerite, $Fe_7Si_8O_{22}(OH)_2$. Am. J. Sci. 277, 735-749.

Flashen, S. S. and Osborn, E. F. (1957) Studies in the system iron oxide-silica-water at low oxygen partial pressures. Econ. Geol. 52, 923-943.

Fyfe, W. S. (1962) On the relative stability of talc, anthophyllite, and enstatite. Am. J. Sci. 260, 460-466.

Gibbon, D. L. and Wyllie, P. J. (1969) Experimental studies of ingenous rock series: The Farrington Complex, North Carolina and the Star Mountain rhyolite, Texas. J. Geol. 77, 221-239.

Gibbs, G. V., Miller, J. L. and Shell, H. R. (1962) Synthetic fluor-magnesiorichterite. Am. Mineral. 20, 543-551.

Gilbert, M. C. (1966) Synthesis and stability relations of the hornblende ferropargasite. Am. J. Sci. 264, 698-742.

_____ (1969) Reconnaissance study of the stability of amphiboles at high pressure. Carnegie Inst. Wash. Year Book 67, 167-170.

_____ and Popp, R. K. (1973) Properties and stability of glaucophane at high pressure. Trans. Amer. Geophys. Union 54, 1223.

_____ and Briggs, D. F. (1974) Comparison of the stabilities of OH- and F-potassic richterites --a preliminary report (abstr.) EOS 55, 480-481.

_____ and Troll, G. (1974) A comparison of the stabilities of OH- and F-tremolite. Int'l. Mineral. Assoc. 9th General Meeting, Berlin and Regensburg, Germany, Collected Abstracts, 84.

Goldman, D. S. and Rossman, G. R. (1977) The identification of Fe^{2+} in the M(4) site of calcic amphiboles. Am. Mineral. 62, 205-216.

Goldman, D. S. and Rossman, G. R. (1977) The identification of Fe^{2+} in the M(4) site of calcic amphiboles. Am. Mineral. 62, 205-216.

Green, D. H. (1973) Experimental melting studies on a model upper mantle composition at high pressure under water-saturated and water-unsaturated conditions. Earth Planet. Sci. Lett. 19, 37-53.

_____ (1972) Crystallization of calc-alkaline andesite under controlled high-pressure conditions. Contrib. Mineral. Petrol. 34, 150-166.

_____ and Ringwood, A. E. (1967) An experimental investigation of the gabbro to eclogite transformation and it spetrological implications. Geochim. Cosmochim. Acta 31, 767-834.

_____ and _____ (1968) Genesis of the calc-alkaline igneous rock suite. Contrib. Mineral. Petrol. 18, 105-162.

Greenwood, H. J. (1963) The synthesis and stability of anthophyllite. J. Petrol. 4, 317-351.

_____ (1971) Anthophyllite. Corrections and comments on its stability. Am. J. Sci. 270, 151-154.

_____ (1979) Thermodynamic properties of edenite. In *Current Research*, Part B, Canada Geol. Survey Paper 79-1B, 363-370.

Griggs, D. T. and Kennedy, G. C. (1956) A simple apparatus for high pressures and temperatures. Am. J. Sci. 254, 722-735.

Grigoriev, D. P., and Iskuld, E. W. (1937) The regeneration of amphiboles from the melts at normal pressure. Am. Mineral. 22, 169-177.

Hariya, Y. and Terada, S. (1973) Stability of richterite$_{50}$-tremolite$_{50}$ solid solution at high pressures and possible presence of sodium calcic amphibole under upper mantle conditions. Earth and Planet. Sci. Lett. 18, 72-76.

Hellner, E. and Schurmann, K. (1966) Stability of metamorphic amphboles: the tremolite-ferroactinolite series. J. Geol. 74, 322-331.

Helz, R. T. (1973) Phase relations of basalts in their melting range at P_{H_2O} = 5 kb as a function of oxygen fugacity. Part I. Mafic phases. J. Petrol. 14, 249-302.

_____ (1976) Phase relations of basalts in their melting ranges at $P(H_2O)$ = 5 kb. Part II. Melt compositions. J. Petrol. 17, 139-193.

_____ (1979) Alkali exchange between hornblende and melt: a temperature-sensitive reaction. Am. Mineral. 64, 953-965.

Hemley, J. J., Montaya, J. W., Christ, C. L. and Hostetler, P. B. (1977) Mineral equilibria in the $MgO-SiO_2-H_2O$ system: I. Talc-chrysotile-forsterite-brucite stability relations. Am. J. Sci. 277, 322-351.

_____, _____, Shaw, D. R., and Luce, R. W. (1977) Mineral equilibria in the $MgO-SiO_2-H_2O$ system: II. Talc-antigorite-forsterite-anthophyllite-enstatite stability relations and some geological implications in the system. Am. J. Sci. 277, 253-383.

Hill, R. E. T. and Boettcher, A. L. (1970) Water in the Earth's mantle: melting curves of basalt-water and basalt-water-carbon dioxide. Science 167, 980-982.

Himmelberg, G. R. and Phinney, W. C. (1967) Granulite facies metamorphism. Granite Falls-Montevideo area, Minnesota. J. Petrol. 8, 325-348.

Hinrichsen, Th. J. (1967) Über den Stabilitatsbereich der $Mg-Fe^{2+}-Al$ Mischkristallreihe rombisher Hornblenden. Teil I: Hydrot Hydrothermole Untersuchungen der Anthophyllit-Ferroanthophyllit Mischkristallreihe. N. Jahrb. Mineral. Monatsch., 257-270.

_____ (1968) Hydrothermal investigations and stability relations of synthetic gedrites. Int'l Mineral. Assoc. Papers Proc. 5th General Meeting, Cambridge, England 1966, 243-258.

Hoffman, C. (1972) Natural and synthetic ferroglaucophane. Contrib. Mineral. Petrol. 34, 135-139.

Holloway, J. R. (1970) *Phase relations and compositions in the basalt CO_2-H_2O system at high temperatures and pressures*. Ph.D. thesis, The Pennsylvania State University, University Park, Pennsylvania.

_____ (1971) Composition of fluid phase solutes in a basalt H_2O-CO_2 system. Geol. Soc. Am. Bull. 82, 233-238.

_____ (1973) The system pargasite-H_2O-CO_2: a model for melting of a hydrous mineral with a mixed-volatile fluid - I. Experimental results to 8 kbar. Geochim. Cosmochim. Acta 37, 651-666.

_____ and Burnham, C. W. (1972) Melting relations of basalt with equilibrium water pressure less than total pressure. J. Petrology 13, 1-29.

_____, _____ and Millhollen, G. (1968) Generation of H_2O-CO_2 mixtures for use in hydrothermal experimentation. J. Geophys. Res. 73, 6598-6600.

_____ and Ford, C. E. (1975) Fluid absent melting of the fluorohydroxy-amphibole pargasite to 35 kilobars. Earth Planet. Sci. Lett. 25, 44-48

_____ and Reese, R. L. (1974) The generation of $N_2CO_2-H_2O$ fluids for use in hydrothermal experimentation: I. Experimental method and equilibrium calculations in the C-O-H-N system. Am. Mineral. 59,587-597.

Huebner, J. S. (1971) Buffering techniques for hydrostatic systems at elevated pressures. In *Research Techniques for High Pressure and High Temperature*, G. C. Ulmer, Ed., Springer-Verlag, New York, 123-177.

_____ and Papike, J. J. (1970) Synthesis and crystal chemistry of sodium potassium richterite $(Na,K)NaCaMg_5Si_8O_{22}(OH)_2$: a model for amphiboles. Am. Mineral. 55, 1973-1992.

Hytönen, K. (1968) A preliminary report on an iron-rich formation near Raahe in the Gulf of Bothnia. Finland Geol. Soc. Bull. 40, 135-144.

James, R. S., Turnock, A. C., and Fawcett, J. J. (1976) The stability and phase relations of iron chlorite below 8.5 kb P_{H_2O}. Contrib. Mineral. Petrol. 56, 1-25.

Jasmund, K. and Shafer, R. (1972) Experimentalle bestimmung der P-T stabilutatsbereiche in der mischkistallreihe tremolittschermakite. Contrib. Mineral. Petrol. 34, 101-115.

Killinc, I. A. (1969) *Experimental metamorphism and anatexis of shales and graywackes*. Ph.D. thesis, The Pennsylvania State University, University Park, Pennsylvania.

Klein, C. (1968) Coexisting amphiboles. J. Petrol. 9, 281-330.

Kohn, J. A. and Comeforo, J. E. (1955) Synthetic asbestos investigations. II. X-ray and other data on synthetic fluor-richterite, -edenite, and -boron edenite. Am. Mineral. 40, 410-421.

Kushiro, I. (1970) Stability of amphibole and phlogopite in the upper mantle. Carnegie Inst. Wash. Year Book 68, 245-247.

_____ and Erlank, A. J. (1970) Stability of potassic richterite. Carnegie Inst. Wash. Year Book 68, 231-233.

_____, Syono, Y. and Akimoto, S. (1968) Melting of a peridotite nodule at high pressures and high water pressures. J. Geophys. Res. 73, 6023-6029.

Lambert, I. B. and Wyllie, P. J. (1968) Stability of hornblende and a model for the low velocity zone. Nature 219, 1240-1241.

_____ and _____ (1970) Melting in the deep crust and the nature of the low velocity layer. Phys. Earth Planet. Interiors 3, 316-322.

_____ and _____ (1972) Melting of gabbro (quartz eclogite) with excess water to 35 kilobars, with geological applications. J. Geol. 80, 693-708.

_____ and _____ (1974) Melting of tonalite and crystallization of andesite liquid with excess water to 30 kilobars. J. Geol. 82, 88-97.

Lindsley, D. H. and Rumble, D., III (1977) Magnetite-ilmenite geothermometer-oxybarometer: An evaluation of old and new data. EOS 58, 519.

Liou, J. G., Kuniyoshi, S., and Ito, K. (1974) Experimental studies of the phase relations between greenschist and amphibolite in a basaltic system. Am. J. Sci. 274, 613-632.

Maresch, W. V. (1973) New data on the snythesis and stability relations of glaucophane. Earth Planet. Sci. Lett. 20, 385-390.

_____ (1977) Experimental studies of glaucophane: an analysis of present knowledge. Tectonophysics 43, 109-125.

Mason, B. (1968) Kaersutite from San Carlos, Arizona, with comments on the paragenesis of this mineral. Mineral. Mag. 36, 997-1002.

McDowell, S. D. and Wyllie, P. J. (1971) Experimental studies of igneous rock series: The Kungnat syenite complex of southwest Greenland. J. Geo. 79, 173-194.

Merrill, R. B. and Wyllie, P. J. (1975) Kaersutite and kaersutite eclogite from Kakanui, New Zealand - Water-excess and water-deficient melting to 30 kilobars. Geol. Soc. Amer. Bull. 86, 555-570.

Millhollen, G. L. (1970) *Melting and phase relations in nepheline syenites with H_2O and CO_2*. Ph.D. thesis. The Pennsylvania State University, University Park, Pennsylvania.

_____ and Wyllie, P. J. (1974) Melting relations of brown-hornblende mylonite from St. Paul's rocks under water-saturated and water-understaturated conditions to 30 kilobars. J. Geol. 82, 589-606.

_____, Irving, A. J. and Wyllie, P. J. (1974) Melting interval of peridotite with 5.7 percent water to 30 kilobars. J. Geol. 82, 575-587.

Mysen, B. O. (1978a) Experimental determination of nickel partition coefficients between liquid, pargasite, and garnet peridotite minerals and concentration limits of behavior according to Henry's law at high pressure and temperature. Am. J. Sci. 278, 217-243.

_____ (1978b) Experimental determination of rare earth element partitioning between hydrous silicate melt, amphibole and garnet peridotite minerals at upper mantle pressures and temperatures. Geochim. Cosmochim. Acta 42, 1253-1263.

_____ and Boettcher, A. L. (1975a) Melting of a hydrous mantle: I. Phase relations of a natural peridotite at high pressures and temperatures with controlled activities of water, carbon dioxide, and hydrogen. J. Petrol. 16, 520-548.

_____ and _____ (1975b) Melting of a hydrous mantle: II. Geochemistry of crystals and liquids formed by anatexis of mantle peridotite at high pressures and high temperatures as a function of controlled activities of water, hydrogen and carbon dioxide. J. Petrol. 16, 549-593.

_____ and _____ (1976) Melting of a hydrous mantle: III. Phase relations of garnet websterite + H_2O at high pressures and temperatures. J. Petrol. 17, 1-14.

_____, Kushiro, I., Nicholls, A., and Ringwood, A. E. (1974) A possible mantle origin for andesitic magmas: discussion of a paper by Nicholls and Ringwood. Earth Planet. Sci. Lett. 21, 221-229.

Naney, M. T. (1977) *Phase equilibria and crystallization in Fe-and Mg-bearing granitic systems*. Ph.D. thesis, Stanford University, Stanford, California.

_____ and Swanson, S. E. (1980) The effect of Fe and Mg on crystallization in granitic systems. Am. Mineral. 65, 639-653.

Nesbitt, R. W. and Hamilton, D. L. (1970) Crystallization of an alkali-olivine basalt under controlled P_{O_2}, P_{H_2O} conditions. Phys. Earth Planet. Interiors 3, 309-315.

Nicholls, I. A. (1974) Liquids in equilibrium with peridotitic mineral assemblages at high water pressures. Contrib. Mineral. Petrol. 45, 289-316.

Oba, T. (1978) Phase relationship of $Ca_2Mg_3Al_2Si_6Al_2O_{22}(OH)_2$ - $Ca_2Mg_3Fe_2^{3+}Si_6Al_2O_{22}(OH)_2$ join at high temperatures and high pressure - the stability of tschermakite. J. Faculty Sci. Hodkaido University Series 4, 18, 339-350.

_____ (1980) Phase relations in the tremolite-pargasite join. Contrib. Mineral. Petrol. 71, 247-256.

Oxburgh, E. R. (1964) Petrological evidence for the presence of amphibole in the upper mantle and its petrogenetic and geophysical implications. Geol. Mag. 101, 1-19.

Peto, P. (1976) Synthesis and stability of edenitic hornblende. In *Progress in Experimental Petrology*, G. M. Bigger, editor, Third Progress Report, Nat. Environ. Res. Council Pub. Serv. D, #6, London, 314 p.

Piwinskii, A. J. (1968) Experimental studies of igneous rock series: Central Sierra Nevada batholith, California. J. Geol. 76, 548-570.

_____ (1973a) Experimental studies of igneous rock series: Central Sierra Nevada batholith, California, Part II. N. Jahrb. Mineral. Monatsh. 5, 193-215.

_____ (1973b) Experimental studies bearing on the origin of the Central and Southern Coast Range granitoids, California. Tschermaks Mineral. Petrogr. Mitt. 20, 107-130.

_____ (1974) Experimentelle Untersuchungen an granitischen Gesteinen von der sudlichen Coast-Ranges, Transverse-Ranges und der Mojave-Wuste, Kalifornien. Fortschr. Mineral. 51, 240-255.

_____ and Wyllie, P. J. (1968) Experimental studies of igneous rock series: a zoned pluton in the Wallowa batholith, Oregon. J. Geol. 76, 205-234.

_____ and _____ (1970) Experimental studies of igneous rock series: felsic body suite from the Needle Point Pluton, Wallowa batholith, Oregon. J. Geol. 78, 52-76.

Popp, R. K., Gilbert, M. C., and Craig, J. R. (1976) Synthesis and x-ray properties of Fe-Mg amphiboles. Am. Mineral. 61, 1267-1279.

_____, _____ and _____ (1977a) Stability of Fe-Mg amphiboles with respect to oxygen fugacity. Am. Mineral. 62, 1-12.

_____, _____ and _____ (1977b) Stability of Fe-Mg amphiboles with respect to sulfer fugacity. Am. Mineral. 62, 13-30.

Ritchey, J. L. and Eggler, D. H. (1978) Amphibole stability in differentiated calc-alkaline magma chamber: An experimental investigation. Carnegie Inst. Wash. Year Book 77, 790-793.

Robertson, J. K. and Wyllie, P. J. (1971) Experimental studies on rocks from the Deboullie Stock, Northern Maine, including melting relations in the water-deficient environment. J. Geol. 79, 549-571.

Robinson, P. and Jaffe, H. F. (1969) Chemographic exploration of amphibole assemblages from central Massachusetts and southwestern New Hampshire. Mineral. Soc. Am. Spec. Paper 2, 251-274.

_____, Ross, M., and Jaffe, H. W. (1971) Composition of the anthophyllite-gedrite series, comparisons of gedrite-hornblende, and the anthophyllite-gedrite solvus. Am. Mineral. 56, 1005-1041.

Ross, M., Papike, J. J., and Shaw, H. W. (1969) Exsolution textures in amphiboles as indicators of subsolidus thermal histories. Mineral. Soc. Am. Spec. Paper 2, 275-299.

Schurmann, K. (1967) Hydrothermale experimentelle Untersuchungen an metamorphen monoklinen Hornblenden, Teil I: Zur stabilitat der cummingtonite. N. Jahrb. Mineral. Monatsh., 270-284.

_____ and Hafner, S. S. (1971) Temperature-dependent distribution of magnesium and iron in cummingtonites. Nature Phys. Sci. 231, 155-156.

Semet, M. P. and Ernst, W. G. (1981) Experimental stability relations of the hornblende magnesiohastingsite: Summary. Geol. Soc. Am. Bull., Part I, 92, 71-74.

Shaw, H. R. (1963) Hydrogen-water vapor mixtures: control of hydrothermal atmospheres by hydrogen osmosis. Science 139, 1220-1222.

Shell, H. R., Comeforo, J. E. and Eitel, W. (1958) Synthetic asbestos investigations: synthesis of fluoramphiboles from melts. U. S. Bureau of Mines, 4517, 35 pp.

Simmons, E. C., Lindsley, D. H., and Papike, J. J. (1974) Phase relations and crystallization sequence in a contact-metamorphased rock from the Gunflint iron formation, Minnesota. J. Petrol. 15, 539-565.

Skippen, G. B. (1971) Experimental data for reactions in siliceous marbles. J. Geology 79, 457-481.

Spear, F. S. (1981) An experimental study of hornblende stability and compositional variability in amphibolite. Am. J. Sci. 281, 697-734.

Stewart, D. C., Boettcher, A. L., and Eggler, D. H. (1979) Phase relations of Kaersutite at upper mantle conditions: implications for its subsolidus origin ultramafic nodules. Trans. Am. Geophys. Union 60, 418.

Stout, J. H. (1972) Phase petrology and mineral chemistry of coexisting amphiboles from Telemark, Norway. J. Petrol. 13, 99-146.

Sykes, M. L. (1979) *Hydrous mineral stability as a function of fluid composition: a biotite melting experiment and a model for melting curves.* M.Sc. Thesis, Arizona State University, Tempe, Arizona.

Thomas, W. M. (1982) Stability relations of the amphibole hastingsite. Am. J. Sci. 282, 136-164.

Troll, G. and Gilbert, M. C. (1972) Fluorine-hydroxyl substitution in tremolite. Am. Mineral. 57, 1386-1404.

_____ and Gilbert, M. C. (1974) Stability of fluorine tremolite (abstr.). EOS 55, 481.

Tuthill, R. L. (1968) *The hydrothermal behavior of basalts in their melting range at 5 kilobars.* M.S. thesis, The Pennsylvania State University, University Park, Pennsylvania.

Vaniman, D. T., Papike, J. J., and Labotka, T. (1980) Contact metamorphic effects of the Stillwater Complex, Montana: the concordant iron formation. Am. Mineral. 65, 1087-1102.

Van Valkenburg, A., Jr. (1955) Synthesis of a fluoro talc and attempted synthesis of fluoro anthophyllite. J. Res. National Bur. Standards, 55, 215-217.

Veblen, D. R. and Burnham, C. W. (1975) Triple-chain biopyriboles: newly discovered intermediate products of the retrograde anthophyllite-talc transformation, Chester, Vermont (abstr.) Trans. Amer. Geophys. Union 56, 1076.

Von Platen, H. and Holler, H. (1966) Experimentelle Anatexis des Strainzer Plattengneises von der Koralpe, Steiermark, ber 2,4,7 and 10 kb H_2O-Druck. N. Jahr. Mineral. Abh. 106, 106-130.

Westrich, H. R. and Holloway, J. R. (1981) Experimental dehydration of pargasite and calculation of its entropy and Gibbs energy. Am. J. Sci. 281, 922-934.

Widmark, E. T. (1974) An edenite forming reaction: hydrothermal experiments. N. Jahrb. Mineral. Monatsh. 7, 323-329.

Wilshire, H. G. and Trask, N. J. (1971) Structural and textural relationships of amphibole and phlogopite in peridotite inclusions, Dish Hill, California. Am. Mineral. 56, 240-255.

Winkler, W. G. F. and Platen, H. V. (1961) Experimentelle Gesteinsmetamorphose. IV. Bildung antaktischer Schmelzen aus metamorphisierten Grauwacken. Geochim. Cosmochim. Acta 24, 48-69.

Wise, W. S. (1969) Geology and petrology of the Mt. Hood area: a study of high cascade volcanism. Bull. Geol. Soc. Am. 80, 969-1006.

Wones, D. R. and Dodge, F. C. W. (1977) The stability of phlogopite in the presence of quartz and diopside. In *Thermodynamics in Geology*, D. G. Fraser, ed., D. Reidel Publ. Co., Dardrescht, Holland.

Wood, B. J. and Carmichael, I. S. E. (1973) P_{total}, P_{H_2O} and the occurrences of cummingtonite in volcanic rocks. Contrib. Mineral. Petrol. 40, 149-158.

Wright, T. L. and Doherty, P. C. (1970) A linear programming and least-squares computer method for solving petrologic mixing problems. Bull. Geol. Soc. Am. 81, 1995-2008.

_____ and Okamura, R. T. (1977) Cooling and crystallization of tholeiitic basalt, 1965 Makaopuhi Lava Lake, Hawaii. U. S. Geol. Surv. Prof. Paper 1004.

_____ and Peck, D. L. (1978) Solidification of Alae Lava Lake, Hawaii. U. S. Geol. Surv. Prof. Paper 935-C.

Yoder, H. S., Jr. (1971) Aluminous anthophyllite: the $MgO-Al_2O_3-SiO_2-H_2O$ systems at 850°C and 10 kbar. Carnegie Inst. Wash. Year Book 70, 142-145.

_____ and Tilley, C. E. (1962) Origin of basaltic magma: an experimental study of natural and synthetic rock systems. J. Petrol. 3, 342-532.

_____ and Kushiro, I. (1969) Melting of a hydrous phase: phlogopite. Am. J. Sci., Schairer Volume 267-A, 558-582.

Chapter 3

AMPHIBOLES in the IGNEOUS ENVIRONMENT

David R. Wones & M. Charles Gilbert

INTRODUCTION *(MCG)*

We define the igneous environment as the pressure and temperature range
existing above the solidus of silicate rocks. Thus, those amphiboles coexisting at some stage in their history with melts (= liquids) are igneous amphiboles.
Data were compiled early on such amphiboles so that the general chemical variations have been known for a long time. While some representative of all the
major chemical classes of amphiboles (iron-magnesium, calcic, sodic-calcic,
and alkali) can be found in igneous rocks, the calcic ones, commonly referred
to as hornblende, are by far the most abundant in the crust.

Figures 1 and 2 indicate in a simplified way the importance of hornblende
as a rock-forming mineral. Particularly in those rocks of intermediate SiO_2
content (diorites-quartz diorites), hornblende is commonly the dominant mafic
phase. Normally, it competes with biotite as the rock bulk composition becomes

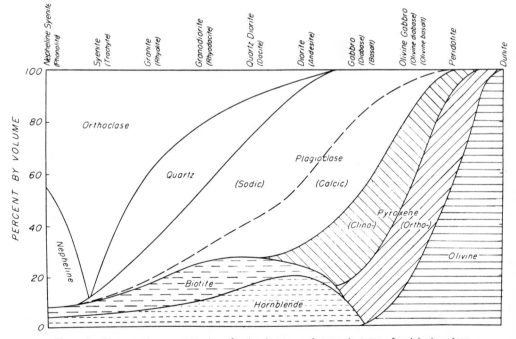

Figure 1. Diagrammatic representation of major igneous rock types in terms of modal mineralogy.
From Washington and Adams (1951).

TABLE 1.

Sources of data on the stability of amphiboles and biotites.

AMPHIBOLES

1.	Ferro-tremolite (= Ferro-actinolite)		Ca_2 Fe_5	Si_8 $O_{22}(OH)_2$	Ernst, 1966
2.	Ferro-pargasite	Na	Ca_2 Fe_4Al Al_2	Si_6 $O_{22}(OH)_2$	Gilbert, 1966
3.	Hastingsite	Na	Ca_2 $Fe_4Fe^{3+}Al_2$	Si_6 $O_{22}(OH)_2$	Thomas, 1977
4.	Ferro-richterite	Na	CaNa Fe_5	Si_8 $O_{22}(OH)_2$	Charles, 1975
5.	Riebeckite-		Na_2 $Fe^{3+}_2Fe^{2+}_3$	Si_8 $O_{22}(OH)_2$	
	Arfvedsonite	Na	Na_2 Fe^{3+} Fe^{2+}_4	Si_8 $O_{22}(OH)_2$	Ernst, 1962
6.	Grunerite		Fe_2 Fe_5	Si_8 $O_{22}(OH)_2$	Forbes, 1977
8.	Anthophyllite*		Mg_2 Mg_5	Si_8 $O_{22}(OH)_2$	Chernosky and Autio, 1979
9.	Tremolite*		Ca_2 Mg_5	Si_8 $O_{22}(OH)_2$	Boyd, 1959
10.	Magnesio-hastingsite	Na	Ca_2 $Mg_4Fe^{3+}Al_2$	Si_7 $O_{22}(OH)_2$	Semet and Ernst, 1981
11.	Pargasite	Na	Ca_2 Mg_4Al Al_2	Si_6 $O_{22}(OH)_2$	Boyd, 1959
12.	Magnesio-riebeckite		Na_2 Fe^{3+}_2 Mg_3	Si_8 $O_{22}(OH)_2$	Ernst, 1960
13.	Richterite	Na	CaNa Mg_5	Si_8 $O_{22}(OH)_2$	Charles, 1975

MICAS

7.	Annite*	K Fe_3	Al $Si_3O_{10}(OH)_2$	Eugster & Wones, 1962 Rutherford, 1969 Hewitt, pers. comm.
7a.	Annite & Quartz			Eugster and Wones, 1962
14.	Phlogopite	K Mg_3	Al $Si_3O_{10}(OH)_2$	Luth, 1967 Yoder and Kushiro, 1969 Wones, 1967
15.	Phlogopite & Quartz			Wones and Dodge, 1977 Wood, 1976
16.	Muscovite & Quartz			Chatterjee and Johannes, 1974

— — — —

*See also Helgeson et al. (1978).

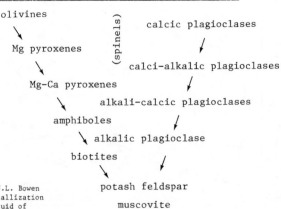

Figure 2. Reaction series developed by N.L. Bowen which attempts to show the order of crystallization (from the top down), beginning with a liquid of basaltic composition undergoing fractional crystallization. From Bowen (1922).

more silicic and more potassic. Some of the controls on amphibole-biotite interaction are discussed below by Wones.

Figure 1 is a reflection of the actual range of bulk chemistry (X), P, T, f_{H_2O}, and f_{O_2} existing through most of the crust. However, ultimate amphibole stability is not limited to the conditions represented in this figure. If H_2O content were to be maintained at a level appropriate to amphibole stoichiometry (about 2 wt %) in liquids of basaltic compositions, then the resulting rock would consist of more than 50 percent amphibole. This was amply demonstrated by Helz's extensive discussion in Chapter 2. Accordingly, the common lack of amphibole, particularly in gabbro but also in basalts, is due to extreme water undersaturation.

The following section discusses amphiboles and biotites as indicators of dehydration and redox reactions in igneous rock suites. Special emphasis is given to granitoid complexes. The last section provides a brief overview of igneous amphiboles according to class.

BIOTITES AND AMPHIBOLES IN IGNEOUS ROCKS: DEHYDRATION REDOX REACTIONS *(DRW)*

There is a great deal of overlap in the stabilities of biotites and amphiboles. Figure 3 is a log f_{H_2O}-1/T plot of end-member amphibole and biotite stabilities taken from the data presented in Table 1. The stabilities of the

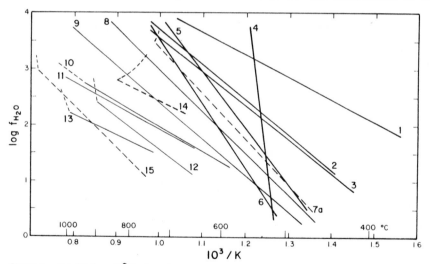

Figure 3. The *log* f_{H_2O}-$10°$/K plot of amphibole and biotite stability curves.
Heavyweight solid curves refer to Fe^{2+}-bearing amphibole end members; lightweight solid curves, Mg-bearing amphibole end members. Heavyweight dashed curves refer to Fe^{2+}-bearing biotite end members; lightweight dashed curves to Mg-bearing biotite end members. Dotted curves at high temperature termini refer to incongruent melting curves. All Fe-bearing curves refer to oxygen fugacities defined by the quartz + magnetite + fayalite buffer. Sources of data and labels of curves are in Table 1. From Wones (1981).

Fe^{2+}-bearing end members are at oxygen fugacities defined by the fayalite-quartz-magnetite assemblage (Hewitt, 1978).

With the exception of grunerite (Forbes, 1977) and -- at low temperatures -- arfvedsonite (Ernst, 1962), Fe^{2+} biotite is more stable than the ferrous amphibole end members. Changes in f_{O_2} change the pattern, however, and in Figure 4 it can be seen that grunerite, arfvedsonite, ferro-pargasite, and hastingsite all have higher stabilities than (annite + quartz), although the maximum thermal stabilities of ferro-pargasite and hastingsite are nearly the same as that of annite.

This pattern is in accord with the crystal chemistry of micas and amphiboles, as the M_1 and M_3 sites in the amphibole structures (see Hawthorne, Volume 9A, Chapter 1) are almost identical to the M_1 and M_2 sites in the mica crystal structure. The M_1 (or M_3)-O_3 ligand is the fundamental bond to be broken in dehydration reactions and should be nearly the same in the micas and the calcic amphiboles, where the M_2 and M_4 sites do not contain Fe^{2+}.

The contrasting stabilities of ferro-tremolite[1] (Ernst, 1966) and grunerite (Forbes, 1977) are remarkable. Gilbert and Popp (Chapter 2, this volume) have given reasons to suggest that the grunerite stability may be at a somewhat lower temperature than that shown here. Nonetheless, the effect of different M_4 cations on the stability of the Fe^{2+}-OH ligand is large, as is the difference in M_2 occupancy.

For the Mg-rich end members, phlogopite has a higher thermal stability than the amphiboles, although at very high oxygen fugacity (see Fig. 4) magnesio-hastingsite has a similar stability. Magnesio-richterite is slightly more stable than phlogopite at lower H_2O pressures. The stability of phlogopite + quartz is very similar to tremolite and is higher than the stability of anthophyllite.

The strength of the Mg-OH ligand in the amphibole and mica structures is an interesting and important problem. The contrast between anthophyllite and magnesio-hastingsite stabilities is extreme, and suggests that Al substitution in the T_1 tetrahedral sites leads to a better articulation of the octahedral and tetrahedral strips. Hazen and Wones (1972, 1978) implied that the better the articulation, the more stable the mica (or amphibole). Thus the amphiboles with all Si in the T_1 and T_2 sites are inherently less stable than those with Al substitutions.

The presence of Fe^{2+} in the M_2 site also tends to give the amphibole a

- - - - - - - - - -

[1]See footnote 1, p. 244: ferro-tremolite = ferro-actinolite.

TABLE 2.   Oxygen buffer curves. $\log f_{O_2} = -\frac{A}{T} + B + C \frac{(P-1)}{T}$

Abbrev.	Assemblage	A	B	C	Reference
HM*	Fe_2O_3–Fe_3O_4	26629	15.29	0.018	Chou, 1978
NNO	Ni–NiO	24930	9.36	0.046	Huebner and Sato, 1970
FMQ	Fe_2SiO_4–Fe_3O_4–SiO_2	25287	8.95	0.110	Hewitt, 1978
MW	Fe_3O_4–$Fe_{1-y}O$	32730	13.12	0.083	Eugster and Wones, 1962
IW	Fe–$Fe_{1-x}O$	27215	6.57	0.055	Eugster and Wones, 1962
FQI	Fe_2SiO_4–SiO_2–Fe	29382	7.50	0.050	Eugster and Wones, 1962
TMWIL	$CaTiSiO_5$–Fe_3O_4–$CaSiO_3$–$FeTiO_3$	30096	11.43	–0.035	Wones, in review
TMQHIL	$CaTiSiO_5$–Fe_3O_4–SiO_2–$CaFeSi_2O_6$–$FeTiO_3$	30939	14.98	0.142	Wones, in review.
GCC	C–CO_2–CO	20586	–0.044	–0.028	French and Eugster 1965

– – – – –
*For HM between 873°K and 1073°K, Chou (1978) recommends

$$\log f_{O_2} = 0.026 + \frac{4381}{T} - .1572 \left[\frac{10^4}{T}\right]^2$$

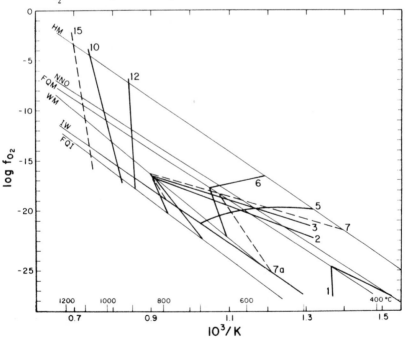

Figure 4. The $\log f_{O_2}$–10^3/K plot of stability curves for Fe-bearing amphiboles and biotites. Hydrous phases are stable at lower oxygen fugacities than the subhorizontal curves and at lower temperatures than the subvertical curves. Sources of data and labels of curves are in Table 1. Buffer curves are from Table 2. From Wones (1981).

higher free energy, as most amphibole ordering schemes (see Hawthorne, Volume 9A, Chapter 1) indicate that Fe^{2+} is preferentially found in M_1 and M_3. Ferrotremolite, the least stable of the calcic amphiboles, has only Si in the T_1 and T_2 sites and Fe^{2+} in the M_2 site. Grunerite remains an anomaly, unless there is some Fe^{3+} in the M_2 and T sites. Its enhanced stability at the relatively high oxygen fugacities of the magnetite-hematite assemblages suggests that this might be the case.

As Gilbert and Popp (Chapter 2, this volume) have indicated, the spread in thermal stabilities between anthophyllite and grunerite is smaller than that between any other pair of Fe- and Mg-amphibole end members.

It can be seen from Figure 3 that Fe^{2+}-OH ligands are inherently less stable than Mg-OH ligands, so that for equivalent structures and Al-Ti substitutions, Mg hydrous silicates are inherently more stable than their Fe counterparts.

In Figure 5, the P_{H_2O}-T curves of muscovite + quartz, selected amphiboles, and biotites are plotted against the H_2O saturated minimum melting curve of the system Ab-Or-Q-H_2O (Tuttle and Bowen, 1958; Luth et al., 1964). Abbott (1981), in a review of the feldspar-quartz-mafic silicate reactions, suggests that

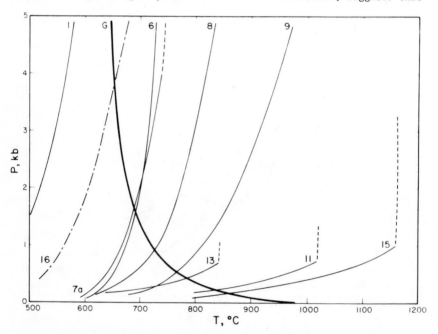

Figure 5. P-T diagram for selected amphiboles and micas from Figure 3. All data are for H_2O saturation. Fe-bearing phases are for oxygen fugacities defined by FMQ buffer. G is the granite minimum melting curve of Tuttle and Bowen (1958). Sources of data and labels of curves are in Table 1.

ferro-edenitic amphiboles would plot at temperatures slightly above those of (annite + quartz).

What we see from Figures 3 and 4 is that the relationships between amphiboles and biotites are very complex and that the thermal stabilities involve not only f_{H_2O}, f_{O_2}, and T but also the activities of FeO, MgO, CaO, SiO_2, and Al_2O_3. In short, the bulk composition of a given magma will determine the sequence of mineral crystallization.

Effect of silica on the stability of amphiboles and biotites

Boyd (1959) found that pargasite reacted with quartz to make plagioclase and tremolitic amphibole. Greenwood (1979) demonstrated that edenite also reacts with quartz to form tremolitic amphibole. Spear (1980) has studied the compositional relations between plagioclase and coexisting amphiboles and demonstrated that sodium-rich amphiboles coexist with sodium-rich plagioclase. Cawthorn (1976a,b) noted that the composition of amphiboles changes progressively with the silica activity of coexisting liquids, and Allen and Boettcher (1978) and Allen et al. (1975) showed a progressive change in the composition of amphibole as a function of silica activity in coexisting melts. Yoder and Tilley (1962) and Green and Ringwood (1967) demonstrated that amphiboles have higher thermal stability in basalts than in andesites (see Helz, Chapter 2, this volume).

Amphibole compositions give us a rough measure of the silica activity of a given system and may be used to show changes in the silica activity of a magmatic system as it crystallizes. Guy (1980) demonstrated that the SiO_2 contents of amphiboles from the Sierra Nevada (Dodge et al., 1968), a continential environment, were higher than those from typical island arc environments (Jakes and White, 1972).

Luth (1967), Modreski and Boettcher (1972), Wood (1976), and Wones and Dodge (1977) demonstrated that phlogopite stability is greatly affected by reactions with phases of varying silica saturation. Carmichael et al. (1974) have suggested silica activity as the thermodynamic basis for rock classification. Figure 6 is a plot of silica activity versus decomposition temperatures at 1000 bars for phlogopite, annite, ferro-pargasite-ferro-tremolite, and pargasite-tremolite. The silica activities are taken from Nicholls et al. (1971).

The stabilities of micas are greatly enhanced by the lowering of SiO_2 activity. Eugster and Wones (1962) showed that the maximum thermal stability of pure annite at 2000 bars was greater by more than 100°C than the stability of annite + quartz. Luth (1967) showed that phlogopite reacted with a series of mineral assemblages of different silica activities over a wide temperature

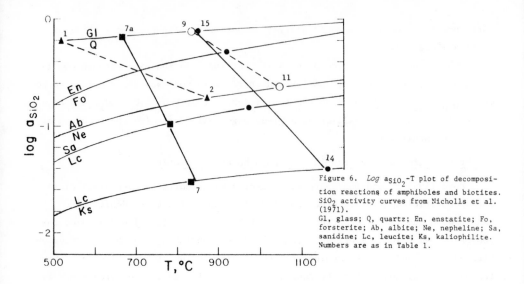

Figure 6. *Log* a_{SiO_2}-T plot of decomposition reactions of amphiboles and biotites. SiO_2 activity curves from Nicholls et al. (1971).

Gl, glass; Q, quartz; En, enstatite; Fo, forsterite; Ab, albite; Ne, nepheline; Sa, sanidine; Lc, leucite; Ks, kaliophilite. Numbers are as in Table 1.

range (Fig. 6). Phlogopite + quartz is the least stable, followed by phlogopite and enstatite, and phlogopite + sanidine in that order. Pure phlogopite is the most stable of the hydrous micas and is more stable than the hydrous amphiboles.

Amphiboles and biotites in Bowen's reaction series

That part of Bowen's (1922) discontinuous reaction series (Fig. 2) that involves amphiboles and biotites has been observed in tonalites and granodiorites. However, this order is commonly reversed. For example, in the Huntington Lake Quadrangle in the Sierra Nevada batholith (Bateman and Wones, 1972), many amphiboles in the tonalite of Blue Canyon and in the Mount Givens Granodiorite contain euhedral biotite inclusions. Some of the plagioclase in these same rocks contain clinopyroxene and biotite inclusions near the cores, but only biotite and amphibole in the rims. Beams (1980) has described similar plagioclase cores in the rocks of the Bega batholith, southeast Australia.

Wones and Dodge (1977) demonstrated experimentally that the H_2O-conservative reaction

$$KAlSi_3O_8 + Ca_2Mg_5Si_8O_{22}(OH)_2 = KMg_3AlSi_3O_{10}(OH)_2 + 2CaMgSi_2O_6 + 4SiO_2 \qquad (1)$$

takes place between 200 and 4000 bars at 755°C with the phlogopite-pyroxene-quartz assemblage as the high-temperature assemblage.

If we define the free energy for the decomposition reaction of biotite and amphibole as

$$G_{phlogopite} + 3G_{quartz} = G_{sanidine} + 3G_{enstatite} + G_{H_2O} \qquad (2)$$

362

$$G_{tremolite} = 2G_{diopside} + 3G_{enstatite} + G_{quartz} + G_{H_2O} \qquad (3)$$

and the fugacity of H_2O by

$$ln f/f^o = (G - G^o)/RT,$$

and use the same standard state, G, for all reactions, then by subtracting (3) from (2):

$$G_{phlogopite} + 4G_{quartz} + 2G_{diopside} = G_{tremolite} + G_{Kspar} + G^1_{H_2O} - G^2_{H_2O} \qquad (4)$$

The difference in the fugacities of water indicates the direction of the reaction. As can be seen in Figures 3 and 4, the phlogopite + quartz reaction crosses the tremolite reaction. Thus, we expect to see a region where clinopyroxene and biotites should coexist in the presence of quartz.

It should be noted that Helgeson et al. (1978) calculated a different stability curve for (phlogopite + quartz) than that found experimentally by Wood (1976) and Wones and Dodge (1977). Data for the decarbonation reactions in the system $KAlSiO_4-CaO-MgO-SiO_2-CO_2-H_2O$ (e.g., William-Jones, 1981) imply that reaction (1) occurs at 370°C and that (tremolite + K-feldspar) is the high-temperature assemblage. Valley and Essene (1980) demonstrated that multiple substitutions in natural biotites and amphiboles tend to make the direction of the reaction equivocal.

For iron-rich systems, the reaction

$$Ca_2Fe_5Si_8O_{22}(OH)_2 + KAlSi_3O_8 = KFe_3AlSi_3O_{10}(OH)_2 + 2CaFeSi_2O_6 + SiO_2 \qquad (5)$$

is so strongly to the right (because annite is stable at much lower H_2O pressures or higher O_2 pressures [Fig. 3] than ferro-tremolite) that we find annite-rich biotites coexisting with hedenbergitic pyroxenes and fayalite (Barker et al., 1975). However, hastingsitic and ferro-edenitic amphiboles are found in alkaline granites (Toulmin, 1964; Lyons, 1972, 1976; Barker et al., 1975; Abbott, 1981), because their stability is enhanced by the Na and Al substitutions in the amphibole. Although the ideal end members, hastingsite and edenite, are not in equilibrium with quartz, the natural amphiboles that are solid solutions between the two are. Reactions involving these latter amphiboles and annite have smaller free energy differences than the ferro-tremolite example noted above.

For the reaction

$$NaCa_2Fe_4AlSi_6Al_2O_{22}(OH)_2 + KAlSi_3O_8 + SiO_2 =$$

$$NaAlSi_3O_8 + CaAl_2Si_2O_8 + CaFeSi_2O_6 + KFe_3AlSi_3O_{10}(OH)_2 \qquad (6)$$

the free energy is lower on the right hand side. Lowering of albite and anorthite activities in plagioclase solid solution will enhance this effect. In
contrast, the lowering of SiO_2 and $KAlSi_3O_8$ activity will shift the reaction
to the left.

It is this latter effect that makes Bowen's reaction series the general
case. Most tonalities and granodiorites have very low activities of $KAlSi_3O_8$
and SiO_2 until the late stages of crystallization. Thus, amphibole crystallizes
earlier and biotites are the late stage minerals. However, in magmas with low
f_{H_2O} and moderate K_2O values, biotite can follow clinopyroxene ahead of amphibole. This effect is seen in the extreme in the ultramafic and gabbroic complexes where biotite, not amphibole, is the interstitial late phase (Jackson,
1961; Huntington, 1979).

Naney and Swanson (1980) have demonstrated this effect in a series of
experiments on synthetic granite and granodiorite compositions. They demonstrated that, for silicate melts near alkali feldspar saturation that contain
normative hypersthene, biotites may crystallize before amphiboles. At higher
H_2O fugacities, the mole fraction of $KAlSi_3O_8$ in the melt is decreased (Burnham,
1979) and the biotites will crystallize after amphiboles. This latter effect is
demonstrated by Ewart et al. (1975) in cummingtonite-bearing volcanic rocks.
Ransome (1898), Larsen and Draisin (1948), Lipman (1971), and Cameron et al.
(1980) have described ash flow tuffs in which biotite and clinopyroxene coexist
with melt. This pair of minerals indicates H_2O fugacities of hundreds of bars
and shows that euhedral biotite phenocrysts found within hornblendes do not
require peculiar interpretations. Speer et al. (1980) demonstrated that petrographic determination of the sequence of crystallization of these mafic silicates can provide useful information concerning magmatic history.

Biotites and amphiboles in alkalic rocks

If we combine the riebeckite-arfvedsonite decomposition reaction and the
annite + quartz decomposition reaction we obtain the reaction

$$Na_2Fe_2^{3+}Fe_3^{2+}Si_8O_{22}(OH)_2 + KAlSi_3O_8 =$$

$$2NaFeSi_2O_6 + KFe_3AlSi_3O_{10}(OH)_2 + 4SiO_2. \qquad (7)$$

At constant f_{H_2O}, the amphibole and biotite stability curves cross in f_{O_2}-T
space and generate curve (7), which normally would be vertical with the annite
+ acmite assemblage on the high temperature side. Figure 7 is a projection onto the f_{O_2}-T plane of the system Na_2O-$KAlO_2$-SiO_2-Fe-O-H at constant pressure in
the presence of quartz. Assuming that the Na occurs only in an $NaFeO_2$ couple

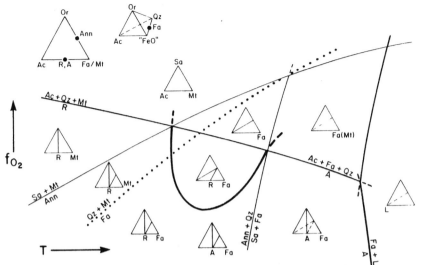

Figure 7. Schematic diagram showing the relationship between biotite and amphiboles in the system $KAlSi_3O_8-SiO_2-NaFeSi_2O_6-Fe-O-H$ at an arbitrary pressure. Or, $KAlSi_3O_8$ (sanidine); Ac, $NaFeSi_2O_6$ (acmite); Qz, SiO_2 (quartz); Mt, Fe_3O_4 (magnetite); Fa, Fe_2SiO_4 (fayalite); R, $Na_2Fe_2Fe_3Si_8O_{22}(OH)_2$ (riebeckite); A, $Na_xNa_2Fe_{2-x}Fe_{3+x}Si_8O_{22}(OH)_2$ (arfvedsonite); Ann, $KFe_3AlSi_3O_{10}(OH)_2$ (annite); l, liquid (Na-rich silicate melt).

and the K as $KAlO_2$, one can project the system from quartz and H_2O into the tetrahedron $NaFeSi_2O_6-KAlSi_3O_8-FeO-Fe_3O_4$. If all the phases occur with magnetite as a ubiquitous phase, then we can represent the system as the ternary $NaFeSi_2O_6-KAlSi_3O_8-FeO$.

The phases riebeckite, annite, sanidine, acmite, and fayalite can be plotted on a compositional triangle with a double degeneracy so that the isobaric invariant point contains three curves, the acmite- and riebeckite-absent one, (annite = sanidine + magnetite); the sanidine-absent one (riebeckite = acmite + fayalite + quartz); and the one represented by equation (7).

Hazen and Wones (1972) have shown that annite always contains some Fe^{3+}; therefore, the slope of reaction (7) in f_{O_2}-T space is not vertical, but has a negative slope.

The riebeckite-acmite-magnetite-quartz curve continues to the fayalite-magnetite-quartz curve, where it terminates and generates a new curve. As Ernst (1962) has shown, the amphibole has changed composition toward arfvedsonite so that it is a solid solution between riebeckite and $Na_3Fe^{3+}Fe_4^{2+}Si_8O_{22}$ $(OH)_2$. The amphibole reacts through oxidation:

$$Na_3Fe^{3+}Fe_4^{2+}Si_8O_{22}(OH)_2 + 0.5O_2 =$$
$$3NaFe^{3+}Si_2O_6 + Fe_2SiO_4 + SiO_2 + H_2O. \qquad (8)$$

This curve intersects the dehydration curve:

$$KFe_3AlSi_3O_{10}(OH)_2 + 1.5SiO_2 = KAlSi_3O_8 + 1.5Fe_2SiO_4 + H_2O, \qquad (9)$$

and yields the reaction:

$$3Na_3Fe^{3+}Fe_4^{2+}Si_8O_{22}(OH)_2 + 2KAlSi_3O_8 + 1.5O_2 =$$

$$9NaFeSi_2O_6 + 2KFe_3AlSi_3O_{10}(OH)_2 + 6SiO_2 + H_2O \qquad (10)$$

This reaction has a positive slope with the biotite-acmite assemblage on the low temperature, high oxygen fugacity side. This curve, as the amphibole changes composition, becomes equivalent to (7), so that the sanidine-amphibole field has a semi-elliptical hole in it.

Sequences of biotites and amphiboles in alkalic rocks are thus quite sensitive to f_{O_2}. One can find pyroxene-biotite-riebeckite paths, such as the cooling history of the Quincy granite in Massachusetts, where sodic pyroxene is an essential mineral, biotite is a late-stage accessory, and riebeckite forms as a late-stage pegmatite mineral or as a filling on slickensided surfaces (Lyons, 1972, 1976). In other sequences, arfvedsonitic amphiboles give way to biotite-pyroxene assemblages, which in turn react in the subsolidus to form riebeckite. This appears to be the case in the Cape Ann granite (Toulmin, 1964), except that the amphibole in this case is more aluminous, and the residual magmatic assemblages are biotite ± olivine. In pegmatites within the Cape Ann granite, quartz and perthite coexist with fayalitic olivine that has been pseudomorphed by quartz, magnetite, and grunerite (see Fig. 5). Upon further cooling, the grunerite has reacted with the perthite to form annite and, at lower temperatures, stilpnomelane. This sequence is subsolidus, and implies that the granitic magma crystallized at temperatures above the stability of grunerite or annite + quartz. As the amphiboles in the granite are interstitial, the further implication is that the original granite magma was relatively reduced, and relatively anhydrous.

Amphibole compositional variations

Popp et al. (1976; 1977a,b) examined the stability of cummingtonite-like solid solution in Fe and Mg as a function of T, f_{O_2}, and f_{S_2}. These data clearly showed how amphiboles can consistently change their Fe^{2+} contents with changes in f_{O_2} and f_{S_2}. Analogous studies on biotites have been carried out by Wones and Eugster (1965), Rutherford (1972), and Tso et al. (1979).

Charles (1977) examined the stability of richterite solutions in Fe and Mg and showed how ordering of Fe and Mg on the several cationic sites influences

the stability of these amphiboles. Wood and Carmichael (1973) had examined
this problem in conjunction with the stability of cummingtonite phenocrysts
in rhyolitic lavas (Ewart et al., 1975).

Cameron (1975) investigated the solvus between actinolite and cummingtonite.
Spear (1980), Oba (1980), and Greenwood (1979) have examined the relations a-
mong tremolite, edenite, and pargasite, and found that a solvus exists between
sodium-poor and sodium-rich amphibole.

Troll and Gilbert (1972) looked at the distribution of fluorine and hydroxyl
between tremolite and fluid and found that amphibole concentrated fluorine less
effectively than biotites, as determined by Munoz and Ludington (1974). Gilbert
and Troll (1974) made further comparisons with micas and found that the latter
always concentrate fluorine over amphibole. Potassium-richterites behave in a
similar way (Gilbert and Briggs, 1974). Holloway and Ford (1975) examined the
melting relations of fluorine-bearing pargasite and demonstrated that the amphibole concentrates fluorine preferentially over the melt.

Gillberg (1964) and Chivas (in press) demonstrated that amphiboles preferentially concentrate chlorine over biotite. Chivas (in press) also showed that
rocks containing hornblende with higher chlorine contents are barren in contrast
to the mineralized rocks whose amphiboles had lower chlorine contents.

Hornblende is potentially as useful as plagioclase in recording magmatic
chemistry. Figure 8 shows a variety of trends from different igneous complexes.

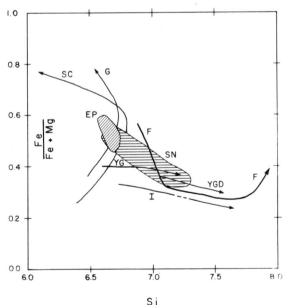

Figure 8. Trends in tetrahedral Si and Fe/
(Fe + Mg) of amphiboles in different igneous
complexes: EP, Eagle Peak zoned pluton,
Sierra Nevada batholith (Noyes, 1978); F,
Finmarka Complex (Czamanske and Wones, 1973);
G, Guadalupe Complex, California (Best and
Mercy, 1967); I, Inamumu pluton, Guadalcanal
(Chivas, in press); SC, Southern California
batholith (Larsen & Draisin, 1948); YG, gabbro
from South Yuat Pluton, New Guinea; YGD,
granodiorite from South Yuat pluton, New
Guinea (Mason, 1978).

In the Finnmarka Complex of Norway, Czamanske and Wones (1973) showed that the amphiboles changed systematically from Fe-, Al-, and Ti-rich hornblendes to Mg-rich tremolites as the magma evolved toward a siliceous residuum. Mason (1978) showed similar trends in the plutonic rocks of Papua, New Guinea, although the variations in Fe/(Fe + Mg) were not as great. Chivas (in press) reported similar trends in mineralized plutons from the Koloula Igneous Complex of Guadalcanal. In these three cases, the change in the amphibole composition reflected changes in both the oxygen fugacity and silica activity of the magma as it crystallized. Chivas (in press) reports a gap in the tetrahedral Si content that may reflect the hornblende-tremolite solvus reported by Oba (1980).

In the Guadalupe Complex, Best and Mercy (1967) showed an iron-enrichment trend in amphiboles from gabbros and closely related granites. Larsen and Draisen (1948) showed a similar variation in amphiboles from the Southern California batholith. In these latter two cases the iron-enriched amphiboles are also enriched in Al^{IV}, which may reflect Na_2O and Al_2O_3 activities in the melt, as well as SiO_2 activity.

Dodge et al. (1968) show a general trend for the Sierra Nevada of amphibole compositions where Si contents increase with lower Fe/(Fe + Mg). Noyes (1978) demonstrated that the Eagle Peak pluton, a zoned pluton in the Sierra Nevada batholith (Bateman and Wones, 1972), has very limited change in amphibole composition throughout the body. This latter property might be expected from plutons in which the amphiboles represent "restite," and the variation within the pluton is due to crystal-liquid separation rather than fractionation. However, a late-stage, sub-solidus reequilibration of the pluton could also lead to uniform amphibole compositions.

Tsusue (1978) showed that amphibole compositions in the granitic rocks of southwest Japan are closely related to bulk rock compositions. Recent detailed studies by Czamanske et al. (1981) of transects across Japan correlate the compositions of the amphiboles, especially Fe/(Fe + Mg), with oxidation state and bulk chemistry.

Amphiboles and the classification of granites

Several different classification schemes have been proposed for granitic rocks that go beyond the modal nomenclature of the I.U.G.S. (Streckheisen, 1973). Buddington (1959) proposed depth of intrusion as the prominent variable and classified granites as catazonal, mesozonal, and epizonal. Burnham (1979) pointed out that catazonal magmas are usually H_2O-rich, mesozonal magmas moderately so, and epizonal magmas contain the least amount of H_2O.

As can be seen from Figure 5, magmas generated from amphibole-rich terranes will have modest H_2O contents that would lead to mesozonal or epizonal style magmas. In a very general way, this observation seems borne out by the general occurrence of amphibole-bearing magmas.

Chappell and White (1974) proposed the I- (Igneous) and S- (Sedimentary) classification system for granitic rocks of southeastern Australia. CaO activities are usually higher in the I-type, leading to hornblende crystallization. Thus, hornblendes are one of the important indicators of I-type granites.

Loiselle and Wones (1979) suggested that granites from anorogenic regions are relatively anhydrous and constitute a group they call "A" that is distinct from the normal I- and S-types. These granites are traditionally rich in alkalies and often distinguished by Na-rich amphiboles. In fact, arfvedsonitic and riebeckitic amphiboles can be used as indicators of peralkaline magmas, where deuteric alteration has made the granite peraluminous. Wones (1981) has given a qualitative comparison of some of the intensive parameters important for amphibole occurrence in these granites.

Ishihara (1977) classified granitic rocks in Japan into magnetite-series and ilmenite-series. Takahashi and others (1980) showed that although such a division somewhat parallels Chappell and White's (1974) I- and S-Type granites, there are variations within both types. Part of that variability is the contamination of a magma by graphite incorporated from the host rocks (Ishihara, 1979).

The oxygen fugacity of a magma can be either intrinsic to the source region or developed during the history of the magma. Sato and Wright (1965) have shown that tholeiitic magmas of Hawaii are usually erupted at oxygen fugacities somewhat above quartz-magnetite-fayalite and may evolve as closed systems to reduced assemblages of fayalite, hedenbergite, and ilmenite. Similar to this pattern is that shown by Muan and Osborn (1956) and Williams (1971) for the system $MgO-FeO-Fe_2O_3-SiO_2$.

Hildreth (1980) has demonstrated a similar pattern for a zoned magma chamber where the top is cooler, H_2O-enriched, and at a lower oxygen fugacity than the deeper portions of the chamber. This can be explained by H_2 diffusion towards the cooler end of a magma column. Czamanske and Wones (1973) suggested that the loss of H_2 during devolatilization of the Finnmarka magma could have led to its oxidation. Lipman and Friedman (1975) suggested that contamination of a magma chamber by oxygen charged ground waters also could lead to oxidation. The magnetite-series granodiorite of the Kofu complex, Honshu, Japan, was converted to a magnetite-free variety where it intruded shale-dominated wall rocks,

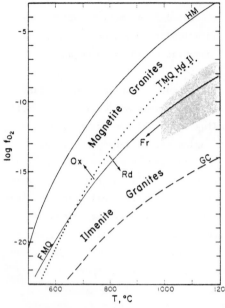

Figure 9. The $\log f_{O_2}$-T plot showing several buffer curves taken from Table 2. Shaded area represents intrinsic oxygen fugacities of mantle derived magmas. Ox represents oxidizing trends through hydrogen loss or oxygen gain during crustal emplacement. R represents reducing trends through hydrogen or carbon gain. Fr represents closed system fractionation typical of layered basaltic magmas.

but remained less reduced where the magma intruded sandstone-rich wall rocks (Ishihara et al., 1976). Kocis et al. (1977) showed that the Narrangansett Pier granite in Rhode Island was reduced locally by carbon contamination from sedimentary inclusions of the Narragansett Bay group.

In Figure 9, the broad areas of magnetite- and ilmenite-series granites are outlined on an f_{O_2}-T plot. Also shown are the buffer curves for FMQ and the ilmenite-hedenbergite-magnetite-titanite-quartz buffer. GCC refers to the graphite-CO_2 equilibrium at one atmosphere. The shaded area is the broad range of mantle-related magmas. The arrow marked Fr refers to the trends of fractionation from such magmas. The curve marked Ox refers to oxidation processes in magma chambers due to either addition of oxygen or the loss of hydrogen. Rd refers to the reduction of a magma by the addition of carbon.

It is important to distinguish between processes that occur after magma formation and those that are intrinsic to the source area. Fugacities of the volatile components may change during migration and crystallization of the magma and be less useful as indicators of the nature of the source region. Yet these interpreted values are powerful indicators of the source areas. Oxidation is a crustal phenomenon. If one can show that a magma is intrinsically oxidized, then one could reasonably infer that its source material had some crustal residence. Thus, oxidized (magnetite-series) granites probably crystallized from magmas that were formed from the melting of crustal material.

Sequences of crystallization are quite important for sorting out these

370

processes. K. Sato (pers. comm.) found that magnetite occurs in the cores of plagioclase phenocrysts, as well as in hornblende and biotite in the major part (magnetite-series) of the Tokuwa grnodiorite, whereas no magnetite was found in the graphite-contaminated rocks along the margin of the granodiorite. This suggests that the contamination took place before significant plagioclase crystallization. Maaloe and Wyllie (1975), in an experimental study of the crystallization of a granite, found that, when buffered by Ni-NiO, all experiments had magnetite as the liquidus phase. The basaltic andesites of the Aleutians (Marsh, 1976) have magnetite as the earliest crystallizing phase, a property quite in contrast to oceanic island tholeiite (Richter and Murata, 1966), where magnetite crystallizes late.

It is important to define clearly the terms oxidizing and reducing. As can be seen from Figures 4 and 9, fayalite and magnetite are both stable over a wide range of oxygen fugacities, but at very different temperatures for a given oxygen fugacity. What is meaningful is the oxygen fugacity of a system relative to some standard. The fayalite-magnetite-quartz reaction is a most useful reference state for granitic rocks. This also corresponds closely with the position of $Ilm_{99}Hm_1$ that coexists with magnetite (Lindsley, 1976; Hewitt, 1978). Oxidized magmas are those that lie in the quartz-magnetite field, reduced magmas are those that lie in the fayalite field.

Phase relations and properties of biotites (Wones and Eugster, 1965) and amphiboles (Popp et al., 1977a; Charles, 1977), when combined with other phases such as titanite (Wones, in review) and feldspar, permit us to refine these more general definitions of reduced and oxidized magmas, so that we can examine relative oxidation states within plutons (Czamanske and Wones, 1973; Mason, 1978; Whelan, 1980) or between plutons (Czamanske et al., 1977, 1981).

BRIEF OVERVIEW OF IGNEOUS AMPHIBOLES *(MCG)*

Iron-magnesium amphiboles

The only member of this class known to occur in igneous rock is cummingtonite, and it is rare (Kuno, 1938). All occurrences are in silicic volcanic rocks except the one reported by Seitsaari (1956) in an amphibole-rich diorite, which Klein (1968) accepted as primary, and the ones reported by Hall (1975) in Eocene hypabyssal plugs. Wilcox (1965) described a number of volcanic glass samples with coeval phenocrysts of hornblende and cummingtonite which Klein (1968) subsequently analyzed. The amphiboles analyzed were not in physical contact, so Klein was unwilling to call all these equilibrium assemblages. One sample, however, had rims of hornblende surrounding cummingtonite cores. This was thought

371

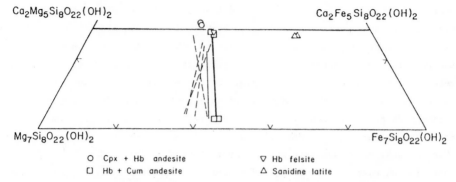

Figure 10. Amphibole quadrilateral showing compositional plots of some analyzed amphiboles from a hypabyssal Eocene igneous suite in Virginia. From Hall (1975). Heavy solid line connects coexisting hornblende and cummingtonite. Dashed lines represent possible coexisting volcanic amphiboles from Klein (1968) and light solid line Klein's "equilibrium" assemblage.

possibly to merit being called an equilibrium pair. Some of these data are shown in Figure 10. These compositions help to establish the miscibility gap existing between iron-magnesium and calcic amphiboles at higher temperatures. Hall (1975) provided additional and complementary data from a series of plugs in Highland County, Virginia. These plugs are exposed at a stratigraphic level and with petrographic and structural characteristics appropriate to a low-pressure emplacement. The coexisting amphibole pair from these rocks, cummingtonite-hornblende, has a tie-line orientation very similar to the equilibrium assemblage of Klein.

Wood and Carmichael (1973) emphasize the importance of cummingtonite phenocrysts as an indicator of P_{H_2O}/P_{total} (see also Fig. 52, point a, and related discussion in Chapter 2, this volume). Their analysis shows that $P_{H_2O} > 0.7-0.8$ P_{total} for cummingtonite to precipitate from silicic liquid. Only if the water content is high enough to approach saturation, thereby dropping the rock solidus in temperature as low as possible while maximizing temperature of stability of the hydrous crystalline phase, could cummingtonite and magma possibly coexist (see the review of work done on cummingtonite stability in Chapter 2). Because cummingtonite is early in many of the silicic lavas in which it occurs, and because that cummingtonite has low fluorine content, it is clear that the entire mass of liquid is initially nearly saturated with H_2O.

Carmichael et al. (1974) also noted that an f_{O_2} control seems to exist for mafic phenocrysts in rhyolitic lavas. From lower oxygen fugacities (close to FMQ) toward higher (near NNO), the sequence of assemblages found was: olivine; orthopyroxene; orthopyroxene + amphibole (cummingtonite or calcic); and biotite and/or amphibole (normally calcic). These assemblages reflect increasing ability to contain ferric iron and -- at higher fugacities -- alkalis as well.

Calcic amphiboles

As the common amphibole class of igneous rocks, a number of excellent studies have been devoted to these types (e.g., Engel, 1959; Wilkinson, 1961; Dodge et al., 1968). All the end members are pyroxene-normative, those with significant A-site occupancy are nepheline-normative, and most are anorthite- and olivine-normative. Thus, hornblendes are typically less siliceous than their hosts, and fractionation of amphiboles should result in silica enrichment of the liquid. The general effects of increased F and of Fe^{3+} are toward promoting normative quartz-saturation. Increased aluminum promotes olivine in the norm.

Several interesting correlations between compositions of amphibole and host rock can be seen in Figures 11, 12, and 13. No distinction is made between extrusive and intrusive varieties of the rock type indicated (e.g., basaltic = basalt or gabbro or essentially any rock whose bulk SiO_2 content falls between 45 to 55 wt %). "Silica-unsaturated" includes syenites and monzonites -- essentially evolved rocks with no quartz. Those from pegmatites may have coexisted only with an H_2O-rich fluid phase and not a liquid. Even where an amphibole originally precipitated from a liquid, it could be expected to have reequilibrated with fluid below the solidus. The xenolithic category represents a limited amount of data from ultramafic and mafic samples occurring as xenoliths, normally in alkaline basalt hosts.

A selection of 245 better quality analyses from Leake (1968) were classified according to rock type. Figure 11 shows these projected onto the plane SiO_2-FeO + Fe_2O_3-Na_2O + K_2O. As rock composition becomes more SiO_2-rich, or evolved, the calcic amphibole becomes more iron-rich. The spread of compositions toward the alkalis is greatest in andesitic-basaltic rocks. In contrast, the spread in Si-Fe is greatest in dacitic-rhyolitic-silica-unsaturated rocks. A distinct change in distribution occurs at the dacitic composition, where amphiboles can be noticeably more Fe-enriched, and at the rhyolitic composition, where the relative silica falls. The rhyolitic and silica-unsaturated categories contain mostly hastingsitic varieties occurring in A-type granitoids (Loiselle and Wones, 1979; Wones, this chapter).

Figure 12 shows amphibole oxidation state as a function of rock composition. Little improvement in the amphibole data base for this sort of plot has occurred since Leake's (1968) compilation because most newer analyzes are done with electron microprobe where ferric-ferrous contents are not determined. Some of the most oxidized amphiboles come from basaltic-andesitic rocks. This may reflect their higher temperature origin and consequent greater opportunity to react with the emplacement environment on cooling.

373

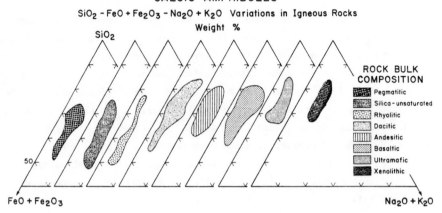

Figure 11. Grouping of calcic amphibole compositions by iron and alkalis according to bulk rock composition, based on 245 better-quality analyses selected from Leake (1968) with limited data added for xenolithic occurrences. No distinction is made between intrusive and extrusive occurrences. "Silica-unsaturated" refers to evolved rock types with no quartz.

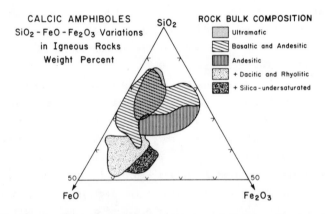

Figure 12. Grouping of calcic amphiboles by FeO-Fe$_2$O$_3$ variations according to rock compositions, based on 245 "better-quality" analyses selected from Leake (1968). No distinction is made between intrusive and extrusive occurrences.

As could be seen in Figure 11, andesitic amphiboles overlap completely with basaltic ones in total iron content but also occupy additional ferric iron space of their own. Some andesites are apparently inherently more oxidized, compatible with other observations (Carmichael et al., 1974). Amphiboles from dacitic, rhyolitic, and silica-undersaturated rocks generally overlap those from basaltic and andesitic rocks but also may be further iron-enriched. Some silica-under-saturated rocks carry amphiboles distinctly more ferric-rich than the rhyolitic and dacitic ones. It may be that all those amphiboles below the composition

374

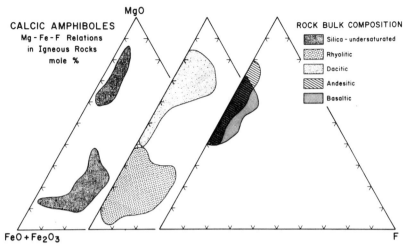

Figure 13. Grouping of calcic amphiboles by fluorine content according to rock composition, based on 245 analyses. No distinction is made between intrusive and extrusive occurrences. From Leake (1968).

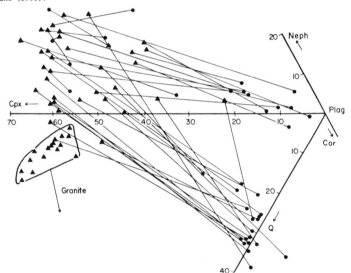

Figure 14. Compositions of amphibole and coexisting magma projected into the basalt tetrahedron, in wt %, from olivine into clinopyroxene-plagioclase-nepheline-quartz. From Cawthorn (1976a).

constriction at $\sim$65 wt % SiO_2 are from A-type granitoids/volcanics and point to a distinctly different petrogenesis from the dacitic-rhyolitic-silica-undersaturated rocks overlapping basalt and andesite.

Figure 13 attempts to delineate fluorine-iron-magnesium relations as a function of host rock composition. Basaltic and andesitic amphiboles have the least fluorine and generally overlap in composition. Surprisingly, rhyolitic and dacitic amphiboles with more than 0.5-1.0 percent fluorine separate rather completely into two populations based on Mg-Fe concentration above 0.5 to 1 wt % fluorine, dacitic ones are Mg-enriched, and rhyolitic ones are Fe-enriched. Even more supprising is the complete separation of amphiboles in silica-undersaturated rocks into two non-overlapping groups. The Mg-rich group has much lower fluorine. The Fe^{2+}-F bond is less favored than the Mg-F bond (see Hawthorne, Chapter 1, Volume 9A) so that F occupancy of the O_3 crystallographic site can determine the Mg-Fe^{2+} ordering scheme over the M_1, M_2, and M_3 sites. However, the Fe^{3+}-F bond may be considerably more energetic since high fluorine contents are not uncommon in the iron-rich hastingsitic amphiboles.

Cawthorn (1976a) has given a perceptive discussion of amphibole-host rock relations utilizing compositional projections into the basalt tetrahedron. An example of one of these diagrams is Figure 14, projected from olivine into clinopyroxene-plagioclase-nepheline-quartz. The solid triangles are amphibole compositions, generally nepheline-normative, and the solid circles are rocks taken to be magma compositions. Cawthorn noted that several distinct clusters of analyses existed in the data set he compiled: one consisted of amphiboles from granites (which do not project as nepheline-normative) whose rock compositions are highly SiO_2-oversaturated; another cluster was nepheline-normative but the rocks were quartz-normative; and the third consisted of strongly nepheline-normative amphiboles whose bulk rocks were also distinctly undersaturated. Cawthorn's interpretation of these data is shown in Figure 15. Two alternative sets of tie-planes are possible: one involving amphibole + quartz; the other plagioclase + orthopyroxene (orthopyroxene equilibria shown in dashed lines). He noted that both do occur and are probably stable over similar ranges of physical conditions, but that the orthopyroxene equilibria occur with more calcic plagioclase, and the quartz equilibria with more sodic plagioclase. A thermal divide was postulated to exist at 11 percent normative nepheline, such that amphibole fractionation from a liquid with less nepheline would produce a trend toward silica-oversaturation while fractionation from a liquid with more than 11 percent nepheline could lead to evolved rocks that are strongly undersaturated.

Cawthorn further attempted to deduce fractionation factors between amphibole and liquid for a number of major elements by plotting amphibole chemistry against mg-value [$= Mg/(Mg + Fe^{2+})$] of the whole rock. MgO and FeO responded well, indicating fractionation factors of 2 for each at higher mg-values (presumably higher temperatures) to factors of 10 and 6, respectively, at lower mg-values (presumably lower temperatures). TiO_2 and Na_2O showed differences

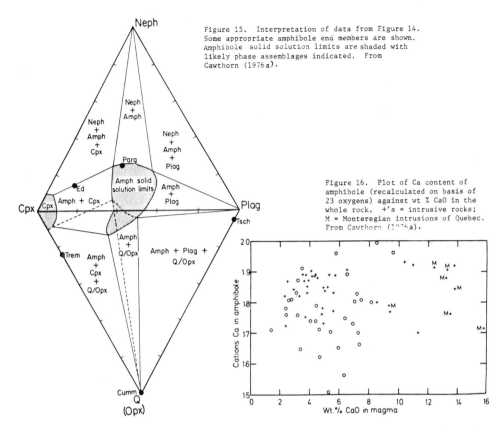

Figure 15. Interpretation of data from Figure 14. Some appropriate amphibole end members are shown. Amphibole solid solution limits are shaded with likely phase assemblages indicated. From Cawthorn (1976a).

Figure 16. Plot of Ca content of amphibole (recalculated on basis of 23 oxygens) against wt % CaO in the whole rock. +'s = intrusive rocks; M = Monteregian intrusions of Quebec. From Cawthorn (1976a).

depending on whether the rocks were extrusive or intrusive: TiO_2, 5-10 to 1-5, Na_2O, 0.6 to 0.25. These factors were thus reasoned to be pressure sensitive, both decreasing with increasing pressure. The TiO_2 increase with temperature, noted by many other workers, was not evident in these data. K_2O showed strong partitioning into the liquid but otherwise did not show special dependence on *mg*-value. CaO showed little sensitivity to rock composition, with most hornblendes containing 1.7-1.9 Ca per formula unit, regardless of rock composition (Fig. 16). A set of titanian pargasitic to hastingsitic hornblendes from hydrous tholeiitic intrusive bodies (Powell et al., 1980) showed an almost constant 1.8 Ca for a range of CaO from 9 to 13 wt %, consistent with Cawthorn's analysis. Interestingly, all those amphiboles in Figure 16 with less than 1.7 Ca were from extrusive rocks, and these were also ones with less than 8 wt % CaO in the rock. The significance of this distribution was not noted.

A valuable regional mineralogic and petrologic study of postmetamorphic granitoids from the southeastern U.S. by Speer et al. (1980) provided data on amphiboles and coexisting phases within one tectonic province. All the bodies

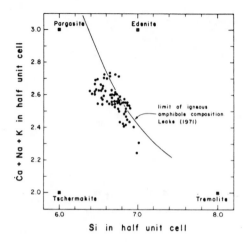

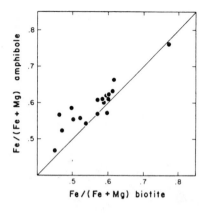

Figure 17. Plot of Si against Ca + Na + K for amphiboles from postmetamorphic, coarse-grained granitoids of the southeastern United States. From Speer et al. (1980).

Figure 18. Distribution of Fe and Mg between coexisting amphiboles and biotites of the postmetamorphic, coarse-grained granitoid bodies of the southeastern United States. From Speer et al. (1980).

contained biotite + potassium feldspar, but nine also contained amphibole, which was typically zoned, not uncommonly with pyroxene cores. These amphiboles are edenites and edenitic hornblendes, and ferro equivalents. Their compositions plot close to the limit of Ca + Na + K, for a specified silicon content, normally found in igneous environments (Fig. 17). Amphiboles in any one pluton have clustered Fe/(Fe + Mg) ratios, with six of the bodies yielding individual averages of 47, 52, 56, 57, 61, and 64. Textures indicated that amphibole crystallized first in some cases, while biotite was first in others. Speer et al. (1980) utilized the argument of Wones and Dodge (1977) that in potassium-rich magmas, low H_2O activity favors earlier precipitation of biotite, contrary to the order of the classic Bowen's Reaction Series (Fig. 2) (also see the discussion in the previous section). The Fe/(Fe + Mg) ratios were slightly higher in amphibole than in biotite (Fig. 18).

A detailed chemical study of amphibole-host rock relations from nonorogenic alkaline plutonic ring-complexes has been presented by Giret et al. (1980). Most of these bodies would be classified as A-type granitoids using the criteria of Loiselle and Wones (1979) (also see the previous section). In contrast, Cawthorn (1976a) used a data base built principally from basic sequences with some I-type granitoids, while the plutons described by Speer et al. (1980) include some possible S-type granitoids. Amphibole compositions were chosen from both silica-saturated (Iskou, Niger; Rallier-du-Baty Peninsula, Kerguelen; Cauro-Bastelica, Corsica; Oslo, Norway) and silica-undersaturated (Tahiti; Courlet Peninsula and Monts Dallons, Kerguelen; Marangudzi; Oslo, Norway)

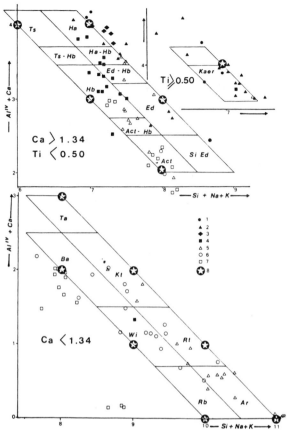

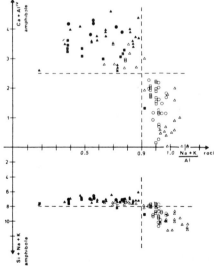

Figure 19 (above). Plots of $(Ca + Al^{IV})$ versus $(Si + Na + K)$ for amphiboles from nonorogenic complexes. From Giret et al. (1980).
Key to symbols: 1 - Tahiti; 2 - Courbet peninsula and Monts Ballons, Kerguelen; 3 - Marangudzi; 4 - Iskou, Niger; 5 - Oslo rift; 6 - Rallier-du-Baty peninsula, Kerguelen; 7 - Cauro-Bastelica, Corsica; 8 - amphibole end members: Ts = tschermakite, Ha = hastingsite, Ed = edenite, Ta = taramite, Kt = katophorite, Ri = richterite, Ar = arfvedsonite, Hb = hornblende, Ba = barroisite, Tr = tremolite, Wi = winchite, Rb = riebeckite, Act = actinolite.

Figure 20 (to the left). Relationship between the composition of amphibole and the agpaitic coefficient of host rock. Symbols as in Figure 19. From Giret et al. (1980).

379

complexes. Based on 1.34 Ca in the formula unit these were divided into two groups to produce Figure 19. Most of the amphiboles with Ca > 1.34 are from undersaturated rocks while those with Ca < 1.34 are from saturated rocks. In one of the saturated series (#6), the amphibole types evolved from katophorite to winchite to ferro-richterite to arfvedsonite. In other saturated series, hastingsitic amphibole was normally early, while sodic-calcic and/or alkalic types crystallized late, with a presumably subsolidus Na-grunerite (also observed in the Pikes Peak series by Barker et al., 1975).

Plotting the amphibole parameters used in Figure 19 against $(Na + K)/Al$ of the host rock (the so-called agpaitic coefficient) produces Figure 20 with resulting distinctive clusters of the data. Where the bulk rock has $(Na + K)/Al < 0.9$, the amphibole has $(Ca + Al^{IV}) > 2.5$ and $(Si + Na + K) < 8$. Giret et al. (1980) argue from these relations that silica-rich and alkali-rich amphiboles crystallize only from alkaline liquids and during the late magmatic or post-magmatic stages.

Normative von Wolff diagrams of these amphiboles and their host rocks are shown in Figure 21, reinforcing in a somewhat different way the point of Figure 14. The line between L and M separates the quartz- and nepheline-normative fields. The three sets of data on the left are for the silica-saturated rock series; the ones on the right, the silica-undersaturated series (except Oslo, which has two distinct series). Tie-lines generally cross the saturation line, with amphiboles more nepheline-normative than rocks.

Giret et al. (1980) schematically depict the different amphibole compositional trends inferred to exist (Fig. 22). The specific substitutions reflected in each of these trends is indicated, while the $Fe \rightleftarrows Mg$ substitution may occur in any. In the saturated associations, the dominant substitution in $(Ca + Al^{IV})$-rich amphiboles is $NaAl^{IV} \rightleftarrows Si$. In the undersaturated associations for these amphiboles, Ti decreases and $CaAl^{IV} \rightleftarrows NaSi$. In $(Ca + Al^{IV})$-poor amphiboles, in this study only found in saturated associations, the substitution $CaAl^{IV} \rightleftarrows NaSi$ produces the main trend, while $Fe^{3+} \rightleftarrows NaFe^{2+}$ produces an offshoot.

In summary, Giret et al. (1980) argue for a break in the evolutionary trends of amphibole composition in alkaline rocks between an early $(Ca + Al^{IV})$-rich, $(Si + Na + K)$-poor group and a later $(Ca + Al^{IV})$-poor, $(Si + Na + K)$-rich group. The early group commonly crystallized *before* plagioclase and the late group commonly *after* alkali feldspar, and in some cases, even after quartz. These later stage amphiboles may also be subsolidus (hydrothermal) -- and thus not strictly igneous in our usage. Giret et al. (1980) believe that a continuum does not exist between hastingsite (calcic amphibole) and arfvedsonite (alkali

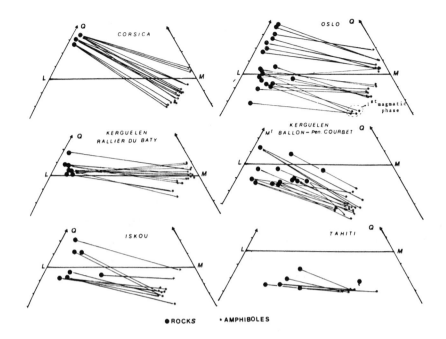

●ROCKS • AMPHIBOLES

Figure 21. Amphiboles and their host rocks plotted on normative von Wolff diagrams (Q = quartz, L = feldspars, M = mafic phases). From Giret et al. (1980).

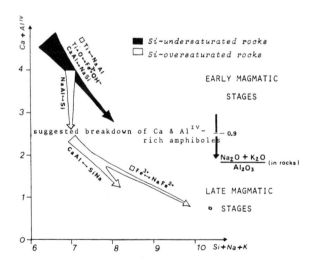

Figure 22. Schematic representation of the different amphibole compositional trends in alkaline ring-complexes. From Giret et al. (1980).

amphibole. This is consistent with the analysis of Ernst (1962), who expected that hastingsite and arfvedsonite would coexist at some relatively sodic plagioclase composition. Giret et al. (1980) suggest that the silicon ranges of the two series are 6.00–7.01 and 6.76–8.00.

Sodic-calcic and alkali amphiboles

Representatives of these classes occur in igneous rocks, but they are found in restricted and special environments. Normatively, richteritic amphiboles carry quartz, alkali metasilicates, and pyroxene, while riebeckitic amphiboles yield sodic pyroxene, alkalic metasilicates, and orthopyroxene and/ or olivine, depending on oxidation state and total iron content. Thermal stabilities of the Mg-end members are quite high (see Chapter 2, this volume), clearly within the range of igneous conditions. Nevertheless, magnesio-richterite and magnesio-riebeckite are rare to nonexistent in such environments, primarily because these environments are aluminous (Ernst, 1960; 1962; Charles, 1977).

The Mg-rich richterites which do occur in igneous rocks are normally enriched in potassium enough to be called potassium-richterites and come close to yielding a formula unit of KNaCa... for the A and M_4 sites. The host rocks are lamprophyres and mica peridotites with coexisting diopside + phlogopite (Charles, 1977). Iron-rich richterites are found in the late stage facies of evolved granitoid rocks (Charles, 1977; Giret et al., 1980). They may be much more common than previously suspected, as indicated whenever detailed microprobe studies have been done; and they may be especially useful in documenting changes in oxygen fugacity during final crystallization. Physical conditions controlling the zoning in late stage amphiboles to ferrorichterite (more reduced) or to riebeckite-arfvedsonite (more oxidized) have not yet been detailed.

The Mg-rich alkali amphiboles are essentially all metamorphic. Only the Fe-rich, Al-poor ones have igneous parageneses. The experimental study of Ernst (1962) (see Chapter 2) did much to elucidate relations among the riebeckite-arfvedsonites. These forms crystallize commonly during the last stages of solidification of A-type granitoids. Phase relations with annite were discussed by Wones in the previous section. Oxygen fugacity strongly controls the character of the solid solution series. Ernst found that these amphiboles in the presence of hematite were nearly stoichiometric riebeckite with a relatively low thermal stability that would not normally permit coexistence with silicate liquid. Thus, so-called "riebeckite granites" or "riebeckite rhyolites" could not have crystallized riebeckite during the magmatic stage. Most such riebeckites

occur as distinctly poikilitic or large single crystals appropriate to formation from a fluid phase during the hydrothermal and subsolidus stages. Under
conditions of lower f_{O_2}, the amphiboles in Ernst's study became more Na- and
Fe^{2+}-rich (arfvedsonitic) with concomitant increase in thermal stability.
Arfvedsonite could and does coexist with liquid. Thus, where granitoids
appear to contain primary sodic amphibole, arfvedsonite, not riebeckite, should
be expected. Alternative explanations involving chemical changes which either
affect the upper thermal stability of the amphibole (F for OH) or lower the
silicate solidus (B for Si) may be applicable in some cases. It is also probable that substitutions involving Na have not been adequately defined. Some
data are available showing amphiboles with three or more Na per formula unit, possibly approaching eckermannite or some of the other extremely Na-rich types
synthetically produced.

Elementary considerations on the role of amphiboles

Extracting information on amphibole paragenesis requires attention to
basic petrographic observation. Two sorts of data are particularly useful:
textural character and order of crystallization. At least four textural types
can be recognized easily (cf. Giret et al., 1980), and these are listed in
Table 3.

A schematic diagram showing rock solidus and liquidus, amphibole stability curve, and precipitation curves for related anhydrous phases illustrates
the importance of determining order of crystallization (Fig. 23). The curves
are arbitrary and no other significant hydrous phase, like biotite, is shown.
The conditions can be taken as $P_{H_2O} = P_{total}$ and at some intermediate oxidation
state where magnetite (Fe_3O_4) is stable. The solidus of the system in which
this bulk rock occurs is taken as temperature-varying, rather than isothermal,
at constant P_{total}. The possible orders of crystallization from the liquid
are: amph→cpx→mt→pc, cpx→amph→mt→pc, cpx→mt→amph→pc, and cpx→mt→pc→amph. An
additional sequence yields a cpx→mt→pc rock showing later subsolidus reaction
to include amphibole. These orders of crystallization are pressure sensitive
from highest relative P_{total} to lowest. The importance of determining point a,
the intersection of the rock solidus and the stability curve of the amphibole,
has been emphasized in Chapter 2. Point a is the lowest pressure where amphibole can coexist with liquid and occurs at its lowest value when $P_{H_2O} = P_{total}$.
Determination that amphibole is the earliest phase to crystallize establishes
a path above point g, implying significant P_{H_2O} and significant P_{total}.

Bulk chemistry affects Figure 23. Point g is probably at the lowest

TABLE 3: Some simple textural types of igneous amphiboles

Texture	Crystallization stage	Comment
#1: EUHEDRAL -Phenocryst -Inclusion	Early	Phenocrysts in andesitic-dacitic-rhyolite at high P_{H_2O} (hornblende: cummingtonite)
#2: WITH CORONA	Middle	Amph + L = reaction products (typically hornblende)
#3: INTERSTITIAL	Late to subsolidus	After pyroxene (uralitic) Typical in calc-alkaline and I-Type sequences (hornblende; ferro-richterite)
#4: POIKILITIC	Late to subsolidus	Typical alkaline (A-Type) granitoid (riebeckite-arfvedsonite)

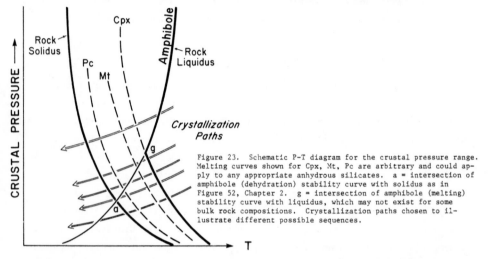

Figure 23. Schematic P-T diagram for the crustal pressure range. Melting curves shown for Cpx, Mt, Pc are arbitrary and could apply to any appropriate anhydrous silicates. a = intersection of amphibole (dehydration) stability curve with solidus as in Figure 52, Chapter 2. g = intersection of amphibole (melting) stability curve with liquidus, which may not exist for some bulk rock compositions. Crystallization paths chosen to illustrate different possible sequences.

pressure value in andesitic systems, migrating to the left and up the liquidus to higher pressure as silica content of the rock increases, and to the right and up the liquidus as silica content decreases. For some granitoid bulk compositions, amphibole stability and liquidus curves may not intersect, so that point g would not exist. The set of anhydrous phases will also change.

H_2O variations obviously affect the curve placements. Lowered H_2O activity will cause an effective shift to the right (higher temperatures) in the melting curves of the anhydrous phases, and a shift to the left in the amphibole stability (lower temperature). This may be simply applied to systems presumed to have crystallized below 4 to 5 kbar, but at higher pressures must be adjusted as discussed in Chapter 2. Thus, curve intersections will normally occur at higher pressure as P_{H_2O} falls relative to P_{total}. Point a will probably range from 0.5 to 8 kbar.

Oxygen fugacity variations will also affect curve placements in Figure 23.

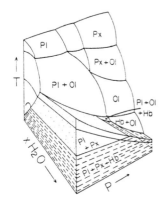

Figure 24. Simplified hypothetical P-T-X_{H_2O} diagram for a high-alumina basalt, drawn in perspective, with origin not shown. Stippled and dashed regions are saturated with H_2O vapor. Below liquidus, pyroxene (Px)-out and olivine (Ol)-in surfaces are shown coinciding. Fields for oxides omitted. Note hornblende (Hb) is a liquidus phase in both vapor-absent and vapor-present regions. Only one symbol shown for pyroxene (Px): liquidus Px is Ca-rich; low-Ca Px probably predominates if Hb is abundant. From Anderson (1980).

As f_{O_2} decreases, magnetite may be restricted and even disappear from the diagram, being replaced by olivine. The importance of the petrographic description cannot be overemphasized as most of the general relations involved in the crystallization of the rock, if available at all, are stored in the textures and order of appearance.

Anderson (1980) has discussed the significance of amphibole in calc-alkaline andesites and basalts; he has offered Figure 24 as a P-T-X_{H_2O} schematic of the relations found in high-alumina basalt. Such a diagram moves one step further than Figure 23 in attempting to incorporate variations in H_2O contents. While the Anderson paper is larger in scope than amphibole stability alone (origin of continental crust, subduction zone magmatic characteristics), it pulls together carefully selected natural phase data on amphiboles and their probable coexisting liquids. Hornblendes appear to be the result of reaction between olivine + liquid where H_2O contents lie between 1.5 and 6 wt %.

In summary, amphiboles play "passive" and "active" roles in the igneous environment. They serve both as meters, recording physicochemical conditions existing within the magmatic system, and as participants, helping to control the chemical evolution of the remaining liquids during crystallization/melting processes. This is because amphiboles are commonly volumetrically abundant enough in major rock types, they have densities high enough for liquid-crystal separation, they have crystallographic sites appropriate to *all* major cations, and they can reflect variable ferrous-ferric ratios with the ability to accept OH, O, and F. Because so many variables are involved, the simplest generalizations are probably the most useful. Site specific studies will always remain necessary, for not until the problems of amphibole parageneses are all solved will the origin of igneous rocks be fully understood.

385

CHAPTER 3 REFERENCES

Abbott, R. N. (1981) AFM liquidus projections for granitic magmas, with special reference to hornblende, biotite, and garnet. Canadian Mineral. 19, 103-110.

Allen, J. C. and Boettcher, A. L. (1978) Amphiboles in andesite and basalt: II. Stability as a function of $P-T-f_{H_2O}-f_{O_2}$. Am. Mineral. 63, 1074-1087.

_____, Boettcher, A. L. and Marland, G. (1975) Amphiboles in andesite and basalt: I. Stability as a function of $P-T-f_{O_2}$. Am. Mineral. 60, 1069-1085.

Anderson, A. T., Jr. (1980) Significance of hornblende in calc-alkaline andesites and basalts. Am. Mineral. 65, 837-851.

Barker, F., Wones, D. R., Sharp, W. N. and Desborough, G. A. (1975) The Pikes Peak batholith, Colorado Front Range, and a model for the origin of the gabbro-anorthosite-syenite potassic granite suite. Precambrian Res. 2, 9-160.

Bateman, P. C. and Wones, D. R. (1972) Geologic map of the Huntington Lake quadrangle, central Sierra Nevada, California. U.S. Geol. Survey Map GQ-987.

Beams, S. D. (1980) *Magmatic Evolution of the Southeast Lachlan fold belt, Australia*. Ph.D. thesis, LaTrobe Univ., Bundoora, 319 p.

Best, M. G. and Mercy, E. L. P. (1967) Composition and crystallization of mafic minerals in the Guadalupe Igneous Complex, California. Am. Mineral. 52, 436-474.

Borley, G. D. and Frost, M. T. (1963) Some observations on igneous ferrohastingsites. Mineral. Mag. 33, 646-662.

Bowen, N. L. (1922) The reaction principle in petrogenesis. J. Geol. 30, 177-198.

Boyd, F. R. (1959) Hydrothermal investigations of amphiboles. *In* Abelson, P. H., (ed.), *Researches in Geochemistry*. John Wiley and Sons, New York, 377-396.

Browne, G. C. and Fyfe, W. S. (1970) The production of granitic melts during ultrametamorphism. Contrib. Mineral. Petrol. 28, 310-318.

Buddington, A. F. (1959) Granite emplacement with special reference to North America. Geol. Soc. Am. Bull. 68, 291-306.

Burnham, C. W. (1979) The importance of volatile constituents. *In* Yoder, H. S. (ed.), *The Evolution of the Igneous Rocks: Fiftieth Anniversary Perspectives*. Princeton Univ. Press, Princeton, N. J., Ch. 16, 439-486.

Cameron, K. L. (1975) An experimental study of actinolite-cummingtonite phase relations with notes on the synthesis of Fe-rich anthophyllite. Am. Mineral. 60, 375-390.

Cameron, M., Bagby, W. C. and Cameron, K. L. (1980) Petrogenesis of voluminous mid-Tertiary ignimbrites of the Sierra Madre Occidental, Chihuahua, Mexico. Contrib. Mineral. Petrol. 74, 271-284.

Carmichael, I. S. E., Turner, C. J. and Verhoogen, J. (1974) *Igneous Petrology*. McGraw-Hill, New York, 739 p.

Cawthorn, R. G. (1976a) Some chemical controls on igneous amphibole compositions. Geochim. Cosmochim. Acta 40, 1319-1328.

_____ (1976b) Melting relations in part of the system $CaO-MgO-Al_2O_3-SiO_2-Na_2O-H_2O$ under 5 kb pressure. J. Petrol. 17, 44-72.

Chappell, B. W. and White, A. J. R. (1974) Two contrasting granite types. Pacific Geology 8, 173-174.

Charles, R. W. (1975) The phase equilibrium of richterite and ferrorichterite. Am. Mineral. 60, 367-374.

_____ (1977) The phase equilibria of intermediate compositions on the pseudobinary $Na_2CaMg_5Si_8O_{22}(OH)_2-Na_2CaFe_5Si_8O_{22}(OH)_2$. Am. J. Sci. 277, 594-625.

Chatterjee, N. D. and Johannes, W. (1974) Thermal stability and standard thermodynamic properties of synthetic 2M-muscovite $KAl_2AlSi_3O_{10}(OH)_2$. Contrib. Mineral. Petrol. 48, 89-114.

Chernosky, J. V. and Autio, L. K. (1979) The stability of anthophyllite in the presence of quartz. Am. Mineral. 64, 294-303.

Chivas, A. R. (in press) Geochemical evidence for magmatic fluids in porphyry copper mineralization. Part I, Mafic silicates from the Koloula Igneous Complex. Contrib. Mineral. Petrol.

Chou, I-Ming (1978) Calibration of oxygen buffers at elevated P and T using the hydrogen fugacity sensor. Am. Mineral. 63, 690-703.

Czamanske, G. K., Ishihara, S. and Atkin, S. A. (1981) Chemistry of rock-forming minerals of the Cretaceous-Paleocene batholith in southwestern Japan and implications for magma genesis. J. Geophys. Res. 86, 10431-10469.

_____ and Wones, D. R. (1973) Oxidation during magmatic differentiation, Finnmarka Complex, Oslo area, Norway: Part II, The mafic silicates. J. Petrol. 14, 349-380.

_____, _____ and Eichelberger, J. C. (1977) Mineralogy and petrology of the intrusive complex in the Pliny Range, New Hampshire. Am. J. Sci. 277, 1073-1123.

Dodge, F. C. W., Moore, J. G., Papike, J. J. and May, R. E. (1968) Hornblendes from granitic rocks of the Central Sierra Nevada batholith, California. J. Petrol. 9, 378-410.

Engel, C. G. (1959) Igneous rocks and constituent hornblendes of the Henry Mountains, Utah. Geol. Soc. Am. Bull. 70, 951-980.

Ernst, W. G. (1960) Stability relations of magnesioriebeckite. Geochim. Cosmochim. Acta 19, 10-40.

_____ (1962) Synthesis, stability relations, and occurrence of riebeckite and riebeckite-arfvedsonite solid solutions. J. Geol. 70, 689-736.

_____ (1966) Synthesis and stability relations of ferrotremolite. Am. J. Sci. 264, 37-65.

Eugster, H. P. and Wones, D. R. (1962) Stability relations of the ferruginous biotite, annite. J. Petrol. 3, 82-125.

Ewart, A., Hildreth, W. and Carmichael, I. S. E. (1975) Quaternary acid magma in New Zealand. Contrib. Mineral. Petrol. 51, 1-27.

Forbes, W. C. (1977) Stability relations of grunerite, $Fe_7Si_8O_{22}(OH)_2$. Am. J. Sci. 277, 735-749.

French, B. M. and Eugster, H. P. (1965) Experimental control of oxygen fugacities by graphite-gas equilibriums. J. Geophys. Res. 70, 1524-1539.

Gilbert, M. C. (1966) Synthesis and stability relationships of the hornblende ferropargasite. Am. J. Sci. 264, 698-742.

_____ and Briggs, D. F. (1974) Comparison of the stabilities of OH and F-Potassic Richterites --A preliminary report: Trans. Amer. Geophys. Union 55, 480-481.

_____ and Troll, G. (1974) A comparison of the stabilities of OH- and F-tremolite. Int'l. Mineral. Assoc., 9th General Meeting, Berlin and Regensburg, Germany, Collected Abstr. 84.

Gillberg, M. (1964) Halogens and hydroxyl contents of micas and amphiboles in Swedish granitic rocks. Geochim. Cosmochim. Acta 28, 495-516.

Giret, A., Bonin, B. and Leger, J. M. (1980) Amphibole compositional trends in oversaturated and undersaturated alkaline plutonic ring-complexes. Canadian Mineral. 18, 481-495.

Green, D. H. and Ringwood, A. E. (1967) The genesis of basaltic magmas. Contrib. Mineral. Petrol. 15, 103-190.

Greenwood, H. J. (1979) Thermodynamic properties of edenite. Canadian Geol. Surv. Paper 79-1B, 365-370.

Guy, R. E. (1980) *The Dinkey Creek intrusive series, Huntington Lake Quadrangle, Fresno County, California.* M.S. thesis, Virginia Polytechnic Institute and State University, Blacksburg, Virginia.

Hall, S. T. (1975) *Mineralogy, Chemistry, and Petrogenesis of Some Hypabyssal Intrusions, Highland County, Virginia.* M.S. thesis, Virginia Polytechnic Institute and State University, Blacksburg, Virginia.

Hazen, R. M. and Wones, D. R. (1972) The effect of cation substitutions on the physical properties of trioctahedral micas. Am. Mineral. 57, 103-129.

_____ and _____ (1978) Predicted and observed compositional limits of trioctahedral micas. Am. Mineral. 63, 885-892.

Helgeson, H. C., Delaney, J. M., Nesbitt, H. W. and Bird, D. K. (1978) Summary and critique of the thermodynamic properties of rock-forming minerals. Am. J. Sci. 278-A, 229 p.

Hewitt, D. A. (1978) A redetermination of the fayalite-magnetite-quartz equilibrium between 650° and 850°. Am. J. Sci. 278, 715-724.

Hildreth, W. (1980) The Bishop Tuff: evidence for the origin of compositional zonation in silicic magma chambers. Geol. Soc. Am. Spec. Paper 180, 43-75.

Hine, R., Williams, I. S., Chappell, B. W. and White, A. J. R. (1978) Contrasts between I- and S-type granitoids of the Kosciusko batholith. Geol. Soc. Australia J., 25, 219-234.

Holloway, J. R. and Ford, C. E. (1975) Fluid-absent melting of the fluorohydroxy-amphibole pargasite. Earth Planet. Sci. Lett. 25, 44-48.

Huebner, J. S. and Sato, M. (1970) The oxygen fugacity-temperature relationships of manganese oxide and nickel oxide buffers. Am. Mineral. 55, 934-952.

Huntington, H. D. (1979) Kiglapait Mineralogy I. Apatite, Biotite, and Volatiles. J. Petrol. 20, 625-652.

Ishihara, S. (1977) The magnetite-series and ilmenite-series granitic rocks. Mining Geol. 27, 293-305.

_____ (1979) Kappameter KT-3 and its application for some volcanic rocks in Japan. Bull. Geol. Surv. Japan 30, 513-519.

_____, Kanaya, H. and Terashima, S. (1976) Genesis of the Neogene granitoids in the Fossa Magna region in Japan. Marine Sci. Monthly 8, 523-528.

Jackson, E. D. (1961) Primary textures and mineral associations in the ultramafic zone of the Stillwater complex. U. S. Geol. Surv. Prof. Paper 358, 106 pp.

Jakes, P. and White, A. J. R. (1972) Hornblendes from calc-alkaline volcanic rocks of Island Arcs and Continental Margins. Am. Mineral. 57, 887-902.

Klein, C. (1968) Coexisting amphiboles. J. Petrol. 9, 281-330.

Kocis, D. E., Hermes, O. D., Cain, J. A. and Murray, D. P. (1977) Re-evaluation of late Paleozoic igneous activity and accompanying contact metamorphism in southeastern Rhode Island. Geol. Soc. Am. Abstr. Programs 9, 286-287.

Kuno, H. (1938) On the occurrence of a primary cummingtonitic hornblende in some dacites from Japan. Proc. Japan Acad. 14, 221-224.

Larsen, E. S., Jr. and Draisin, W. M. (1948) Composition of the minerals in the rocks of the Southern California batholith. Int'l. Geol. Congress (Great Britain). Part II, Problems of Geochemistry, 66-79.

Leake, B. E. (1968) A catalog of analyzed calciferous and subcalciferous amphiboles together with their nomenclature and associated minerals. Geol. Soc. Am. Spec. Paper 98, 210 p.

Lindsley, D. H. (1976) Experimental studies of oxide minerals. *In* Rumble, D., III, Ed., *Oxide Minerals,* Reviews in Mineralogy 3, L61-L88.

Lipman, P. W. (1971) Iron-titanium oxide phenocrysts in compositionally zoned ash-flow sheets from southern Nevada. J. Geol., 79, 438-456.

_____ and Friedman, I. (1975) Interaction of meteoric water with magma: an oxygen-isotope study of ash-flow sheets from southern Nevada. Geol. Soc. Am. Bull. 86, 695-702.

Loiselle, M. C. and Wones, D. R. (1979) Characteristics and origin of anorogenic granites. Geol. Soc. Am. Abstr. Programs 11, 468.

Luth, W. C. (1967) Studies in the system $KAlSiO_4-Mg_2SiO_4-SiO_2-H_2O$: I. Inferred phase relations and petrologic applications. J. Petrol. 8, 372-416.

_____ Jahns, R. H. and Tuttle, O. F. (1964) The granite system at pressures of 4 to 10 kilobars. J. Geophys. Res. 69, 759-773.

Lyons, P. C. (1972) Significance of riebeckite and ferrohastingsite in microperthite granites. Am. Mineral. 57, 1404-1412.

_____ (1976) The chemistry of riebeckites of Massachusetts and Rhode Island. Mineral. Mag. 40, 473-479.

Maaloe, S. and Wyllie, P. J. (1975) Water content of a granite magma deduced from the sequence of crystallization determined experimentally with water-undersaturated conditions. Contrib. Mineral. Petrol. 52, 175-191.

Marsh, B. D. (1976) Some Aleutian andesites: their nature and source. J. Geol. 84, 27-45.

Mason, D. R. (1978) Compositional variations in ferromagnesian minerals from porphyry copper-generating and barren intrusions of the Western Highlands, Papua, New Guinea. Econ. Geol. 73, 878-890.

Modreski, P. J. and Boettcher, A. L. (1972) The stability of phlogopite and enstatite at high pressures: a model for micas in the interior of the earth. Am. J. Sci. 272, 852-867.

Muan, A., and Osborn, E. F. (1956) Phase equilibria at liquidus temperatures in the system $MgO-FeO-Fe_2O_3-SiO_2$. J. Am. Ceramic Soc. 39, 121-140.

Munoz, J. L. and Ludington, S. D. (1974) Fluoride-hydroxyl exchange in biotite. Am. J. Sci. 279, 396-413.

Naney, M. T. and Swanson, S. E. (1980) The effect of Fe and Mg on crystallization in granitic systems. Am. Mineral. 65, 639-653.

Nicholls, J., Carmichael, I. S. E. and Stormer, J. C., Jr. (1971) Silica activity and P_{total} in igneous rocks. Contrib. Mineral. Petrol 33, 1-20.

Noyes, H. (1978) *Comparative Petrochemistry of the Red Lake and Eagle Peak Plutons, Sierra Nevada Batholith.* Ph.D. dissertation, Massachusetts Inst. of Tech., Cambridge.

Oba, T. (1980) Phase relations in the tremolite-pargasite join. Contrib. Mineral. Petrol. 71, 247-256.

Popp, R. K., Gilbert, M. C. and Craig, J. R. (1976) Synthetic and X-ray properties of Fe-Mg orthoamphiboles. Am. Mineral. 61, 1267-1279.

_____, _____, and _____ (1977a) Stability of Fe-Mg amphiboles with respect to oxygen fugacity. Am. Mineral. 62, 1-12.

_____, _____, and _____ (1977b) Stability of Fe-Mg amphiboles with respect to sulfur fugacity. Am. Mineral. 62, 13-30.

Powell, B. N., Gilbert, M. C. and Fischer, J. F. (1980) Lithostratigraphic classification of basement rocks of the Wichita province, Oklahoma. Geol. Soc. Am. Bull. 91, Part II, 1875-1994.

Ransome, F. L. (1898) *Some Lava Flows of the Western Slope of the Sierra Nevada, California.* U. S. Geol. Surv. Bull. 89, 74 pp.

Richter, D. H. and Murata, K. J. (1966) Petrography of the lavas of the 1959-1960 eruption of Kilauea Volcano, Hawaii. U. S. Geol. Surv. Prof. Paper 537-D, 12 pages.

Rutherford, M. J. (1969) An experimental determination of iron biotite-alkali feldspar equilibrium. J. Petrol. 10, 381-408.

_____ (1972) The phase relations of aluminous iron biotites in the system $KAlSi_3O_8$-$KAlSiO_4$-Al_2O_3-Fe-O-H. J. Petrol. 14, 159-180.

Sato, M. and Wright, T. L. (1965) Oxygen fugacities directly measured in magmatic gases. Science 153, 1103-1105.

Seitsaari, J. (1956) Some new data on the blue-green hornblende from the Tampere Schist belt. Bull. Comm. Geol. Finland 28, 41-46.

Semet, M. P. and Ernst, W. G. (1981) Experimental stability relations of the hornblende magnesiohastingsite. Geol. Soc. Am. Bull. 92, 71-74.

Spear, F. S. (1980) NaSi-CaAl exchange equilibrium between plagioclase and amphibole. Contrib. Mineral. Petrol. 72, 33-41.

Speer, J. A., Becker, S. W., and Farrar, S. S. (1980) Field relations and petrology of the post metamorphic, coarse-grained granitoids and associated rocks of the southern Appalachian Piedmont. In Wones, D. R., ed., Proceedings: The Caledonides in the U.S.A., Virginia Polytechnic Institute and State University. Memoir No. 2, 137-148.

Streckheisen, A. L. (1973) Plutonic rocks. Geotimes 18, 26-30.

Takahashi, M., Aramaki, S. and Ishihara, S. (1980) Magnetite-series/Ilmenite-series vs. I-type/S-type granitoids. Mining Geol. Spec. Issue 8, 13-28.

Thomas, W. M. (1977) Preliminary stability relations of the hornblende hastingsite, and the effect of Fe^{3+} for aluminum replacement in amphiboles. (Abstr.) Am. Geophys. Union Trans. 58, 1244.

Toulmin, P., III (1964) Bedrock geology of the Salem quadrangle and vicinity, Massachusetts. U. S. Geol. Survey Bull., 1163-A, 1-79.

Troll, G. and Gilbert, M. C. (1972) Fluorine-hydroxl substitution in tremolite. Am. Mineral. 57, 1386-1403.

Tso, J. L., Gilbert, M. C. and Craig, J. R. (1979) Sulfidation of synthetic biotites. Am. Mineral. 64, 304-316.

Tsusue, A. (1978) Coupled substitutions within the amphiboles in the granitic rocks of southwest Japan. In K. Aoki, Ed., Collected Abstracts of Researches on Rock-forming Minerals.

Tuttle, O. F., and Bowen, N. L. (1958) Origin of Granite in the Light of Experimental Studies in the System $NaAlSi_3O_8$ - $KAlSi_3O_8$ - SiO_2 - H_2O. Geol. Soc. Am. Memoir 74, 153 p.

Valley, J. W. and Essene, E. J. (1980) Calc-silicate reactions in Adirondack marbles: the role of fluids and solid solutions. Am. Geol. Soc. Bull. 9, 114-117, 720-815.

Washington, H. S. and Adams, L. H. (1951) The chemical and petrological nature of the Earth's crust. Ch. 5, 81-106. In Gutenberg, B., Ed., Internal Constitution of the Earth, 2nd revised ed., Dover, 439 p.

Wager, L. R. and Brown, G. M. (1967) Layered Igneous Rocks. W. H. Freeman, San Francisco, 588 p.

Whelan, J. (1980) Aspects of Granites and Associated Mineralization. Ph.D. dissertation, Australian National University, Dept. of Geol. Canberra, A.C.T., Australia.

Wilcox, R. E. (1965) Volcanic-ash chronology. The Quaternary of the United States (a review volume for the VII Congress, Int'l Assoc. Quaternary Res.), 807-816.

Wilkinson, J. F. G. (1961) Some aspects of the calciferous amphiboles, oxyhornblende, kaersutite and barkevikite. Am. Mineral. 46, 340-354.

Williams, R. J. (1971) Reaction constants in the system Fe-MgO-SiO_2-O_2: intensive parameters in the Skaergaard Intrusion, east Greenland. Am. J. Sci. 271, 132-146.

Williams-Jones, A. F. (1981) Thermal metamorphism of siliceous limestone in the limestone in the aureole of Mount Royal, Quebec. Am. J. Sci. 281, 673-696.

Wones, D. R. (1967) A low pressure investigation of the stability of phlogopite. Geochim. Cosmochim. Acta 31, 2248-2253.

_____ (1981) Mafic silicates as indicators of intensive variables in granitic magmas. Mining Geol. 31, 191-212.

_____ (in press) A reexamination of the significance of titanite-magnetite-quartz assemblages in granitic rocks. Am. Mineral.

_____ and Dodge, F. C. W. (1977) The stability of phlogopite in the presence of quartz and diopside. In Fraser, D. G., Ed., Thermodynamics and Geology, Reidel Dortrecht, 229-247.

_____ and Eugster, H. P. (1965) Stability of biotite: experiment, theory, and application. Am. Mineral. 50, 1228-1272.

Wood, B. J. (1976) The reaction phlogopite + quartz = enstatite + sanidine + H_2O. Progress in Experimental Petrology, Natural Envir. Res. Coun. Pub. Series D, No. 6, 17-19.

_____ and Carmichael, I. S. E. (1973) P_{total}, P_{H_2O}, and the occurrence of cummingtonite in volcanic rocks. Contrib. Mineral. Petrol. 40, 149-158.

Yoder, H. S. and Kushiro, I. (1969) Melting of a hydrous phase: phlogopite. Am. J. Sci. 267-A, 558-582.

_____ and Tilley, C. E. (1962) Origin of basalt magmas: an experimental study of natural and synthetic rock systems. J. Petrol. 3, 342-532.